1965

THE ANIMAL KINGDOM

THE

George G. Goodwin

ASSOCIATE CURATOR OF MAMMALS,
THE AMERICAN MUSEUM OF NATURAL HISTORY

Charles M. Bogert

CURATOR OF AMPHIBIANS AND REPTILES,
THE AMERICAN MUSEUM OF NATURAL HISTORY

Dean Amadon
E. Thomas Gilliard

ASSOCIATE CURATORS OF BIRDS,
THE AMERICAN MUSEUM OF NATURAL HISTORY

Christopher W. Coates CURATOR
James W. Atz ASSISTANT CURATOR,

AQUARIUM OF
THE NEW YORK ZOOLOGICAL SOCIETY

John C. Pallister

RESEARCH ASSOCIATE, INSECTS,
THE AMERICAN MUSEUM OF NATURAL HISTORY

ANIMAL KINGDOM

THE STRANGE AND WONDERFUL WAYS OF MAMMALS, BIRDS, REPTILES, FISHES AND INSECTS. A NEW AND AUTHENTIC NATURAL HISTORY OF THE WILDLIFE OF THE WORLD.

FREDERICK DRIMMER, M.A.
EDITOR-IN-CHIEF

VOLUME III

GREYSTONE PRESS, NEW YORK

3598-10M

LIBRARY OF CONGRESS CATALOG NUMBER 53-11687

Designed by Sidney Feinberg

MANUFACTURED IN THE UNITED STATES OF AMERICA
AMERICAN BOOK—STRATFORD PRESS, INC., NEW YORK

BOOK IV: Fishes of the World

CHRISTOPHER W. COATES

JAMES W. ATZ

Fishes—Their Whys and Wherefores

ASK ANYONE what creatures live in water, and nine times out of ten the first answer will be "fish." A vast and colorful horde of other living things make their home in the oceans, lakes, rivers, streams, and swamps of the earth, but to man the fish has always been the most important of water dwellers.

And for good reason. Since before the dawn of history, man has relied upon the fish as food, wresting a good part of his livelihood from the water. He has found a thousand cunning ways to satisfy his needs with this creature, from making tools of its skeleton, a fertilizer of its flesh, a bone-building medicine of the rich oil in its liver, right up to using the fish itself as a decoration in his home.

Fishes dominate the waters of our planet. There are more fishes—and more different kinds of them—than of any other good-sized animals living wholly or partly in water. Today we are able to recognize more than twenty-five thousands of fishes—as many species as there are of mammals, birds, reptiles, and amphibians put together.

What is a fish? Don't suppose this question is naive. To cover so diverse a group of animals with a single definition—one that will include all the kinds of fishes and at the same time exclude all living things that are not fish—is difficult. Fishes are so varied in the nature of their bodies and the way they use their organs, that exceptions turn up for almost every characteristic of fishes in general. For example: a number of fishes have no scales; a few have no fins; a few lack jaws; some do not breathe primarily by means of gills; and others spend practically as much time out of the water as in it.

After gathering together a number of the features unique among fishes, and taking account of the exceptional fish that lacks one or another of them, we arrive at the following definition: A fish is a cold-blooded, aquatic vertebrate with gills and a two-chambered heart.

Like most definitions, this one needs some explaining to make it fully understandable. A vertebrate is, briefly speaking, an animal with a backbone, and this characteristic alone is sufficient to separate fishes from all the invertebrates (animals without backbones)—which include such creatures as insects, spiders, shellfish of all sorts, starfish, and their relatives, all kinds of worms, sponges, and jellyfish—and also from the near-vertebrates (protochordates), the acorn-worms, sea-squirts, and lancelets.

The fact that fishes are cold-blooded, that is, have a body temperature which more or less closely follows that of the water or air in which they live, clearly distinguishes them from birds and mammals. (We must say "more or less" because a very few fishes, such as the tunas, maintain a body temperature which is somewhat higher than that of the water surrounding them.)

The fact that fishes have a two-chambered heart also separates them from the amphibians and reptiles and from the birds and mammals—all of which have three- or four-chambered hearts. The gills, too, are an important feature of fishes. Although some fishes do not depend on their gills for breathing, these organs are always present, even though they may consist of only a few undeveloped filaments.

Fishes are aquatic, with no exceptions whatsoever. Those that spend hours or perhaps days at a time out of water, still must periodically return to that element to keep from becoming dried out. Some fishes can live for months without water, and a very few even for years, but they can do this only when inactive, in a state of suspended animation. All active fishes require at least enough water to bathe their bodies and keep their respiratory, or breathing, organs moist.

Actually, it is much easier to distinguish fishes from other generally similar aquatic animals than you might gather from what we have said. You can tell fishes from whales and porpoises by their tails; in fish the tail is vertical, like a rudder, while in whales and porpoises it is horizontal. A snake and an eel can be distinguished at a glance: the snake has no gill-openings, but the eel has. Tadpoles have no paired fins, and this marks them off from all but a very few fishes—and these few exceptional fishes are so untadpole-like that they could never be confused. Recognizing fishes, you can see, is more difficult in theory than in practice.

WHERE FISHES LIVE

More than seven-tenths of the earth's surface is covered with water, and practically all of this vast area is inhabited by fishes. The seven seas, the many lakes, streams, ponds, and swamps all accommodate typical groups of fishes of one kind or another.

Ocean waters contain by far the greatest proportion of fishes—both in number of species and individuals. In the sea, fish are found from shallow, temporary tide pools down to the utmost depths of the ocean; in fact almost everywhere except uninhabitable regions such as the lower levels of the Black Sea, which are completely devoid of oxygen. Some fishes are what might be called "blue water" dwellers, living out in the middle of the ocean and never seeing or coming close to land during their whole lives. Others remain near shore, around coral reefs, or at the mouths of rivers. Still others live on the bottom, be it rocky or muddy, in calm depths, or near surf-washed beaches.

Fresh-water fishes are subject to even greater extremes in the waters they inhabit. The streams of the world—from source to mouth —provide living places for various types of fish. Fishes are found in mountain torrents and sluggish rivers, ice-cold lakes and hot volcanic springs, foul swamps and clear, crystalline pools, soda-charged waterholes and acid lakes, sun-heated ponds and murky caves. Some fishes even make temporary pools their homes, and when these dry up, the fishes either travel overland to find water elsewhere, or hole up in mud until the rains come; they may also die, but leave their drought-resistant eggs behind to carry on the race.

Few of these waters are entirely isolated from all others, and there are fishes adaptable enough to live in more than one kind. For instance, a number can thrive in either fresh or salt water, or in places either warm or cold.

So it is not surprising that fishes, being subjected to such diverse conditions of existence, should show widely different structures and functions, and should vary so greatly in their life histories and patterns of behavior. But this variety of dwelling places alone does not account for the diversity of fish life, because in a single, relatively uniform locality, as that around a coral reef, as many as two hundred species may be found—eloquent evidence that there are additional factors involved in the evolution of fish.

There is hardly anything that lives in water, either plant or animal, that is not eaten by some fish. Fishes prey extensively upon one another, too. Most bizarre perhaps are those relationships in which fishes make their homes inside living sponges, snails, bivalves, starfish, and sea-cucumbers, or in which they share the burrows of shrimps and worms, or live among the stinging tentacles of jellyfishes and sea-anemones.

We shall look more closely at the many wonderful features of fish life—the relationships between fishes and other animals and among the various kinds of fishes—in the "biographies" of various fishes, later on.

THE FISH'S BODY

A typical fish, such as the striped bass, is roughly spindle-shaped, tapering at each end. Its muscular, streamlined body is beautifully constructed for fast and efficient movement through the relatively dense medium of water. The rear end of the body, including the tail fin, serves as the principal means of locomotion through the water; its motion from side to side causes the fish to move forward. The caudal, or tail, fin plays only a minor part in this process, although it does make for more precise movement. The fins along the midline of the dorsal surface (the back) and on the midline of the ventral surface (the belly) behind the anus, or vent (called "dorsal" and "anal" fins, respectively), act as keels or stabilizers, and the two sets of paired fins, the pectorals and the pelvics (corresponding to the limbs attached to the shoulders and hips of other backboned animals) are used in stopping, turning, and other maneuvering.

In the water, the fish has to move up and down, as well as from side to side and forward and backward; except for the birds and bats, few vertebrates face this problem. As a consequence, fishes have an extreme nicety of adjustment and interaction of fins and flexible body. Even breathing is integrated, because the discharge of water through the gill covers tends to move the fish forward, and so is compensated for—chiefly by movements of the pectoral fins.

HOW FISHES REMAIN SUSPENDED IN WATER

In order to remain suspended in the water without constantly swimming to keep from sinking to the bottom or floating to the surface, many fishes have bodies with nearly the same density as the water surrounding them. Flesh and bone are heavier than water, of course, but, to compensate for this weight, many fishes, the striped bass included, have a swim bladder, or air bladder, which is a long sac, filled with gas, between the stomach and the backbone. In some fishes

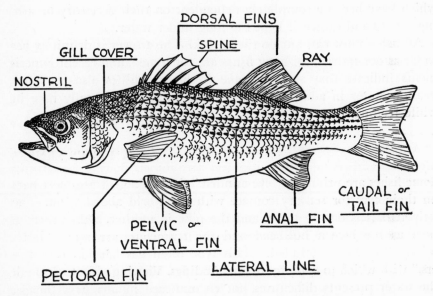

UNDERSTANDING THE FISH
This illustration shows a typical fish, the striped bass, with the principal fins and other external organs labeled. Spines are sometimes found in other fins besides the dorsal. Only the pelvic and pectoral fins are paired.

this bladder opens into the gullet; in others, like the striped bass, it is sealed off completely. In either case, however, the volume of gas inside can be changed to suit different conditions. Air bladders are also sometimes used as breathing organs, as aids in hearing, and in the production of sound. A good number of fishes get along without them, mostly bottom-inhabiting forms, but even some that live in mid-water, such as certain sharks and the Atlantic mackerel, lack an air bladder.

THE WAY FISHES BREATHE

The striped bass breathes by taking in water through its mouth and passing it through its gills and out under its gill covers. The gills are so constructed that they can extract oxygen which is dissolved in the water and throw off carbon dioxide into it. Several groups of fishes also have accessory breathing organs which enable them to breathe in directly the air above the surface. Such species often live in stagnant or warm water, where the amount of dissolved oxygen is low and that of asphyxiating carbon dioxide is high. Among these fishes are ones which have become completely dependent on their accessory breathing organs and drown if kept too long under water.

All fishes must eat, but do they drink? The answer is definitely *yes* so far as ocean-dwelling bony fishes are concerned, and recent experiments indicate that at least some fresh-water fishes also regularly swallow water in addition to what they might accidentally take in while feeding.

A FISH'S SENSES

Some fishes are primarily "eye-minded," depending for the most part on their eyes for sensory contact with the world about them. The striped bass is one of these, and the pike is another. Other species, such as the brown bullhead and the sturgeons, are more "taste-minded" or "smell-minded." This type often has barbels, or "feelers," with which to explore its surroundings. Viewing objects through the water presents difficulties not encountered in air; nevertheless, numerous fishes show real ability to see sharply. Witness the accuracy with which the trout or the bass strikes at the fisherman's fly. So far as known, fishes are also able to perceive colors.

Fishes have ears, although they are hidden away inside their heads. Like other vertebrates, fishes use their ears to keep their balance and to detect sound waves. Fishes are also equipped with a system of small canals that lie under the skin and communicate with the exterior by a series of pores. Part of this complex organ is visible externally; it is known as the "lateral line," and is quite apparent in the striped bass. It "feels" many of the numerous vibrations transmitted through the water, thereby acting as a sort of long-distance touch. Not all fishes have lateral lines, however.

In fishes, the nose is not connected to the mouth, except in a handful of species. Fishes use their noses only to smell, not to breathe—with the exception of the electric stargazer and its very close relatives, and perhaps certain eels. Smell and taste are rather difficult to tell apart under water; at any rate there is a lot of evidence that fishes can be acutely sensitive to chemical substances. Many of them have taste buds over much of their bodies, and thus are able to detect the presence of food even with their tails. Usually barbels and other sensory organs are especially well equipped with taste buds.

BIRTH AND CARE OF THE YOUNG

The vast majority of fishes reproduce themselves by means of eggs that are both laid in the water and fertilized there. Their eggs are usually spherical, less than one-eighth of an inch in diameter, and may sink or float. A few kinds of fishes give birth to living young, and a still smaller number lay eggs that have already been fertilized while inside the female. Although most fishes show no concern toward their eggs, quite a number make nests for them, guard them, and otherwise care for them until they hatch. A few of these also watch over the fry when they hatch from the eggs. With few exceptions, it is only the male fish who makes the nest and performs the "nursery" duties; in certain species both parents cooperate, and in others the female alone cares for the eggs and young.

POPULAR NAMES OF FISHES

Many hot arguments have been held over the proper popular name for a given fish. It usually turns out that both sides were right; a fish having a certain popular name in one part of the country may be called by a different one somewhere else. What we call the zebra fish, for example, is also known as the lion fish, turkey fish, butterfly cod, devil fish, dragon fish, stingfish, firefish, and fireworks fish.

The better recognized a fish is, the more popular names it seems to have; for instance, no less than forty-four different names have been recorded for the well-known largemouth black bass. At one time or another this fish has been called green bass, white bass, gray bass, yellow bass, spotted bass, striped bass, straw bass, moss bass, mud bass, rock bass, river bass, lake bass, marsh bass, bayou bass, and cow bass.

It has also been called a green or white trout, a white salmon, a green or yellow pond perch, and a southern chub. Many of these names have been traditionally attached to entirely different species. Many are confusing in that a member of the fresh-water black bass and sunfish family cannot very well also be a member of the perch or the salmon and trout family.

An effort to straighten out this confusion has recently been made by the American Fisheries Society, the Outdoor Writers Association of America, and the Board of Conservation of Florida, working through the University of Miami. Each has published a valuable check list of fishes that includes a careful selection of popular names. Since it is clearly impossible for us to list even a part of the multitudinous synonyms belonging to most fish of the succeeding series of "biographies," we have followed these authorities, especially the first, in our choice of popular names.

FISHES OF LONG AGO— AND THEIR DESCENDANTS TODAY

Fishes form the oldest group of vertebrates, that is to say, they were the first backboned animals to develop on the earth. The earliest fossil record of them dates back to the Ordovician period, some four hundred million years ago.

These fish, which we call "Ostracoderms" (meaning "shell-skinned"), were heavily armored and had no jaws. The head and front part of the body were encased in a shieldlike, bony, external cover. Most species were small, and all of them were certainly not "built for speed." They apparently poked along the bottom, sucking in dead organic matter for food, and depending on their armor for protection. None of these ancient fishes is alive today; they have been extinct for the last 280 million years. Their nearest living relatives are the jawless fishes—the lampreys and hagfishes—of the class Cyclostomi ("circular mouthed").

During succeeding millions of years other groups of armored fishes appeared and disappeared. Sharks first show up in geological deposits that are somewhat more than three hundred million years old. Their descendants constitute the class Chondrichthyes ("cartilage-fishes"), which have gristle instead of true bone in their skeletons.

About the same time the first of the class Osteichthyes ("bony fishes") appeared on the earth. This group, which now contains the vast majority of fish species, differs from the others in having true bone in at least some part of the skeleton. Because of the various highly specialized members of the group, it is hard to find characteristics that are common to all species. All have jaws and at least one pair of nostrils, but some lack fins or scales; in fact, practically every fish characteristic is lacking in one species or another, or is so modified as to be hardly recognizable.

One very old group of bony fishes—that comprising the crossopterygians (a name meaning "fringed fins")—is of especial interest, because it was from them that the first backboned land animals, the amphibians, evolved. Although at one time the fringe-fins were the chief animals of prey in fresh water, only two salt-water species are known to be alive today. These "living fossils" are the East London coelacanth and the Anjouan Island coelacanth. With their close relatives the lungfishes, the fringe-fins constitute one of the major divisions of the bony fishes, the subclass Choanichthyes ("nostril fishes") —so called from the fact that they, or their ancestors, had a nose that connected with the mouth.

With the exception of five species of lungfishes and two fringe-fins, all of the living bony fishes are included in the subclass Teleostomi ("perfect mouth"); these are the ray-finned fishes. The scientific name refers to the presence of true bone in the structure of the jaws and skull; the popular name to the structure of the fins, by which these fishes can be distinguished from the fringe-fins. Although a few of the ray-fins have fins with a fleshy base like those of the fringe-fins, the arrangement of the bones inside is fundamentally different.

One point concerning the evolutionary status of fishes should be emphasized. Although they belong to the most ancient group of backboned animals, and a number of them which are still alive today can be called "living fossils" because of their similarity to ancient types, the vast majority of species are as up-to-date, geologically speaking or in an evolutionary sense, as any bird or mammal. Most fishes of today represent highly specialized lines of descent that were undergoing evolutionary change at the same time that the amphibians, reptiles, birds, and mammals were evolving to their present state. Therefore, fishes, in their own way, are just as "modern" or "advanced" as any of these so-called "higher creatures."

THE PROTOCHORDATES, MYSTERY ANIMALS

Earlier in this chapter we made reference to these near-vertebrates. Unless you are a frequenter of certain rocky seashores or have fished for the lancelets in China, you have probably never seen a protochordate. In fact, few people even know of their existence. Zoologists, on the other hand, are well aware of them, but in many ways the protochordates are mystery animals to scientists as well as laymen.

The protochordates are not fishes, although they live in water. Everyone has heard about "missing links" and how they provide key information about the course that evolution has taken. By rights, protochordates should be missing links. They have, at some time during their lives, a rod-shaped structure (notochord), the forerunner of the backbone. Thus they stand between the animals without backbones (the jellyfish, shellfish, starfish, insects, worms and all the rest) and those with them (the fishes, amphibians, reptiles, birds and mammals). But instead of solving the problem of how some backboneless creatures through eons acquired backbones, the protochordates have simply created new problems of their own. Instead of being a key, they turned out to be a headache. In other words, careful study of these animals has failed to reveal the course of evolution.

But the exact location of the protochordates in the scale of life is mainly the concern of scientific specialists. These animals are also interesting in their own right because of the most peculiar lives they lead. They may be separated into three principal groups: the sea-squirts, the acorn worms, and the lancelets.

Sea-squirts are aptly named, for if you touch one it is likely to send forth a couple of small jets of water. Most likely you would mistake the creature for a bit of marine plant life or at best some sort of sponge. It is a small, sac-like object fastened at one end to a rock and bearing two small holes at the other. The body is encased in a jacket or tunic which gives it the appearance of a small bag and from which it gets the name of tunicate.

Sea-squirts or tunicates live only in the sea, many of them on rocks that may be exposed at low tide, others in deeper water, and still others in the water itself, floating free. One of the fascinating things about the fixed sea-squirts is that they start out life as tiny, free-swimming, tadpolelike creatures which soon settle down, lose the tail and gradually assume the typical adult tunicate shape—or lack of it if you will. They spend the rest of their lives in one spot, more like plants than animals. Like plants, some tunicates can reproduce themselves by budding. Whole colonies arise from the buds of a single individual. Tunicates feed on microscopic organisms which they filter out of the water.

Acorn worms live in the mud and are seldom seen. Like the sea-squirts, they are strictly marine. They may be only two inches in length or as long as two feet, but they are rarely any bigger around than an ordinary pencil. At the front end, they have a rounded proboscis which fits into a collar, and it is from this structure that they get their popular name. In the manner of earthworms, although they are not worms at all, these animals swallow quantities of earth or mud from which they digest the organic matter, and, like earthworms, they leave their castings on the surface near the entrance to their burrow.

The lancelets are transparent, fishlike animals, two inches or less in length, which inhabit sandy beaches in many parts of the world. They spend most of their time hidden in the sand, only the snout projecting above the surface. Occasionally they dart about, but they soon return, usually burrowing tail first. Although they look a good deal like a small fish, lancelets do not have eyes or ears, nor do they have a brain, heart or skeleton. They feed on microscopic organisms which they strain out from a current of water flowing through the mouth and out past the gills.

Despite their small size, lancelets are so abundant at one spot near Amoy in southern China that they are fished for food. It has been estimated that about 35 tons are taken during a single season. This is equivalent to more than a billion individuals.

FISH ARE BIG BUSINESS

The economic importance of fish is greater today than ever before and is steadily growing. Statisticians predict that much of the vital protein food necessary to nourish our ever-increasing human population—of which perhaps half is underfed even today—will come from marine (salt water) fisheries. At present, approximately twenty-five million tons of fish are procured from the sea each year. Investigations of ways and means to increase this yield are now being vigorously pursued in many parts of the world. In the United States, the total estimated catch of salt and freshwater fish for one recent year was more than 3,850,000,000 pounds, valued at well over $200,000,000.

Sportsfishing has become enormously popular of late, especially in the United States. There, during the year ending June 30, 1951 more than sixteen million fishing licenses were issued, providing a revenue of more than thirty-five and one-half million dollars. Trade experts estimate that sportsfishing provides an income of about 150 million dollars each year to tackle manufacturers, boat captains, bait dealers, and others engaged in the business end of "fishing for fun."

A third industry connected with fish has recently become quite important—that concerned with the keeping of fishes as pets. One estimate places the number of people who maintain captive fishes in America at ten million. A large fish-importing trade has been built up, as well as the domestic breeding and rearing of tremendous numbers of small tropical freshwater fishes, goldfish, and aquatic plants. Along with this, there has developed an extensive tank-and-appliance manufacturing business. Little fish are now big business; approximately 150 different species of "tropicals" and forty kinds of aquatic plants are regularly available on the market today.

Lampreys and Borers—Modern Primitives

THE LAMPREYS and borers are the most primitive of living animals with backbones. Eel-shaped, jawless, scaleless fish with a single nostril, they lack the paired fins we find in most other fishes. For feeding, they possess a rough, rasping tongue, with which they scrape away an entrance to the body cavities of other fishes.

In all, we are acquainted with about fifty species of these creatures (class Cyclostomi, a word meaning "circular mouths"). They range from six inches to about three feet in adult size.

All of the borers, which include the hagfishes and slime-eels, are ocean dwellers, and lay relatively large eggs with a protective, horny shell. Unlike the lampreys, they seldom, if ever, are able to attack living prey, but eat their way inside fishes that are injured, or trapped in gill nets (nets that catch on the gill covers when the fish tries to back out). The borers devour their victims completely, except for head, skin, and the larger bones.

The Sea Lamprey, *Petromyzon marinus,* is a repulsive-looking fish with a mode of life that befits its appearance. It has a long, eel-like body, covered with scaleless skin that grades from whitish on the belly to grayish blue on the back in young adults, older individuals becoming mottled. Its only fins are a small caudal (tail) fin and two small dorsal (back) fins. It has a pair of well-formed eyes, and behind each of these stretches a series of seven holes which lead into the gills. A single nostril opens midway between the eyes.

Instead of jaws, the lamprey has a round, sucking mouth, lined with more than a hundred sharp teeth and containing a pistonlike tongue also armed with teeth. With its sucking mouth the lamprey fastens itself onto a fish, then rasps a hole in it, and sucks out its blood and body fluids. Lampreys sometimes attach themselves to large sharks and to boats and are capable of overtaking and fastening onto motorboats traveling fifteen miles per hour. Occasionally they attach themselves to human swimmers, but do not feed on them, although they have been known to cut out lumps of tissue from whales to which they have fastened themselves.

There are about twenty-five different kinds of lampreys, and they are found in both fresh and salt waters of many parts of the world. Those that live in the ocean, like the sea lamprey, go into fresh water to spawn. In the spring full-grown sea lampreys, ranging from about two to three feet in length, enter streams on our Atlantic coast. They sometimes employ their sucker-mouths to ascend waterfalls and rapids, and always use them to build their nests. Both male and female cooperate in moving stones to form a depression in which the small eggs, sometimes more than 200,000 are laid. After one spawning, lampreys die. The young larvae do not resemble their parents at all and are called ammocoetes. For at least three years they burrow in the mud, feeding on small bits of organic matter that they sift out of the ooze. Finally they change into the adult form and go back to the sea.

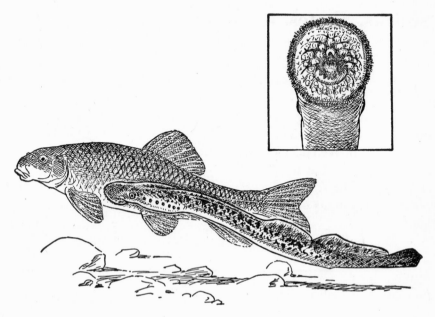

THE MOST PRIMITIVE OF ALL FISHES
The sea lamprey is in many ways the most primitive of living animals with backbones. It attaches itself to a fish, as in the picture (where it is shown on a white sucker), rasps a hole in the creature, and sucks out the blood and body fluids. The inset shows the sucking mouth of the lamprey, which has a large number of sharp teeth, and contains a tongue also provided with teeth.

Sea lampreys, however, can remain in fresh water all their lives, as is the case with the descendants of those that found their way through the Welland canal into the Great Lakes. Here the sea lamprey is considered a serious pest because it is believed to destroy large numbers of lake trout. In the ocean, too, this species attacks many commercially valuable fish. Although eaten today only in restricted localities, sea lampreys were considered a delicacy during the Middle Ages, and were used for food in the northeastern United States until about one hundred years ago. Not all lampreys prey on other fish; the brook lampreys do not feed at all as adults, but simply reproduce and die.

Sharks, Skates, Rays, and Chimeras

NOT EVERY SHARK is a fear-inspiring giant, yet some are even more than that. They range in size from two feet to about sixty feet in length. We encounter them in ocean waters throughout almost all of the world, but seldom where it is extremely cold. A few species run up into the fresh waters of tropical rivers, and three or four are regular inhabitants of fresh-water lakes in Central America and Thailand.

Sharks are flesh-eaters, and some are extremely savage in their habits, as we shall soon see. Most of them give birth to living young, but a number lay eggs with horny cases; fertilization is always internal. You may be surprised at the enormous variety among the sharks: about 235 species are known.

Most of the skates and rays live in the sea, although the sawfishes and some of the skates go far upstream, and some of the rays live permanently in fresh water. The bodies of these strange animals are very much flattened, and usually their pectoral fins are so expanded they remind us of wings. The skates undulate these fins to drive themselves forward, while the rays flap them like wings, flying through the water. In size these fishes range from monsters twenty feet across the wings to those less than one foot in width. So far as we know, the skates lay eggs with horny cases, while the rays have living young. Scientists have named and described several hundred species.

The weird-looking chimeras are at home in the deep waters of the oceans, where they are only rarely seen. These blunt-nosed fishes attain lengths of roughly three feet. They lay large eggs with horny capsules.

The sharks, skates, rays, and chimeras are different from most fishes in a number of odd and interesting ways. For one thing, all of them have gristle instead of true bone in their skeletons. They have jaws, two sets of paired fins, and a curious covering of spiny scales which gives the skin a texture like the surface of a file. Known as placoid scales, these are found only on fishes of this group.

These creatures also lack the true gill covers of the bony fishes; instead, the sharks, skates, and rays have from five to seven pairs of gill clefts, each opening to the outside, while the chimeras have a single opening on each side, formed by a fold of the skin—not a bone-supported, muscle-controlled organ like the gill covers of almost all bony fish. Sharks, skates, rays, and chimeras differ from the bony fishes in several other fundamental ways, and are so distinct that some zoologists do not consider them to be fishes at all. We place them in a class by themselves—the Chondrichthyes, a name meaning "gristle fishes."

The Sand Shark, *Carcharias taurus,* is one of the commonest sharks of the Atlantic seaboard. It is of little economic importance, however, as a source of food, leather, or vitamin A (from the liver). Typically sharklike in appearance, it has a prominent snout, five gill-slits on either side behind the eyes, an undershot jaw ringed with several rows of sharp triangular teeth, and a tail with the upper lobe much longer than the lower one. Predominantly light bronze in color, its rough skin, called "shagreen," has a metallic luster when viewed under water.

A number of species of sharks are dangerous to man; but the sand sharks look more sinister than they really are, for they have never been known to attack human beings. Their relative, the gray nurse of Australia, has a very bad reputation, though, and has contributed its share to the more than two hundred recorded shark attacks from that continent for the years 1840 to 1940. From 1919 to 1949 inclusive, seventy-seven authenticated shark attacks on Australian swimmers and bathers are on record, in addition to thirty-three on professional divers. More than two-thirds of the swimmers and bathers died from the wounds they received. (The gray nurse is only a distant relative of the nurse shark of Florida and the West Indies.)

The largest sand sharks on record measured almost eleven feet in length, but the species does not feed on large prey, voraciously eating many kinds of smaller fishes instead.

Females give birth to living young, a single one at a time, which is especially well-developed at birth. Evidence indicates that the single fetus actively swims about inside the reproductive tract of its mother and that it feeds upon undeveloped eggs that apparently are specially shed into the uterus to provide nourishment for it.

The Mako, *Isurus oxyrinchus,* is a savage, streamlined shark of the warm Atlantic, renowned for the fighting qualities it shows when hooked. Most game fishermen regard it and its close relative, *Isurus glaucus* from the Pacific and Indian Oceans, more highly than any other shark. These species take rapidly moving bait, and then swim fast and hard with it, sometimes leaping as high as ten feet or more out of the water in their efforts to escape. They are also known to attack deliberately the man or boat that has them fast. The record Pacific mako was twelve feet long and weighed one thousand pounds. The Atlantic form is said to reach thirteen feet.

Makos are eaters of fish and can capture speedy ones like mackerel. They attack larger fish, too. The Atlantic mako fights with the swordfish, and whole swordfish as well as many pounds of swordfish flesh have been found in its stomach. In the Pacific, makos fight with the black marlin.

The Great White Shark, *Carcharodon carcharias,* is also called "the man-eater," a title that it well deserves, since it is undoubtedly the most dangerous of all sharks. Not only does it maim or kill bathers, but without provocation it will sometimes attack small boats. Few living creatures are safe from its huge appetite. Sea lions, seals, sea turtles, sharks, tuna, and a large variety of other fishes have been found

THE MOST DANGEROUS OF ALL SHARKS
The great white shark is known as "the man-eater." It occasionally injures or kills swimmers, and sometimes attacks boats. Its appetite is huge: sea lions, seals, and other large creatures have been found in the stomach of the shark. However, the piranha of South America is a more dangerous fish than this one.

—sometimes in a whole condition—in white sharks' stomachs. This shark also eats garbage and offal, at least occasionally.

The white shark inhabits temperate and tropical oceans all over the world, coming near shore fairly frequently in some regions.

One specimen was thirty-six and one-half feet long, but mature females are usually about fifteen feet long, and few individuals are found larger than this. A twenty-one-foot specimen weighed seven thousand pounds. The females bear living young.

The Thresher Shark, *Alopias vulpinis,* has an enormously elongated upper lobe of its tail fin which is often longer than all the rest of its body. This fin is apparently used in capturing prey. Riding herd on a school of fish, the thresher swims 'round and 'round them, all the while splashing with its great tail. Gradually it forces them closer and closer together, and finally goes in for the kill. Sometimes two threshers will work together in this fashion. Occasionally, the tail is used to strike prey such as sea birds and fish. The old belief that the thresher shark teams up with the swordfish to attack whales is untrue.

This temperate and tropical species occurs in the Atlantic and eastern Pacific, but whether the form found in the western Pacific and Indian oceans is the same species or not is still undecided. Thresher sharks grow to a length of twenty feet or more, about half of which is composed of the tail. The females bear living young, two to four at a time, about three feet long.

Threshers are harmless to man, although they sometimes cause trouble by becoming entangled in fishing nets.

The Nurse Shark, *Ginglymostoma cirratum,* is a sluggish species that spends much of its time lying quietly on the bottom in the shallow waters of the tropical Atlantic. It is well known in Florida, where it is extensively fished for its hide, considered the best from any American shark for the production of leather.

Nurse sharks have large broods, as many as twenty-six young being born at a time. Newly born nurse sharks are less than a foot in length and generally show numerous spots that are usually lost as they grow up. Their ground color ranges from gold to light brown. Although nurse sharks mature at about five feet, individuals as long as fourteen feet have been caught. They feed mostly on creatures like crabs, shrimp, spiny lobsters, squid, and sea urchins, and on small fish.

The Whale Shark, *Rhincodon typus,* is the largest of living fishes. Accurately measured specimens forty-five feet long are on record and some of sixty feet have been reliably reported. No one knows just how much such monsters weigh, but the estimated weight of a thirty-eight-foot example was nearly 26,600 pounds.

Found in all tropical seas, the whale shark occasionally ventures into temperate waters. It sometimes gathers in schools. Often it basks or feeds at the surface, and is so fearless or lazy, that it is sometimes rammed by ships.

The whale shark eats only smaller invertebrates and fishes. It has a large mouth with very small teeth and a strainer-like apparatus at the gills. Swimming open-mouthed through schools of little fish or aggregations of other small sea animals, the whale shark engulfs them. The water is then forced out through its gills, and the animals are caught on the specially contrived gill arches which act like sieves. There are also reports that this shark feeds in a vertical position, head up, and that it sucks in its prey.

The whale shark's back and sides are distinctively marked with round white or yellowish spots that show up plainly against the dark gray or brown of the skin.

The Smooth Dogfishes, *Mustelus canis* of the western Atlantic and *Mustelus californicus* of the eastern Pacific, are small sharks that attain lengths of about five and two and one-half feet, respectively. They do not inhabit the open sea, but usually remain quite near shore.

What we say here applies to the Atlantic species, but the Pacific one is undoubtedly quite similar. Crabs and lobsters are its chief food, but small fish, worms, squid, and other mollusks are also eaten. Garbage is taken if available. Dogfish have about six rows of flattened, pavement-like teeth, employed for crushing rather than shearing as are the more pointed teeth of many sharks. Scientists have shown, by marking individual teeth in the rear rows, that the dogfish's back teeth gradually move forward, replacing those lost at the front edge of the mouth. Since new ones are constantly being formed, to move forward as those in front break off or are worn away, the shark has a never-ending supply of teeth. The sand at the bottom of the shark tank in the old New York Aquarium was filled with hundreds of discarded teeth.

Other experiments have shown that the smooth dogfish seeks its prey by smell rather than sight, even though it has well-developed eyes. This is probably true of many other kinds of sharks, but whether it holds for the fast-swimming oceanic ones is questionable.

Some sharks lay large eggs covered with horny capsules. In others the eggs hatch while still inside the mother, and the young sharks complete further development before being liberated. In the smooth dogfish, which produces living young, there is an intimate, placenta-like union between the bloodstreams of the mother and her offspring, by which the embryo is provided food and other necessities in a way similar to that in the mammals. The period of development within the mother is about ten months, and the litters of four to twenty baby dogfish, about fourteen inches long, are born in late spring and early summer. Since smooth dogfish are of little commercial importance and are believed to be destructive to other fishes, their abundance is sometimes an annoyance to fishermen.

The Tiger Shark, *Galeocerdo cuvier,* occurs in tropical oceans all over the world, and strays into temperate waters during the summer. No one is sure whether its popular name arises from its voracious habits and prominent, sickle-shaped teeth, or from the stripes and blotches displayed by smaller specimens. At any rate, tiger sharks are considered the most dangerous species in some areas, and are proved man-eaters around Australia.

Tiger sharks up to thirty feet in length have been reported, but the longest on fully authenticated record was an eighteen-foot specimen. When born they are about one and one-half feet long. The size of litter varies greatly; from ten to eighty-two young have been found in various females.

Most remarkable are the feeding habits of tiger sharks; practically everything edible—and much that is not—has been found in their stomachs. Their food ranges in size from small crabs to giant sea turtles and other large sharks. Spiny lobsters, horseshoe crabs, snails, octopuses, squid, fishes of all sorts, sea snakes, birds, and sea lions are all eaten by them. They capture sting rays which often leave their spines embedded in the shark's jaws. All kinds of offal are eagerly swallowed, including the heads and hooves of cows and horses, and whole dogs, cats, and goats; even human corpses. Such indigestible things as old boots and clothes, tin cans, and sacks of coal have also been taken from their maws.

This abundant species is fished for its hide and also, to some extent, for its liver. As with numerous other sharks, its flesh is palatable and is used for food in certain localities.

The Soupfin Shark, *Galeorhinus zyopterus,* from the coast of California and Baja California, has long been well known to the Chinese, who consider its fins superior to almost all others as an essential ingredient of certain soups. The fins are cut off and thoroughly dried, in which condition they can be shipped. Before they are used, they are soaked in warm water, and the cartilaginous rays, that in life gave the fin its strength, are separated from the flesh. Then these rays are sliced up and boiled with meat, chicken, vegetables, and so forth, to make soup.

Not until 1937 did the soupfin shark become generally known. At that time an intensive fishery for this species was instituted to obtain its liver, which had been found to be extraordinarily rich in vitamin A. Since soupfin livers sold for as much as thirteen dollars a pound, and an average female's liver might weigh as much as fifteen pounds, small fortunes were made on a few boatloads of these sharks. Within three years, however, the number of sharks taken fell off to such an extent that many fishermen had to abandon the fishery. It is believed most probable that this reduction in numbers may have resulted from over-fishing, because the soupfin shark is apparently a slow reproducing and maturing species.

Male soupfin sharks mature at a length of about five feet, the females at a somewhat larger size. The young are born alive, and an average brood consists of thirty-five individuals.

Other species of sharks are also important for the considerable amounts of vitamin A that are contained in the oil of their livers.

The Hammerhead Shark, *Sphyrna zygaena,* has one of the strangest heads found among fishes. Its skull is flattened into two long, narrow, squared-off projections, at the extreme ends of which are located the eyes and nostrils. No one has been able to explain the utility of this bizarre arrangement except that the placing of the paired sense organs further apart may allow more accurate location of prey or enemies—much in the way that a wider base between two observation points permits more accurate range-finding for artillery.

The food of hammerhead sharks consists mostly of various fishes, including its own kind, other sharks, skates, and sting rays. There are several authenticated accounts of hammerheads attacking human bathers. Since they reach a length of thirteen feet, they are capable of doing considerable harm. In the shark fisheries of the West Indies and Florida, hammerheads are used both for leather and liver oil. As many as thirty-seven embryos have been found in a single female. The young are about twenty inches long, and their "hammers" are folded back alongside the body to make birth easier.

A SHARK WITH A HEAD LIKE A HAMMER
The hammerhead shark, with one of the oddest heads in the finny kingdom, is truly a weird-looking creature; the eyes and nostrils are in the two long, squared-off projections of the skull. Hammerheads grow to thirteen feet in length, and occasionally attack swimmers. Two sharks are shown here with their prey, a cownose ray.

In the Atlantic, there are five species of hammerheads, but exactly how many exist in the rest of the oceans is not known.

The Little Skate, *Raja erinacea,* is the best known of the half-dozen species of skates that are found off the northeastern coast of the United States. Like practically all skates, it lives mostly on the bottom and the greater part of its food consists of bottom-inhabiting animals such as crabs, shrimps, worms, sea squirts, bivalves, squid, and small fishes. It has numerous rows of small, rounded teeth set in a pattern resembling a tile pavement.

Skates are relatives of the sharks, much flattened from back to belly, with a roughly triangularly shaped body, and a long, thin tail. The large triangular pectoral fins, extending out on either side of the body, are the principal means of locomotion. These fins are undulated from front to rear, not flapped like wings as are those of some rays. The more or less rigid tail, with two small fins attached at its end, acts as a steering device to a certain extent.

The eyes are located quite close together on top of the head, while the mouth is underneath. The gill slits are also on the underside. Instead of taking water in through the mouth and passing it out through the gill slits, as do the sharks during breathing, skates use their spiracles, which are two valved openings just behind the eyes. Water enters through the spiracles and passes out through the gill slits. Thus the problem of remaining on the bottom and inhaling without taking in debris—as would happen if the mouth were used—is solved.

The little skate is usually not more than twenty inches long, but may attain a length of two feet. Females lay eggs inclosed in a rectangular, blackish, leathery case, measuring about one and three-quarters by one and three-eighths inches, at each corner of which a thin, hook-shaped prong is attached. Similar egg cases are laid by other skates. They are sometimes found washed up on the beach and called "mermaids' purses." The eggs of the little skate are laid during the late spring and the summer and probably take several months to hatch.

There are seventy-five or more skates belonging to the genus *Raja,* and they inhabit most of the world's cool seas. Some of them occur in quite deep water. The largest species are about eight feet long.

The Atlantic Torpedo, *Tetranarce occidentalis,* **and the Pacific Torpedo,** *Tetranarce californica,* possess powerful electric organs that are strong enough to knock a man off his feet in certain circumstances. At the New York Aquarium, we measured the electrical discharges of a large local specimen and found them to be about two hundred volts and 1600 watts. There is no doubt that such electrical powers are an excellent means of defense. It is believed that torpedoes also use their electricity to obtain food, by stunning fishes and other creatures before eating them, because relatively large fish have been found in their stomachs without a single mark on their bodies. Only by shocking them into insensibility could the torpedoes have overpowered these fish without damaging them in any way. Moreover, a Neapolitan species of electric ray has been observed shocking mullet into insensibility and then swallowing them whole.

In appearance torpedoes are distinguished from other rays by their round, disklike body, large tail fin, and soft naked skin. Some of them are said to attain weights of two hundred pounds, but the average Atlantic torpedo weighs about thirty pounds. Weights of more than fifty pounds have been recorded for the Pacific torpedo. Torpedoes are born alive and are capable of producing electricity even before birth. There are quite a number of different kinds of electric rays, most of them found in tropical seas.

The Sawfish, *Pristis pectinatus,* that occurs on the southeastern and Gulf coasts of the United States, has a snout elongated into a flat, blunt blade, on each side of which is a single row of twenty-four to thirty-two strong, sharp teeth. This sawlike structure is about a third as long as the fish's body and is a formidable weapon in even a small specimen. In the largest ones of twenty feet, it may be a foot wide at its base and six feet long, with teeth projecting well over two inches on either side.

The mouth of the sawfish is located on the underside of the head and is equipped only with small blunt teeth. It is the "saw" which is used to obtain food. With a nicely gauged sideswipe the sawfish impales a fish on one of the teeth, then swims to the bottom with it and there scrapes it off, quickly swimming over the fish to engulf it—before it can recover, should it not be completely incapacitated.

The "saw" may also be used in a more haphazard fashion, the sawfish swimming into a school of fish and rapidly striking from side to side. The dead or injured fish can then be devoured more or less at leisure. Sawfish have also been reported as rooting out crustaceans and other invertebrates with the "saw."

Sawfish live in shallow, tropical, salt waters and the brackish ones around tidal inlets and river mouths. They also travel upstream into fresh water well beyond the region of tidal influence. They give birth to broods of as many as twenty young, which are born fully armed with a "saw"! At this time, however, it is soft and flexible and covered with a membranous sheath.

There are about six different kinds of sawfishes. Although they have a sharklike body, sawfishes are really rays, as can be seen by the location of their gill openings, which are underneath the head rather than on the sides, as in the sharks.

A FISH THAT IS ARMED TO THE TEETH

The sawfish uses its "saw" to catch its food. It impales a fish on one of the teeth, then scrapes it off, and swallows it before it can revive. Also, the sawfish swims into a school of fishes, striking them down left and right, thus getting more food. Even the young are born fully armed with a "saw."

The Sting Ray, *Dasyatis centrura,* hides at the bottom of seas, bays or rivers, its flattened disk-shaped body concealed by sand or silt and by its camouflaging coloration. When stepped on by some unwary person, the sting ray quickly swings its long, flexible tail up and around so that it drives into the leg of the unfortunate person a spine that is toothed like a saw. This spine is located on the top surface of its tail, halfway between the base and tip. The excruciating pain that almost invariably follows such an injury is caused by some type of poison that the spine introduces into the wound. Pain, swelling, dizziness, and nausea may be so intense that hospitalization is necessary. In a few instances death is said to have resulted.

There are several dozen different species of sting rays, and they are found in all warm seas and in a number of tropical rivers. They range in size from a giant Australian form, that attains weights of about 750 pounds, to small fresh-water ones that are the size of a pancake. The Sting ray, *Dasyatis centrura,* which is the one most commonly seen on the northeastern coast of the United States, reaches a length of twelve feet, although specimens over six feet long are rare. So far as known, all sting rays have living young.

THE STING RAY AND ITS POISONOUS SPINE

Sting rays are found in warm seas and tropical rivers. In Australia, one sting ray grows to 750 pounds; fresh-water rays, however, are much smaller. Halfway down its tail the sting ray has a spine with teeth like a saw, which it drives into the leg of anyone who steps on it. Poison is injected into the wound, causing intense pain and, occasionally, death.

The Devil Ray, *Manta birostris,* grows to weights of more than three thousand pounds, and is the largest of all the rays. It has a diamond-shaped body that may be twenty feet across from wing-tip to wing-tip, a long thin tail, and a pair of prominent "horns" projecting out from the head just in front of the eyes. These "horns" are really a pair of fins, called "cephalic" fins. They probably help the devil ray in obtaining the small sea creatures upon which it feeds.

Devil rays inhabit the warmer ocean waters. They apparently spend a good deal of time at or near the surface, "flying" through the

Marine Studios, Marineland, Fla.

37223

College of St. Francis
JOLIET, ILL.

CAUTION IS THE WATCHWORD IN DEALING WITH SHARKS
Although a number of sharks are proven maneaters, the vast majority of the nearly 250 known
species have never been known deliberately to attack man. Nevertheless, sharks are so well
equipped with dangerous rows of teeth that few persons would not treat them with great caution.

water by slowly and gracefully flapping their great triangular "wings," or lying quietly, basking in the sun. Their common name gives a wrong idea of their habits, for they have never been known to harm a man or a boat deliberately, although they have capsized or demolished a number of boats in their Herculean efforts to escape when harpooned. Perhaps it is their forbidding appearance and great size that have given them the name of devil ray and made them much feared.

The female devil ray has a single large youngster at a time. One eighteen-foot, twenty-three-hundred-pound female which was caught, contained a young devil ray just about to be born; the young one weighed twenty-eight pounds.

Fringe-Finned Fishes and Lungfishes —Among Earth's Greatest Oddities

THESE STRANGE CREATURES are among the most fascinating oddities on earth. Their forerunners, the ancient fringe-finned fishes (crossopterygians) were at one time the chief animals of prey in fresh water. There were great numbers of them, and they thrived for untold ages. But they died out millions of years ago. Or that, in any event, was the opinion of scientists until two were discovered alive in ocean waters quite recently.

Why should we dwell on these fishes of ages past? They are of great scientific interest, since it was from them that all land animals with backbones—the amphibians, reptiles, birds, and mammals—developed.

In these ancient types, we find that the paired fins, and sometimes the other fins, too, consist of fringed lobes. The rays and membrane of the fins are attached to a fleshy, scale-covered base, which contains supporting bones. These bones are so arranged that with relatively little change they could have become the support of a limb instead of a fin. Many fossil fringe-fins used the air bladder as a lung to breathe atmospheric air. These are two reasons why we believe the fringe-fins were the ancestors of the first backboned land animals, the amphibians.

The lungfishes are in several ways similar to the fringe-fins, but differ from them in the way the jaws are attached to the skull and in other characteristics. After studying the lungfishes and comparing them with fossils, some experts have come to the conclusion that the lungfishes are an offshoot of the fringe-fins that has become degenerate in a number of ways. Lungfishes have lobe-shaped paired fins, which may, however, be no more than mere ribbon-like structures, as in the African and South American species living today. They also have nostrils that open into the cavity of the mouth and an air-bladder that serves as a lung. Strangely enough, they do not breathe air through their nostrils, however, apparently using them only for smelling underwater. Many of the internal structures of the lungfishes resemble the ones in amphibians.

The lungfishes of today are but a remnant of those that lived in the past. Five species are still alive, all inhabiting tropical fresh waters. Three very similar forms come from Africa, one from the Amazon and Paraguay Rivers of South America, and one from Queensland, Australia.

The East London Coelacanth, *Latimeria chalumnae,* was unknown until 1938, when a fishing boat off the coast of South Africa pulled in a five-foot, blue, rough-scaled fish with strange, fleshy bases to several of its fins and a peculiar triangle-shaped tail. Although the boat crew decided to save the queer fish, they did not realize the sensational nature of their unique catch.

As it turned out, the fish belonged to a group supposed to have become extinct sixty to seventy million years ago—about the same time that the dinosaurs disappeared from the earth. Moreover, this ancient group of fishes originated about 400 million years ago and is the one that includes the ancestors of all land vertebrates (backboned animals).

Through an unfortunate series of circumstances all of the internal soft parts and much of the skeleton of the East London coelacanth were discarded before it was examined by any expert. Therefore, strangely enough, the anatomy of some of its fossil relatives is better known. As a result of the first catch in 1938, an intense search was started for more specimens, in the hope that we might learn more about this "living fossil." In late 1952 fishermen took another coelacanth, and Professor J. L. B. Smith, leading South African ichthyologist, was rushed by plane to the scene of the find. He succeeded in

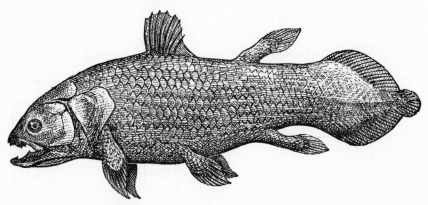

RETURNED FROM THE PAST
The East London coelacanth belongs to a group of fishes that was supposed to have become extinct from sixty to seventy million years ago. In 1938, a fishing boat off the coast of South Africa pulled in a five-foot, rough-scaled specimen. Late in 1952, a native fisherman caught another coelacanth of a different species in the same general region. Both finds caused a great stir in the scientific world.

preserving the specimen, to the delight of the scientific world. Most surprising of all, the fish turned out to be a different species. Scientists are now wondering more than ever what rarities still remain undiscovered in the depths of the sea.

The African Lungfish, *Protopterus annectens,* has been known to live longer without food and water than any other backboned animal. Specimens have been kept alive in a natural state of suspended animation in blocks of hardened mud for more than four years, after which they were "awakened" successfully to take up a more ordinary life for a fish.

When the waters of its native tropical streams, lakes, and swamps commence to dry up during times of unusual drought or during regular annual dry seasons, the lungfish sinks into the mud. Being an air-breather, it is little inconvenienced so long as the mud remains quite soft; but when it begins to harden, the fish has to struggle to the surface to obtain a gulp of air. Nevertheless, the lungfish continues to force its way upward periodically, until at last the surface has become quite hard, and all that remains to indicate the fish's presence is a breathing hole scarcely larger in diameter than a lead pencil.

Underneath in the still pliable mud, the lungfish now prepares itself for its summer rest, or "estivation," as it is called. It folds its tail over its head, coming to rest in a tight U-shaped position, head and tail uppermost. Its skin secretes a thin covering, protecting all but the mouth of the fish against undue drying out. The mud gradually hardens all around it, and finally it is completely encased as if in stone. Profound changes in the working of the body parts of the immobile

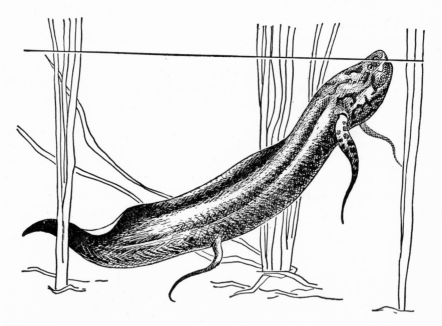

THIS ONE "SLEEPS" AND BREATHES AIR
The African lungfish provides us with a remarkable example of an animal that can live for a long period of time in a natural state of suspended animation. Some lungfish have existed in blocks of hardened mud for more than four years, and have afterwards resumed their usual life. Normally, lungfish must come to the surface for air, or drown.

lungfish take place, enabling it to live at a very slow rate, so to speak, and to withstand the accumulation of waste products in its blood. When the rains return and soften the hardened mud, the fish is aroused from its "sleep" and soon begins to feed voraciously, principally on other fishes and on snails and bivalves.

The lungfish has small gills, but must have access to air or it drowns. About once every twenty minutes it comes to the surface to swallow a gulp of air, passing the gas into a pair of air bladders or lungs that open into the gullet. Among the many other unusual features of structure found in the lungfish are a pair of nostrils that open from the exterior into the mouth; in this respect lungfish differ from almost all other kinds of fishes. The lungfish has a long body with long dorsal and anal fins that seem to come together in a sharp point to form the tail. The pectoral and pelvic fins are merely long, tapering ribbons. Scales are small and completely embedded in the skin. In color it is brown or tan with black or dark brown mottling.

The male lungfish prepares a clear area among dense plant growth on the muddy bottom, and there the female lays her eggs. These are about one-eighth of an inch in diameter and are guarded by the male and kept supplied with fresh water by vigorous movements of his tail. After about eight days they hatch, and the young are also guarded for awhile. Young lungfish are unusual in having external gills—four pairs of them—like those seen in a number of amphibians. As the fish mature, these organs gradually disappear. Lungfish attain a size of at least three feet. They are a popular food with native Africans.

The African lungfish is widely distributed in the fresh waters of tropical Africa. There are two other closely related African species, one of which reaches a length of at least six feet.

Sturgeons and Paddle Fishes
—Famed for Their Eggs

T HE STURGEONS are famed for their eggs, which we eat as caviar. Although these fishes are dwellers in the sea for the most part, they leave salt water and go up into rivers to lay their eggs. There are some sturgeons, however, that live permanently in streams and lakes. Perhaps as many as twenty-five species exist; their cousins the paddle fishes, are far fewer in number, and like the sturgeons make their home only in the Northern Hemisphere.

Although the sturgeons and the paddle fishes are not close relatives of the sharks, they remind us of them in several ways. For one thing, they have little true bone in their skeletons—mostly these are gristle. (Thus the sturgeons and paddle fishes are placed in the order Chondrostei—"gristle-boned.") Five rows of bony plates protect the bodies of some; others are almost completely naked-skinned. Scientists look upon them as primitive forms of the ray-finned group of the bony fishes.

The Atlantic Sturgeon, *Acipenser oxyrhynchus,* roots up sand or mud with its pointed, flattened snout to obtain the small, bottom-inhabiting invertebrates and fishes upon which it feeds. On the underside of its snout is a row of four barbels, or feelers, that are undoubtedly used to detect food, and behind these is the sucking mouth, which can be protruded. The rather long body has five longitudinal rows of large, bony plates, the fish's scales. The tail is sharklike, the upper lobe being much longer than the lower.

Atlantic sturgeon are found on both sides of the Atlantic from the St. Lawrence River to the Carolinas in the west, and from Scandinavia to the Black Sea in the east. During the spring they enter large

1424

rivers, and travel upstream to spawn. Large numbers used to be caught at this season for their flesh, which is especially fine when smoked, and for their eggs, which are one of the original sources of the caviar of commerce. The eggs are adhesive, heavier than water, and a little larger than one-eighth of an inch in diameter. An average female contains over one and one-half million of them.

PRODUCER OF CAVIAR
The Atlantic sturgeon is a long fish covered with a tough skin and bony plates. It uses its strange snout to burrow in the bottom for food. The average female produces in excess of one and a half million eggs; prepared and salted, these are known as caviar.

Fully grown Atlantic sturgeon are usually about seven or eight feet long, but eighteen-foot specimens are said to have been caught on both sides of the Atlantic Ocean. At present, in the United States and Canada at least, the Atlantic sturgeon is relatively rare, and is apparently becoming more scarce all the time.

The White Sturgeon, *Acipenser transmontanus,* is the largest fish found in North American waters. It is native to the coast and rivers of the northwest of the United States, and has been reported to attain a weight of eighteen to nineteen hundred pounds. One twelve-and-a-half-foot female weighed 1,285 pounds. Unfortunately, this valuable commercial fish is now very rare, and is probably dying out. Heavy fishing, pollution, and large dams that keep it from reaching its breeding grounds upstream have all taken their toll.

The Beluga, *Huso huso,* also a sturgeon, is the largest fresh-water fish in the world. It is found in the Volga, Dnieper, and other European rivers, and in the Caspian and the Black seas. A specimen of this aquatic giant, weighing 3,210 pounds, is on record, and several exceeding two thousand pounds are known. One fish of 2,250 pounds was fourteen feet, two inches long, and a 2,680-pound female contained over 320 pounds of eggs, or roe, enough to provide caviar canapés for an army.

The Paddle Fish, *Polyodon spathula,* has been called the most remarkable fresh-water fish in North America because of its many bizarre and unique features. Its naked body—it has scales only on part of the tail—is quite sharklike in general appearance, but its head is entirely different from that of any other type of fish. Projecting out from the front is a long, flattened snout, about one-third to one-half as long as all the rest of the fish. Beneath this paddle-shaped projection is the wide mouth, the lower jaw of which can be dropped down to form a truly cavelike opening. The tiny eyes are located alongside the base of the paddle. The gill covers are large and soft and end toward the rear in a heavy triangular point.

The paddle fish feeds upon small aquatic creatures like freshwater shrimp, water fleas, and aquatic insects. It also eats some vegetable matter. Its paddle is undoubtedly used to detect the presence of food, for it is well provided with nerves and sense organs, and is swung from side to side in an exploratory fashion while the fish swims. When it encounters any tiny creatures, the fish opens its mouth wide and literally swims over its food, the water passing out through the gill-chambers, while small objects are retained by the gill rakers which act like a sieve.

The reproductive habits of paddle fish are still a mystery despite the efforts of numerous scientists to find out how, when, and where they lay their eggs. The smallest paddle fish ever caught was about five-eighths of an inch long and at this size did not yet have a paddle. It is believed that the fish spawns in the main channels of large rivers in the Mississippi system. Sexual maturity is reached when the fish is between thirty-nine and fifty-five inches in length. Maximum length exceeds six feet and maximum weight 150 pounds. The flesh of the paddle fish is usually smoked, and the eggs are used as caviar.

THE MOST REMARKABLE NORTH AMERICAN FISH
An odd creature indeed is the paddle fish—it looks rather like a shark in some respects, but its head is quite unlike that of other fish. It possesses a long, flattened snout, shaped somewhat like a paddle, which is used for detecting food, and under this is a wide mouth. The tiny eyes are located at the base of the paddle. Except for a part of its tail, this fish is without scales.

Only two species of paddle fish exist today—one in the rivers of China, the other in the United States.

Gars and Bowfins—Fresh-Water Savages

THE GARS and the bowfins are rugged-looking fishes, extremely fierce and voracious in their habits. Because of the havoc they wreak among other living things and because their flesh is ill-tasting, they are most unpopular with fishermen. Conservationists point out, however, that these predatory fishes frequently keep the hordes of suckers, catfish, and minnows in check, and thus help to maintain the balance of nature.

Although today not many members of this group exist—we know of only ten species of gars and one of the bowfins—in the remote past they were far more numerous. Some of these ancestors lived in Europe, but today we do not find the bowfin outside the fresh waters of the United States and Canada, and the gars live only in North and Central America and Cuba. Sometimes, however, they stray into brackish and salt water. They make up the order Protospondyli.

The Longnose Gar, *Lepisosteus osseus,* with its long, beaklike jaws bearing strong, conical teeth throughout their length, is a prime example of a fish that preys on other fishes. Stealthily it glides alongside a prospective victim and with a sudden swift, sideward snap, securely impales the fish on its needle-sharp teeth. Usually the prey is caught crosswise, but it is eventually juggled around so that its head points toward the gar's mouth and is then swallowed whole. Feeding is often done at night. In many places gars are considered a serious menace to food, game, and forage fishes, but this has been proved true in only a limited number of cases.

On the other hand, longnose gars themselves seem well protected against their enemies by the heavy, diamond-shaped scales that cover their body like a coat of mail. So hard they can turn the sharpest knife, these scales are of a type commonly found on ancient fishes,

1428

but absent among the more recently evolved, streamlined, fast-swimming species and their descendants. Although the gar's scales are jointed with one another, they do not make a very flexible covering, and this may be one reason why gars are sluggish creatures, rarely moving rapidly except while feeding. The body of the longnose gar is round and long. The dorsal and anal fins are located just in front of the tail.

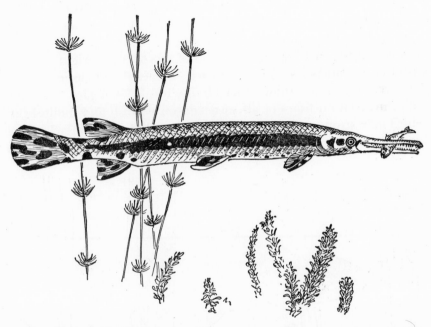

A FISH THAT EATS FISH
The longnose gar has a taste for fish, and its long, beaklike jaws and strong, conical teeth are excellent equipment for catching them. The gar swims quietly beside its prospective prey, then suddenly snaps its jaws to the side, impaling the victim on its sharp teeth. In general, the gar is a slow-moving creature.

Periodically, as the water in which they live becomes foul or too warm, gars rise to the surface and take a gulp of air. They spawn in shallow water, usually among weeds, during the spring. The numerous eggs are adhesive; a fifty-six-inch female, weighing thirty-two pounds, contained 77,150 of them. A maximum length of five feet is attained. Longnose gars are widely distributed from Quebec and Vermont to Florida, and from the Great Lakes, excepting Lake Superior, to northern Mexico.

The Alligator Gar, *Lepisosteus spatula,* from the lower Mississippi valley and other streams draining the Gulf Coast, is the second largest fresh-water fish in North America. There are authentic records of specimens more than nine feet long and unconfirmed ones of twelve and fourteen feet. One female that was nine feet, eight and one-half inches in length, weighed 302 pounds.

The Bowfin, *Amia calva,* represents the last living survivor of a group of fishes that was relatively abundant in the geological past in Europe and North America. Now found only in fresh waters from Vermont to Florida and the Great Lakes to Texas, the bowfin holds its own very well with numerous fishes of more recent origin. In fact, it is often considered a scourge of such "modern" gamefishes as bass and perch, just as are those other "living fossils," the gars.

Bowfins feed on fishes of all sorts and on crayfish and mollusks as well. Their strong, sharp-toothed jaws enable them to attack quite large fish. Even small birds sometimes fall victims to their voracious

A FISH THAT SOMETIMES EATS BIRDS

With its sturdy jaws and powerful teeth, the bowfin, an American fresh-water fish, will attack other big fish and even some birds. The male is remarkably "domestic"—not only does he make a sort of nest for his mate, but he also protects the eggs and the young that emerge from them.

appetites. Although they fight hard when hooked, they have never found favor with sportsmen. Nor are they considered a desirable food, except in a few scattered localities. They reach lengths of over two feet and weights of more than ten pounds, females being larger than males.

The stocky body of the bowfin is round in cross-section and covered with dark olive scales, shading to lighter underneath. During the breeding season, the pectoral, pelvic, and anal fins of the males become bright green. Males also show a large black spot at the upper base of the tail fin.

The male bowfin prepares a nest in late spring by clearing a space among the plants and making a small depression in the bottom, where the female lays large numbers of eggs, between one-sixteenth and one-eighth of an inch in diameter. These are adhesive and become attached to plants and rootlets within and surrounding the nest. The male guards the eggs until they hatch, that is, from four to fourteen days, depending on the temperature. For the first few days, the newly hatched fish attach themselves by means of a sucking disk to the plants or bottom. After that they become free-swimming, and are herded about in a school by the male, who still bravely protects them for a month or more, sometimes until they are three or four inches long.

Bowfins have gills of unusual microscopic structure that are thought to aid them in breathing when in foul waters. They also can breathe air by taking a gulp at the surface and passing the gas into the specialized air bladder.

Our Most Important Fishes—Herring, Salmon, Pike, and Their Relatives

---

Econowically, this is our most valuable group of fishes —it provides us with about twenty million tons of commercial fish each year. In this tremendous assemblage we find all the herring-like forms, the salmons and the trouts and their relatives, the pike and pickerels, and a host of other species. They inhabit both fresh and salt waters of all the oceans and the continents, from the Arctic and the Antarctic to the Equator, and from the depths of the sea to high mountain streams.

The two families most important to our commerce are the herring, shad, and sardines (Clupeidae) and the salmon and trout (Salmonidae). In fact, the herrings and their relatives rank first in economic importance among all the families of fishes. They occur in all seas, and include more than 150 different species. Some of them enter fresh water, frequently to spawn. A few live only in fresh water, but the majority never leave the sea.

The salmon and trout were originally found only in the fresh and salt waters of the Northern Hemisphere, none naturally dwelling further south than California, Georgia, Spain, the Caspian Sea, and the Kamchatka Peninsula. Man, however, has introduced them into suitable waters over much of the world. They either live their entire life in fresh water or spend part of it in the sea, returning to fresh water to spawn. As many as one hundred species have been listed, but the actual number is considerably less than this.

The pike, the muskellunge, and the three species of pickerels (family Esocidae) are all native to the fresh waters of North America, with the pike also found in Europe and Asia. There are three or four species of American mudminnows and a single European one; they are fresh-water forms and are generally classified as a single family (Umbridae).

Among the other well-known fishes—and here we are mustering only a few names from the great finny legions of this order—are the tarpons and ten-pounders, the bonefish, the pirarucu, the milkfish, the whitefishes and ciscos, the grayling, the smelt, and the Alaska blackfish.

Although many of these fishes are highly specialized and of relatively recent evolution, the group (order Isospondyli, a name meaning "equal vertebrae") as a whole is not advanced, and contains some of the most primitive of bony fishes. We identify its members by the lack of spines in the fins and by the fact that the pelvic fins (if the fishes have them), are located toward the rear of the body. Scientists identify these fishes mostly by the structure of the skull and upper jaw.

The Tarpon, *Tarpon atlanticus,* has become a famous gamefish because of its fighting qualities and leaping powers. Since its flesh is often coarse and bitter, it is seldom eaten and therefore is not of commercial importance as a foodfish. The largest tarpon ever caught by means of tackle weighed 247 pounds and was almost seven and one-half feet long. It is known, however, that the tarpon sometimes reaches weights of three hundred pounds and lengths of nearly eight feet.

Tarpon are handsome, silvery fish with large shiny scales, a prominent mouth, and a long fine extension of the rear portion of the dorsal fin. They are inhabitants of the tropical Atlantic Ocean, normally not far from shore. They are frequently found in brackish waters, far up tropical rivers, and in lakes. Evidently tarpon can live for years in fresh water. They usually range from Florida and the Gulf Coast to Brazil, but straggle as far north as Nova Scotia. They frequent the west coast of Africa and are common in the West Indies, but rare in Bermuda.

Very few data were available on the tarpon's life history until the New York Aquarium, in 1938, established a laboratory on the west coast of Florida, in the heart of tarpon country, to study this fish. We now know that tarpon mature when about seven years old and four feet long, and that their numerous eggs are undoubtedly laid in open waters and sink to the bottom, and that very young tarpon go through a number of different stages before they assume a typical tarpon-like appearance. It was also discovered that the characteristic habit of "rolling," in which tarpon break the water surface, is for the purpose of obtaining atmospheric air, which is stored in the fish's air bladder. Despite their large, well developed gills, tarpon die if denied access to the surface even though kept in pure, rapidly flowing seawater.

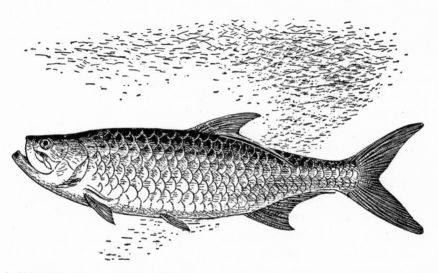

A FIGHTER AND A HIGH-JUMPER

Although it is too bitter to make good eating, the tarpon is famed as a gamefish. It may grow to nearly eight feet in length, and weigh as much as three hundred pounds. Fishermen esteem it because it puts up a good fight, often leaping surprisingly high.

A smaller species of tarpon lives in the Indian Ocean and western Pacific. It, too, often enters rivers and remains for considerable lengths of time in fresh water.

The Bonefish, *Albula vulpes,* grows by shrinking! For some time during its early development this fish looks entirely different from the adult, being transparent, long, and very compressed, that is, extremely thin from side to side. At this stage it is called a "leptocephalus larva." After reaching a length of about three and one-half inches, it begins a remarkable transformation. The fish actually shrinks in size—as much as three-fourths of an inch in four days. Meanwhile, its ribbon-like body gradually takes on the cylindrical, tapering shape of the adult bonefish and also acquires some of the silver coloring for which the species is famous. Its fins move into their final positions, and its head assumes the usual bonefish shape, with a characteristic piglike snout overhanging the small mouth. During this process of growth the fish shrinks to less than one-third of its former length.

After taking on the typical form of an adult, the young one-inch bonefish begins to grow in the usual fashion. It generally reaches a weight between two and five pounds, but can grow much larger. The record bonefish ever caught with fishing tackle weighed sixteen pounds and was thirty-eight inches long. Like its distant relative, the tarpon, the bonefish is a great fighter when hooked and is highly esteemed as a gamefish.

Although adult bonefish travel in small groups or are solitary, the young are often found in sizable schools. They frequently come in with the tide to feed on mud flats. Burying their snouts in the soft bottom, they search for mollusks and crustaceans which they crush with their blunt teeth. Sometimes the water is so shallow that their silvery tails project above the surface as they grub for food. Adults also feed in this manner.

Bonefish have been found in tropical seas and inlets throughout the world. On the Atlantic coast of North America they occur as far north as Cape Cod, but are not numerous north of Florida. On the Pacific coast they have been taken as far north as Monterey, but seem to be nowhere common.

The Atlantic Herring, *Clupea harengus,* is one of the most numerous of all of the backboned animals on earth. A single gigantic school, or shoal, may contain three billion individuals, and there are undoubtedly scores of such shoals in the North Atlantic. They are easily captured in great numbers with nets and are perhaps the most important single foodfish in the world. About three and one-quarter billion pounds are caught annually—to be consumed fresh, salted (pickled herring), salted-and-smoked (kippered and red herring), and canned.

Herring are quite beautiful with their silvery, iridescent sides and deep steel-blue backs. They grow to be about seventeen inches long and may live for twenty years. This is very rare, however, for, before they reach an age of ten years, the vast majority of herring are eaten by the innumerable animals that prey upon them, including other fishes, squid, whales, and man.

The food of the herring consists of the small, floating animals that abound in northern seas. Sometimes they feed by simply swimming open-mouthed through masses of these creatures, straining them out with their gill-rakers, which are numerous, dense, bristle-like projections in the region of the gills, that act like sieves. All water entering the mouth and eventually passing over the gills must pass through the gill rakers, leaving behind all but the finest particles. At other times herring chase somewhat larger prey, snapping up such creatures one at a time.

Herring gather into large shoals, more or less inshore, to spawn at almost any time of the year, depending on the particular locality and race of fish involved. Astronomical numbers of eggs are laid, for each female produces about thirty thousand. The eggs are heavier than sea water and adhesive, sinking and sticking to whatever plants, stones, or bottom they happen to touch. Hatching takes place from ten to forty days later, depending on the temperature; the colder the water, the slower the development of the fish in the egg.

The Pacific Herring, *Clupea pallasi*, is not as economically important as the Atlantic herring. Somewhat more than one billion pounds are caught each year. Its habits are similar to those of the Atlantic species. It spawns in large groups, mostly on kelp beds and among eel grass, from mid-winter to June, depending on the latitude. The heavy, sticky eggs hatch in one to three weeks.

The American Shad, *Alosa sapidissima,* was once much more abundant than it is today. Its life cycle, like the salmon's, makes it especially vulnerable to human mismanagement. Each year, from January to July according to the latitude, adult shad leave the sea, where they have been feeding on small ocean creatures, and run up the rivers of our Atlantic coast to spawn. The males or buck shad weigh from one and one-half to six pounds, while the females or roe shad weigh from three and one-half to eight and, rarely, up to twelve pounds. They select shallow water over pebbly or sandy areas for reproduction. The average female lays about thirty thousand pale pink or amber eggs which neither float nor sink, but rest lightly on the bottom. They hatch in six to ten days. The young shad remain in fresh water until the fall, when they move into brackish and, later, salt water. Their parents return to the sea very soon after egg laying.

While traveling up rivers and streams, shad used to be caught with great nets almost a mile long that sometimes stretched from shore to shore. So many were caught that they were used as fertilizer. In this way whole "runs" were undoubtedly destroyed. The pollution of rivers and the erection of dams, destroying the breeding places of the shad or preventing the adults from reaching them, are two other ways in which man has thoughtlessly destroyed this delicious and valuable natural food resource, and is continuing to destroy it.

In 1871 the shad was introduced into the Pacific coastal waters of the United States, where it has now become fairly well established from Southern California to Alaska.

The Pilchard, *Sardina pilchardus,* when young is called the sardine and is the object of an important fishery in France, Portugal, and Spain. As adults, too, when they are approximately seven inches long, pilchards are fished commercially. They inhabit most of the Mediterranean Sea and the waters off the western coast of Europe from North Africa to the British Isles. They migrate along the coast and are found further north during the summer and autumn.

Pilchards look somewhat like herring, to which they are quite closely related. They lay their floating eggs offshore, the time of the year depending on the temperature of the water. This means that the further south that the fish are, the earlier in the year they spawn.

The name "sardine" is derived, we believe, from the island of Sardinia, and goes back to antiquity.

The California Sardine, *Sardinops caerulea,* supports one of the largest fisheries in the United States. During the 1936-37 fishing season well over one and one-half billion pounds of California sardines were taken by the United States and Canada and either canned or "reduced," the latter being the process of making oil and meal out of the fish. In addition, many hundreds of thousands of pounds were used as bait, in fishing for tuna, for example.

Since that season, however, there has been an alarming decrease in the weight of sardines caught, for any given amount of fishing effort. To find the cause of the reduced catch and prevent permanent damage to the industry, an extensive program of scientific investigation has been set up. The object is to find out anything about the California sardine that might have a bearing on its response to heavy, continuous fishing. In effect, this means that practically everything about the sardine's life history and its relation to its surroundings must be determined. Consequently, fishery experts are now learning many facts about the California sardine—things that ought to be known about all economically important fish and which, unfortunately, are known about very few.

California sardines first spawn when they are two, three, or four years old and from a little more than seven to a little less than ten inches long. Spawning takes place from late winter to early summer, principally fifty to two hundred miles off the coast of southern California. Each female lays about one hundred thousand eggs. These float about on the surface for two or three days, when hatching takes place. Adult sardines are rovers, and it is believed that this tendency soon shows itself in the young. At any rate, schools of sardines, great and small, make extensive and complicated migrations that investigators are only beginning to understand. In their travels, these fish range all the way from southeastern Alaska to the southern tip of Baja California, but they apparently spend more time in California waters than anywhere else.

Like its relative the pilchard, the California sardine feeds on minute floating plants and animals, which it strains out of the sea by means of a sievelike structure near the gills.

The Menhaden, *Brevoortia tyrannus,* is today the basis of the largest single fishery in the United States. Between 800 and 900 million pounds are taken off the Atlantic and Gulf coasts each year, mostly by special boats equipped with purse seines (long, flat nets with a drawstring to close the bottom after a shoal of fish is encircled). This means that well over a billion menhaden are captured each year.

This great fishery provides very little food for man, although the roe of the menhaden is very similar to that of the American shad, and a few have been canned. By far the greatest part of the catch is "reduced," that is, converted into fish meal (used in hog, cattle, and poultry feeds), oil (used in soaps, paints, insecticides, and in many other industries), and fertilizer. In all, there are five different species of menhaden, but this species is the one most common off the northeastern coast.

Menhaden feed principally on the myriads of microscopic plants found floating near the surface of the sea, which they filter out of the water with their fine, sieve-like gill apparatus. They swim through the water with open mouths, and it has been estimated that as much as seven gallons pass into their mouths and out past their gills each minute. The average length of the menhaden is about one foot and they seldom exceed fifteen inches. They lay floating eggs. In the vicinity of New York, the peak of the spawning season is in May and June.

The European Anchovy, *Engraulis encrasicholus,* is best known to Americans as a canned delicacy—after its tender, oily flesh has been processed into filets or into paste. It is a common fish in the Mediterranean Sea and on the western coast of Europe from North Africa to Norway, where it migrates, with the change of season, in large schools. It spawns during the spring and summer, laying floating eggs that hatch in a few days. Like the eggs of most anchovies, these are ellipsoidal (longer than wide or thick) in shape. The vast majority of floating fish eggs are spherical, but no one has yet advanced any reason why anchovy eggs should not conform to the general rule.

The various anchovies are small, flesh-eating fishes that, as a rule, live in schools, more or less near shore in temperate and tropical seas over most of the world. They somewhat resemble herring in their body shape and silvery color but differ in having a short snout in front of large eyes, and a receding lower jaw that seems to fit inside the upper one, giving the fish a peculiar "chinless" look. In South America especially, anchovies ascend streams, and some may live permanently in fresh water.

Nearly ninety New World species have been described; there are undoubtedly quite a number that live in the Old World. Of the several American anchovies only the Pacific Anchovy, *Engraulis mordax,* is utilized to any extent for food, and the greater part of the catch of this species is used as bait rather than for human consumption. The Pacific anchovy ranges from Baja California to British Columbia. It grows to a length of about seven inches.

The Milkfish, *Chanos chanos,* is prized for food through much of the Orient, where it is the most valuable of all the fishes cultivated in ponds, being especially important in Java and the Philippines. Although it is normally found only in salt or brackish water, it does very well in fresh, and can be reared in both salt- and fresh-water ponds. At certain seasons of the year, tremendous numbers of milkfish fry appear along the coast. They are scooped out and planted in ponds, where they put on size rapidly, growing as much as twenty inches within one year.

Little or nothing is known about the spawning habits of milkfish, for they never reproduce in captivity. This does not limit the usefulness of the fish, however, since there is always an abundant supply of fresh stock to be obtained from nature. Milkfish are quite widely distributed in shallow water from the Red Sea and east coast of Africa, through the Indian Ocean and East Indies, to southern Japan, New South Wales, Hawaii, and the Pacific coast of Mexico.

The milkfish has a slender body with a small head and a large, widely forked tail. It is colored a brilliant, metallic, silvery blue or green above, silver along its sides, and white below. It has no teeth and feeds on tiny plants and animals which it strains out of the water with a special accessory gill apparatus. A swift, powerful swimmer, the milkfish can leap more than twenty feet in the air. Adults range from about twenty-eight to sixty inches in length.

The Pirarucu, *Arapaima gigas,* is the most important foodfish of the Amazon River. It is usually speared or harpooned and its flesh cut into thin slabs to be dried in the sun. It is probably the largest freshwater fish in South America, but authorities disagree on the maximum size it may attain, some claiming fifteen feet and four hundred pounds, other twelve feet and three hundred pounds, and still others only seven feet. Undoubtedly the first of these estimates is too generous; no recently caught example has exceeded eight feet. Today the largest specimens fished are seldom more than five feet long or weigh more than 175 pounds.

The pirarucu has a shape all of its own. It has a somewhat cylindrical body and a rather small, flattened head. The mouth, however, is quite large. Dorsal and anal fins are located far to the rear, almost surrounding the small rounded tail fin. The body is covered with very large scales, colored olive green toward the front of the fish and gradually becoming more and more tinged with scarlet toward the rear, until they are quite red near the tail.

The range of the pirarucu includes much of the Amazon Basin and British Guiana. The fish is an air-breather and drowns if kept under water. It constructs a nest and cares for its eggs and young. Because of a shortage of these valuable fish, the Brazilian government has undertaken experiments in growing the pirarucu in ponds.

The Atlantic Salmon, *Salmo salar,* probably has been studied more than any other fish, but there are still many things not understood about it. For example, no one can yet explain how salmon manage to return to the same river, even the identical tributary, in which they were hatched—after spending years out in the trackless ocean. That they do this has been demonstrated by tagging or otherwise marking young fish and then catching them again years later, in the same stream. Occasionally "stray" salmon turn up in other river systems, but they usually go back to their so-called "parent stream" to spawn. This behavior is not inherited, for, if salmon still within the egg are transplanted from one stream to another, they will in later life return to the river in which they were hatched, not to the one in which their parents lived. Just what "landmarks" enable the fish to "recognize" any particular stream are still a mystery, as well as how the fish can "remember" them for several years.

The migrations of the Atlantic salmon are sometimes very extensive. While in the sea, they may travel as far as fifteen hundred miles to feeding grounds, and their journey upstream may be several hundred miles long, as in the Rhine River. During sea migrations, their sustained rate of speed has been calculated to be as high as forty-five or even sixty miles a day. Many Atlantic salmon migrations are relatively short, however, including most of those made on the Atlantic coast of North America. In some places the fish spends its whole life in fresh water, migrating from lakes into streams. These Atlantic salmon are called "landlocked."

The age at which the Atlantic salmon returns to spawn varies from one to five years. The largest individuals weigh about twenty pounds, although there are some records of rare fish that tip the scales at eighty pounds or more. As the fish become ripe (sexually mature), they lose their sleek, steel-blue and silvery colors and become a dull, reddish brown. The males often develop grotesque, hooked jaws. so distorted that they cannot completely close their mouths. The reason for these changes is unknown. As a rule, salmon do not feed once they have entered fresh water. This may mean going practically a whole year without food in those instances where a very long river trip is involved. Occasionally they will eat, however, and will strike at fishermen's flies.

Upon reaching the spawning area, the female Atlantic salmon begins to construct her nest or redd. She lies on her side, strongly arches her back and with her tail beats the gravelly bottom. This, together with the rather strong current, causes small stones, gravel, and sand to rise off the bottom and be carried some distance downstream. Over and over again the female beats the stream bottom, at intervals testing the depression she has made by sinking into it with extended anal fin. As the redd becomes deeper, the male begins to court the female by entering it with her. He has won this right by driving off other males and may have to continue doing so throughout the spawning. Digging the redd sometimes takes several days, but at last, when it is from six to twelve inches deep, the female signifies that she is ready to spawn, the male immediately comes to her side, and the eggs are laid and fertilized. After laying a batch of eggs, the female quickly moves upstream a foot or two and once more lying on her side, stirs up the bottom so vigorously with her tail that the eggs are covered by displaced gravel in less than a minute. Now the female is ready to complete another section of her redd to hold the next batch of eggs. Thus she may progressively move upstream until finally all her eggs have been laid.

Is it any wonder that many Atlantic salmon do not survive this arduous business of perpetuating the race? Few live to spawn a second time, and those that do almost invariably spawn in streams in which the journey from the sea is not very long. An Atlantic salmon that has spawned four times is extraordinary. Such a fish would be at least twelve years old, having spent two or three years in the sea between each spawning migration. Landlocked Atlantic salmon apparently survive spawning more often than do those coming from the sea.

On the northeastern coast of North America, Atlantic salmon spawn in the fall. The eggs do not hatch until five or six months later, that is, until April or early May. Young salmon may live for three years in fresh water before going to sea; in some places they may stay in streams for five or six years. After reaching the ocean, they grow very rapidly on the fish and shellfish they find there. At this time they lay down stores of fat that will enable them to dispense with eating during spawning and the migration associated with it.

The Atlantic salmon is native to the coast of Europe from the northern part of Norway to the northern part of Spain and as far east as the Caspian Sea. On western Atlantic shores it once existed from Delaware northward. It has been exterminated, however, in all the streams of the United States except a very few in Maine. Although salmon have been reported able to negotiate natural barriers eighteen feet high, man-made dams, locks, and other obstructions, together with pollution and the destruction of suitable spawning beds, have proved too much for this magnificent fish.

The Rainbow Trout, *Salmo gairdneri,* has confused scientists and laymen alike for many years. The problem has been: When is a rainbow not a rainbow? The principal controversy concerned the trout known as "steelhead." These resemble rainbow trout, but are colored quite differently, being silvery with a bluish head and back, instead of greenish with a reddish gill cover and lateral stripe. It is now generally agreed that steelhead trout are merely sea-going rainbows, or, to put it another way, that rainbow trout are "landlocked" steelheads. In a few places, however, rainbow trout have been found to assume the steelhead coloration while remaining in fresh water. But there are several other types of rainbow-like fish whose status is still in doubt. Some ichthyologists hold that the Shasta trout, the Kamloops trout, the Kern River trout and others are all separate species. They are believed to be only geographical varieties, that is, subspecies, by other scientists, and a few of them are considered by certain experts to be not enough different to require a special name. At any rate, it is agreed that all of them are closely related to one another.

These trouts originally occurred only on the West Coast of the United States, from southern California to southeastern Alaska. Rainbows now exist all over the world, however, having been widely introduced into suitable lakes and streams where sportsmen have wanted to fish for this gamy species. They are at present found throughout the northern United States and Canada, and they have been successfully transplanted to Europe and the British Isles, Argentina, Chile, Venezuela, South Africa, East Africa, Madagascar, Mauritius, India, Ceylon, Australia, New Zealand, Tasmania, Hawaii, and Panama. One of the reasons why rainbow trout have been established in so many faraway lands is that their eggs can be transported long distances. If kept cold, moist, and free from jarring, they will stay alive for many weeks, developing so slowly that there is ample time to make long trips with them before they hatch. For example, rainbows were first introduced into New Zealand through a shipment of eggs from California in 1877—long before air express.

In fact, rainbow trout respond well to all phases of artificial culture. The eggs are gathered by "stripping," a process in which the ripe females are carefully taken out of water and freed of their eggs by gentle pressure. The eggs are then fertilized with milt (the product of the male reproductive glands) collected from ripe males. They are allowed to develop in carefully watched trays bathed in cold running water. Females have been kept captive for as long as fourteen years, being stripped on ten to twelve occasions during this time.

Some rainbow trout remain in fresh water all their lives—even when they have access to the ocean. Others enter the sea when a year or more old, taking on the steelhead coloration. They return to their "parent stream" for spawning at an age of three to six years. Spawning occurs in winter or early spring, but steelheads enter streams almost any time of the year, sometimes apparently only to feed. Like the Atlantic salmon they may spawn more than once. Rainbows also construct their redds and lay their eggs in almost exactly the same way as do Atlantic salmon.

The usual adult rainbow trout weighs from two to eight pounds, but thirty-six- to fifty-two-and-one-half-pound giants have been reported.

The Cutthroat Trout, *Salmo clarki,* gets its name from the slash of bright red that it has underneath its lower jaw. It was once more widely distributed through our Far West than it is today. Each of the main river systems from Alaska to California seemed to have its own particular kind of cutthroat. This trout has now been replaced by transplanted species in many places or destroyed by pollution and other disturbances of its natural waters. When rainbow trout are introduced into cutthroat streams, the two species hybridize, but their offspring are either completely sterile or nearly so.

Those cutthroat trout that live on the western coast of North America often enter the sea when two or three years old, remaining there for a year or more before returning to fresh water to spawn. Some coastal, and all inland fish of course, spend their whole lives in fresh water. Coastal fish tend to spawn in the winter and very early spring. Those further inland spawn in spring or summer.

The record sized cutthroat trout weighed forty-one pounds and was thirty-seven inches long. In some places, however, mature cutthroats rarely exceed a single pound.

The Brown Trout, *Salmo trutta,* can live in warmer waters than other trouts. This is one of the reasons it has been so widely transplanted throughout the world. It occurs naturally in Europe, from

Iceland and Norway to the Mediterranean, and also in Corsica, Sardinia, and Algeria, and as far east as the Himalayas. It has now been transplanted to most of the northern United States and to Canada, Argentina, South Africa, Ceylon, Australia, Tasmania, and New Zealand. It is not generally considered as fine a gamefish as other trouts, but its hardiness and ability to thrive under conditions unfavorable to other species make it a valuable fish.

There are sea-running races of brown trout, as well as those that remain in fresh water at all times. Those that spend part of their lives in salt water are quite differently colored from the others, and once were thought to be a different species. Both kinds spawn only in fresh water, as do all other trout and salmon.

The eggs of the brown trout are spherical and a little less than one-fifth of an inch in diameter. Like the eggs of all trout and salmon, they are a little heavier than water and are slightly adhesive when first laid. They would be quickly washed downstream by the rapidly flowing current, were it not for the special manner in which they are laid. The female first digs a hole in the gravelly bottom that is six to eight inches deep to receive her eggs. This is the beginning of the trout nest, which is called a redd. When about to lay her eggs, the female sinks down to the bottom of the depression she has dug. The redd is so placed in relation to the current that the water passing over it produces a slight eddy. Therefore the water directly over the bottom where the eggs are laid actually moves upstream. This unexpected state of affairs was discovered by an investigator who placed crystals of potassium permanganate (a strongly colored chemical) in redds that were being dug by brown trout, and discovered that the red-stained water traveled upstream, against the main current. This is the principal reason why the eggs are not washed away while they are being laid. The eggs stick to the bottom and this also helps prevent their being swept downstream. As soon as she has laid a batch of eggs, the female immediately starts to dig a new depression slightly upstream from the old one and in so doing displaces small stones and gravel that drop into the hole and soon cover the eggs completely. Safely resting under six to eight inches of clean gravel, the eggs are well protected from egg-eating fish and other animals and from smothering by mud or silt. Here they remain from forty to seventy days, when they hatch.

Brown trout spawn in the late fall. They may reproduce seven times during their lifetime and undoubtedly can survive more than seven spawnings. Those that must endure the hardships of an upstream migration from the sea spawn less often than those living entirely in fresh water. This species often attains weights of about seven pounds, but has been known to reach thirty-nine and one-half pounds.

The Brook Trout, *Salvelinus fontinalis,* is one of America's favorite fresh-water gamefish. Its delicious flesh, trim appearance, and brilliant yet not gaudy colors, combined with its wariness and its spunkiness when hooked, make it a fisherman's dream fish. Unfortunately this prince of sportsfish requires pure, cold water and so has become increasingly scarce as such waters have become more and more rare.

Brook trout vary greatly in size, depending on the supply of suitable food and perhaps the size of the body of water in which they live. In small streams or cold-water ponds the maximum weight ever attained may be as little as one or even one-half pound. In rivers or lakes, however, five-pound specimens may be regularly taken. The largest brook trout ever caught weighed fourteen and one-half pounds.

Like most trout and salmon, brook trout eat a variety of foods. In some places insects make up more than 90 per cent of their food. When this is the case, brook trout rarely exceed nine inches in length. Larger individuals feed mostly on other fishes and on crayfish, with an occasional frog or salamander, although they continue to eat insects when available.

Most brook trout remain in freshwater all their lives, but on the northeastern coast of the United States and Canada some of them migrate to the sea for short periods. Spawning may take place either in flowing streams, quiet spring beds or gravelly shallows in lakes. Most other species of trout and salmon depend on the fast flowing current in which they construct their nests, or redds, to help them move excavated material from the depression in which the eggs are laid, or to help cover up the eggs after spawning. Since brook trout can spawn in still waters, their behavior is modified accordingly. Although digging is apparently done in approximately the same manner by both the brook trout and the Atlantic salmon, the female brook trout covers her eggs with slow sweeps of her body, actually brushing small stones and gravel over the eggs with her anal fin and tail.

Spawning takes place in October, November, and December, and the eggs usually hatch in February. One experimenter subjected captive brook trout to gradually decreasing amounts of light over a period of about a month. He found that they became ripe several months ahead of the regular spawning season. This indicates that the shortening of hours of daylight in the fall is one of the principal stimulants to reproduction of the brook trout in nature. Brook trout have been crossed with brown trout in hatcheries; the hybrids are hardy, handsome fish, but apparently completely sterile.

Brook trout are native to eastern North America from Labrador to Georgia, and do not occur naturally west of the Mississippi except in parts of Iowa and Minnesota. They have now been introduced throughout the western United States and the provinces of Canada, and into parts of Europe, Argentina, and New Zealand. They belong to the group of trout known as chars, which in general are smaller than other trout, have a somewhat different arrangement of teeth from them, and possess smaller scales. As with all other trout and also the salmons, the natural home of the chars is in the fresh and salt waters of the northern part of the Northern Hemisphere.

The Lake Trout, *Salvelinus namaycush,* is the largest of all the trouts, and only one of the species of salmon equals or exceeds it in size. Individuals weighing twenty pounds are fairly common. The biggest specimen ever taken with rod and line weighed sixty-three pounds and was forty-seven and one-half inches long, but lake trout weighing about one hundred pounds have been caught commercially either with nets or set-lines.

Man has extended the range of this game and commercial fish by transplantation so that it is now found both west and south of its former natural boundaries. In addition to lakes in northern United States, Canada, and Alaska, lakes in California, the Pacific Northwest, Peru, Bolivia, and New Zealand today harbor lake trout that were originally put there by man.

Lake trout often inhabit depths of eight hundred feet or more in larger lakes, but spawn during the fall on gravel-covered or rocky areas in relatively shallow water. No nest or redd is constructed, although a common spawning area is cleaned by a number of fish, mostly males. No pairing takes place, and as many as three females and seven males may press together, spawning as a group. In captivity they have lived as long as twenty-four years.

The Red or Sockeye Salmon, *Oncorhynchus nerka,* forms an important part of the most valuable fishery resource of the United States. It is one of five species of Pacific salmon that yield around six hundred million pounds of fish each year to commercial fishermen in Oregon, Washington, and Alaska. It ranks second to the Pink Salmon, *Oncorhynchus gorbuscha,* in total quantity caught, but first in quality for canning.

Each year millions of salmon leave the sea and enter the streams in which they were hatched, travel as far as two thousand miles to spawning beds, lay their eggs, and then die. On their way upstream great numbers are caught in traps and nets, principally for canning. In recent years a grave new hazard to the successful completion of the Pacific salmon's life cycle has appeared, namely, great dams erected for hydroelectric power, irrigation, and flood control. Fish-ladders, elevators, and locks have been provided to permit fish to get over or bypass these otherwise insurmountable barriers. Nevertheless, enormous numbers of very young salmon, traveling down to the sea, are destroyed in the turbines and violent whirlpools of the dams themselves and in the irrigation ditches into which they are often diverted. For these and other reasons there has been a serious decline of salmon in many of our rivers.

Regardless of whether they travel long or short distances or remain in fresh water all their lives, as a few of them do, the Pacific salmon all die very soon after spawning is completed. All pink salmon spawn when two years old, but the life span of the other species is more variable. Sockeye salmon range from three to eight years in age when they return to fresh water, the great majority of them being four or five. At this time they generally weigh about six pounds.

At sexual maturity the male sockeye salmon changes from a greenish or silvery blue to a blood-red body with a green head, while the female becomes a somewhat darker red. The male also develops a strongly hooked jaw, showing prominent teeth. Migration upstream takes place during the summer. Spawning occurs during the fall, most often on gravelly shallows of tributaries to lakes. The female digs a nest, or redd, by lying on her side and rapidly vibrating her tail, thus creating currents that displace stones, gravel, and sand on the bottom. Both the female and male—the latter stands by, at least during the latter part of the nest building—defend the nesting site against other fishes. The male also frequently courts the female by gently nudging her with his snout, caressing her with his body and fins, and quivering by her side. During a female's spawning activities, several different males may be attendant on her, for the defending male is not always successful in driving off rival suitors and is sometimes himself driven off. When the saucer-like depression is completed, some eggs are laid and fertilized and immediately covered by the female. Several excavations, either immediately upstream from the first one or in some new locality, may be made before all the eggs of a single female are laid.

Young sockeye salmon appear in the spring. They pass down to the lakes and usually remain there for a year, sometimes two or three, before they proceed to the sea. At all sizes sockeye salmon feed principally on small aquatic crustaceans.

In many lakes in the Far West there are sockeye salmon that never enter salt water. These are usually much smaller than ocean-going ones. Some of them have been introduced into one or two places in Maine, Pennsylvania, Connecticut, and New Zealand.

The Lake Whitefish, *Coregonus clupeaformis,* is still one of the most valuable of fresh-water foodfishes in North America, even though the catch has become greatly reduced in numbers—presumably from overfishing. It is generally distributed through the Great Lakes and various smaller lakes in Maine, New York, Michigan, Wisconsin, Minnesota, and all the Canadian provinces as far north as Alaska. In the region of Hudson's Bay it spends considerable time in brackish water. To the natives of Northern Canada the whitefish is an important source of food and is preferred above all other fishes.

Lake whitefish are more or less oval or spindle shaped, with an olive back and silvery sides and belly. Considerable variability in size, shape and other characteristics is found from area to area and sometimes even from lake to lake. A maximum size of twenty-six pounds has been recorded. In some places maturity is not reached until the fish weigh three pounds; in others mature fish weighing less than an ounce are known.

Spawning usually takes place in the fall in relatively shallow water. The eggs are heavier than water and lie on the bottom. Hatching takes place after approximately twenty weeks. The food of the lake whitefish consists of crustaceans, aquatic insects, mollusks, and, to a lesser extent, small fishes.

There are about thirty-five different species of whitefishes and their close relatives, the ciscos and tullibees. They are found around the polar regions, in the salt waters of the extreme north, and in the fresh waters of northern Europe, Asia, and North America.

The American Smelt, *Osmerus mordax,* usually spends most of its life in the sea, coming into fresh water only to spawn. There are, however, a number of places in which it is landlocked, that is, in which it has no access to the ocean and therefore spends its whole life in fresh water. It occurs naturally on the Atlantic coast from Labrador to New York and in the St. Lawrence River, Lake Champlain, Lake Ontario, and their associated streams. About 1912 it was introduced into the other Great Lakes, where it gradually became more and more abundant. At first it was thought that the smelt would eventually outstrip most of the native fishes and become a pest, and its exact effect on fishes like lake trout is still debated. After the smelt had increased sufficiently, however, a valuable fishery developed, and many millions of pounds were taken both by commercial and sports fishermen. Then in the early 1940's almost all the smelt in the upper Great Lakes disappeared. The reason for this remains a mystery, although there is a little evidence that some epidemic disease was responsible. Today, apparently, the smelt is slowly coming back.

American smelt are caught in a variety of ways: by hook and line, by dipping with hand-nets while they proceed upstream to spawn, by gill nets, and with special nets set under the ice. Smelt may attain a size of somewhat more than a foot, but most adults are considerably smaller.

Spawning takes place in very early spring, sometimes just after ice has left the water. Smelt that have been living in salt water do not go far upstream, even spawning in slightly salty water in certain instances. Those that live permanently in fresh water spawn in small streams or the shallow parts of lakes. During egg laying a single female is generally attended by several males. The eggs are sticky when first laid and adhere to any aquatic plants, sticks, stones, or gravel that they touch.

In all, there are roughly a dozen species of smelt and their relatives, the capelin and eulachon, inhabiting the northern seas around Asia, Scandinavia, Canada, and Alaska.

dekens   *Weyerhaeuser Timber Company*

JUMPING THE FALLS ON ITS WAY TO SPAWN
The Chinook or king salmon, an important foodfish, is the largest of all our salmon — it may attain a weight of 125 pounds. A native of the North Pacific, it ascends streams from California to Alaska, and also in northeastern Asia, to lay its eggs. It shows almost incredible agility in overcoming barriers such as waterfalls, determinedly making its way to the breeding grounds.

The Atlantic Capelin, *Mallotus villosus,* runs onto beaches out of water to spawn. During the late spring, schools of capelin gather just beyond the waves breaking on gravelly beaches. There, the males seek out the females, each one attaching himself to the side of his prospective mate, or two males flanking a single female on either side. Together they swim vigorously toward shore just ahead of an incoming wave. As they settle on the beach, they scoop out a small hollow with rapid strokes of their tails, and then the eggs are laid and fertilized. The spawning act takes only a few seconds and may be completed in time for the fish, by paddling furiously toward the deeper water, to ride the same wave back out to sea, or they may have to wait for the succeeding one.

Male capelin are slightly larger than females and have longer pectoral fins. During the reproductive season they exhibit along their sides two rows of pointed scales covered with thickened skin. It is by means of these ridges that the males are able to cling to the females during spawning.

The average female capelin lays about thirty thousand eggs. These eggs, each about one thirty-second of an inch in diameter, are adhesive and become attached to bits of sand or gravel. Most of them are probably buried in the gravel of the beach by the action of the waves, but a good many are washed to sea or eventually exposed to sun and air. In the water, they are eaten by winter flounders and other fishes, including capelin themselves, and on dry land they are destroyed by maggots, drying out, and high temperatures. Those eggs that are properly protected hatch in two weeks to a month, depending on the temperature. Capelin also spawn in water somewhat off-shore, generally laying their eggs over sandy bottoms.

Spawning capelin average about seven inches long. Their maximum length is about nine inches, and they ordinarily live to be from five to seven years old. They feed on small creatures floating in the sea. Capelin habitually live out in the ocean, coming inshore only during the spawning season. In their migrations they are followed by large numbers of Atlantic cod, which sometimes pursue them almost onto the beaches. Not only do cod feed voraciously upon them, but Atlantic salmon and other fishes, as well as seals and sea-birds, live largely upon capelin at certain times of the year.

In Newfoundland, the capelin is taken in great numbers during the spawning season. Salted and dried, smoked, fresh, or frozen, it is used for human consumption. It is also used fresh for cod bait, and large amounts are employed as fertilizer. The fish is also of economic importance in Finland and other countries where spawning runs take place.

The capelin inhabits the north Atlantic and Arctic Oceans from Hudson's Bay to Scandinavia. It occurs as far south as the coast of Maine, but rarely spawns there. The closely related Pacific Capelin, *Mallotus catervarius,* is found in the north Pacific and Arctic Oceans as far south in the east as the state of Washington.

The Pike, *Esox lucius,* often lies in wait for its prey, and when some unsuspecting fish swims by its weedy lair, it dashes out with split-second speed to snap it up. Sometimes, instead of lying in wait, it stalks its prey, the stealthy approach being followed by the same death-dealing sprint. The pike's great voracity is well known; fishes large and small, frogs, snakes, crayfish, and even birds and mammals have been found in its stomach. Small specimens feed on crustaceans, worms, and insect larvae. They become principally fish-eaters when they grow up. Pikes consume an enormous amount of food in the course of a year.

The long, sturdy body of the pike is usually olive or greenish gray with light yellow spots on the sides, shading into the whitish or yellowish belly. Younger specimens are marked with light bars rather than spots. A greenish, silvery variety of pike showing no pattern at all has recently appeared in Minnesota waters. The pointed jaws of the pike are lined with numerous sharp teeth. Although teeth that are broken off or worn down are replaced, the idea that the fish sheds its teeth regularly each summer has definitely been proved untrue. As in many species of fishes that catch their prey by making short dashes, the dorsal and anal fins are located towards the rear, near the tail.

Pikes are found throughout the Northern Hemisphere in Europe (excepting Spain and Portugal), northern Asia, and in North America south to British Columbia, Montana, Nebraska, Missouri, the Ohio valley, and New York. They prefer quiet, weedy waters. The record pike caught by rod-and-reel weighed forty-six pounds, two ounces, and was fifty-two and one-half inches long. Specimens weighing more than fifty pounds are known. Pikes are most frequently taken by trolling, that is, fishing with a hook that is drawn along or through the water, but they may also be still-fished with live bait. In winter they are lured, then speared through the ice. Besides being a highly esteemed gamefish, the pike is a foodfish of minor importance.

Soon after the ice melts in early spring the pike spawns. Numerous barely adhesive eggs, heavier than water and not quite three-sixteenths of an inch in diameter are laid, usually among plants or decaying vegetation. Spawning generally occurs in shallow water during daylight hours, each female being accompanied by one, two or three males. Hatching occurs in one to four weeks, depending on the temperature. Hybrids between the pike and the muskellunge and the chain pickerel are found in nature, undoubtedly resulting from the fact that they may sometimes carry on their reproductive activities in the same area at the same time.

The Muskellunge, *Esox masquinongy,* is one of the prize gamefish of North America. It attains a weight of over one hundred pounds, and specimens weighing more than fifty pounds are caught every year. The official record fish caught by means of angler's tackle weighed sixty-four and one-half pounds and was fifty-eight inches long. Like the pike, the muskellunge is a savage fighter.

The muskellunge is often confused with the pike, but can usually be distinguished by its lack of scales below the level of the eye on both the lower cheeks and gill-covers. The pike lacks them only on the gill-covers, its cheeks being fully scaled. The scales on the body of the muskellunge are also relatively smaller than those on the pike; the sensory pores under the lower jaw are smaller and more numerous; and the number of rays under the gill-covers is greater. There are also differences in color pattern and in shape of head and body, but these are less pronounced and liable to be misleading. In general, however, muskellunge tend to be darker than pike and to carry dark spots or bars rather than light ones.

Fully as voracious as the pike, the muskellunge leads the same sort of life. It generally prefers somewhat colder and deeper waters, however, and tends to be more solitary in habit. It spawns a little later than does the pike, and in open waters, rather than among weeds. Both species' spawning areas and seasons overlap sometimes, which explains the presence of natural hybrids between the two. Muskellunge can grow very fast; when only two months old they may be six inches long. Such specimens eat ten to fifteen minnows every day.

The Central Mudminnow, *Umbra limi,* makes out well even under the worst of living conditions. It can exist in stagnant pools, and, if these dry up, it burrows into the mud and awaits the return of water. Neither high nor low temperatures greatly inconvenience it; it is often the only species of fish to survive a very severe freeze. In fact, it frequently is the only fish ever to be found in the shallow, muddy ponds, swamps, and bog-pools it inhabits. Mudminnows are also found in more favorable surroundings, most often among plants and over muddy bottoms.

Mudminnows eat a great variety of small objects, both animal and vegetable, living and dead, although they are principally flesh eaters. They are small fish, seldom exceeding four inches in length. At first glance they appear to be a drab dark brown, but close examination reveals a rather attractive mottled pattern.

It is the female mudminnow who takes care of the nest and eggs, guarding them and carefully picking out and devouring any that do not develop. In all other North American fishes that build nests, it is the male who keeps house, although in a few of the catfishes both parents may share that task. Spawning takes place in the spring.

The central mudminnow ranges through the Great Lakes region, east to Lake Champlain and south to Tennessee and has been transplanted to parts of northwestern Europe. Another closely related species of mudminnow is found along the Atlantic Coast.

Minnows, Characins, Catfishes, and Their Relatives

THE BULK of our fresh-water fishes—the creatures that throng the lakes and streams of the world—are members of this great group. The minnows, characins, catfishes, and all their motley array of relatives comprise it—they total perhaps five thousand different species, all told. Among them we find dwarfs as well as giants, and maximum size ranges from a scant one inch to as much as ten feet.

One might well be puzzled by the meaning of the scientific name of the group: "little bones-bladder" (order Ostariophysi). But it does describe the outstanding feature of all of the fishes in this order: the Weberian apparatus, a chain of small bones which connect the fish's inner ear with its air bladder. We suppose these help it to detect movements, sounds, and changes in pressure.

Three main groups of fishes are included in this group: the first made up of the suckers and buffalo fishes (family Catostomidae), the minnows, carps, barbs, etc. (Cyprinidae), and the loaches and weather fish (Cobitidae); in the second we place the tetras, piranhas, hatchet fishes, etc. (Characidae) and their relatives, including the electric eel and other gymnotid eels (Gymnotidae); and the third is composed of the dozen or more families of catfishes.

The suckers are mostly from North America, with only two species found in Asia. The cyprinids hail from Asia, Europe, North America, and Africa. Loaches inhabit Asia, Europe, and northern Africa. The characins range from Texas through Central America and most of South America, and are well known in Africa; while the gymnotid eels are found only in South and Central America. Unlike the other groups, the catfishes are found in both salt and fresh waters. About two thousand species of them occur in warm salt and brackish waters all over the world, and in the streams and lakes of every continent.

The characins are a most varied group—we find them ranging in size from one-inch midgets to six-foot monsters, and from inoffensive vegetarians to voracious flesh-eaters, such as the piranhas and the Goliath Tiger Fish, *Hydrocyon goliath,* of tropical Africa, which is the largest of all the characins. Some characins are shaped like minnows, some like darters, pikes, or snakeheads, and many have contours different from any other fish. A number of the smaller, brightly colored species are popular with tropical fish fanciers. Most species lay small, more or less adhesive eggs, and show no parental care of either eggs or young. A few, however, build nests and guard their eggs. One great oddity, the Splashing Samlet, *Copeina arnoldi,* lays its eggs out of water on overhanging leaves. The dutiful male remains near the eggs and periodically splashes water upon them to keep them moist.

There are about fifty species of gymnotid eels, the largest of which is the famous electric eel, the only one with great electrical powers.

The other species seldom exceed three feet in length, but all the species have long bodies, with the vital organs confined to the front one-fifth of the body. Dorsal and tail fins are lacking; the principal means of locomotion is the long anal fin, which is undulated, enabling the fish to move either forward or backward—seemingly with equal ease.

The catfishes range in size from tiny, one-inch species to those reaching lengths of ten feet and weights of well over six hundred pounds. Their great variety of body forms and the many structural peculiarities shown by them defy brief description, and their habits, if anything, are even more varied. A few are equipped with unique devices for breathing atmospheric air, enabling them to live in mud holes and swamps, and even out of water, for long periods. Some of these, and other catfishes, too, can "sleep" through a dry season in the mud at the bottom of a dried-up stream or pond, and live for months without food or water in a state of suspended animation. A few can travel on land and do so for fair distances. In one African family, there are species that habitually swim upside down.

There are more than a dozen blind catfishes—a greater number than in any other group of fishes. Most of them inhabit caves, but two or three burrow in the bottom of open streams. There are tiny catfishes no bigger than one-inch toothpicks that live in the gills of other fishes, sucking blood from them. Others gnaw holes through the sides of larger fishes in order to obtain blood—somewhat like the way the lampreys feed.

Reproductive habits among the catfishes are also most variable. Many construct nests and care for their eggs—and sometimes for their young, too. One or two species build a raftlike affair of plants and frothlike bubbles which are blown by the fish, to hold the eggs. In one whole group the males carry the eggs and young in their mouths for as long as two months—until they are well developed and able to fend for themselves. A few female catfishes carry their eggs in a layer attached to their bellies, and some armored catfish males carry the eggs in enlarged folds of their lips. Still other catfishes simply lay their eggs on plants or stones, and pay no more attention to them.

The White Sucker, *Catostomus commersoni,* has often been accused of consuming large quantities of the eggs of trout, but there is no proof for this—no eggs have been found in the stomachs of white suckers, nor have these fish been observed eating trout eggs. It is true, however, that white suckers eat the eggs of other fishes when they are available; apparently trout eggs are not easily obtained by them. Other foods of this species include insect larvae, mollusks, crustaceans, worms, and algae and other aquatic plants.

The mouth of the white sucker is located underneath its short, blunt snout, and, as you might expect, a great deal of its food is procured from the bottom. The body is slender and cylindrical. In males it becomes darker during the spawning season and develops a black band lying along the side above a rose-colored one. In the early spring, white suckers leave the lakes, pools, and rivers where they usually live, and crowd into smaller streams to spawn in swift water over gravelly bottoms. Occasionally they also lay their eggs in quiet pools. The eggs are pale yellowish in color and about three thirty-seconds of an inch in diameter when first laid. Being heavier than water, they come to rest among the pieces of gravel, where they remain from five to twenty days, depending on the temperature, before they hatch. During spawning, two or more males flank the larger female, pressing against her sides. They are helped to maintain their position by the many tiny, hard, conical growths, called "pearl organs," that develop along their bodies and fins during the time for breeding.

White suckers are widely distributed east of the Rocky Mountains from Labrador and the Mackenzie River system in northern Canada, south to the Gulf states. Their greatest importance is as a forage fish, that is, as food for various commercial and gamefishes. They are eaten by man, however, in fair quantities in some places, being taken mostly during the spawning migration. They reach a length of over twenty inches. Because they multiply rapidly—more than one hundred thousand eggs may be produced by a large female—and are easily raised in fish hatcheries, white suckers are becoming increasingly important as bait fish.

The suckers, including the buffalo fishes, chubsuckers, redhorse suckers, and quillback, make up a family of nearly ninety species.

The Bigmouth Buffalo Fish, *Megastomatobus cyprinella,* prefers the sluggish waters of large rivers, bayous, and shallow lakes. It ranges from southern Canada to Texas and is most common in the Mississippi valley. It has been transplanted into southern California.

The bigmouth buffalo fish is a stocky fish with an elliptical body. The mouth is sharply angled upwards. Its food consists of both vegetable and animal matter, the latter including insect larvae and mollusks. Reproduction takes place in the spring, when the bigmouth buffalo fish lays adhesive eggs which hatch in about nine days at 60° Fahrenheit.

Buffalo fishes are the basis of one of the most valuable of North American inland fisheries. There are three or four species of commercial importance of which the bigmouth buffalo fish is probably the most numerous and definitely the largest. In fact it is the largest species of all the suckers, reaching a length of four feet and a weight of sixty-five pounds.

The North American Minnows are the most numerous single group of fresh-water fishes on that continent—and one of the most important, too. Most of them do not reach a large size, but they provide the bulk of the food for practically all the larger fish-eating commercial and game fishes. A few, such as the Fallfish, exceed one foot, and the relatively gigantic Colorado Squawfish, *Ptychocheilus lucius*, attains a length of five feet and a weight of eighty pounds.

The squawfishes are fish-eaters, but most minnows feed on very small animals and on aquatic plants. Minnows inhabit many different types of water, from glacial lakes to warm springs and from tiny mountain brooks to broad silted rivers. Included in the more than four hundred different species are the shiners, chubs, dace, stonerollers, squawfishes, and the hitch.

Minnows are often mistaken for the young of larger fishes, but can be distinguished from them by their lack of teeth on the jaws (they have instead a few large teeth in their throats), the presence of a Weberian apparatus (described at the start of this chapter), the absence of scales on the head, the location of the pelvic fins back towards the rear of the body, the lack of spines in any of the fins, and the presence of less than ten main fin rays in the single dorsal fin. Any fish not having all these characteristics is not a North American minnow.

The reproductive habits of these minnows are quite variable. In a number of species, the males excavate shallow pits in gravel or sand to receive the eggs. In others they gather piles of small stones to make a nest. Among these species is the Fallfish, *Semotilus corporalis*. Although the males never exceed eighteen inches, they perform great feats of strength in moving large stones—as much as three and one-half inches in diameter—and may construct a nest eighteen feet in circumference and three feet high at the center. Still other species of minnows lay their eggs in crevices of logs or on the under surfaces of stones and other submerged objects, after which they are guarded and cared for by the male. Finally, there is a whole group that builds no nest of any sort and shows no parental care, simply allowing the eggs to fall on gravel or sand or into aquatic vegetation. Among those species that build nests, the males are usually larger than the females and develop beautiful, bright coloration during the spawning season, which is in spring or summer. At this time they also develop small horny growths, the pearl organs.

The North American minnows belong to the family Cyprinidae, of which the rasboras, danios, bitterlings, carps, goldfish, barbs, gudgeon, and roach are also members. This is the largest single family of fishes, containing roughly two thousand species. A species, *Catlocarpio siamensis,* from southeastern Asia, reaches lengths of nearly ten feet, and is the largest of all the cyprinids.

The Common Shiner, *Notropis cornutus,* is one of the most abundant of North American minnows and is widely used as a bait fish. It is found in many streams and lakes throughout the continent east of the Rockies, from southern Canada and Maine to the Gulf states and North Carolina. It reaches a length of eight inches.

Males are generally larger than females, and during the spawning season their sides become tinged with red, and their other colors become intensified. Females remain practically the same color all the year 'round, that is, olive green or gray above and silvery below. Males also develop breeding tubercles around the head, on the back, and on the pectoral fins; these are undoubtedly of use in fighting, digging and mating.

During spring and early summer males gather on gravel or sand beds in streams, awaiting the appearance of females ready to spawn. Sometimes nests up to about one foot in diameter are dug, by inserting the head between small stones and dislodging them, thus cleaning away the silt and sometimes creating a slight depression. Whether or not a nest is constructed, the males constantly vie with one another for the best position in the area. They rush around one another, trying to butt their rivals, and also indulge in a kind of display behavior in which two opponents tensely swim together side by side for a few feet before returning to the spawning area. Usually the largest male holds the position farthest upstream, with perhaps twenty others jockeying for position behind him. When a female appears near a male on the spawning ground, he displays to her in a peculiar manner, and they embrace for a fraction of a second during which time perhaps fifty orange-colored eggs about one-sixteenth of an inch in diameter are laid. These soon become adhesive and stick to pebbles and grains of sand.

Frequently common shiners use the nests of other species of minnows as places in which to lay their eggs. It is undoubtedly this habit that leads to the production of the several kinds of well-known hybrids, involving the common shiner and other minnows. Scientists believe that when common shiners happen to spawn at the same moment a pair of some other species is doing so, the sexual elements may become mixed in the water, creating natural hybrids.

Common shiners feed at the surface, on the bottom, and in midwater. They consume both plant and animal matter. The former consists mostly of algae and tiny plants called "diatoms"; the latter includes many insects and crustaceans, worms, and small fishes.

The Bluntnose Minnow, *Hyborhynchus notatus,* lays its eggs on the under surface of such natural objects as rocks, logs, strips of bark, and mussel shells, and artificial ones like boards, tile, tin cans, and pieces of flat metal or tar-paper. The male prepares the nesting site by hollowing out a cavity beneath the object just big enough for him to enter and then cleaning off the lower surface where the eggs will be attached. Several females lay in a single nest, usually at night, and as many as five thousand eggs may finally be present in a large one. The male guards the eggs most bravely, protecting them from other fishes and from leeches and snails. He also circulates water around them and keeps them free from sediment. Frequently several males build their nests alongside one another, each fish apparently recognizing his own place and living at peace with his neighbors.

The male bluntnose minnow assumes a darker coloration at the onset of the time for breeding. He also develops three rows of hard, conical growths across the rounded snout. These protuberances are used in nest digging and in butting other fishes. The spawning season extends through the spring and summer. The eggs are about one-sixteenth of an inch in diameter and are adhesive. They hatch in from six days to two weeks, and the young are about one-fifth of an inch long.

No parental care over them is shown. Male bluntnose minnows grow to be about four inches long, females about three. Some live to be at least four years old. They feed mostly on tiny plants and animals.

The range of the bluntnose minnow includes most of the eastern half of the United States and Canada, from Quebec and North Dakota to Virginia and the Gulf states. Because of their large numbers, wide distribution, and ability to withstand different living conditions, bluntnose minnows are among the most important forage minnows. Since they do not compete with gamefishes for food to any extent, yet provide them with excellent food themselves, they may be considered doubly valuable.

The Red Rasbora, *Rasbora heteromorpha,* occurs in streams and lakes of Sumatra, the Malay Peninsula, and Thailand. It is perhaps the best-known member of the very numerous group of small, freshwater fishes called rasboras. Its renown arises from its beauty and its ability to thrive in home aquaria. Since 1906, the year it was first imported alive into Europe, it has been one of the most popular of the fishes kept as pets.

Red rasboras reach a length of about one and three-quarter inches. Their bodies are tinged with a lovely rose color, over which a delicate, shifting rainbow plays. Each side, from the mid-point of the body to the tail, carries a roughly triangular, purplish-black mark, which contrasts beautifully with the rest of the fish. Above this is a golden line, usually more brilliant in males than females. The fins are tinted red and yellow.

The adhesive eggs are usually laid on the under side of the leaves of aquatic plants. The mating pair turn on their backs to deposit and fertilize them. The eggs hatch in about one and one-half days.

The Bitterling, *Rhodeus amarus,* uses a living fresh-water mussel as a nursery. At spawning time in the spring, the female grows a long tube or ovipositor that may become as long as she is, that is, about three inches. Both the male, who assumes a bright red nuptial livery, and the female indulge in courtship behavior in which they seem to pay much more attention to some particular mussel lying half exposed on the bottom than to each other. Suddenly, with a motion so fast that its exact details are still a matter of question, the female inserts her ovipositor into the exhalant or excurrent siphon (the tube that discharges water) of the bivalved mollusk and lays one or two ellipsoidal eggs inside. The male immediately performs his part, the eggs being fertilized while inside the mollusk. This procedure is repeated many times over the course of several days, more than one mussel being used by a single female. The eggs become lodged among the gills of the mussel, and two to three weeks later, tiny bitterlings emerge from their strange shelter.

LAYING EGGS IN A MUSSEL
The bitterling uses a living fresh-water mussel as a nursery. After the female has laid her eggs in the mussel, the male fertilizes them there. This fish, a native of central Europe, was introduced into New York waters and thrived there for some time, using American mussels for its eggs.

Bitterlings are found in central Europe. They use at least two different species of European mussels as a hatching place for their eggs. For a while at least, they successfully maintained themselves in the United States after being introduced into New York waters. It was found that two different American mussels could also be utilized by the fish. There are several Asiatic species of bitterling-like fishes, including three or four from Japan.

The Carp, *Cyprinus carpio,* has proved a mixed blessing to man, but the good service it has done far outweighs the bad. It has provided countless people with wholesome, high-protein food at most reasonable cost. Although considered inferior in taste and too full of bones by many—including most North Americans—the fact remains that the fish is delicious when properly prepared.

Even in the United States, where carp are considered an inferior foodfish by the great majority of people, more than seventeen million pounds are caught annually, mostly for food. The carp is by far the most important species employed in the extensive culturing of fishes in ponds that is carried on in Europe and the Near East, and is one of the most important in the Far East. It is also raised for food in parts of South America and Africa. No accurate estimate of present-day, world-wide consumption of carp has ever been made; nevertheless, it is safe to say that more carp are eaten by man than any other fresh-water fish.

Originally a native of Asia—and probably of Europe, too—the carp is now found on all the continents, and also in outlying places like Madagascar and the Hawaiian Islands. Some authorities believe it was introduced into Europe during the thirteenth century. In 1872 a few specimens were carried from Germany to California; four or five years later some were brought over to Maryland. With much enthusiasm and little discretion carp were soon transplanted into the waters of most states. The species was introduced into Africa and South America somewhat later. In many of these places carp have become a nuisance or actually a menace to other, more valuable, kinds of fishes. Because of their hardiness, adaptability, and high breeding rate, carp tend to compete severely with native forms and, sometimes, to replace them. They destroy vegetation and thus the breeding grounds and shelters of many species, but worst of all, their habit of rooting up the bottom for food can so stir up and cloud the water with sediment as to render it unsuitable for desirable fishes.

Carp were undoubtedly the first of all fish to be domesticated; the Chinese have raised them in ponds for at least twenty-five hundred years. There are three principal varieties used in pond culture today: the mirror carp, which has a reduced number of scales, scattered over the body with bare skin in between; the leather carp, which has no scales at all or only very few around the base of the fins; and the fully scaled, wild type. A number of special strains have also been developed, showing varying degrees of rapidity of growth, economical use of food, resistance to disease, and the like. Under good domestic conditions, carp attain a weight of three pounds by the time they are three years old. If carp ponds are fertilized to increase the growth of microscopic plants and animals and the fish are artificially fed, they will yield as much as twelve hundred pounds of fish per acre each year. Since carp are primarily vegetarian, they can use plants directly as food, although they will eat a variety of small animals and animal products as well.

The eggs of the carp are about one-sixteenth of an inch in diameter. They are adhesive, and in nature are laid on water plants. Spawning takes place in spring and early summer, often being accompanied by much splashing and other commotion as the female swims about, closely attended by several males. Females can produce tremendous quantities of eggs, all of which, however, may not be laid at one time. Hatching occurs from about five to twenty days after laying, the length of time depending on the temperature of the water.

Carp live well in captivity; some specimens have been kept alive for more than thirty years. A maximum weight of eighty-three and one-half pounds has been reported, but rarely is forty pounds exceeded.

The Goldfish, *Carassius auratus,* was first domesticated by the Chinese one thousand years ago. Wild goldfish are more or less dull silver and bronze in color—similar to the carp, to which they are related, but from which they are entirely distinct, even though the two species can cross. Comparing the two, carp can be identified by the presence of two pairs of short barbels on the upper jaw. In nature, goldfish often show a golden condition, apparently resulting from the reduction or lack of black pigment cells; it was from such specimens that the first domestic yellow-gold or red-gold fish were developed. The natural home of the wild goldfish is in southern China, and both young and old are used for food there today.

Various fancy strains, such as fantails and veiltails, were originated by the Chinese relatively early, and the Japanese carried on this work after the introduction of goldfish into their country at about the beginning of the sixteenth century. It is not definitely known when the goldfish was first brought to Europe, but evidence indicates that it was imported into England during the first half of the eighteenth century. By about 1785 goldfish bowls had become popular household decorations in that country. Goldfish may have come to the United

States as early as 1850; at any rate some had already escaped into the Schuylkill River by 1858. Unfortunately, when these fish revert to the wild state, all the beautiful, fancy-colored individuals disappear, leaving only dull, unprepossessing fish with feeding habits that make them a nuisance and even a threat to native fishes. Wild goldfish are now also found in Europe, Madagascar, Hawaii, Australia, and much of the Orient.

The goldfish are omnivorous, that is, they eat all sorts of animal and vegetable matter; most people that keep them do not realize the great variety of foodstuffs their pets will consume if given the opportunity. Goldfish have no jaw teeth and so can eat only small items and soft materials like algae. Much time is spent grubbing and picking about the bottom, and this is what makes them undesirable tenants in natural waters. Goldfish should never be allowed to escape into the wilds because they can easily become a pest.

Spawning takes place in the spring and summer. Males develop numerous, small growths on the head, gill covers, and pectoral fins; and females become heavy with eggs. The eggs are adhesive and are scattered on plants as the female swims through them, pursued by one or more males. A medium-sized fish lays as many as one thousand eggs at a single spawning and may spawn more than once in a season. At about 60 degrees, hatching occurs in nine days. Newly hatched fry are about one fifth of an inch long, and have a prominent yolk-sac. They do little or no swimming for the first two days, while the yolk is being absorbed, but then they start actively to search for microscopic and near-microscopic food. Goldfish have lived long lives in captivity—for at least twenty years on good authority. The ordinary ones can reach lengths of two feet, but rarely do so because they are confined in relatively small tanks or pools.

The amazing results that can sometimes be obtained through selective breeding cannot be better shown than with the goldfish. An astonishing number of differently colored and shaped types have been developed at one time or another during the long history of this fish as a domestic animal. There are red-, orange-, yellow-, blue-, and black-hued strains. Fish lacking dorsal or tail fins have been bred. Enormously enlarged fins, some of them doubled, are well known. Fish with telescopic eyes, with shortened, egg-shaped or comma-shaped bodies, or with large wartlike growths on the head have been developed. Perfect examples of some of these types are extremely difficult to obtain, since thousands of individuals must be weeded out—even among the offspring of specially selected parents—before the right one is found. Such fish have sold for as much as seven hundred dollars each.

The Barbel, *Barbus barbus,* is the only member of the large group of barbs found north of the Alps. The great majority of the several hundred different species come from Africa and tropical Asia eastward to the East Indies. We find the barbel in France and Germany and other central and southern European countries as well as in a few rivers of eastern England.

The body of the barbel is rather long. Its mouth is crescent-shaped with thick lips and is located on the under side of the snout. There are two pairs of barbels, one on the snout, the other at the corners of the mouth. The barbel usually feeds by grubbing on the bottom for a large variety of animal and vegetable matter.

In May and June barbels spawn, laying eggs, which are heavier than water, over gravelly bottoms. The eggs of the barbel are believed to be more or less poisonous, and it is considered good practice to remove them from a female fish very soon after catching.

The barbel is one of the medium-sized barbs. Many of this group are small—of a size that perfectly suits them for home aquaria. A few are very large, the mahseers of India, for example. These are famous gamefishes that attain weights well over one hundred pounds and perhaps exceed two hundred. In England the maximum recorded weight of the barbel is twenty pounds, but larger specimens are known on the continent.

The Gudgeon, *Gobio gobio,* is a small, bottom-inhabiting fish of streams, lakes, and ponds in England, Wales, and Ireland, and on the continent, excepting Greece, Spain, and Portugal. Towards the east, it is found in Russia, Turkestan, Siberia, and Mongolia. It rarely exceeds six inches in length, although specimens two inches longer are known.

The gudgeon has a small crescent-shaped mouth located on the underside of the snout, with a single barbel on either side. Its food consists of small crustaceans and mollusks, insect larvae, worms, and fish eggs and fry. During the spring and summer gudgeons lay their small, adhesive eggs on gravelly shallows. Despite its diminutive size, the gudgeon fights gamely when hooked. Comparatively speaking, though, fishermen have always considered it an easy fish to catch. As a result its name has become a synonym for a creature that may be duped without trouble—Shakespeare used the word that way. The gudgeon makes a delightful morsel when cooked, but many prefer to use it as a bait fish.

The Roach, *Rutilus rutilus,* is probably the most sought after of all fresh-water fishes in England and Scotland; more anglers try their skill against this species than any other. In most places, catching roach requires both skill and patience, for the fish are quite wary. Unfortunately, once caught, they are not too well liked for food because of their bony flesh and sometimes muddy flavor. The record specimen ever caught by rod-and-reel weighed three pounds, fourteen ounces. Such a fish is about eighteen inches long. Individuals more than two pounds in weight are uncommon, and any over one pound is considered a good catch.

Roach inhabit quiet fresh waters in northern Europe and Asia. Sometimes they also are found in brackish waters. They feed on vegetable and animal matter, usually near the bottom. Spawning takes place in the spring, when the fish migrate from deeper waters, where they have spent the winter, to weedy shallows or small streams. They lay numerous small eggs which are heavier than water and which hatch in about eleven days. The roach can hybridize with at least three different fishes of its own family in Europe and the British Isles, and these hybrids have been found in nature.

The Weather Fish, *Misgurnus fossilis,* is supposed to indicate coming changes in the weather by dashing frantically around its tank. The fish makes an interesting aquatic pet, but its ability as a weather prophet seems to have been exaggerated.

Weather fish inhabit fresh waters of central Europe, east to the region of the Caspian Sea. They are bottom forms that hide most of the daylight hours, sometimes digging their long, thin, round bodies into mud or sand. A length of at least twenty inches is sometimes reached. The weather fish employs its intestine for breathing atmospheric air in addition to the more usual respiration by means of gills. It rises to the surface and swallows some air which passes through the stomach and is stored in a bulge in the intestine located just behind the stomach. Here the vital exchange of gases takes place, and finally the "bad" air is voided through the fish's vent.

Around the mouth of the weather fish are five pairs of small barbels, giving it the appearance of having quite a mustache. These are undoubtedly used in feeding, since the fish grubs around a good deal and also takes in quantities of disintegrated matter, apparently sifting out tiny edible particles. In the spring thousands of small, adhesive eggs are laid, usually at night.

The Neon Tetra, *Hyphessobrycon innesi,* created a sensation among tropical fish fanciers when it was introduced into Europe and the United States in 1936. The first specimen to reach the United States arrived from France on the airship *Graf Zeppelin,* and cost several hundred dollars. Neon tetras had been discovered far up the Amazon in the region where Brazil and Peru meet, and after many difficulties a few specimens were finally brought out alive. Today large shipments of them are regularly made from Brazil to the United States, and they are now one of the standard items in the large business of importing tropical fresh-water fishes for home aquaria.

Few fresh-water fish can rival the neon tetra for sheer brilliance of color; the fish really lives up to the name of "living jewel." It is a small species, mature specimens being about one and one-half inches long. Its general body color is a neutral light gray, but the lower part of the rear of the body and base of the tail are colored bright red, and running along each side, from the eye almost to the tail, is an iridescent blue-green band, so brilliant that it seems to arise from some electrical apparatus or molten metal rather than living tissue.

Although neon tetras have bred in captivity a number of times, they do so far too seldom to supply the great demand for them among fanciers of tropical fish, and so must be imported regularly. During spawning a pair swims through aquatic plants, the female scattering two to fifteen small, slightly adhesive eggs that may or may not become attached to the vegetation. This process is repeated at frequent intervals until perhaps two hundred eggs have been laid—a matter of two to three hours. The eggs hatch in about two days. The fry are minute, almost transparent creatures that hide among plants or hang motionlessly at the surface of the water.

The Blind Cave Characin, *Anoptichthys jordani,* comes from a single, small cave in the state of San Luis Potosi, Mexico—and nowhere else. In captivity, on the other hand, it is common all over the United States, in Europe, and elsewhere. This is because it has become one of the popular small "tropical fishes" of home aquarists. It is safe to say that there are many more blind cave characins living in aquaria far from their native dwelling place than exist in the Mexican cave.

Even though the cave characin is blind, its eyes being reduced to a pair of degenerate capsules more or less buried under the skin, it can hold its own in a tankful of other tropical fish in full possession of all their faculties. Although it may bump into plants, rocks, and other tank accessories when first placed in an aquarium, it very soon learns to avoid these obstacles and will swim directly towards one, unerringly turning away from it just before striking it. If you change the location of an object, the fish must again learn where it is.

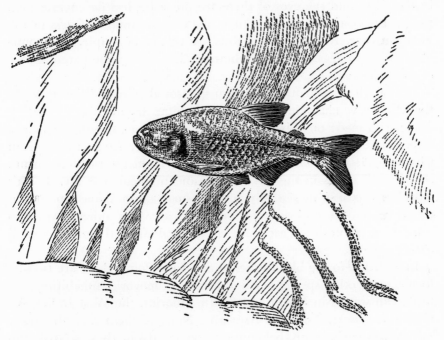

THIS FISH IS BORN BLIND

The blind cave characin is a popular fish in the home aquarium. It comes from only one place—a single, small cave in the state of San Luis Potosi, Mexico—and nowhere else. However, it has been shipped to fanciers all over the United States and to Europe. Although it is actually blind, it soon learns to adjust itself among a tankful of normal fish, and does not suffer particularly because of its handicap.

Blind cave characins quickly learn about the feeding procedure in any particular tank and never suffer from lack of food despite the fact that they must compete with eyed fish. They generally feed on the bottom, scurrying around with such energy that, if anything, they get more than their share of food. They exhibit little nicety of taste, eating practically anything. In nature their principal food consists of the droppings of the thousands of bats that inhabit their cave.

Besides having only degenerate eyes, the blind cave characin lacks the dark pigment present in the great majority of fishes. When first taken from the cave, it is pinkish white, but after being exposed to light for some time, it becomes silvery. Its ears, too, have degenerated through the ages. It does, however, possess a greater number of taste buds than does its nearest eyed relative. Living in light has no effect on its eyes whatever; many generations have been hatched and raised in the light, and the eyes of these are not a bit less degenerate than the eyes of fish that lived all their lives in the total darkness of the Mexican cave. Reproductive habits are relatively simple. The somewhat adhesive eggs drop to the bottom, and there is no parental care of any sort.

In 1940 the New York Aquarium sponsored an expedition to study the blind cave characin in its native habitat. One of the interesting discoveries made on this trip was that the blind fish were evidently interbreeding with their eyed and pigmented relative, the Mexican Characin, *Astyanax mexicanus*. A whole series of intermediate forms, showing all stages in the lack of eyes and pigment, was found. This cross has also been successfully made in small tanks. Later exploration revealed that in the same region there are four other caves also containing blind fishes, each slightly different from the other, but all closely related.

In addition to the blind fishes of San Luis Potosi there are twenty-five or more other species of blind fishes in the world, inhabiting subterranean waters in North and South America, the West Indies, Africa, Madagascar, Asia, and Australia. None of them is at all closely related to the characins, belonging to several distinctly separated families of fishes. In the United States, there are two species of blind catfishes that have been taken from artesian wells in Texas, and about eight species of blind fishes, belonging to a special family of their own, the Amblyopsidae, that inhabit a number of the limestone caves in the Midwest and Midsouth.

The Piranha, *Serrasalmus nattereri,* has killed perhaps more human beings than any other fish. Although it reaches a length of only ten and one-half inches, it is one of the most savage of all fishes, and no creature is too large or powerful to be attacked by it.

Its short, broad jaws are each equipped with a row of strong, triangular, razor-sharp teeth that fit into one another very closely. So powerful are the jaw muscles that only the hardest ironwood or metal can resist. Ordinary fishhooks, for example, are quickly snapped in two, and fingers or toes are amputated with grisly ease. With each bite, the piranha neatly removes from its prey a piece of flesh about the size of a large olive, this being clipped off and swallowed whole with machine-gun rapidity. The fish seems to go berserk when any blood is let, madly snapping in all directions, even biting its own companions in its frenzy.

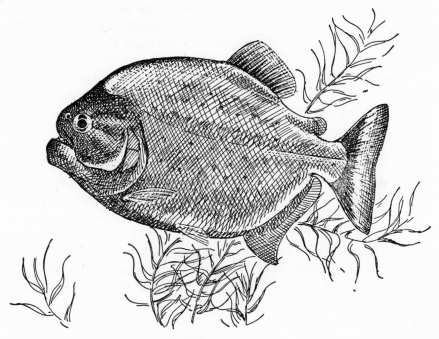

MOST DANGEROUS OF ALL FISHES
In spite of its small size, it is probable that the piranha has taken more human lives than even the deadliest of the sharks. "Caribe" ("cannibal") is the name the Spaniards gave this dangerous creature; when it tastes blood it will even attack its own kind. The piranha is a South American fresh-water fish.

Large numbers of piranhas gather wherever food is available. They have been known to strip the flesh from the bones of a living one-hundred-pound capybara in less than one minute and a four-hundred-

pound hog in less than ten. Horrible stories about people being literally eaten alive by these bloodthirsty fish have been fully corrobo-
rated. Wherever they are found, piranhas are generally the most
feared of water creatures. Their usual food consists of other fishes, but
mammals, birds, and reptiles—in fact any sizable creatures that accidentally or deliberately get into water—are frequently destroyed. Piranhas also eat fruit and can be caught on hooks baited with balls of
dough.

The piranha is a rather deep-bodied, compressed fish with a blunt,
bulldog-like profile—the upper part almost vertical, the lower jaw
projecting beyond the upper part of the face. It is colored silvery blue
with a light red anal fin. During the spawning season, the underparts
of the male become a brilliant red. Little is known about the reproductive habits of piranhas. They have been reported as laying adhesive eggs on submerged plants and roots and constructing a shallow
nest on sandy bottoms. The parents are said to attack viciously anything approaching their eggs.

There are four dangerous species of piranhas, and they inhabit
South American streams that drain into the Atlantic from northern
Argentina to Venezuela. Not every river harbors them, but the Amazon, Orinoco, Paraguay, Parana, and Sao Francisco Rivers all have
one or two species. *Serrasalmus nattereri* is the most widely distributed of all, being found in the Guianas, Venezuela, Brazil, Paraguay,
Uruguay, and northern Argentina. The largest species is *Serrasalmus
piraya,* found only in the Río Sao Francisco, which reaches a length
of at least twenty inches.

The Streaked Hatchet Fish, *Carnegiella strigata,* is one of the fresh-
water flying fishes and is capable of traveling through the air for distances of perhaps six feet or more over the shaded forest streams and
pools of the Guianas and the Amazon, where it lives. Unlike the marine flying fishes, hatchet fishes do not glide, but actually flap—or
rather, vibrate—their arched pectoral fins, like wings; their flight is
therefore similar to that of insects rather than airplanes. Although
they will fly to escape from a fish that is pursuing them, they never
fly ashore by mistake, and while they will take off toward the open water when in danger of being caught by a net, they cannot be forced to
fly towards a nearby shore, no matter how much they are harassed.
Perhaps this unerring knowledge or instinct of the limits of their

aquatic environment is what prevents them from ever flying in the tanks in which tropical fish fanciers keep them as pets.

To operate their "wings," hatchet fishes have tremendously developed pectoral (breast) muscles attached to a very large "sternum" or breastbone like that of birds. This structure projects forward and downward, giving the fish a chest that is semicircular in profile and triangular in cross-section, coming to a rounded, knife-thin edge. The muscles that move the pectoral fins or "wings" may constitute as much as one-quarter of the total weight of the fish; in more ordinarily shaped species they make up less than one one-hundredth.

Streaked hatchet fish reach a length of one and three-quarter inches. They feed principally on small insects floating on the water surface. They lay eggs that float. About ten different species of hatchet fishes are known, all from northern South America or Panama.

The Electric Eel, *Electrophorus electricus,* is the most powerful of all the electric fishes. At the New York Aquarium we have measured hundreds of specimens and have found that the average maximum voltage is in excess of 350; and that at maximum power, an external current of about one-half an ampere at two hundred to three hundred volts may be drawn—that is, a hundred or more watts. This is enough to knock down a horse or to stun a man, and there are records of people having been killed by the electric eel's discharges, or drowned when they fell unconscious into the water after being shocked.

One of our medium-sized eels, about three feet long, produced discharges of 650 volts. These are the greatest we have ever recorded. One single discharge from even this particular eel is not as much, electrically, as a single discharge from a medium-sized torpedo. But the electric eel can continue to discharge for long periods of time, at a rate that varies from three hundred to thirty discharges a second— whereas the torpedo quickly becomes fatigued, after not more than fifty or so discharges.

Despite its great power, the electric eel cannot operate ordinary electric appliances and incandescent lamps. This is because each discharge lasts only about two one-thousandths of a second—while it takes an incandescent lamp, for example, as long as one-fiftieth of a second to heat up enough to be visible. The electric eel generates direct current, and the front end of the fish is always positive to the rear.

Electric eels use their electricity both to obtain food and to protect themselves. They are toothless, spineless, and scaleless creatures that swallow whole the small fishes and frogs stunned by their discharges. They inhabit the Amazon, Orinoco, and other smaller river systems of northern South America, usually being found in slow-moving, rather shallow backwaters. They are sluggish, and spend much time lying quietly in the water, only moving periodically to come to the surface for a gulp of air. The roof and floor of the mouth are specially modified to enable the fish to breathe atmospheric air, and if denied access to it electric eels drown in about ten minutes.

The electric eel is not at all related to the true eels, and, although it has a long, rather thin body, it completely lacks the sinuous grace and streamlined contours of the American eel and its relatives. With the exception of an expanse of salmon red or yellowish green on the belly and throat, the electric eel is a more or less uniform dull gray. The pectoral fins are very small. There is no dorsal or caudal fin at all, but the anal extends along the whole posterior four-fifths of the fish. By undulating this long fin the fish moves about, backwards and forwards with equal ease.

Practically nothing is known about the life history of electric eels. They undoubtedly lay eggs, but exactly where or when is pretty much of a mystery. The fish apparently disappear from their normal haunts during the rainy season, presumably going into flooded swamp lands, and at the end of that season they reappear with a cloud of small eels, an inch or so long, swimming about their head. The sex of this parent, or whether both sexes take care of the young, is unknown, but at least one parent is reported to do so until the young are five or six inches long. It is not until this time that they can produce enough electricity to defend themselves or procure food. By the time an electric eel has reached a length of about three feet, it has attained its maximum voltage, and subsequent growth only slightly increases the voltage but considerably increases the amperage. Maximum length is about nine and one-half feet.

The vital organs of the electric eel are confined to the first fifth of its length, all the rest being tail. Almost two-thirds of the tail is composed of the electric organs. These are made up of electric tissue which operates in essentially the same fashion as nerve tissue, and for this reason the electric eel has become very important in physiological and medical research.

Although sensitive to electricity, the electric eel is not harmed by its own discharges or those of its fellows. On the contrary, when an individual discharges, all others in the vicinity gather about the spot, apparently searching for food. The only "harm" done by these powerful currents seems to be the formation of opaque spots on the lenses of the eyes. All but the smallest electric eels have these, a circumstance suggesting that electric eels are apparently dependent on their own

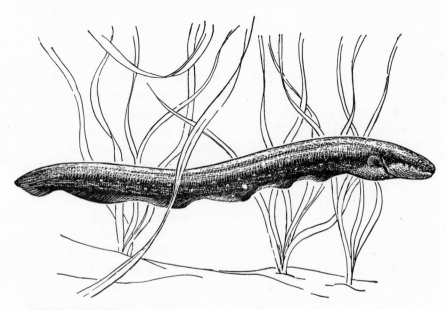

A LIVING DYNAMO

The electric eel is capable of producing more electric discharges than any other electric fish, including the torpedo; the voltage easily paralyzes or kills small fish and frogs, and is sufficient to stun a man. As a result, this fish is greatly feared by the Indians of the Orinoco and Amazon, where it is found. The electric eel is a slow-moving creature and devoid of teeth—without its charge it would be hard put to defend itself or find food.

electric discharges, operating as a sort of radar, to explore their surroundings. Whenever an electric eel moves about, it produces a series of low-powered discharges, and these are used to locate objects in its environment. At least one other species of gymnotid eel also produces small electrical discharges for the same reason; the Electric Mormyrid, *Gymnarchus niloticus,* does so in a similar manner.

The Sea Catfish, *Galeichthys felis,* carries its eggs and young in its mouth for about two months, during which time it does not eat. Only the males play the role of living incubator, and they have been reported as becoming rather scrawny toward the end of their long period of fasting. While the eggs, and later the young fish, are being carried about, the male's mouth becomes quite enlarged, and even then it sometimes seems as if he could hardly hold his offspring in—so great is their bulk.

The eggs of the sea catfish are among the largest of all the bony fishes, ranging from one-half to three-quarters of an inch in diameter. Relatively few are produced by each female, but the indications are that a single female can produce more in one season than a single male can carry. The largest number of eggs ever found in a male's mouth was forty-eight; the usual number ranges from ten to thirty. Before the spawning season, which is in June and July, the females develop peculiar, fleshy, hooked growths on the inside margins of their pelvic fins. Presumably these hooks are used during the laying and fertilization of the eggs, for what evidence we have indicates that the eggs are in some way transferred to the mouth of the male without ever touching the bottom.

The eggs hatch in about a month. The young fish remain in the mouth of the father for almost another month, however, not only until their large yolk sac has been absorbed but until they are at least two inches long. While still under parental care they feed on their own account, but whether they do while still in their father's mouth or whether they venture outside to eat, returning for shelter and in case of emergency, is unknown. The male parent, on the other hand, does not eat at all during the whole period. Most of the stomachs of incubating males that have been examined were completely empty; a few had an egg or two in them.

Sea catfish inhabit shallow brackish and salt water bays during the spring, summer and fall. During the winter they apparently go into deeper water. This is a common species along the coast of the Gulf of Mexico, becoming rarer as one proceeds north; a specimen occasionally is found as far north as Cape Cod. The sea catfish occurs as far south as Yucatan.

The food of the sea catfish is most variable and may include crabs, shrimp, a number of other invertebrates, fishes, algae and various seagrasses, and garbage. The species grows to a length of slightly more than sixteen and one-half inches, but males less than half that length have been found carrying eggs. The under side of the skull of the sea catfish, and that of many of its ocean- and inlet-dwelling relatives, has two rounded, long prominences arranged more or less at right angles to each other. These are often considered to represent Jesus of Nazareth on the cross, and the skulls are used as icons in some parts of Latin America. The fish is therefore called the "crucifix fish."

The Brown Bullhead, *Ameiurus nebulosus,* inhabits shallow, quiet, fresh waters in the eastern part of North America, from Manitoba to New Brunswick in the north, to Texas and Florida in the south. It has been introduced along the west coast and now thrives in California, Oregon, Washington, and British Columbia. It is now also found in parts of western Europe and on several of the Hawaiian Islands. The brown bullhead is remarkably hardy, being able to exist in waters too foul for practically all other fishes. It can also live for weeks at a time down in the mud, when the water of its lake, pond, or stream dries up.

The most prominent feature of the brown bullhead is the four pairs of long barbels or "whiskers" located on the chin and between the eyes and mouth. These are used to explore its surroundings, the bullhead apparently depending on them more than on its eyes. The body is without scales. There is a single stout spine in the dorsal fin and in each pectoral fin; it is these that cause the unpleasant pricks that result when the fish is not handled properly. The brown bullhead does not have any poison glands associated with its spines.

Although looked down on by many fishermen, the brown bullhead has provided many anglers with pleasure, and a great many people with cheap yet tasty and nourishing food. It takes the hook most readily, and its flesh is firm, white, sweet, and relatively boneless. The usual length is less than one foot but specimens half again as long are known.

The food of the brown bullhead is quite varied; this fish apparently eats whatever is most available. Insect larvae and adults, crustaceans, mollusks, fishes, frogs, leeches, and worms are all taken. Plant material may be consumed in quantity, and at times fish eggs or garbage may be the chief item in its diet.

Brown bullheads prepare a nest for their eggs. This is usually in some cavity under rocks, roots, or logs, or within an abandoned muskrat hole; even objects like old tin pails may be used. Occasionally a shallow, dish-shaped nest is dug more or less out in the open. A large number of cream colored eggs about one-eighth of an inch in diameter are laid. There may be more than two thousand of them and they adhere to one another, forming one or more clumps. Either the male alone or both parents together may care for the eggs and young. The eggs are vigorously shaken by the fish's pelvic fins, and are taken into the mouth, "chewed" and then spat out. Hatching may occur in less than a day or may take as long as ten days. Young bullheads move about together in a school, forming a dense, black cloud of tiny fish upon which the attending parent or parents "ride herd."

The Stonecat, *Noturus flavus*, the madtoms, and a number of tropical species of catfishes do have, unlike the brown bullhead, poison glands in their spines and can inflict very painful and slow-healing wounds.

The Electric Catfish, *Malapterurus electricus*, has been known since ancient times. The fish was familiar to the Egyptians and also to the Greeks and Romans, and Arab writers during the Middle Ages told of its use as a love charm and as a therapeutic shocking-machine. It was first scientifically described in 1789 and imported alive into Europe in 1880; yet even today very little is known about its life history or the exact way its organs work.

Electric catfish are found through most of the western and central parts of tropical Africa and along the River Nile. They grow to a length of about four feet. They have a cylindrical body, brownish or grayish in color, with no scales and only a very small, adipose (fatty) dorsal fin located near the tail. Surrounding the mouth are three pairs of long "whiskers." It is perhaps significant that the electric catfish, which is well able to defend itself by means of electric shocks, completely lacks the spines or armor so common among most other species of catfishes.

Little is known of the mode of life of the electric catfish save that it inhabits rivers and swamps. It is reported as eating algae, worms, and fish, but its exact diet in nature has apparently never been recorded. In captivity it cannnot be kept with other members of its species; in any tank, one and only one electric catfish survives. Nothing is known of its reproductive habits.

There is no doubt that the strong electric shocks which the electric catfish is capable of producing are used defensively, but whether they are also employed offensively, that is, to stun prey, is still a question. What reports there are on the strength of the electric discharges of the fish appear quite different from one another. We have measured a number of specimens ranging from about four to eight inches in length and have found their maximum discharge to run about eighty volts. The electric organ consists of a special, gelatinous coat of tissue that covers most of the body just under the skin.

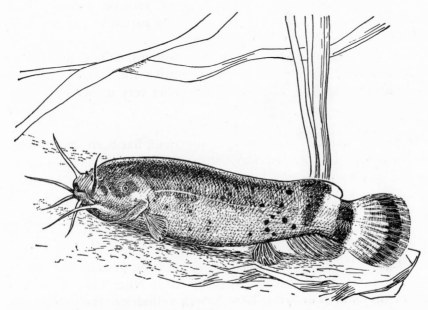

CATFISH WITH AN ELECTRIC CHARGE
The "bewhiskered" creatures called catfish are well known to fishermen in Europe, America, and Australia; less familiar is the electric catfish of Africa. An eight-inch individual is capable of producing a charge of eighty volts. In earlier times the electric catfish is said to have been used in the treatment of epilepsy.

The Whiptail Loricaria, *Loricaria parva,* at first glance looks like a living fossil, a creature out of the dim past, when all fishes were flattened and heavily armored. The truth of the matter is, however, that the family of armored catfishes to which the whiptail loricaria belongs is among the most specialized or "modern" of all the catfishes, and that it consists of not a few relics, but of a flourishing group of more than four hundred different species, inhabiting almost all the fresh waters of tropical South and Central America.

The whiptail loricaria reaches a length of about eight inches. It has a depressed head that is semi-circular in outline and shield-shaped, followed by a roughly triangular body that tapers to a long whisk of a tail, terminating in a small fin with a long ray, or whip, at its upper edge. The whole fish is covered with bony armor, the head and fore-part of the body being sheathed in an inflexible case, and the rest of the fish in movable, overlapping plates. The color is grayish brown with darker transverse bands and blotches.

A CATFISH WITH A COAT OF ARMOR
The whiptail loricaria belongs to the family of armored catfish. With its flattened, heavily armored body it looks like a fish of ancient times but it is really a thoroughly "up-to-date," modern fish. Here a male rests on a batch of eggs, guarding them and keeping them clean.

Like other armored catfishes, the whiptail loricaria spends most of its time on or near the bottom and is most active during the hours of twilight and darkness. It feeds on organic matter which it sucks up from the bottom, on algae scraped from rocks, or on plants. Its sucker-like mouth is located on the underside of the head. The mouth is often employed to hold the fish in place—for example, on the vertical side of a stone or the glass walls of an aquarium. Many armored cat-fishes live in swift-flowing streams and use their mouths to keep from being washed downstream by the current. At least one species is able to inch up high waterfalls, in spite of the strong flow of water, by means of its sucking mouth.

In preparation for spawning a pair of whiptail loricaria clean off a rock or bit of hard bottom. The forty or so large, amber eggs are carefully cared for by the male who rests directly upon them, cleaning them with his mouth and fanning them with his large pectoral fins. After eight to ten days, the eggs hatch into baby fish about three-eighths of an inch long. The father shows no interest in his offspring, however.

Whiptail loricaria are native to fresh waters in Paraguay and southern Brazil.

The Eels—Fishes Like Snakes

An eel is just an eel to the person who does not know the fishes of this group well. But once you start to examine them closely, you will find many remarkable contrasts among them. Some are large, brightly colored, savage animals whose bite may be poisonous—at the other extreme are tiny, inoffensive, burrowing creatures that look and behave like worms. Even these are interesting: you would be astonished at the rapidity with which they can dig themselves into the sand or mud, tail first.

As recently as seventy-five years ago, the life story of the eels was one of the great riddles of nature. Up to that time, no one knew how they bore their young or what stages they passed through. The ancients thought these curious snakelike fishes arose through spontaneous generation from "the bowels of the earth" or the morning dew, or came from horsehairs that fell into water or from small beetles or the gills of other fishes.

So far as we now know, all eels lay their eggs in salt water. The young pass through a flat, transparent stage, at which time they hardly look like eels at all. Most species remain in the sea all their lives, but some live for long periods in fresh water, returning to the sea to lay their eggs.

The eels are very long, have tiny scales or none at all. They lack spines in their fins and have a characteristic kind of upper jaw. None of them possesses pelvic fins; some also are without pectorals, and a few have no fins whatsoever. The giants of the group (order Apodes, meaning "footless") range in length up to ten feet and in weight to more than one hundred pounds. Among the twenty or so families are the common edible eels of Europe and eastern North America and their relatives (Anguillidae), the conger eels (Leptocephalidae), and the moray eels (Muraenidae).

The fishes of this order might be called the "true eels," although sometimes we reserve that term for members of the family Anguillidae. At any rate, a number of wholly unrelated fishes are termed eels, among them the slime-eels and lamprey eels, the gymnotid eels or knifefishes, the synbranchid or swamp-eels, the mastacembelid or spiny eels, the cusk-eels and the rock-eel. Except for the long, supple body, these fishes have little in common.

The American Eel, *Anguilla rostrata,* was for many years a mystery fish. Although it was well known in the lakes, ponds, and streams of eastern North and Central America and of Bermuda and the West Indies, its life history puzzled scientists and laymen alike. No one knew where or when this important foodfish spawned; no one had ever seen the egg or young of the eel. When, after years of patient, careful work, the life cycles of both the American eel and its European cousin were revealed, for sheer strangeness and fascination they exceeded all expectations.

Mature female American eels, one and one-half to six feet long and about seven to twelve years old, migrate to the coast, entering the sea in the fall. To accomplish this they must sometimes travel overland, which they probably do at night, and while out of water they breathe through their skin. Mature males do not have to travel so far, since they grow up near the coast in brackish water. (They are usually smaller than the females, ranging from about twelve to eighteen inches in length.)

The goal of the eels' journey is an area in the Atlantic Ocean a few hundred miles southwest of Bermuda, in and around the Sargasso Sea. Here in mid-winter they spawn and then die.

The young eels are tiny, flattened, transparent creatures that do not remotely resemble eels—we call them leptocephalus larvae. They slowly make their way back towards the continent and arrive on our eastern coast in the spring less than a year and a half after they were spawned. By this time they have assumed an eel-shaped but transparent form. They are a little over two inches long. Soon they begin to darken, and those destined to be females start their long migration up streams. Now they are called elvers.

The European Eel, *Anguilla anguilla*, has a similar life history, but takes three years to change from leptocephalus larva into elver. In all, there are sixteen different species of eels that are closely related to the European and American ones. They are found throughout most of the warm temperate and tropical seas, with a notable exception of the eastern Pacific. There are none of these eels on our Pacific coast.

Under certain conditions, in captivity for example, eels never mature and have lived for as long as fifty-six years without showing signs of becoming reproductive adults.

The Conger Eel, *Conger oceanicus*, looks like the American eel in a general way. But we can quickly recognize the conger eel by its dorsal fin, which arises just above and behind the small pair of pectorals. In the American eel this fin begins a long way back from the pectorals. Moreover, the American eel has minute scales embedded in its skin—the conger eel has no scales whatsoever.

The life history of these two species is also somewhat different. Conger eels spend all of their lives in salt water and only make a relatively short migration offshore into deeper waters to spawn. The tiny eggs float, and the young fish go through a leptocephalus stage before becoming eel-shaped. At this stage they are very small, flattened, transparent creatures, so unlike their parents that for a long time they were thought to be a different kind of fish. Not until 1886 —when some leptocephalus larvae were kept in captivity while they underwent their remarkable transformation into small conger eels— was their true identity demonstrated.

The conger eel is widely distributed on both sides of the Atlantic, but does not occur on the west coast of the United States. Those from Europe are generally considerably larger than those found off our shores, where specimens over four feet long are unusual. These are females, males attaining about two and one-half feet. The largest conger eel on record weighed 128 pounds and was about eight feet long.

The Green Moray, *Gymnothorax funebris,* is as ferocious as it looks. It has a powerful, sinuous body that may be six or more feet long, and strong jaws armed with many sharp teeth. Although sometimes used for food, it is greatly feared by West Indian and Bermudian fishermen and divers who come into contact with it.

Its solid green color results from a layer of bright yellow slime that covers its slate-blue, tough, scaleless skin. Other morays, of which there are over a hundred, are marked with all sorts of stripes, bars, spots, and blotches. They can be distinguished from other kinds of eels by the lack of pectoral and pelvic fins and their small, round gill openings.

Morays inhabit coral reefs as a rule, and in captivity seem most contented when they can squeeze themselves into some hole or crevice. They retain their savage dispositions in the aquarium; tankmen never become familiar with them even though morays sometimes learn to feed from the hand.

Killies, Guppies, and Their Relatives
—Small but Useful

THE KILLIES, guppies, and their relatives compose a colorful group. All are small, but man has found a use for them. Some are valuable research animals, others help prevent the breeding of mosquitoes, and a few are famous as household pets—inside glass, of course.

There are more than five hundred species in this group (order Cyprinodontes, a name meaning "toothed carp"). Most of them inhabit fresh water, but we find a small number in brackish or salt waters. The biggest size of any of them is about one foot. They lack spines in the fins, and the poor development or absence of the lateral line on the body (although it is well developed on the head) is noteworthy. The best-known families are: the North American cavefishes (Amblyopsidae); the egg-laying topminnows or killifishes (Cyprinodontidae); the live-bearing topminnows (Poeciliidae); and the four-eye fishes (Anablepidae).

We know about eight species of North American cavefishes. With one or two exceptions they are small pink and white fishes without eyes, that inhabit cold, limestone caves in the central part of the United States. The two hundred or so egg-laying topminnows are found on every continent except Australia and include such interesting creatures as the mummichog and the desert minnows, together with a number of popular, colorful home-aquarium fishes. The well-known guppy, and the platyfishes, swordtails, and mollies belong among the live-bearing topminnows. This family was originally found only in North, South, and Central America and the West Indies, but several of its members have been deliberately or accidentally introduced into many other parts of the world.

The Mummichog, or Killie, *Fundulus heteroclitus,* can live in polluted and diluted sea water that would quickly be fatal to most salt-water fishes. Although primarily a salt-water fish, it often goes into brackish and fresh waters of its own free will, especially in the spring. It can also withstand drastic changes in temperatures and can live out of water for a considerable time.

As might be expected with so adaptable an animal, the mummichog is very common and occurs in large numbers throughout the greater part of its range, from the Gulf of St. Lawrence to Texas. It is a shallow-water fish but is sometimes supposed to go into deeper water offshore during the winter. The toughness and availability of the mummichog have made it a favorite laboratory animal, both for experiments and teaching. Hundreds of scientific papers about it have already been published, and more are written each year. The mummichog has aided man in other ways, too, namely, as a bait fish and as a destroyer of salt-marsh mosquitoes.

Mummichogs are killifish and belong to a large group of fishes called topminnows because as a rule they live just under the water's surface. Their mouths equip them to feed at the surface, the lower jaw being extended and the upper jaw foreshortened so that the mouth opens practically at a level with the top of the head. A wide variety of foodstuff, both plant and animal and both living and dead, is consumed by the mummichog. Maximum size is from five to six inches, the females being slightly larger on the average than the males.

The male mummichog is more brightly colored than the female, and during the breeding season, which is early spring to late summer depending on the latitude, his colors become especially bright. It has been shown by experiments that this type of color is strongly influenced by male hormones (internal secretions produced by the testes). At breeding time the males pursue the females ardently and fight fiercely with one another. The sticky eggs are laid on the bottom or on stones or plants. They hatch in from nine to eighteen days, and the young are further advanced in development than are most baby fishes just hatched from the egg.

The Desert Minnow, *Cyprinodon macularius,* is one of a number of fishes that live in the creeks, springs, and water holes of American deserts. Like several of them, the desert minnow is able to withstand high temperatures that would rapidly kill the great majority of fishes. Desert minnows have been found in natural waters that reach 100° Fahrenheit and have lived comfortably in captivity at 102 degrees. (This is the temperature of a warm bath.) The highest temperature at which an American fish has definitely been found living in nature is 104 degrees, in a hot spring near Death Valley, and the fish involved is a close relative of the desert minnow.

Strangely enough, the desert minnow can also withstand low temperatures, nearly down to freezing in certain circumstances. It is also quite tolerant of changes in the amount of salt and other dissolved chemicals in the water surrounding it. It can live in water that is either fresh or quite heavily charged with chemicals.

The desert minnow is found through a large part of the southwestern United States, the state of Sonora in Mexico, and Baja California. Adults are about two inches long. Males are a pale blue color that is especially bright during breeding. Females are brownish and more slender than males. The males are pugnacious during breeding; they fight lustily with one another at this time. The adhesive eggs are laid singly or in clusters, and stick to the bottom or to plants. Young desert minnows grow very rapidly and become mature in less than four months. There is evidence that the fish breeds the year 'round in some of the warm springs it inhabits.

The Guppy, *Lebistes reticulatus,* has introduced more people to the problems and satisfactions of keeping tropical fishes as pets than any other member of that group of small, warm fresh-water species now maintained in home aquaria all over the world. Its bright colors, incessant activity, interesting reproductive habits, and, above all, its extreme hardiness have made it one of the most popular and best known of all fishes.

Scientists, too, appreciate some of these characteristics, and guppies have been employed in studies and experiments for the past thirty years with ever-increasing frequency. The guppy has proved beneficial in still another way. In fact the first use to which the fish was put was to aid in the control of the mosquitoes carrying that world-wide scourge, malaria—by eating up their aquatic larvae.

Originally found in the streams, ponds, ditches, and the brackish, coastal waters of northern South America, Trinidad, Antigua, Barbados, and the Windward Islands as far north as St. Lucia, the guppy has now been transplanted to many parts of the tropical world, including such widely separated localities as Ceylon, Singapore, Borneo, Tahiti, the Hawaiian Islands, and Argentina. Not all the introductions were for the purpose of mosquito control, however. A few were accidental, the fish escaping from captivity in garden pools. Others were made by fish fanciers simply "for the fun of it"—a very dangerous practice, since foreign animals can become veritable plagues: witness the rabbit in Australia and the carp in the United States. Fortunately, the guppy does not seem to have become a pest in any of those widespread places in which it has become established, except on the island of Mauritius, where it is said to be very destructive to the eggs of certain edible fishes and crayfishes.

So numerous in parts of its original home that it is called the "millions fish," the guppy is apparently as successful in the wild as it is in captivity. It feeds on a variety of small foods such as adult and larval insects, the eggs of other fishes, and algae. In turn, the guppy is preyed upon by a number of larger fishes and by some birds.

In nature male guppies rarely exceed three-quarters of an inch, while females regularly grow to twice that length. Males are colored with patches of pastel reds, oranges, yellows, greens, and violets and with a few black spots. So various are their color patterns that no two seem exactly alike.

Fanciers have taken advantage of this great natural variability to create dozens of differently colored strains by selective breeding. Experiments have shown that these masculine colors are under the influence both of the heredity and the hormones of the fish; they are inherited, but need the presence of the male hormone for full development. Female guppies have deeper bodies than males and lack their bright colors. In captivity, however, some strains that have malelike coloration have been developed through selective breeding. Fancy strains of albino guppies, golden guppies, and guppies with peculiarly shaped tails are also now established.

Guppies are viviparous, that is, they bring forth their young alive. Under the best of conditions, females can have their first brood in less than three months. First broods are quite small in number, but the female continues to grow after reaching maturity, and for this reason and others, her broods become larger, too. The average maximum number of young born at one time is in the neighborhood of fifty, but broods as large as 126 have been reported. The minimum time between broods is twenty-three days but usually twenty-eight or more days elapse. The young are nurtured within the female's ovary, not the uterus as in mammals; but it has been shown that, like the mammal, the mother fish contributes nourishment to her developing offspring. Fertilization is effected by means of the gonopodium, the modified anal fin of the male.

Male guppies seem to be ardent gallants, for they court the females almost incessantly. The latter seldom take any heed of their antics, however, save to flee from the attentions of some too-persistent suitor. Females have had as many as eight broods after being isolated from all other fish. This is made possible by the ability to store the male sexual element for many months.

Guppies live to be about three years old. In nature, and captivity too, young are born the year 'round, although reproductive activities are usually more intense at some seasons of the year than at others.

The guppy was first imported alive into Germany in 1908. At that time, its correct scientific name was generally thought to be *Girardinus guppyi*. This name had been proposed in honor of Dr. Robert

Lechmere Guppy, a scientist who lived on Trinidad. Some five years later it was definitely shown that, according to the international rules of scientific nomenclature, the fish's correct name was *Lebistes reticulatus*, but by the time this fact became known, the popular name, guppy, had become too well established to be changed.

The Mosquito Fish, *Gambusia affinis,* has been transplanted into more than seventy different countries to help man in his never-ending battle against the mosquitoes, especially those that transmit malaria.

Originally found in northeastern Mexico and much of southeastern United States—as far north as southern Illinois and New Jersey—this small fish, since 1905, has been introduced into every continent except Australia. It has become a tenant of such far-flung islands as Cyprus, Ceylon, Guadalcanal, Samoa, Tahiti, Hawaii, the Marianas, Fijis, Philippines, Carolines, Ryu-Kyus, and Celebes. Within the United States, the fish has been carried to the West Coast, and a cold-resistant strain has become established as far north as Chicago. The mosquito fish is now the most widely distributed fresh-water fish in the world.

Although mosquito fish do not totally eliminate mosquitoes that breed in the water they inhabit, they have been found highly efficient in keeping the number of those pests quite low. One captive adult female was seen to consume more than 150 mosquito larvae in the course of ten hours. Such gluttony would undoubtedly be rare under most natural conditions, but the observation gives an idea of the ravenous appetites exhibited by these small fish.

Female mosquito fish occasionally reach a length of two and one-half inches; usually they are about one and three-quarter inches long. Males are smaller, never attaining one and one-half and rarely exceeding one and one-quarter inches. This difference in size results mostly from females continuing to grow throughout life, while males practically cease growing once they have attained adulthood. Females also live longer than males, the maximum life span in nature usually being not more than fifteen months. In any given locality there are almost always many more females than males.

In tropical regions, mosquito fish breed all year 'round, but where winters are cool or cold, they breed only during the warmer months. The young are born alive, an average brood consisting of forty to fifty babies. These are about five-sixteenths of an inch long at birth, and as many as 315 young have been found inside a two-and-one-half-inch female. Females have a brood every three to four weeks, but in the north at least, have no more than four or five broods before old age sets in. All this adds up to a tremendous reproductive capacity for a live-bearing animal and helps to explain the usefulness of the mosquito fish in reducing the number of mosquitoes.

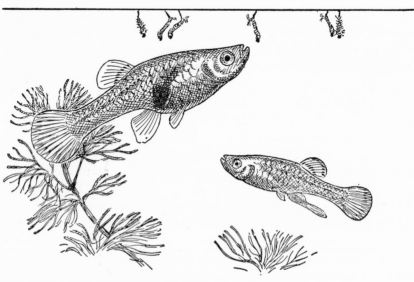

THIS FISH HELPS US BATTLE DISEASE
One of the world's greatest sanitation workers is the mosquito fish, shown here in the act of attacking mosquito larvae at the surface of the water. Thanks to the efforts of this creature, the activity of malaria-bearing mosquitoes has been sharply curtailed. Once found only in the United States, the mosquito fish has been introduced into more countries than any other fresh-water fish.

Male mosquito fish are easily distinguished from females by the presence of a gonopodium, the modified anal fin used in fertilization. The development of this structure—and of other masculine characteristics too—has been shown to be dependent upon the presence of male sex hormone. As in many other live-bearing fishes, it is possible for the female mosquito fish to have several broods after a single contact with a male. As many as five successive litters have been observed in females that were isolated in small aquaria.

The food of mosquito fish does not consist solely of mosquito larvae, of course. They will eat practically any animal, provided it is small enough, and also small plants, especially algae. They are also not averse to eating their own young, both in captivity and nature.

The Common Platyfish, *Xiphophorus maculatus,* is endowed with a more extensive series of fixed color patterns than any other backboned animal in North America, and perhaps in the whole world. More than 150 different color varieties of common platyfish have been found in nature, and, with further collecting, still more will undoubtedly be discovered. Platyfishes show several kinds of black spotting, located on many different parts of the fish's body and fins. If the three different red-pigmented patterns and the one or two blue ones —that are also found in combination with the black ones—are considered, the total number of color varieties would be several times 150.

Except for this extreme variability of color pattern, the common platyfish is not a fish of striking appearance. It grows to a length of a little more than two inches, females being slightly larger than males. A male can be easily distinguished from a female by his gonopodium, which is the anal fin modified into a sticklike organ used in fertilization.

The female common platyfish gives birth to living young. At the height of her reproductive capacity she has a brood every twenty-eight days. The period of gestation is only twenty-one days, however, for the new brood does not start to develop until a week after the preceding one has been born. At birth, baby platyfish are a little less than a quarter of an inch long. They are able to swim and immediately seek shelter among floating plants at the top of the water if these are available. The largest brood on record is that of a wild-caught female who had 168 babies just ready to be liberated.

Common platyfish inhabit lowland fresh waters of the Atlantic drainage in British Honduras, Guatemala, and southern Mexico, excluding Yucatan. They prefer slow-moving, weedy waters, but have been found in a number of different types of streams, lakes, ponds, ditches, and temporary pools. They feed on both small animals and plants.

Tropical-fish fanciers are well acquainted with the common platyfish. Since 1907, when the first living specimens were imported into Germany, they have been one of the hobby's favorites. Fish breeders have developed a number of colorful strains, including blue, gold, black, and red ones. One popular strain, the wagtail, was originated at the New York Aquarium. In this, the rays of all the fins are heavily pigmented, giving to them a black, lacelike effect.

The Mexican Swordtail, *Xiphophorus helleri,* is a close relative of the common platyfish. It, too, is a popular fish with home aquarists and was first imported alive into Germany in 1909, two years after the platyfish. One of the first things the German aquarists discovered was that the swordtail and platyfish could be cross-bred. From these crosses a number of beautifully colored hybrids developed. For example, all of the red platies and swordtails we commonly see in pet shops and home aquaria are hybrids; one may have to go back many generations, however, to discover the original cross.

It is a strange fact that although the common platyfish and the swordtail are frequently found in the same ponds and streams of Mexico, they never hybridize in nature. Apparently they will only cross-breed in the confines of an aquarium.

The outstanding feature of the Mexican swordtail is the "sword" which is carried by the males. This is a long, pointed extension of the lower part of the tail fin. The largest swordtail males are more than six inches long and about half of this length is made up of sword. To what use the fish puts its sword is not known. It has been suggested that the sword is displayed during courtship, but whether it actually excites or entices the female is questionable.

Swordtails are found in the Atlantic drainage of Honduras, British Honduras, Guatemala, and Southern Mexico, excluding Yucatan. They seem to prefer higher, cooler waters than the common platyfish, although the two species, as mentioned before, often live together.

Certain kinds of platyfish-swordtail hybrids regularly fall victim to black cancer, called "melanoma," and they have therefore been used in medical research on this disease. In the Genetics Laboratory of the New York Aquarium, located in the American Museum of Natural History, there are hundreds of tanks containing special strains of different kinds of platyfishes and swordtails that are being studied and experimented with in many ways. These fishes are fast becoming aquatic counterparts of the white rat and guinea pig.

The Foureye Fish, *Anableps anableps,* which cruises at the surface, has eyes so wonderfully constructed that it can see above and below water at the same time. The pupil of the eye is actually dumbbell-shaped, and the fish swims with the upper part out of water and the lower part submerged. This arrangement and the difference in curvature of the corresponding parts of the lens are such that objects both above and below the surface of the water are focused on different regions of the retina at the same time. Thus, foureye fish can be aware of what is going on in two elements at once.

The fish seem very alert, too, for they are among the most difficult of all fishes to catch. At the slightest disturbance or movement on shore, foureye fish skitter away. They appear to know exactly how a net works, and more often than not whole schools will escape capture by hurdling the top. Nor will they take the fly or be angled in any other manner. Some fishermen capture them with cast-nets at night, at which time they can be blinded by torches, and museum collectors have resorted to shooting them with scatter-shot. Despite the difficulties of capture, foureye fish are sold for food in some South American markets. They reach a length of about one foot.

Foureye fish inhabit fresh or brackish waters in streams, lakes, and tidal flats. Their somewhat elongated, cylindrical bodies are flattened on top, and as they swim at the surface, only their eyes project out of the water, these being elevated as in a frog. The fish feed on algae and on insect adults and larvae and small crustaceans, found at or near the water surface. Foureye fish are born alive. They are one and three-quarter inches long at birth, and a nine-inch female may have from six to thirteen in a single brood. The female's ovary, in which the eggs are produced and the young nurtured, contains an elaborate apparatus for the nourishment of the developing offspring.

This species of foureye fish is found in northern South America along the Atlantic drainage and in Trinidad. There are two other species, one from South America and the other from southern Mexico and much of Central America.

Needle Fishes, Flying Fishes, and Halfbeaks

Fishes of this group are fascinating natural entertainers. Needle fishes skitter about the surface of the water like living javelins; halfbeaks are flip-flop artists and wrestlers; and flying fishes are aquatic aviators. They live mostly at the surface of tropical and warm temperate seas, and range in length from about one inch to five feet.

Some fifty needle fishes or marine gars—thin but savage hunters—comprise the family Belonidae. From sixty to seventy-five different halfbeaks (family Hemirhamphidae) have also been accounted for. Several members of both these groups enter streams and lakes occasionally, and others do so regularly.

In certain lakes and streams of southeastern Asia, the East Indies, and the Philippines, there are small halfbeaks that never live in the sea. Unlike other members of the order, some of these give birth to living young. The Siamese selectively breed one of them, *Dermogenys pusillus,* for combat, as they do the better-known Siamese fighting fish. These tiny halfbeak males fight by grasping each other with their jaws and wrestling, sometimes for hours at a time. The family Exocoetidae is made up of the flying fishes, of which there are about sixty species.

The fishes of this order have curious jaws, to which they owe their scientific name (Synentognathi—it means "with inner jaws"). You can recognize them by the lack of spines in the fins and by the high attachment of the pectoral fins. The dorsal and pelvic fins are located to the rear and the lateral line has a low position.

The Atlantic Needle Fish, *Strongylura marina,* lives at the surface of waters along the east coast of the United States, from Maine to Texas,

1494

and it seems admirably equipped for the predatory life it leads. Its silvery body is cylindrical and extremely thin; a specimen six inches long is scarcely bigger around than a lead pencil. About one-fifth of its total length is occupied by its jaws which are prolonged into a narrow, bill-like structure and lined their whole length with numerous sharply pointed teeth. It preys almost exclusively on small fish. The needle fish usually catches its victim crosswise between its jaws, artfully juggles the hapless fish about until it faces the mouth, and then swallows it whole, head first. Occasionally shrimp are also caught and eaten.

The eggs of the Atlantic needle fish are provided with tufts of long tendrils, which entangle the eggs with any object they touch. Development apparently takes an unusually long time even at high temperatures. So far as known, these fish reproduce during the summer. For a while, the lower jaw of the young needle fish is much longer than the upper one; not until it reaches a total length of at least six inches does its upper jaw approach the lower one in size. Atlantic needle fish four feet long are on record, although very few exceed two and one-half feet.

This species is much given to leaping and skittering over the water's surface, like a silvery javelin. It also occasionally hurdles small floating objects like sticks. Other species of needle fishes indulge in this peculiar behavior quite frequently, jumping again and again over a floating straw, twig, stick, leaf, feather, or piece of paper. No completely satisfactory explanation of these antics has yet been forthcoming. In certain instances it seems as if the fish are trying to scrape tiny parasites off their bodies. Another possible explanation is that they are playing, but no one knows just what "animal play" is, especially among fishes.

Like a good number of other needle fishes, the Atlantic species travels up streams and can be seen living in fresh water.

The Halfbeak, *Hyporhamphus unifasciatus,* seems actually to possess half a beak! It has a short upper jaw, only about one-half an inch long in the largest specimens, but its lower jaw is much longer, being eight or more times the length of the upper one. There are no teeth on the projecting jaw, nor does it ever seem to be used as a spear or broadsword. When food is seized by the halfbeak, the upper, not the lower, jaw is moved. In the present fragmentary state of our knowledge about these fishes, the exact function of this peculiar structure remains a matter of guesswork.

Halfbeaks feed on small crustaceans, mollusks, and on vegetable matter, mostly algae. They spawn in the summer, laying semi-buoyant eggs. Very small individuals have no beak, but when they are slightly longer than one-half inch the lower jaw begins to elongate. A maximum size of about one foot is attained.

This species is found from Massachusetts south through the West Indies, and it is common south of Chesapeake Bay. Like other half-beaks, it habitually lives at or near the surface. Specimens have been seen flipping themselves over small floating objects such as match boxes and bits of seaweed. The fish swims up to the object and places the tip of its lower jaw just under it. A violent flip follows, and the fish lands on the other side, generally facing in the opposite direction. This performance may be repeated a half-dozen times. What it means is a mystery. Some species of halfbeaks make great leaps over the water or propel the forepart of their body out of it, sculling themselves along with their tails, which is the only part remaining in the water. This behavior closely resembles the taxiing of their relatives, the flying fishes.

The Twowing Flying Fish, *Exocoetus volitans,* is the commonest flying fish of the Atlantic and is also found in the warm portions of the Indian and Pacific Oceans. It is a truly oceanic fish, most frequently seen in tropical mid-oceans. It reaches a length of seven inches.

This fish has greatly enlarged pectoral fins, and these constitute its wings. With them the fish can glide through the air—which it often does when disturbed by a ship or pursued by some larger fish. The twowing flying fish has no teeth and feeds upon plankton (minute plants and animals floating at or near the surface of the sea).

Ripe specimens have been taken during the first half of the year. The eggs are smooth and are pelagic, that is, they float at or near the surface of the open sea.

The Atlantic Fourwing Flying Fish, *Cypselurus heterurus,* is one of the species of flying fishes seen from shipboard by travelers sailing around Florida and the West Indies and in the Mediterranean. In this species both the pectoral and pelvic fins are enlarged, giving the fish two pairs of wings.

For many years it was argued whether flying fishes flapped their wings like birds or glided like airplanes. Anatomical studies have shown the former method to be an impossibility, since flying fishes completely lack the bulky muscles necessary to work flapping wings —such muscles as compose the meaty breast of a bird. Nevertheless, many observers claimed that they saw the fishes' wings move, especially during the first stages of flight.

A study of the structure of flying fish from the viewpoint of the airplane designer has proved that their wings are sufficiently well designed to support them in gliding flight. Very careful observations in nature confirmed this and revealed just how the flying fish starts and maintains its glide; they also showed that the so-called "wing flapping" was an optical illusion created in part by the instability of the fish when taking off. Finally, stroboscopic photography, which shows the successive steps of a movement, no matter how rapid, confirmed what had been previously deduced from theory and from wind-tunnel experiments.

Swimming very rapidly in the fashion of most fish—with pectoral and pelvic fins held close to the body—the fourwing flying fish drives the front part of its body out of water into the air. It then spreads its great pectoral fins or wings, and these provide enough lift to sustain the body in the air—all except part of the tail. The lower lobe of the tail fin of flying fishes is half again as long as the upper one. With this lobe acting as a scull, the fish taxis for perhaps a hundred feet, accelerating all the while. Finally the fish spreads its pelvic fins and the added lift raises the tail out of the water. The fish now glides freely above the ocean's surface.

The usual flight of a fish of this type covers roughly fifty yards and lasts not quite three seconds. The speed of flight averages about thirty-five miles per hour, being about forty at the start and twenty-five at the finish. Much longer flights are possible, however; flights lasting thirteen seconds have been recorded with a stop watch. Like good pilots, flying fish generally take off into the wind, and it is entirely possible that they take advantage of wind currents during flight, for they have considerable maneuverability in air and can bank and adjust the angle of their wings.

Often the fourwing flying fish allows the lower lobe of its tail fin to drop back into the water during flight and then taxis some more, regaining flying speed. Any single flight usually contains only one or two such leaps, but as many as eleven successive leaps have been observed before the fish finally dropped back into the water completely.

These compound flights naturally last longer than do the simple ones. The fish may remain out of water—except for its tail fin—for half a minute or so, and may travel a quarter of a mile. Ordinarily flying fish glide from three to six feet above the water's surface, but air currents may lift them much higher—onto the decks of ships for example.

To end its flight a fourwing flying fish simply closes its wings and falls into the water, sometimes head first, sometimes belly first, occasionally even upside down. Flights are made both at night and in the daytime. Flying fishes seem to be attracted to lights, and a number meet untimely deaths by crashing into ships, landing on decks, and flying through portholes at night.

The Atlantic fourwing flying fish is dark above and silver below in color. The wings, that is, the pectoral fins, are a uniform gray with a single lighter band extending obliquely outwards across them. Younger specimens have their wings quite differently marked. In fact the fish goes through a remarkable series of changes involving both color and structure as it grows up. Among other things, the young up to a length of at least three inches have a pair of prominent barbels on the chin. All this was quite perplexing to scientists, who described the young stages under a number of different names and confused them with other species of flying fishes. A maximum length of somewhat over one foot is attained by the Atlantic fourwing flying fish.

The food of flying fish apparently consists only of small animals and plants floating in the sea. Young specimens have been seen poking around in floating seaweed and catching small creatures there. Flying fishes are themselves preyed upon by a number of different fishes, the most noteworthy being the dorado, or dolphin. Certain sea birds live almost exclusively on flying fish.

Reproduction in the Atlantic fourwing flying fish occurs during the summer. The one-sixteenth-inch spherical eggs are attached to each other by means of numerous tendrils which run out from the surface. They are also attached to very long filaments so that they look like groups of tiny beads on somewhat tangled skeins of fine cotton thread. These filaments are found wrapped around all sorts of floating objects like seaweed, sticks, branches, cork, pumice, and the discarded straw wrappings of wine bottles. The utility of this arrangement becomes apparent when we realize that the eggs and threads are heavier than water, and if they were not buoyed up, they would sink to their death in the cold, sunless depths of the sea. The young are about one-fourth of an inch long when first hatched. For some time they remain in or around their floating cradle before taking up an existence in the open sea.

The Atlantic fourwing flying fish has been found as far north as Massachusetts and Norway, but occurs in numbers only in warm waters. The thrill of unexpectedly seeing a group of these fish suddenly leave the water and gracefully sail through the air for a hundred feet or more before dropping back into the sea is a memorable one.

The California Flying Fish, *Cypselurus californicus,* grows to a length of eighteen inches and is probably the largest of all flying fishes. It occurs in schools from Point Conception south along the West Coast to Baja California. It is one of the four-winged types, and is colored deep blue on its back and sides and silvery white on its belly. This species is one of the sights around Santa Catalina Island, where its spectacular flights are watched by numerous tourists.

FLYING FISH WITH FOUR WINGS

The California flying fish, a four-winged creature that is deep blue above and white below, may reach a length of a foot and a half. It travels in schools, and a group of these fish breaking the surface and launching themselves into the air present a spectacle that is not soon forgotten.

Flying fishes make delicious eating, but are nowhere caught in sufficient numbers to support a large fishery. They are commercially caught during certain seasons of the year, however, off Barbados, India, and the Celebes. In the latter two places they are lured by bunches of leaves and twigs which the fishermen throw on the surface of the sea. The fish congregate about this floating material to lay their eggs. The California flying fish is regularly taken with gill-nets, but is not used for food to any extent. Instead it is employed as bait for marlin fishing.

The life history of the California flying fish is practically unknown. The eggs and larval stages have been described, but where the eggs are normally laid is a mystery. They are about one-sixteenth of an inch in diameter and rather evenly covered with filaments. Without doubt they are laid on floating objects or seaweed. Young California flying fish possess a peculiar semicircular, many-fingered outgrowth on the chin during one stage of their development. This modified barbel is red in color.

Cods and Their Relatives
—Leading Foodfish

THE CODS and their relatives are important to us as foodfish. The cod, tomcod, haddock, pollack, coalfish, cusk, ling, whiting, hake, and stockfish, all of which are used for food, are among the 150 known species of a single family (Gadidae). Mostly they inhabit northern seas; relatively few are found in the tropics or Southern Hemisphere. They spend a good deal of time on or near the bottom, but are not deep-sea dwellers. The largest member is the Atlantic cod; most, however, are much smaller, weighing less than five pounds.

The grenadiers and rattails (family Macruridae) are deep-sea creatures with long, tapering bodies; both the second dorsal fin and anal fin run into the pointed tail fin with no perceptible break. This large family is found in all of the oceans, including the Arctic and Antarctic.

The fishes of this order show a peculiar mixture of both primitive and advanced characteristics. Their distinguishing features include the arrangement of bones in the skull; the position of the ventral fins in front of the pectorals, near the throat; and the lack of spines in the fins (save for a single one in the dorsal of some of the grenadiers), which gives them their scientific name, order Anacanthini ("without spines").

The Atlantic Cod, *Gadus callarias,* annually provides the fishermen on the North American banks off the northeastern coast of that continent with more than a billion pounds of fish. Newfoundland takes almost half of this, with Canada, France, the United States, and Portugal sharing most of the rest. Other European countries, however, are also represented on the Banks.

Cod held first place in the New England fisheries for many years and was a mainstay of early American economy. One of the principal reasons for this was that cod salts down especially well, and salting was the only way large quantities of fish could be preserved in those days. With the development of modern methods of refrigeration, the haddock has supplanted the cod because it can be fileted more easily and is somewhat more available geographically.

Today codfish filets and steaks are principally sold fresh or frozen. Some, however, are salted, smoked, or processed into fish flakes. Codfish oil, or cod-liver oil, was the first economical source of Vitamin D, the sunshine vitamin, and although it is still an important one, it is at present much more important for the Vitamin A it contains.

Most American fishermen catch cod with otter trawls (nets dragged along the bottom, with two boards to keep the mouth of the net open). Sinking gill-nets, traps, and pound-nets (large fixed nets with small openings) are also employed. Hook-and-line fishing is used extensively by Europeans, some of the long lines carrying as many as three thousand hooks. Trawling and line fishing are employed a great deal because cod live on or near the bottom, belonging to that great group of commercially important fishes called "groundfish," which includes the various cods and their relatives (haddock, pollack, coalfish, ling, cusk, hake, and whiting), the flatfishes (halibut, flounders, turbots, and soles), the rockfishes (rosefish, bocaccio, chilipepper, etc.) and the sablefish.

Atlantic cod are found in water as deep as 250 fathoms but in the western North Atlantic are rarely taken deeper than 150 fathoms. They prefer cold water, not inhabiting any warmer than 50 degrees. They therefore frequent the coast of Connecticut, New York, and New Jersey only during the colder months, and further north move offshore during the summer. In Europe the Atlantic cod straggles as far south as the Bay of Biscay. It is an important foodfish in the Irish and North Seas and in Scandinavian waters.

IT SWELLS EUROPEAN AND AMERICAN LARDERS

One of the most important foodfishes of the world, the Atlantic cod is at home in the cold waters of the North Atlantic. The flesh is not especially tasty, but has been a staple food for hundreds of years. The crude oil from the cod's liver is used in tanning leather, in making soap, and in tempering steel; refined, it is a popular source of vitamins.

Commercially caught cod generally range from two and one-half to twenty-five pounds, but fifty-pound individuals are not unusual. The largest Atlantic cod on record was more than six feet long and weighed more than 211 pounds.

Atlantic cod mature from the age of two years on, roughly half of them being capable of reproduction by the time they are five years old. This is an extremely prolific species; a forty-inch female can produce annually from three to four million eggs, and one seventy-five-pound specimen was estimated to contain more than nine million. The season for spawning varies greatly from region to region, beginning as early as January in some places and ending as late as October in others. The eggs are buoyant and roughly one-sixteenth of an inch in diameter. Depending upon the temperature, they hatch in ten to twenty days. Development takes as long as forty days if the salt water is as cold as 32 degrees.

The newly hatched cod is about five thirty-seconds of an inch long and floats upside down, being held in that position by its yolk sac, which is lighter than water, for about two days. For the following two and one-half months the baby Atlantic cod remains a member of the plankton—the enormous mass of floating or weakly swimming organisms of the surface of the ocean. It feeds on various tiny animals that float there along with it, and is fed upon in turn by others. When about one inch long it sinks to the bottom. By this time it has assumed the general shape of the adult fish.

The food of the Atlantic cod is most varied, and the fish feeds both on the bottom and in mid-water, and occasionally at the surface. Squid, clams, mussels, crabs, lobsters, shrimp, sea-squirts, worms of all sorts, sea-urchins, sea-cucumbers, and brittle-stars are among the invertebrates it consumes. It also eats many kinds of fishes, including young members of its own species. Occasionally even a duck has been found in the stomach of a large cod. Rate of growth varies in different localities; off the coast of Maine, cod attain an average of fourteen pounds in two years and twenty pounds in three.

The Haddock, *Melanogrammus aeglefinus,* is the basis of the most valuable American commercial fishery of the north Atlantic Coast. About 150 million pounds are landed yearly, almost all being fished by means of otter-trawls. Most haddock is sold fresh or frozen, but a considerable amount is smoked, and then is known as finnan haddie. The haddock is also a valuable foodfish in the North Sea and around Iceland.

Haddock are similar to the Atlantic cod in having three dorsal fins, two anal fins, a single barbel under the lower jaw, and the pelvic fins located far forward in front of the pectorals, besides lacking spines in all fins. It differs from the cod in that its lateral line is black instead of light, in the presence of a dusky blotch on its sides just over the pectoral fins, and in the height and pointed triangular shape of its first dorsal fin. It does not grow nearly as large as the cod; the largest specimen ever caught was forty-four inches long and weighed between thirty-six and thirty-seven pounds.

In New England waters, haddock mature at three or four years of age, at a weight of two to three pounds; around Newfoundland, where waters are colder, maturity is reached a year or so later. Spawning takes place from March through June. The small floating eggs hatch in two to four weeks, depending on the temperature. The young fish do not leave a planktonic existence until about three months old, when they are between one-fourth and one-half inches long. They then take up life on the sea bottom, near which they remain the rest of their lives.

Practically every kind of invertebrate inhabiting the bottom where it lives is eaten by the haddock. In addition, some swimming animals like squid, shrimp, and fish are consumed. Haddock are known to live fifteen years or longer.

The European Hake, *Merluccius merluccius,* ranges from Iceland and the coast of Norway to northwest Africa and the Mediterranean Sea. It is an important foodfish, over seventy million pounds being taken by British trawlers alone in the course of a single year.

Although the European hake feeds in midwater, it is taken by trawls (which operate along the bottom) because it rests on the bottom during the day, catching fishes, crustaceans, and squid at night. In the late spring or summer, European hake move inshore to spawn, and in the winter move off into deeper waters. The tiny eggs are planktonic, that is, they float at the surface of the sea. The young are also planktonic and do not take to the bottom until somewhat over an inch long. Female European hake grow larger and mature later than do males. A two-year-old female is about eight inches long; a thirteen-year-old fish may be more than forty inches long.

The Silver Hake, *Merluccius bilinearis,* the Pacific Hake, *Merluccius productus,* and the Stockfish, *Merluccius capensis,* are close relatives of the European hake. The silver hake, found from Newfoundland to the Bahamas, is becoming more and more popular as a foodfish; the Pacific hake, which occurs from southern California to Alaska, is hardly used for food at all. The stockfish, however, is the most important commercial fish of South Africa. It is principally taken by trawls in depths as great as one hundred fathoms, although the fish frequents water as deep as five hundred fathoms. The stockfish attains a length of four feet and feeds on midwater creatures such as squid, fish, and crustaceans.

The Burbot, *Lota lota,* is the only fresh-water member of the cod family. It is found in Europe, Siberia, and northern North America as far south as Connecticut and the basins of the Great Lakes, the Missouri River, and the Columbia River. It inhabits cool streams and lakes, the latter to a depth of seven hundred feet. The burbot can easily be distinguished from all other fresh-water fishes by the presence of three barbels—a single stout one on the chin and a pair of smaller ones on the snout—and by its slender, dark-colored body with long anal and dorsal fins and the absence of spines and prominent scales.

This fish is one of North America's neglected aquatic resources. Although it is occasionally used as food, its repulsive appearance apparently discourages its wide use in the United States, despite its edibility and availability. Like its salt-water relatives, it has a liver very rich in vitamins, and this has been used as a source of these food factors by a few commercial enterprises.

The maximum size of the burbot in the United States and Canada is thirty inches with a weight of ten pounds. The species feeds voraciously, principally on other fishes and on insect larvae, crayfish, and fish eggs. In the dead of winter or very early in the spring, the burbot spawns, numerous males and females gathering together at night into balls somewhat less than three feet in diameter. Here the eggs are laid and fertilized. They are heavier than water and lie on the bottom. One female twenty-seven and one-half inches long contained well over one million of them.

Oarfishes, Opahs, and Ribbon Fishes
—Including the Sea-Serpent

Although this group of fishes is little known—even among experts on fish—it has a claim to fame: one of its members is largely responsible for that most famous of all mythical creatures, the sea-serpent. The oarfish, which belongs to the family Regalecidae, is undoubtedly the prototype of most of the tales about snakelike sea monsters, stories which have been part and parcel of the lore of the sea since ancient times, and which regularly crop up in the newspapers and magazines of today.

The fishes of this group are most diverse in body shape. But they do have in common the ability to protrude their jaws in a way different from all other fishes, (hence their scientific name, order Allotriognathi, or "strange jaws") and also a few other special features in bony structure.

The ribbon fishes or dealfishes, which have long, ribbon-shaped bodies, comprise the family Trachypteridae. The dorsal fin stretches almost the whole length of the fish and has a crest at its front end. The strange tail fin has a tiny lower lobe and a relatively tremendous, triangular, upper one. There are few species, mostly inhabiting ocean waters. The Opah, *Lampris regius,* is the sole member of the family Lampridae. It is a large fish with a body compressed from side to side but deep from back to belly and with more or less sickle-shaped pectorals, pelvics, and forward portion of the dorsal fin. The opah is of world-wide distribution in temperate and tropical seas.

The Oarfish, *Regalecus glesne,* is responsible for many of the stories about sea-serpents. Its body is long and ribbon-shaped, being extremely narrow from side to side. The fish reaches a length of twenty feet and a weight of perhaps six hundred pounds. When it swims, it throws its elongated body into great serpentine curves. Oarfish apparently live in the open ocean in many parts of the world and sometimes at least swim at the surface.

Down the whole length of the oarfish's back is the dorsal fin and the first dozen or so rays of this are greatly elongated, forming a crest or mane on top of the head. When the oarfish is excited, this crest is erected. The body is silvery and the fins coral red.

Is it any wonder that sailors, coming upon this rare, queer creature undulating its great sinuous body and flashing its brilliant red crest, have sworn that they saw a sea-serpent? Not all such tales are based on the oarfish, but undoubtedly a good many are.

Squirrel Fishes and Firefly Fishes

THE BEST-KNOWN members of this group undoubtedly are the night-prowling squirrel fishes (family Holocentridae). We know about seventy species, dwellers in tropical ocean waters, usually near shore, all around the world. These curious creatures have large eyes and rough, good-sized scales, and are usually colored red. They rarely exceed one foot, but a few species become twice that long.

Perhaps even odder are those armored denizens of eastern waters, the pinecone fishes (two species comprise the family Monocentridae). These small fishes have thick, spiny scales, forming a coat of mail over the body; the spines of the dorsal fin alternately angle out to the left and right, instead of being vertical as in the vast majority of fishes. Pinecone fishes are found in the tropical and temperate Indian and Pacific oceans, in fairly deep water. They possess a pair of small luminous organs located just under the lower jaw.

But light-producing organs are much more spectacularly developed in the family Anomalopidae from the tropical Pacific and Atlantic, as we shall soon see. There are two or three species, including the firefly fish. Other less well-known families are also included in this, the Order Berycoidei ("like the *Beryx*"), which takes its name from the *Beryx*, a typical genus.

This group of fishes exhibits both primitive and advanced features. The dorsal, the anal, and the ventral fins have spines in their forward portions. The ventrals are located either to the front, under the pectorals—the advanced, more "modern" arrangement—or somewhat toward the rear, but not all the way back as in the primitive, older fashion. Some of the bony structures are advanced, others primitive.

The Squirrel Fish, *Holocentrus ascensionis,* usually remains hidden during the day in its native home, and leaves its hiding place at night to forage for food. In captivity, however, it soon begins to venture forth regularly during daylight hours. A number of fishes are capable of radically changing their natural way of life when brought into captivity, adapting themselves to changed conditions in a remarkable manner, and the squirrel fish is one of them.

In common with a number of night-prowling and deep-sea fishes, the squirrel fish is colored red. It also shows silvery and brownish tinges, and its prominent eyes are deep black. It has a single sharp spine on each cheek.

Although not caught in large numbers, this fish is often used for food when it is captured. Maximum size is usually about one foot, but two-foot specimens are known. Squirrel fish inhabit the ocean waters of Bermuda and those from Florida southward to Brazil.

The Firefly Fish, *Photoblepharon palpebratus,* swims about the coral reefs of the Banda Sea in the East Indies, flashing its light organs like a great aquatic firefly. Under each eye is a flattened, semi-circular organ, with a diameter somewhat greater than that of the eye itself, that shines with a bright light. Although this light is emitted continuously, the fish is able to turn it on or off by covering or uncovering the organs with a fold of black tissue that works very much like an eyelid. The fish reaches a length of about four inches.

The light organs are shallow and contain numerous bacteria of a special sort, which are the actual source of the light. These bacteria are evidently nurtured by special tissues or secretions of the fish, and are dependent on them for the proper kind of growth. The fish thus provides food and shelter for the bacteria, while they in turn provide their host with a continuous supply of living light.

GLOWWORM, OF THE SEA
The firefly fish carries its own "searchlights"—under each eye it has a large oval spot emitting a bright light. The fish can cut off the flow of light by means of a fold of tissue that works like an eyelid. In reality the glow is produced by a colony of bacteria dwelling under the eye of the firefly fish.

No one knows to just what use the firefly fish puts its light-producing organs. Some claim that they act as searchlights, others that they are employed in signaling, but the evidence for either of these functions is inconclusive. Banda Islanders, however, make good use of them, cutting out the luminous organs and using them as bait for fishing at night. While on the hook they remain lit for as long as eight hours.

Bone-Protected Fishes—Sticklebacks and Their Relatives

IT WAS the amazing home life of the sticklebacks that first called people's attention to the complicated "love life" of certain fishes and made them aware that the world of the fish is far from a simple one. Home aquaria first became fashionable in the middle of the nineteenth century in England, and the stickleback or tittlebat was one of the most popular of aquatic pets, since it thrived and reproduced readily in captivity.

In a stormy session of the Pickwick Club, Samuel Pickwick, Esq., reported on the Theory of Tittlebats and he took no little pride in presenting his Tittlebatian Theory to the world. This was Dickens' way of poking fun at the little groups of aquatic nature enthusiasts that sprang up in England at that time. They were the forerunners of our tropical fish and goldfish societies, of which there are several hundred in existence today.

The sticklebacks are small, fierce fishes—the largest is only about six inches long—which we find in the fresh and salt waters of the cooler parts of the Northern Hemisphere. Some species live in fresh water exclusively, others in salt. Still others, such as the threespine and fourspine sticklebacks, are found in both types and in brackish waters of varying salt content. In all species of sticklebacks, the males are good fathers—they build a nest to receive the eggs, which they guard and otherwise care for. There are about a dozen different species of sticklebacks, all members of the family Gasterosteidae.

The tube-snouts are cousins of the sticklebacks but belong to the family Aulorhynchidae. They look like very long sticklebacks. One species, *Aulorhynchus flavidus,* dwells along the Pacific coast of

1510

North America, from southern California to Alaska. It attains a length of six and one-half inches.

The sticklebacks and their less-known relatives have a number of peculiarities in their bony structure, as well as two or more free spines in front of the dorsal fin. The pelvic fins are placed close behind the pectorals, and the body is usally either armored along the sides with bony plates or completely encased in a series of bony rings. It was for this reason that the order was named Thoracostei, or "bony chests."

The Threespine Stickleback, *Gasterosteus aculeatus,* darts about and hovers in water the way a hummingbird does in air. Everything about this small fish seems to indicate intensity of effort, and even when it remains stationary with its tiny pectoral fins vibrating and its tail characteristically curved to one side, it appears, like a steel spring, ready to jump into action—which it does, dashing off to catch some small creature for food, to court some likely female, or to fight with some male, or other intruding fish.

Adult threespine sticklebacks are usually about two and one-quarter inches long, but in some places they grow to a length of four inches. Their spindle-shaped body seems well protected by two large spines (and one small one) on the back, one large spine on either side of the belly, and a number of flat, bony shields, or scutes, on the sides in place of ordinary scales. The mouth has numerous sharp teeth.

Good use is made of these various weapons, for sticklebacks are pugnacious, attacking fish much larger than themselves with both teeth and ventral spines. It has been claimed that the spines also afford them protection against larger fish which would otherwise eat them. Although this may be true in some instances, goodly numbers of sticklebacks are consumed by fish and birds. The number of scutes present varies from none to thirty-six, and depends on the salt content and temperature of the water in which the fish lives; the more salty the water and the lower the temperature, the greater the number of scutes.

As we have seen, threespine sticklebacks inhabit both salt and fresh waters. The species is found throughout the northern portion of the Northern Hemisphere. In North America it occurs as far south as Virginia and southern California on the coasts, and the Lake Ontario Basin inland. In a few places sticklebacks are so abundant that they are caught in great numbers; they are pressed for their oil, and the residue is used as fertilizer.

For its size the threespine stickleback is as ferocious as any fish; it kills and sometimes eats fish as large or larger than itself. It feeds principally upon small crustaceans and insects, but also eats the eggs and fry of other fishes. Its appetite is enormous. One specimen ate seventy-five quarter-inch fish within five hours, and two days later consumed sixty-two more.

The reproductive habits of the threespine stickleback are quite complicated and have been studied by numerous naturalists and experimental zoologists. During spring and summer the male develops a bright red throat and belly and selects a bit of bottom in quiet water that he defends against all other fishes, especially other male sticklebacks. He builds a nest of bits of aquatic plants, cemented together by a sticky thread-like secretion manufactured by his kidneys. Sometimes, instead of building a nest, he digs a hole in the ground and lines it with this secretion. Females are vigorously courted with zig-zag "dancing," chasing, nipping, and butting. Finally the female follows the male to his nest and enters it, or is forced to enter it—both coaxing and coercion seem to play a part in the process. She lays her relatively large eggs, measuring about one-sixteenth of an inch in diameter, and then, strangely enough, leaves by burrowing or boring a new exit from the nest, rather than backing out of the one she entered. In fact the male, sometimes at least, prevents her from backing out by nips and butts. The male then enters and fertilizes the eggs. Several females are usually enticed or driven to lay in a single nest, each being chased away when her duties have been performed. For about six days the male parent guards his nest and circulates water through it by fanning with his pectoral fins. After the young have hatched, the nest is generally torn open, but the fry are carefully returned to the site when they stray away. Finally, either the young become too adventurous for the male to control their wanderings or he loses interest in them, and the family group disperses.

The Fourspine Stickleback, *Apeltes quadracus,* differs from the three-spine species in lacking bony scutes and in the triangular cross section of its body, as well as in the number of spines in front of the dorsal fin. Common in salt and brackish water along the east coast of North America from New Brunswick and Nova Scotia to Virginia, this species is occasionally also found in fresh water. It reaches a length of about two and one-half inches, but most adults are less than one and one-half inches long.

Spawning occurs in late spring and summer. The male constructs a nest, usually near the base of some aquatic plant. With the aid of a sticky, threadlike secretion from the kidneys, he weaves the stalks to gether with bits of other plants, until a small, cup-shaped basket is formed. Females are then courted assiduously, and after one or more have laid their eggs in the nest, he builds a "roof" over it. This con tains two tiny holes just large enough for the male to put his snout into—in order to suck fresh water over the eggs.

One male may construct a nest of three or four stories, successively adding to the structure from the top. At the same time he must guard them all and keep them in repair, ventilate the eggs within the lower

BUILDING HIS NEST

The fourspine stickleback builds a nest much the way a bird does. As shown in the illustration, the male weaves portions of water plants into a sort of basket, using growing stalks as the framework. After the female of his choice has laid her eggs in the nest, he roofs it over, and looks around for another mate.

stories, entice females to fill up the latest addition, and now and then take time out to feed. Such males with as many as four nests going at once have been described as the busiest things among fishes.

The eggs are yellowish spheres, about one-sixteenth of an inch in diameter. They hatch in about six days at 72° Fahrenheit.

Seahorses and Their Relatives

To MANY PEOPLE the little seahorse is one of the most fascinating of fishes. Its small head actually resembles a horse's, and the creature holds it upright as it swims along with an air of serious dignity. No other fish is so frequently used as a motif for jewelry, book-ends, ash-trays, lamps and other decorative furniture, to say nothing of all the book plates, advertisements, trade marks and emblems in which seahorses have appeared. The seahorse has become the symbol of ocean life.

But the seahorse is only one of the odd types we find in this order. Trumpet fishes, cornet fishes, snipefishes, and shrimpfishes are also among the important members of the group. Its variety is one of its most impressive features. Looking casually at the three sub-orders (each contains two families), we are hard put to discover much resemblance among them. One thing they all seem to have in common, however—a small mouth located at the end of a tubelike snout. It is inside their bodies, rather than outside, that these fishes are most alike, and the order name, Hemibranchi ("half-gills") highlights the fact that their gills are small and differently shaped from those of other fishes.

Joined, bony armor completely covers the seahorses and pipefishes (family Syngnathidae). We know more than 150 different pipefishes, ranging from tubelike forms with well-developed caudal fins to others with a grasping tail and a head and body that remind us of the typical seahorse. Pipefishes, as a general rule, are at home in weedy shallows along tropical shores, but we do encounter a few in temperate ocean waters. Several species frequently enter streams, and there are some tropical ones found only in fresh water. The largest forms are about two feet long.

One of the rarest and most amazing of seahorselike fishes is the Leafy Seadragon, *Phycodurus eques,* of South Australia. Its head, body and tail are covered with leaflike growths—the whole animal looks for all the world like a piece of seaweed and is a miracle of natural camouflage. It is about one foot long.

AN ANIMATED PIECE OF SEAWEED
One of the oddities of the fish world is the leafy sea dragon, a dweller in Australian waters. This relative of the seahorse has extensive leaflike growths of skin which stream out around it in the water, so that the fish can rarely be distinguished from the seaweed among which it lives. Only three or four specimens of the leafy sea dragon have ever been found; these strange creatures measured some twelve inches in length.

Curiously enough, in all of the pipefishes and seahorses the female, after producing the eggs, turns them over to the male for care. He carries them either in a broodpouch or attached to the under part of his body. Nature, we see, has devised many ways of accomplishing a single end. (In the related family Solenostomidae of the Indian and west Pacific oceans, however, the female carries the eggs.)

The trumpet fishes (family Aulostomidae) and the cornet fishes (family Fistulariidae), are each a small group of tropical ocean fishes. Superficially, the trumpet fishes appear to combine the features of the pipefishes and seahorses and the barracudas, while the cornet fishes at first glance look like marine gars (needle fishes). There are about half a dozen kinds of cornet fishes; they attain lengths of six feet or more, and are used for food. The trumpet fishes—we know only one or two species—grow to be about twenty inches long.

The snipefishes (family Macrorhamphosidae), possess an unmistakable shape with a long snout, a short body, and a single strong spine in the dorsal fin. They inhabit tropical seas, and the largest of the dozen or so species reaches a length of about one foot.

The shrimpfishes (family Centriscidae), are encased in plates of translucent bone. Their two dorsal fins project straight out to the rear, being located where the tail fin usually is. The tail fin is turned so that it projects downward next to the anal. There is sharp disagreement as to how the shrimpfishes swim. Some observers claim they swim vertically, that is, belly first with the long snout pointed upwards. Others claim they swim with the snout pointed down, the back proceeding first. Still others state that they progress in an ordinary fashion, horizontally with the snout first. There are less than six species of these small fishes, inhabiting the tropical Indian and western Pacific Oceans.

The Northern Pipefish, *Syngnathus fuscus,* has a long body, covered with ribbed bony plates through which the small fins project. Its long snout is tipped by a tiny, toothless mouth, and it feeds principally on small crustaceans common in the seaweed and shore plants among which it lives. This species is found from Nova Scotia to North Carolina, usually quite close to shore. It reaches a length of one foot.

During courtship the male and female embrace, their bodies making two intertwining S-shaped curves. The female deposits a batch of eggs by means of a long ovipositor (egg-laying organ) into a pouch that the male has on his underside. The pair then separates, and the male works the spawn further down into the pouch with various gyrations before egg deposition is commenced again. The eggs remain in the pouch for some time, being carried about by the male until they hatch.

Because of this peculiar reversal of the usual part played by the sexes in reproduction, male pipefishes were for many years quite understandably thought to be the females. After their correct sex was first reported, in 1831, a forty-year controversy ensued before the matter was finally settled. In some species of pipefishes the eggs are carried in open grooves along the belly rather than in closed pouches.

The Western Atlantic Seahorse, *Hippocampus hudsonius,* has a head like that of a horse, an external skeleton like that of an insect, a prehensile, or grasping, tail like that of a monkey, eyes that can be moved independently like those of a chameleon, and a pouch for carrying its offspring like that of a kangaroo. Few animals have such an extraordinary assortment of characteristics!

Seahorses are found in tropical and temperate seas throughout the world. They usually inhabit shallow water, but some have been found in floating seaweed far from land. About fifty different species are known. The largest, *Hippocampus ingens,* of the west coast of the Americas from the extreme southern part of California to northern Peru, attains a length of one foot. The common western Atlantic seahorse averages about four inches in length and has been known to reach seven and one-half. The Dwarf Seahorse, *Hippocampus zosterae,* of Florida never exceeds two inches.

The unique shape of seahorses, with their head held at a right angle to their upright body, makes them resemble nothing so much as a knight on the chessboard. The whole body is encased in jointed armor —an external skeleton that they possess in addition to the more usual internal skeleton of all backboned animals. The mouth is a small, traplike affair located at the tip of the long snout. More than half of the total length of the seahorse is made up of the tail, which is rectangular in cross section, flexible, and prehensile. The fish spends much time holding fast to undersea objects by means of this organ.

The deliberate behavior of the seahorse gives it a dignity lacking in most fishes. Its progress is always slow, for the fish must depend upon the movements of its small dorsal and pectoral fins to swim about. Since these fins are more or less transparent and unnoticeable, the seahorse gives the appearance of moving through water without effort of any sort. Actually each part of these fins may vibrate back and forth as fast as thirty-five times per second. The usual position of the body is more or less vertical; horizontal or head-down positions are taken only infrequently.

HORSE OF THE SEA

An object of great interest to visitors at the aquarium is the seahorse. This curious fish swims along with what impresses us as remarkable dignity, or else it rests on some underwater object, to which it attaches itself by its tail. It is the father seahorse, pictured above, that cares for the young—he possesses a pouch, in which he carries the eggs about until they are hatched.

Seahorses feed on small crustaceans which they snap up with their tiny, toothless jaws and swallow whole. They pursue this small prey with gravity and preciseness at the same slow pace that seems to mark their whole existence. Because of their finicky feeding habits—and also their absolute dependence on pure sea water—seahorses are difficult to maintain in captivity. This is too bad, because otherwise no other aquatic creature would approach their popularity as pets.

Reproduction in the western Atlantic seahorse takes place during the late spring and summer. The female seahorse, not the male, is said to do the courting. At any rate, she grows an ovipositor, a special organ with which she deposits her eggs in the pouch of the male. This pouch is located on his belly just before the tail and has a single small opening at its front end. The eggs are fertilized at this time. While they are contained within the pouch, the opening is sealed, so it is obvious that the male must at least supply oxygen to his growing offspring. The highly developed state of the walls of the pouch during incubation indicates that food, too, is supplied to the young. Of course, their waste products must also be removed. The father seahorse, then, truly acts like a mother, carrying and nurturing the young until birth.

In the western Atlantic seahorse, the young are born after about forty-five days of incubation within the male's pouch. If the struggles and gyrations of the father fish are any indication, getting rid of his brood is a difficult and exhausting task. Frequently the male presses his full pouch against rocks or shells as if trying to dislodge the young. The 150 to 200 babies, each a quarter-inch long, may be born over a period of several days. The dwarf seahorse has much smaller broods numbering less than ten young, and the whole procedure of birth may take place in less than a quarter of an hour.

Silversides, Mullets, and Barracudas

In this group we find creatures that are fish food, fish eaters, man food—and man-eaters. Some are so small you can catch them with your hands; others are longer than a man, and catching them requires great skill and strength.

A silvery band along each side helps us to recognize most of the more than 150 species of silversides. (They make up the family Atherinidae.) Besides the silversides proper, this family has other members —the whitebaits, the Australian rainbow fishes, the grunion and the jack-smelt. Although they are mostly at home in tropical oceans, many of them regularly enter brackish water, and a number spend their whole lives in the fresh waters of streams or lakes. The largest species—dwellers in the temperate zones—reach a length of between one and two feet.

The mullets are no small family, either. We know more than one hundred different kinds (family Mugilidae). The largest species reach a good two and one-half feet and a weight of nine pounds. Several are valuable as food; for example, *Mugil dobula* is one of the two most important commercial fishes of Australia. During the spawning season many of the mullets leave the tropical or temperate ocean waters, in which they spend most of their time, for brackish or fresh waters. A number are permanent fresh-water inhabitants.

Swift hunters and ferocious killers, the barracudas—there are twenty different kinds or so in the family Sphyraenidae—prowl all the warm seas. One of the largest of these pikelike fishes is the great barracuda of the western Atlantic, a creature as fearsome as any we encounter on land. Not so formidable are the other members of this order, the threadfins (family Polynemidae). These fishes live near the shores of tropical seas, sometimes entering fresh water, perhaps to spawn. Adults are usually less than one foot long, but a few species exceed six feet. They have peculiar pectoral fins, each one of which is separated into two parts; the upper part is quite ordinary, but the lower part consists of about a half-dozen long, separate threadlike rays, for which the fish are named. In the Indo-Pacific regions, the threadfins (there are about twenty-five different kinds) are sought as food.

All the fishes in this order—Percesoces, meaning "perch-pikes"—have spines on their fins. Still, unlike the true spiny-rayed fishes, which we shall encounter in the next chapter, their ventral fins are located back on the belly rather than near the throat. They have two dorsal fins.

The Common Silverside, *Menidia menidia,* dwells in enormous numbers along the shores of the Atlantic from Nova Scotia to Florida. Great schools of these small, light-colored fish can often be seen in very shallow water in bays or inlets or near sandy or gravelly beaches. They frequently venture into brackish water.

Silversides are characterized by their slender shape, two dorsal fins and a wide silvery band that runs from head to tail. They reach a maximum length of six inches. Their food consists of all sorts of tiny creatures, belonging to the crustacean, mollusk, and worm groups of invertebrates. They also eat algae and other very small plants, and fish eggs, too—including their own.

The common silverside spawns from early spring to late summer, depending on the latitude. The eggs are about one-sixteenth of an inch in diameter and are provided with a tuft of long, gelatinous threads. Ripe fish gather in shallow water to deposit their eggs which, being slightly heavier than sea water, sink to the bottom, and become attached to plants and other underwater objects by means of the sticky threads. Hatching takes place in one to two weeks or more, depending on the temperature.

This species is not ordinarily used for food, although its close relative *Menidia beryllina* provides the delicacy, whitebait. The common silverside is nevertheless of no little economic importance, because of the abundant food it provides for so many other larger food and gamefish.

The Grunion, *Leuresthes tenuis,* is regularly caught with the bare hands—on land! This unbelievable mode of fishing is made possible by the equally unbelievable spawning habits of the fish, which lays its eggs out of water on various beaches of southern and Baja California.

From March until July or August, grunion spawn a day or two after each new and full moon. They begin their reproductive activities from fifteen to forty minutes after the night high tide. At this time grunion can be seen riding in with the waves and swimming further on to the beach as the waves recede, thus being left stranded on the sand. Each incoming female is accompanied by several males. After she "hits the beach," she digs herself, tail first, into the soft wet sand by twisting and turning, until she is buried up to her pectoral fins. The males curve around her on top of the sand as closely as possible. The female then lays a batch of eggs underground. As she struggles to free herself, leaving her eggs behind, the milt (sexual secretion) of the males is carried down to fertilize them.

Now both sexes wiggle back toward the sea, catching up with a wave that eventually carries them back into the deeper water. The whole process may take less than half a minute, but several minutes out of water seem to do the grunion no harm.

The eggs remain in the moist sand until the next series of extra-high tides, two weeks later, come and wash them out. Two or three minutes after the eggs have been freed, the baby grunions hatch out and are carried out to sea. The marvelous adjustment of the fish to its living conditions is apparent. The eggs are laid just after the extra-high tides following the new and full moons, tides that will not be equalled in height for two weeks. Thus for this length of time the eggs will be safe from premature exposure. Nor will the eggs hatch if the succeeding extra-high tide should fail to uncover them. They will remain, development suspended, until the next one, that is, until a month after they were laid. So long as they remain covered with sand the eggs will not hatch. In fact, the eggs are ready to hatch about a week after being laid. They have even successfully developed in running water in the laboratory, showing that burying in sand is not necessary. The eggs are about one-sixteenth of an inch in diameter and salmon pink

FISHES THAT COME ASHORE TO LAY THEIR EGGS

Sometimes thousands of grunion are seen at one time on the beaches of California, for these fish lay their eggs on land. There the eggs remain until a very high tide carries them back to the ocean, where they hatch. Shown in the foreground is the female depositing the eggs, with the male circling about her. Their sojourn ashore rarely lasts more than a few minutes, but they can remain out of water for quite a while without harm.

in color. The newly hatched young are about one-quarter of an inch long and relatively well developed; they are able to swim immediately.

During the height of a spawning run there may be so many grunion on the beach that walking there without stepping on them is impossible. The sight of thousands of these slender, silvery, six-inch fish on a moonlit beach is a memorable one. In order to protect the grunion—an excellent foodfish which was becoming quite scarce—all types of special grunion-collecting equipment, such as nets, have been forbidden, and only the bare hands may be used to capture them. In addition, the state of California has ruled that no grunion at all may be taken during April and May.

Most of the grunion's life is apparently spent near sandy beaches from Point Conception south to the northern portion of Baja California. This is the only place in the world where these fish exist. Young grunion grow rapidly, and by the spring following their hatching they are about five inches long and soon are ready to spawn themselves. They usually live to be two or three years old, and rarely four.

The Striped Mullet, *Mugil cephalus,* feeds on tiny floating plants which it sieves out of the water, on algae which it scrapes off stones, pilings, and the leaves of aquatic plants, and on organic matter from the bottom, which it sifts out of mouthfuls of silt and mud. To help it digest its food, which is mostly vegetable matter, the striped mullet has a gizzard, very similar to that found in birds, where the food is ground up by the action of thick muscular walls covered inside with a horny lining. The mullet's intestine is also relatively long and coiled, permitting more complete digestion and absorption.

When it is young, the striped mullet has the more usual type of short intestine and a good set of teeth. It feeds on small floating animals and plants at this time. As it grows older, its teeth become reduced to tiny bristles, while its intestine becomes longer and more coiled. These changes occur at the beginning of adult feeding habits. Experts disagree as to just where young striped mullet are born, that is, whether the adults lay their eggs in bays and other inside waters, or along exposed shores. We have little scientific information about the eggs, even though spawning fish have once been described. According to this report, each ripe female was accompanied by several smaller males who huddled close to her on all sides during the process of egg laying. It is agreed that reproduction takes place from November to February in Florida waters.

The striped mullet has a world-wide distribution in temperate and warm seas. Along the Atlantic coast of North America it is found from Maine to Florida but rarely occurs north of Cape Cod. Its range extends along the Gulf coast, Mexico, Central America, and south past Brazil. On the Pacific coast it is found from central California to Chile. It is present in the Mediterranean and was well known to the ancients there. It ranges down the west coast of Africa at least as far as the Congo, and all around the Indian Ocean. It is rare in the Indo-Australian archipelago, but is a common fish along much of the Asiatic coast, including the Philippines and Japan.

In many places in the Orient and in Hawaii, the striped mullet is reared in brackish or sea-water ponds. In nature the fish often ventures into the brackish or fresh waters of streams.

Wherever it occurs in large schools, the striped mullet is an important foodfish. In the southern United States about thirty-seven million pounds are taken each year. On the west coast the fish is beginning to become popular as a foodfish, and as a gamefish, too, when taken on light tackle with a dry fly. It grows to a length of about two feet.

The Great Barracuda, *Sphyraena barracuda,* deserves its reputation for ferocity. It has been called the "tiger of the sea"; few fishes seem better equipped, both mentally and physically, to destroy other living creatures. Fearless and apparently inquisitive, a barracuda is not frightened away by the antics of a swimming man as would be almost any other fish. Many of the supposed shark attacks on bathers in the West Indies are the work of this dreadful fish.

With one swipe of its great jaws a barracuda can remove the whole lower-leg muscle of a man or maim his arm or leg so badly as to make surgical amputation necessary. The fish's teeth are pointed, razor-sharp, and they overlap one another, fitting rather closely between the corresponding members on the opposite jaw. From two to four large canines (fangs)—extending three-quarters of an inch beyond the gums in fair-sized specimens—are located on either side of the front part of the upper jaw. One or two are placed at the tip of the lower jaw. Whenever teeth become broken or worn out, they are replaced by new ones that grow in beside the old.

The long pikelike body of the great barracuda seems admirably adapted to sudden dashes through the water. The fish's usual food consists of other fish, which it carefully stalks, then attacks with terrific speed, the strike being almost too fast for the eye to see. Great barracuda have been seen herding a group of snappers, grunts, angelfishes, and others, and not one of this group of prospective prey was able to make a dash to liberty.

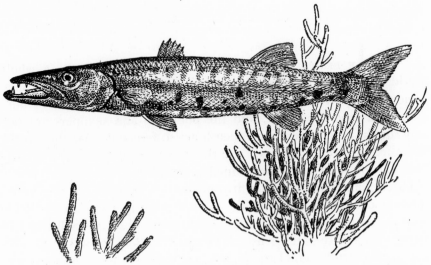

TIGER OF THE SEA
The great barracuda, at home in the waters off the West Indies, Bermuda, and Florida, will attack almost any living thing, including human beings. The sharp, pointed teeth of this tiger of the sea can with one bite practically amputate a man's arm or leg. Barracudas often grow to a length of six feet or more.

The reproductive habits of the great barracuda are a mystery, although it is suspected that it spawns in the early spring and that its eggs float on the surface of the ocean. It grows to be ten feet long, but few individuals exceed half that length.

Rarely is a great barracuda ever found further north than the Carolinas. Small specimens, however, are not uncommon in Bermuda. Its usual home is the West Indies, but it also occurs south to Brazil. This seems to be the most dangerous to man of all the barracudas. The Northern Barracuda, *Sphyraena borealis,* of the east coast of the United States and the Pacific Barracuda, *Sphyraena argentea,* of the west coast are both completely harmless. At least one species in the East Indies, however, has been authentically credited with attacks on men.

The Spiny-Rayed Fishes

I F FISHES interest you at all, you will discover a whole world of wonder in this, the largest single group of bony fishes. Among its species, perch, bass, and sunfish are the delight of both sport and food fishermen; and the pompano and snappers are eagerly sought table delicacies. Bluefish are so ferocious that they might be called "wolves of the sea," and the dorado, or dolphin, is a shining example of incarnate, streamlined speed.

Queer habits and abilities are common in members of this order. The conchfish dwells within the shell of a living giant sea snail; the leaffish is a master of camouflage in imitating dead leaves floating in the water; and the archer fish shoots tiny "bullets" of water. Finally, the grunts, drums, croakers, pigfish, and weakfish have the ability to make sounds—in the water and out of it—to such an extent that schools of certain species around a vessel at anchor will keep the people aboard awake all night.

In a number of ways we can consider the spiny-rayed fishes the peak development of present-day forms—that is, the highest point of a whole line of evolutionary progress. Judged by the number of species alive today, they are the most successful of all of the orders of fishes. In total number of individuals, they stand far ahead of all other salt-water fishes. The spiny-rayed fishes are, in effect, the typical modern fish.

Being typical, they lack the radical, bizarre anatomical features possessed by more highly specialized—and therefore more limited—fishes. They are, nevertheless, extremely different from family to family. These two facts make it difficult, if not impossible, to define them accurately, except in technical terms meaningful only to the expert. Moreover, the experts themselves have had difficulty in defining the group and in deciding exactly what fishes should or should not be included in it.

1526

This vast order, the Percoidei ("perchlike") contains about seventy-five families, including such well-known fishes as the perches, sunfishes, basses, groupers, snooks, snappers, grunts, porgies, weakfishes, goatfishes, and jacks. They have spines in some of their fins, and the pelvic fins, if present, are located well forward, near or directly under the pectorals. Although they have many characteristics in common, they are perhaps best identified by those features they do not possess. For example, they lack the Weberian apparatus of the minnows and catfishes, the irregular shapes of the flatfishes, the accessory gill chambers of the climbing perch, and the peculiar arrangement of cheekbones of the scorpion fishes. Only a fraction of the large number of existing families is mentioned here, since many of them are unknown except to scientists and local specialists.

The Yellow Perch, *Perca flavescens,* furnishes both commercial and sports fishermen with a highly valued catch. About six million pounds are taken commercially each year in the Great Lakes region, and no one knows the weight of the millions of yellow perch caught by anglers. We find the fish east of the Rockies from northern Canada south to Kansas, Missouri, Illinois, Indiana, Ohio, Pennsylvania, and South Carolina.

Yellow perch inhabit lakes, ponds, and the quiet parts of streams. They have been introduced into the West Coast and further south, but these transplantations have not been very successful. Yellowish sides with six to eight dark vertical bars distinguish the yellow perch from other North American fresh-water fishes. The largest specimen ever taken by rod-and-reel weighed four pounds, three and one-half ounces, but the usual maximum weight is about one pound with a length of about twelve to fifteen inches.

In the spring, long, adhesive bands, containing tens of thousands of eggs, are laid over weeds, sticks, and sunken branches, usually at night. The eggs hatch in somewhat less than a month. The food of the yellow perch is quite varied, including insect larvae and adults, crustaceans, mollusks, worms, fishes, and algae and other plant material. When adult, the fish no longer eats plants, but only animal matter.

The perches, pikeperches, and darters comprise the family Percidae, a fresh-water group with about ten species in northern Asia and all of Europe except Spain and Portugal, and with a few more than 100 species in North America, east of the Rockies. The vast majority of the different species are darters, which are exclusively North American. The largest members of this family range up to about three feet in length and twenty-five pounds in weight.

The Pikeperch, *Stizostedion vitreum,* has a tricky name. It is indeed related to the perch, but not to the pike. In appearance it is not at all pikelike, being approximately spindle-shaped and having two dorsal fins and relatively short jaws. It is at home east of the Rockies from central and southern Canada to Nebraska, Arkansas, Alabama, Georgia, and North Carolina. Not native to New Jersey, Connecticut, and eastern Pennsylvania, it has been successfully introduced there, as well as into many bodies of water within its original range. It prefers large, cool lakes and clear rivers.

Pikeperch are flesh-eaters, feeding mostly on other fishes, but also on insects, crustaceans, and amphibians. Although specimens weighing as much as twenty-five pounds have been reported, any more than ten are rare, and the usual weights run less than five. The record angler's catch was slightly more than three feet long and weighed twenty-two and one-quarter pounds.

Shortly after the ice melts or in the very early spring, pikeperch spawn. They often migrate up small streams to lay their numerous eggs, but sometimes deposit them in the shallow parts of lakes. Spawning occurs at night. The eggs are heavier than water, and lie on the bottom. They are about one-twelfth of an inch in diameter. Hatching takes place in a week to a month, depending on the temperature.

There are three different pikeperches generally recognized in North America, and altogether they yield in the neighborhood of ten million pounds of highly edible fish to commercial fishermen in the United States—almost entirely in the region of the Great Lakes. In addition, a considerably larger amount is imported from Canada. Two of the generally recognized pikeperches, the Yellow Pikeperch, or Walleye Pike, and the Blue Pikeperch, are geographical varieties of *Stizostedion vitreum.* The third is a separate, somewhat smaller species, the Sauger, *Stizostedion canadense,* which occasionally cross-breeds with the yellow pikeperch.

The Johnny Darter, *Boleosoma nigrum,* lives on the bottom of lakes and streams, mostly in shallow water among rocks, or on gravel and sand. It is a small fish, becoming as a rule not more than two and one-half inches long at the maximum, although specimens nearly an inch longer have been measured. Its food consists of small crustaceans and insects and algae. Sometimes Johnny darters eat the eggs of other fishes. This species is widely distributed from southern Canada to Colorado, Alabama, and North Carolina.

Johnny darters spawn in the late spring and summer. The eggs are laid on the undersurface of a submerged stone, mussel shell, or other object; the pair swims upside during the process of egg laying. The male, who is somewhat larger than the female and more strikingly colored than she is during the reproductive season, guards the eggs. He also circulates water around them by vibrating his tail under them, and cleans them by turning on his back and brushing them with his body and pectoral fins. The eggs are amber in color and about one-sixteenth of an inch in diameter. They hatch in about three weeks at about 65° Fahrenheit.

There are about one hundred different darters, all of them in North America, but none in the Pacific drainage. They are small fishes; one species is adult at the size of one inch, and the "giant" of the group is the Logperch, *Percina caprodes,* which attains a length of eight inches. Most darters live in streams, always on or near the bottom and frequently among the stones in riffles. Species that do not exhibit parental care of their eggs, lay them on plants or on the bottom, or bury them in sand, and then abandon them.

The Thin Snook, *Centropomis undecimalis,* you can most easily recognize by its low, sloping forehead, its pointed snout, and its undershot jaw. This fish is used both for food and sport. It occurs from Florida and the Gulf Coast south to Brazil, frequently traveling up rivers for many miles. The thin snook feeds on a variety of creatures such as smaller fishes, crabs, and shrimps. It attains weights of more than fifty pounds but averages only about four. Very little is known about the life history of this fish, although it is an important foodfish along the Gulf Coast.

The snooks belong to the family Centropomidae. They occur along the coasts on both sides of South and Central America as far north as Florida in the east and Baja California in the west. They are also found along the shores of tropical west Africa. There are at least eight different species. Other fishes included in the family are the numerous, small glassfishes of shallow, salt, brackish, and fresh waters of the Indian and western Pacific regions, and the perchlike fishes of the genus *Lates,* which are important foodfishes in Africa and southeastern Asia and the East Indies.

The Conchfish, *Astrapogon stellatus,* often makes its home in the cavity of very large marine snails called conchs. These mollusks, belonging to the genus *Strombus,* are used as food, and when they are taken off the bottom they close up the opening to their shells, trapping inside any small conchfish that is using them as a shelter. Later, while lying on the bottom of the collecting boat or in the market, the snail relaxes and the fish falls out, much to the surprise of any beholder.

Not all conchs contain conchfish, however, nor does every conchfish live within a conch. These fish also inhabit living sponges and bivalves and the empty shells of dead conchs; they most probably make use of a wide variety of objects for shelter. When kept in an aquarium, they hide during the day, appearing only when it is dark; most likely in nature they rarely leave their conch except at night.

The color of the conchfish is quite variable. At night it may be almost white, and by day, dark brown. Sometimes a single, slanted, very dark line runs across the cheek; at other times there may be four different lines on the head and body. The pelvic fins are unusually long, but whether they serve any special purpose is unknown. A length of two inches is attained.

Conchfish feed largely on small crustaceans. They occur in Bermuda, the West Indies, and southern Florida. Reproduction begins in August. As in many other species of cardinal fishes, the male carries the eggs around in his mouth.

The cardinal fishes make up the family Apogonidae. They are small fishes, found generally in shallow, tropical salt waters, and comprise one of the most populous groups living among East Indian coral reefs and around the Philippines. Several inhabit depths as great as sixteen hundred feet, and some live in fresh water. Many of them are red or pink in color.

The Smallmouth Black Bass, *Micropterus dolomieu,* rivals the best of the trouts and salmons in popularity as a fresh-water gamefish. Originally distributed through most of the Great Lakes drainage and the Ohio, Tennessee, and upper Mississippi river systems, the smallmouth black bass has been introduced into practically every state and most of the Canadian provinces. It has also been quite successfully transplanted to South Africa and less so to the British Isles and the European continent. Its favorite living places are clear, cool lakes and streams that are not too small and have little vegetation or mud.

The average adult smallmouth black bass weighs from one and one-half to three pounds, but especially large ones may attain weights of more than eleven pounds. Such specimens are usually quite old. Experts have found that the smallmouth can live to be at least fourteen years old in nature. It grows rather rapidly when an ample food supply is present, and may reach a length of ten inches in three to six years; it becomes sexually mature in four to six years.

The spawning season begins when the water becomes sufficiently warmed by the spring sun, that is, from late April to the end of June, depending on the latitude and weather. The males gather over sunny, gravel- or rock-covered areas, usually where the water is three to six feet deep. Each male establishes a territory that he vigorously defends against other fish, especially other bass.

By assuming a nearly vertical position, head uppermost, and fanning the bottom with his tail, the male starts to construct his nest. He roots up the bottom, loosening debris so that it may be fanned away, and carries larger pebbles and other objects away in his mouth.

The nest may take two days or more to build. It is a saucer-shaped depression, as much as four feet in diameter, if the male that made it is a large one. No speck of sediment is allowed to settle for long on any stone within the nest, nor is any fish, crayfish, snail, or worm allowed to remain in it. The male cleans and guards his nest continuously.

Soon females approach the nesting area, and the males try to drive them into their nests. Eventually a female enters one of the nests and lays her adhesive eggs on a small patch of the polished stones lying on the bottom. More than one female may spawn in the nest of a single male. The females retire after laying their eggs, their duties as a parent being completed.

It is the male's job to care for the eggs and young. He gently fans the eggs with his pectoral and tail fins and attacks all creatures that come near them. When they hatch, three or four days later, he also fans and watches over the helpless fry. In three to twelve days, the young begin to swim about. Then the male conducts them into shallow water near shore where he continues to stand guard over them, usually for two to nine more days, but sometimes for as long as twenty-eight.

The food of recently hatched smallmouth black bass consists of small crustaceans like water fleas. As they grow larger, the fish begin to eat insects. When about one and one-half inches long, they start to catch small fishes, and at twice this size crayfish are added to their diet.

The Largemouth Black Bass, *Micropterus salmoides,* as you might expect, may be distinguished from the smallmouth by the size of its mouth, which extends back past the eye. Also, it has an almost complete division between the two parts of its dorsal fin. Scientists at present recognize three species of black basses besides the smallmouth and largemouth. The habits of all of these are basically alike, but they differ in a number of details. For example, the largemouth black bass is typically found in weedy, mud-bottomed, still, or sluggishly moving fresh waters, in contrast to the smallmouth which occurs in cooler, clearer, generally more rapid waters.

The largemouth originally lived further south than the smallmouth; its range extended from northern Canada through the Great Lakes and Mississippi river systems to Florida and northeastern Mexico. Because of its greater adaptability to warm, still waters, the largemouth black bass has been employed extensively in pond culture and has been introduced over most of the United States and Canada and such places as France, Germany, South Africa, and Hawaii.

Largemouth black bass spawn in the spring, more or less in the same way as do smallmouth. The nest may be located on muddy areas, however, in which case the adhesive eggs are laid on the roots of aquatic plants, on sticks, or on other objects besides stones. The male guards his school of young fish until they are an inch or more in length, that is, for many days he rides herd on them and drives off possible enemies. There may be four thousand or more young in such a school, so the father has no small task in watching over all of them. Having attained a size of about an inch, the young lose their tendency to school and become solitary—until winter time when they gather together again in the deeper parts of their home waters, as do many of the black basses and sunfishes when the water becomes cold.

The record largemouth black bass ever taken with hook and line weighed twenty-two and one-quarter pounds and was thirty-two and one-half inches long. Specimens weighing twenty-five pounds have been reported.

It is generally believed that most fishes can distinguish colors, but in the largemouth black bass we have definite indications of this faculty. One investigator was able to train the largemouth to distinguish between red or yellow and the other primary colors quite easily. Green and blue were more difficult for the fish to tell apart. The careful attention fishermen pay to the color of their flies may therefore be very worth while.

The Pumpkinseed, *Lepomis gibbosus,* has provided many a boy with his first fishing experience. Found almost everywhere through its range, a ready taker of all sorts of bait—even when the bait hides a bent pin—and an excellent panfish, the pumpkinseed is a beginner's gamefish second to none. It bites most of the year and can even be successfully fished through the ice in some localities. Pumpkinseeds are found in a variety of habitats, but most frequently in the weedy parts of ponds, lakes, and streams. They occur naturally from southern Canada to South Carolina, west to Pennsylvania, Iowa, and the Dakotas, but have been introduced into California, British Columbia, and France, among other places.

The pumpkinseed belongs to the family Centrarchidae, a group that also includes the black basses, sunfishes, crappies, rock bass, warmouth, and Sacramento perch—in all about thirty species. This family is confined to North America, no member of it existing anywhere else unless introduced there by man. The largest species is the largemouth black bass; the smallest, the pygmy sunfish from the southeastern United States, which is adult when about one inch long.

As in the great majority of sunfishes, the male pumpkinseed builds a nest and takes care of the eggs and young. One of the most characteristic views of North American fish life consists of a colony of male pumpkinseeds, each on his easily discernible, round nest, all closely arranged along some sunlit, shallow, sandy or rocky area near the shore of a pond or lake. Breeding takes place during the late spring or early summer, and, as a true member of the sunfish family, the male pumpkinseeds actively build and court only when the sun shines brightly.

The male constructs the nest by fanning vigorously with his tail. At the same time, by rapidly backing water with his pectoral fins, he prevents the forward motion that would ordinarily result from this action. Since he rotates through a complete circle while keeping his head up and more or less over the same spot, the result is a circular, cleaned or excavated area, with a diameter just about twice the length of the fish. After the eggs are laid and hatched, the male does not guard his offspring very long, as the black basses often do.

Similarity in reproductive habits among the sunfishes is undoubtedly one of the main reasons why so many of them hybridize in nature. For example, the pumpkinseed naturally crosses with the warmouth and the green, yellowbelly, longear, bluegill and orangespotted sunfishes. The hybrids produced are perfectly healthy fish with a rate of growth more rapid than that of either parent, but they are all sterile.

PUMPKINSEED ON PATROL

The pumpkinseed, found in many parts of the United States, is a fish that is easy to catch, and hence is popular with the novice fisherman. Its breeding habits are most interesting— the male clears a round area at the bottom of shallow water simply by fanning with his tail and then, as pictured above, guards the eggs deposited there by the female.

The food of the pumpkinseed is quite varied and includes principally insects and their larvae, snails and small crustaceans like water fleas, together with lesser amounts of worms, leeches, tiny fishes, freshwater sponges, and aquatic vegetation. Although they have been

inches long, but the largest one of which there is any kind of authentic record is reported to have weighed 125 pounds. Males grow more slowly than females. The food of the striped bass consists of a large variety of smaller fishes and crustaceans.

The Black Sea Bass, *Centropristes striatus,* is one of more than four hundred members of the large family of true sea basses, the Serranidae. This group includes the groupers and hinds from salt water, the white and yellow basses from fresh water, and the striped bass and white perch that live in both kinds of water. The great majority of fishes in this family inhabit temperate or tropical seas, however. The black basses, it should be noted, belong to a separate group of fishes.

Black sea bass are popular with so-called "deep-sea fishermen," since they inhabit rocky bottoms at least a couple of fathoms deep and take the hook regularly. They are also of some importance as a commercial foodfish. They seldom exceed four pounds, although the record angler's catch weighed more than eight pounds.

The black sea bass straggles as far north as Maine and occurs as far south as Florida and rarely the Gulf Coast, being most common off the Middle Atlantic States. It feeds on squid, crabs, and other fishes.

Reproduction takes place in the late spring. The eggs are pelagic, that is, they float freely at the surface of the open ocean, and are slightly more than one thirty-second of an inch in diameter. They hatch in about five days. Males are more brightly colored than females being blue-black with bright blue and white spots here and there. Older males develop a fatty hump over the back of the head during the breeding season. Its function is unknown. Males are larger than females and live to be at least twenty years old, whereas no females over half that age have been discovered. Among younger fish females predominate, but among the older ones males are much more numerous. A microscopic examination of the internal organs of numbers of black sea bass revealed that after the fifth year or so, many females gradually turn into males! So far as known, no sex-reversed individual functions both as male and female at one time. Instead, many black sea bass start out as egg-producers and later in life become functioning males.

The Spotted Jewfish, *Promicrops itaiara,* is the largest of all the American groupers—it may reach a weight of 750 pounds. Most are considerably smaller, however. In all, there are nearly forty different kinds of groupers and grouper-like fishes in the salt waters off the southeastern and Gulf coasts of the United States, and the West Indies. Many of them are used for food; they are usually caught by hook-and-line. The spotted jewfish is no exception, being regularly eaten in Key West.

This species feeds on other fishes and on spiny lobsters. Those 350-pound specimens kept in the New York Aquarium seemed especially fond of dogfishes, which they swallowed whole. One of these giant jewfish would slowly approach an unwary two-and-one-half-foot dog-fish and suddenly open wide its jaws. The dogfish, sucked into the gaping maw by the strong current produced, would quickly and completely disappear. At other times the large fish simply lay on the bottom and waited until a likely morsel swam by, before opening its cavernous mouth to engulf it. Presumably these are the ways spotted jewfish feed in nature, since they are sluggish and are usually found on the bottom near coral formations and sunken wrecks or under rocky ledges. They occur on both the east and west coast of tropical America, from Florida to Brazil, and from Lower California to Peru.

Although the spotted jewfish possesses limited powers of altering its coloration, many other groupers are phenomenal quick-change artists. For example, the Nassau Grouper, *Epinephelus striatus*, has at least eight different color phases, ranging from cream to dark brown. The fish can assume them at a moment's notice, and may show several in the course of a minute. The spotted jewfish can take on four color patterns: dusky black, dark gray with black blotches, creamy white with black blotches, and almost entirely creamy white.

As many as six distinct patterns have been seen in individuals of some species of fishes within only a few moments. These remarkably rapid transformations result from the contraction and expansion of the pigment in thousands of tiny pigment cells in the skin of the fish. There are four or five different kinds of them distributed in various ways over the body. The multitude of color changes are produced by the pigment expanding and contracting in different combinations. Some fishes definitely change their colors to match their surroundings. In these the ability to alter their pigment patterns appears to help protect them from enemies, but in the groupers—and many other fishes, too—the color patterns seldom seem to hide the fish. What purpose they serve, if any, is unknown. All that we can be certain of is that some patterns are definitely associated with flight, hiding, resting, fighting, and other activities.

Very little is known about the life history of the groupers save that they lay eggs, supposedly in the spring.

The Tilefish, *Lopholatilus chamaeleonticeps,* was the victim of one of the most famous of natural disasters known to have overtaken a fish. The species was not discovered until 1879, when a cod-fishing vessel happened to catch some in deep water off Massachusetts. Since it was a large fish of good commercial possibilities, it was investigated by the United States Bureau of Fisheries and found to be abundant within a circumscribed area ranging from about 90 to 150 fathoms in depth, all of a rather definite water temperature. Hardly had the new fishery become established, however, when vessels, arriving in New York from Europe in 1882, reported seeing vast numbers of dead and dying fish, most of them tilefish. Perhaps 7,500 square miles of sea were covered by these fishes; at least one and one-half billion dead tilefish were seen.

As far as known, the catastrophe was caused by a sudden, drastic, but short-lived drop in water temperature brought about by some meteorological or geological event. For ten years not a tilefish was caught, and it was believed that the species had become extinct. But in 1892, eight fish were taken. From then on their numbers gradually increased until, by 1916, over eleven and one-half million pounds were being taken annually. Since that time, however, the demand for tilefish has fallen off to such an extent that it is at present hardly ever commercially fished.

The coloration of the tilefish is most attractive. Its back is bluish green and its sides yellow or pink, both dotted with yellow. Its belly is rose and white, and its head is reddish towards the top, white below. It has a large well-toothed mouth and a peculiar, stiff, triangular, fatty flap projecting upward just in front of the long dorsal fin. Tilefish may reach a weight of fifty pounds, but the usual maximum weight is somewhat less.

Tilefish live on or near the bottom and feed on bottom-dwelling invertebrates, crabs being the most important single item of food. Occasionally they eat other fishes. Spawning takes place in the summer, and the small eggs float. The family Malacanthidae, to which the tilefish belongs, is principally found in tropical seas. Most of its members are smaller than the tilefish, not exceeding eighteen inches, and none possess the adipose, or fatty, flap.

The Bluefish, *Pomatomus saltatrix,* has been likened to an animated chopping machine. When a school of these ferocious, streamlined, sharp-toothed killers moves into a school of mackerel, menhaden, or herring, the carnage is truly colossal.

Instead of completely devouring their prey, the bluefish swing through the group, wildly biting and slashing, and leaving most of their victims with half a body or with great pieces bitten out of them. When their stomachs are filled, they apparently disgorge what they have eaten and begin all over again. Like blood-crazed dogs running amok in a herd of sheep, they seem to kill only for the joy of killing. After two unusually large schools of predator and prey have met, the trail of blood and maimed fish floating on the sea has been said to stretch for miles. When feeding inshore, bluefish have been known to drive thousands of menhaden right out of the water on to the beach.

Young bluefish, called snappers, emulate their parents, but do almost all of their feeding inshore, and on smaller prey. They grow rapidly, more than doubling their length in about three months during the summer. Just where or when they are spawned is not known. Ripe bluefish are occasionally taken during the late spring or summer on the Atlantic Coast, so it is presumed that reproduction takes place around that time. What little evidence there is, indicates that the eggs are laid over the continental shelf (the off-shore, underwater plain bordering a continent), perhaps fairly close to shore in some instances.

The demand for bluefish usually exceeds the supply—both at the fish market and among sports fishermen. Roughly six million pounds are caught by commercial fishermen each year, and probably an equal amount by anglers. The fish are taken principally with nets or by trolling. Bluefish weighing fifty pounds were reported to have been taken in the old days, but today's maximum is only half that large.

We do not always find the bluefish where we would expect to. Although it is a widely distributed oceanic fish, there are large parts of the sea from which it is completely absent. Bluefish roam the temperate and tropical Atlantic, regularly traveling as far north as Maine during the summer and appearing off Florida and the Gulf Coast during the cold months. This north-and-south migration does not always closely follow the thermometer, however; the movements of bluefish are to a certain extent erratic, and independent of the temperature of the water in which they live. Bluefish are also found off the east coast of South America, on both sides of Africa, in the Mediterranean Sea, in the Indian Ocean, and around Australia. This fish is rare through most of the East Indies and completely absent in the Central and North Pacific. It is the only member of the family Pomatomidae, and is distinguished from all other fishes on the basis of internal features and a unique combination of external ones.

The Horse Mackerel, or Saurel, *Trachurus trachurus,* is not a mackerel, but belongs to the family of jacks. It is an oceanic fish, widely distributed in the Atlantic, rare to the west and north but common to the east and south. Its most distinguishing feature is a series of large scutes, or plates, that cover the lateral line from head to tail. This structure has a sharp dip in it about halfway down the fish's body.

The tiny buoyant eggs are laid during the summer. The young, which are less than one eighth of an inch long when hatched, apparently live near the surface of the open sea at all times. From a size of about one-half inch to nearly three inches, they are frequently found around jellyfish, under whose umbrella they take shelter. The horse mackerel feeds upon young herring and pilchard and at times large schools of them have appeared offshore to feed. It reaches a length of thirty inches and is caught commercially on the west coast of South Africa.

The jacks, scads, pompanos, runners, pilot fish, banded rudder fish and yellowtail, as well as the horse mackerel, are members of the family Carangidae. More than two hundred species are known from all the tropical and warm temperate seas of the world. Several species run many miles up tropical rivers. Practically all are edible, and some are taken in sufficient numbers to be important food fishes. They are strong swimmers and often take the hook avidly, being therefore popular with sportsmen.

The Pilot Fish, *Naucrates ductor,* frequently follows ships and large fish, especially sharks. The ancient Greeks believed that it would guide sailors who had lost their way at sea, showing them how to reach port. Whales, too, were supposed to be guided by pilot fish. This fish also played a part in classic Greek mythology and was held sacred in some places.

Observations in nature and in public aquariums have shown these beliefs—still held today by numbers of people—to be erroneous. The pilot fish does accompany slow-moving vessels and sharks, sometimes remaining very close to them for long periods of time. The reason for this behavior cannot very well be to guide the ship or large fish, however, because the pilot fish *follows* rather than leads. The prospect of scraps from the ship's galley or odd bits from the shark's roughly torn prey is a much more likely reason for the peculiar attraction. Moreover, oceanic fishes of several sorts seem to be drawn to floating objects, and some species are characteristically found resting under them. Scientists suggest that living in the open ocean, where there are very few things to see, has made these fishes especially sensitive and likely to be attracted to any object that comes into view.

The young of the pilot fish frequently take shelter beneath floating seaweed and jellyfish or among the stinging tentacles of siphonophores like the infamous Portuguese man-of-war. These small pilot fish look so different from the adult that for a long time they were thought to be different species. Instead of being streamlined, they are short, rather grotesque creatures with relatively enormous eyes and numerous spines about the head. They are hatched from small, floating eggs.

The trim body of a grown pilot fish is distinctly marked with five broad, dark vertical bands. The four small spines placed just in front of the dorsal fin and the keel on each side of the base of the tail fin are also characteristic. A size of at least two feet is attained. The pilot fish ranges throughout the tropical and warm temperate seas of the world.

The Common Pompano, *Trachinotus carolinus,* is perhaps the most renowned of American tropical marine foodfish and one of the outstanding epicurean delights among seafoods. Its average weight is not more than two pounds, and less than a million pounds are marketed annually. The demand exceeds the supply, however, and many more pounds would be consumed if more fish could be caught.

The finely scaled body of the common pompano has its dorsal and anal fins almost identically located and both fins have their first few rays prolonged into a sharp-pointed, triangular extension so that one fin seems a mirror-image of the other. The color of the common

pompano is bluish green above, shading into silver below, with yel
lowish fins.

The fish are often prevalent near the surf. Young specimens are
frequently thrown on the beach where they flip-flop back towards the
sea to be picked up and carried away by the next wave. Young pompanos are hardy and can live out of water longer than many other species. Common pompanos feed on the eggs and young of other species
and on various kinds of shellfish. When adult, they have very few
teeth or none at all, but their small bony jaws apparently serve them
quite adequately. Nothing is known of the pompano's reproductive
habits save that an extended spawning season during the late spring
and early summer is indicated on the Gulf Coast.

POPULAR ON THE TABLE

The common pompano, which dwells along the Gulf and southern Atlantic coasts of North
America, is highly esteemed as a foodfish. Pompanos are common near beaches, and
young ones are often washed ashore. Flippity-flop, the fish make their way back to where
the water will engulf them again. The adult pompano, pictured above, may grow to a
length of eighteen inches.

The Yellowtail, *Seriola dorsalis,* schools off the coast of California and southward. It takes live or trolled bait eagerly and is noted for its long rapid runs when hooked. Commercial fishermen employ purse seines to catch yellowtail off the Mexican coast, but are prohibited from using this method in California waters. The fish is sold both fresh and canned. The usual maximum size is about twenty pounds, but fish weighing more than eighty pounds are on record.

Although superficially it looks like a relative of the tunas, the yellowtail is a true member of the family Carangidae. Its spindle-shaped body is beautifully colored, bluish above and silvery below with a conspicuous yellowish band running from eye to tail. As befits so streamlined a fish, the yellowtail pursues such fast-swimming prey as mackerel and flying fish as well as sardines, herring, and shrimp. Spawning is said to take place in the spring, but practically nothing is definitely known about the life history of this fish.

The Dorado or Dolphin, *Coryphaena hippurus,* feeds on flying fishes. These often take to the air to escape, and the dorado has been described as flushing them like quail. Their flight into another element may frequently be to no avail, for the dorado often swims as fast as a flying fish can fly, and snaps up the hapless creature when it drops back into the water. The fastest accurate estimate we have of the dorado's speed is a little more than thirty-seven miles per hour, as measured from a moving ship. While in pursuit of prey, the dorado often leaps from the water itself.

Like a brilliantly colored knife, this fish cuts through the water, its narrow, long, triangular body being admirably designed to offer little water resistance. Its powerful tail is tipped with a deeply forked caudal fin, and along the whole back runs a soft, many-rayed dorsal. Larger specimens, especially males, have very high foreheads that may rise almost perpendicular to the long axis of the body. Because young specimens lack this character, they were originally described as different species. At one time, in fact, there were nearly a score of different kinds of dorado listed; now it is believed that there is only one species, or at the most two. They make up a family of their own, the Coryphaenidae.

Dorados are renowned for their coloration. A group of them can fill the water with electric blue flashes, it has been said. Luminous blues, royal purples, radiant greens and rich gold are all incorporated

into their color scheme. This changes so rapidly that it practically
defies description, save to say that the fish's back is relatively dark
and its belly quite light. Soon after capture, the vivid colors fade, going through a whole series of striking variations—as if some secret fire
within the fish had been extinguished, leaving the exterior gradually
to cool.

IN PURSUIT OF THE FLYING FISH
The dorado, a large, powerful fish of the warm seas, will frequently launch itself into the
air as it pursues its favorite prey, the flying fish. A speedy swimmer, the dorado will also
swim along below the fish in flight, and seize it when it descends to the water. The flesh
of dorados is succulent, and they enjoy considerable popularity as gamefish.

Within recent years the dorado has become a popular gamefish.
The largest one ever caught on hook-and-line weighed sixty-seven and
one-half pounds and was sixty-eight and one-half inches long; which
is close to the maximum size the fish ever attains. Dorados are excellent eating, but not enough are caught to make them a regular market fish.

The dorado is an oceanic fish that is found in most warm seas. On
the Atlantic coast of the United States it ranges as far north as Cape
Cod and on the Pacific it is found off southern California. Little is
known of the fish's life history. Undoubtedly it lays floating eggs,
probably in the spring in the region of the West Indies. Partly

grown individuals are frequently found in numbers around or under floating objects like logs or bunches of Pacific kelp or Atlantic sargassum weed and gulf weed. The ancients took advantage of this habit and set bundles of reeds in the water to attract dorado, which were then caught with hook-and-line.

The Gray Snapper, *Lutjanus griseus,* has often been called the most intelligent of fish. Described as wary, alert, strong, swift, and adaptable, it has been held up as an excellent example of the highest development in modern, spiny-rayed fishes.

Gray snappers can be found throughout the West Indies and Bermuda where they often are the most noticeable element in the fish population. North of Florida the species occurs only as a straggler, although it has been picked up as far north as New Jersey. To the south it is found along the coast of Central and South America to Brazil. Shaped like a typical spiny-rayed fish with a single dorsal fin, pelvic fins far forward and its large jaws armed with sharp teeth, the gray snapper seems well equipped to meet the necessities of underwater existence. Its usual maximum size is five pounds, but individuals weighing as much as eighteen pounds have been reported.

In behavior the gray snapper reminds one of nothing so much as "a guy always out to make a buck." Groups of them can be found around docks, stones, mangrove swamps, and coral reef formations, hungrily alert for any food that might become available. They usually do their hunting at night, however, feeding on crabs, shrimps, squid, worms, and small fishes. They sometimes can also be seen actively feeding during the day, however. A gray snapper will slowly stalk its prey until from one to three feet away from it. Then with a sudden burst of speed it dashes forward, seizes the unfortunate victim, turns sharply and returns more slowly to the general area from which the rush was started, to await more food. Bits of floating seaweed are often examined intently for some morsel that might be lurking in them. Gray snappers will swim close to shore, paralleling the course of people walking along the beach, so they can catch the crabs that, frightened by the people, scuttle into the water. Scraps of all sorts from kitchen or galley are avidly taken—even such things as bread, potatoes, and beans, that one would suppose to be not very tasty to a fish which lives chiefly on animal food.

Because of their obvious alertness and aggressiveness, gray snappers

THE GIANT GROUPER DOES NOT FEAR MAN

The spotted jewfish is one of the largest of the whole grouper tribe, reaching a weight of at least 750 pounds. In captivity these fish quickly learn to recognize the person who feeds them and to take food from the hand. A specimen as large as this one could easily swallow a 2½-foot dogfish.

have been employed in experiments by scientists interested in animal behavior. It has been discovered that they can distinguish between various colors and patterns of their prey and can easily be taught to avoid certain types by associating them with a distasteful flavor or other unpleasant stimulus, provided by the experimenter.

In some places gray snappers can hardly ever be caught with hook-and-line, but in others they are not so wary. They are hard fighters when hooked and are used for food.

The Lutjanidae, the family of snappers, comprises some 250 species of fishes from tropical and warm temperate ocean waters, mostly near shore. They are hard-hitting, flesh-eating fishes, and provide good sport when hooked. A number are extensively used for food, including the Mutton Fish and the Schoolmaster of the West Indies.

The Red Snapper, *Lutjanus aya,* ranks with the pompano as one of the most famous foodfish of tropical marine waters. It is also renowned for its lovely rose-red color; a red snapper served for dinner on a well-garnished plate looks as marvelous as it tastes. This bright color distinguishes it from most other snappers, but there is at least one other species of red-colored snapper with which it has been confused.

The red snapper inhabits deep water in the Gulf of Mexico, the Caribbean Sea and adjoining regions. It is fished by hook-and-line. The principal area for the fishery is located on the Campeche Banks off the coast of Yucatan; other smaller banks are scattered off the Gulf Coast of the United States and Mexico. We know practically nothing about the life history of the fish. What little evidence there is indicates that it spawns in the deep water in late spring or summer. It is known to attain a weight of seventy-nine pounds.

The Bluestriped or Yellow Grunt, *Haemulon sciurus,* is usually striped with chrome-yellow and lavender-blue, but these bright colors can be temporarily lost, the fish becoming entirely gray. During the day bluestriped grunts gather in groups around coral formations and underwater growths, and at night they scatter to feed on small crustaceans, mollusks, worms, and brittlestars. Their range is from Florida and the West Indies southward to Brazil. They are also found in Bermuda.

As in many other grunts, the lining of the mouth is a brilliant red. Often, two bluestriped grunts will approach each other head on, and one will suddenly open wide its mouth, plainly displaying the bright interior. The other will then follow suit. Often the two will approach each other so closely that the top and bottom of their jaws touch. Then they will back off slightly and repeat the strange performance. The exact significance of their maneuvers is not known, but it seems quite possible that they are a warning or recognition display by which the fish are told of the presence or intent of their fellows. Other species of grunts perform in a similar manner. The bluestriped grunt grows to a length of about one and one-half feet.

The grunts, family Pomadasyidae, are closely related to the snappers, differing from them most prominently in the arrangement of teeth. Like the snappers they inhabit tropical and warm temperate seas, are flesh-eaters and are much used for food. Among the grunts are the margates, porkfish, pigfish, and tomtate.

The Pigfish, *Orthopristis chrysopterus,* makes distinct grunting sounds when it is hooked, revealing by its behavior as well as its appearance that it belongs to the grunt family. It is caught both by anglers and commercial fishermen, but is a foodfish of only minor importance. Usually it is most tasty, but once in a while an individual with a distinctly bad odor and taste turns up. This unpleasant quality is acquired by eating acorn-worms, which are peculiar worm-shaped creatures (not really worms at all), whose bodies are strongly scented with an evil-smelling chemical similar or identical to iodoform. The great majority of pigfish eat less odoriferous bottom-inhabiting creatures such as small crustaceans, bivalves, worms, and a few starfish.

At about two years of age pigfish spawn for the first time. They are then somewhat over eight inches long. At the latitude of North Carolina, spawning may begin as early as mid-March and extend through June, the height of activity occurring in May.

The female lays her eggs inshore early in the evening. They are perhaps half the size of a pinhead, float at the surface and hatch in about one and one-half to three days. The newly hatched pigfish is only about one-sixteenth of an inch long and floats helplessly on its back, with its relatively large yolk-sac uppermost. By the time it is three days old, it has absorbed practically all of the yolk, has assumed an upright position, has started to grow fins and is able to swim. It is of course still completely at the mercy of its surroundings and remains so for some time.

The pigfish occurs along the coast of the United States from Massachusetts to Texas, but it is uncommon north of Virginia. During the cold months it disappears from its usual inshore haunts, returning in the spring in a rather thin and run-down condition. Just where it spends the winter remains a mystery. The maximum size is about fifteen inches.

The Northern Scup, *Stenotomus chrysops,* often falls victim to otter-trawls, pound-nets, floating traps, purse-seines and hook-and-line, since there is a good demand for it. The otter-trawl—in which the net is spread apart by two large boards—accounts for most of the catch. Some twenty million pounds of northern scup are sold commercially each year.

These fish spawn in the bays and other inshore waters of southern New England and the Middle Atlantic States from May to August. The tiny buoyant eggs hatch in forty hours at 72 degrees. The larvae are less than one-eighth of an inch long; by their first winter they have grown to about three inches. Adult northern scup average about one pound. Scup are bottom feeders, and gather in groups to eat crustaceans, mollusks, worms, and small fishes.

The Sparidae or porgy family, to which the northern scup and the sheepshead belong, contains more than one hundred different species. They are found mostly along tropical and warm temperate shores, but some live in quite cold water, especially around South Africa and southern Australia. Here the largest species seem to occur; for example, the Musselcracker, *Cymatoceps nasutus,* of South Africa grows to weigh more than one hundred pounds. In these regions the sparids are among the most important fishes used for food.

Fishes of this family are also of commercial value along the east coast of North America and in the West Indies, the Mediterranean Sea and the Red Sea, in which regions the greatest number of species occurs. They are relatively rare in the western Pacific, still rarer in the central portion and on the west coast of South America, and are absent from the west coast of North America. A few of the sparids enter brackish and fresh water.

The Sheepshead, *Archosargus probatocephalus,* was once common around New York and was a commercially important species in Chesapeake Bay and on the coast of the Gulf of Mexico. To the regret of fishermen, it is now unknown in the vicinity of New York, has practically disappeared from Chesapeake Bay and has greatly declined along the Gulf Coast. The reason for this striking decrease in abundance is a mystery.

The sheepshead has been recorded as far north as the Bay of Fundy, but it seldom appeared north of Cape Cod and then only during the summer and early fall. From North Carolina southward it is a year-'round resident. It occurs as far south as Tampico, Mexico. Very game when hooked and very tasty when served, the sheepshead is popular with sports and commercial fishermen. It reaches a length of thirty inches and a weight of twenty pounds, but averages no more than six.

The seven dark vertical bands on the body of the sheepshead are distinctive. The single dorsal fin is strongly spined, as is the anal. Prominent incisor teeth give its mouth a somewhat "buck-tooth" appearance. It has a long digestive tract of the kind usually associated with fishes that feed on vegetation, but it eats both aquatic plants and shellfish.

The eggs are very small and float, hatching in about forty hours at 77 degrees. Spawning takes place in the spring. When they are only half an inch long, baby sheepsheads already resemble their parents. Their rate of growth is slow.

The Tripletail, *Lobotes surinamensis,* disappointing to relate, does not have three tails. Still, looking at it, you might almost think it lived up to its name—the rear portions of its dorsal and anal fins are quite large, and form, with the caudal fin, three distinct lobes, all about the same size, giving the illusion of three tail fins.

Adult tripletails are mottled dark brown; younger fish are lighter in color. They reach a length of three and one-half feet and a weight of at least forty-one pounds. They are good eating, but are nowhere caught in sufficient quantity to make them a regular market fish. Tripletails frequent a variety of coastal regions, including the mouths of rivers—where they congregate around jetties, wrecks, fallen tree-tops, and so forth—and over rocky or coral bottoms. They range from Cape Cod to Florida and the Gulf Coast, and further south. A few have been taken in the Mediterranean. They occur along the tropical east coast of Africa and the eastern Asiatic coast from southern Japan to Australia, including the East Indies. They are also occasionally found in other warm ocean waters.

The spawning of the tripletail is believed to occur during the late summer in the tropical western Atlantic. The eggs and larval fish have yet to be described. Young individuals about three and one-half inches long remarkably resemble dead leaves floating on the sea, not only in appearance but in behavior. Observations of a small captive specimen revealed that it habitually lay on one side at the surface of the water, usually with its head slightly down, moving only by means of its transparent pectoral fins. If slightly disturbed, the fish seemed to rely on its deceptive resemblance, because it would move away quite slowly, never abandoning its posturing. If thoroughly disturbed, say by a net, it would dart away for about eighteen inches, then immediately resume its leaf-mimicking behavior. When mangrove leaves were thrown into its tank, the small tripletail carefully moved over among them, in effect schooling with the leaves!

The tripletail belongs to the family Lobotidae, a small group of three or four species. Two of them are confined to salt, brackish, and fresh waters of India, Burma, southeastern Asia and the East Indies and one has been reported from the Pacific coast of Panama.

The Atlantic Croaker, *Micropogon undulatus,* is named for the noise that it produces. When the fish is out of water, the sound is like a very low, rasping croak, but under water it has been described as consisting of rapid drum rolls that resemble the distant sound of a pneumatic drill being driven into asphalt. It can be heard through at least twenty-five feet of water. The fish accomplishes this by rapidly vibrating the walls of its swim bladder (air bladder) by means of two special muscles attached to it. The swim bladder is apparently modified to provide a noise-making apparatus, having a peculiar shape with two hornlike extensions at the front end and a single taillike one at the rear.

Most members of the family Sciaenidae, to which the Atlantic croaker, the weakfishes, and the drums belong, are capable of producing sounds. The significance of this ability is not understood, although it may well have social import, that is, the fish may employ it to communicate with one another. Both male and female Atlantic croakers can produce sound, but the male's apparatus is more robust than the female's, and he is said to produce a louder sound. In the weakfish, only the male has the muscles necessary for noise production, or "drumming," as it is called.

The study of underwater fish sounds has become increasingly important. With the development of hydrophones for listening beneath the surface in order to detect submarines and other vessels, it became necessary to recognize those sounds made by the natural inhabitants of an area, so that they might be accurately distinguished from those made by motors and propellers. The bottom of the sea turned out to be quite a noisy place, with snapping shrimp and a number of fishes being among the loudest of all aquatic life. We now have recordings of many of these sounds.

The underslung mouth, minute barbels on either side of the lower jaw, and slight extension of the middle of the tail fin distinguish the Atlantic croaker from other members of its family. The eggs of this fish have not yet been described, but studies on the condition of ripeness in grown fish and the appearance of very small ones in different localities indicate that spawning extends from August until January on the east coast of the United States, and from October to February on the Gulf Coast. This is an unusually long reproductive season for an egg-laying fish.

Croakers are one of the principal foodfish of the Middle Atlantic States. They are also extensively caught by anglers. They average about one pound, the maximum being five or more. Croakers themselves feed mostly upon small animal life, including crustaceans, worms, bivalves, and snails.

The family Sciaenidae includes several fishes of economic importance as foodfishes. There are about 150 species in all, most of them from shallow, warm, salt water. Some species venture into colder regions, however, some into mid-ocean and some into brackish water. A few tropical species live more or less permanently in fresh water. One species, the Freshwater Drum, *Aplodinotus grunniens,* occurs in streams and lakes from Guatemala to Canada.

The Red Drum or Channel Bass, *Sciaenops ocellata,* can be most readily recognized by the round, black spot on the upper part of the base of the tail fin. This well-known food and game fish is found from New York to Texas, but exists in large numbers only south of Chesapeake Bay. The largest specimen ever caught with rod-and-reel weighed eighty-three pounds and was fifty-two inches long.

From the presence of ripe adults and the appearance of very young specimens, scientists judge that spawning takes place in the late fall and winter. In Texas the height of the reproductive season apparently falls in October. The eggs and larvae are unknown, however. The principal food of the red drum consists of shrimp, crabs, and small fishes.

The Black Drum, *Pogonias cromis,* has been known to make so much noise, when gathered in a school near a ship at anchor, that it has kept sailors awake at night. The fish's swim bladder is especially well developed, with tough, thick walls, and attached to it are special muscles which, when contracted, cause the hollow sac to vibrate, producing the sound.

DRUMMER OF THE DEEP
The common drumfish, or black drum, which dwells along the Atlantic coast of the United States, is able to produce a drumming sound by contracting the muscles of its swim bladder. Note the barbels at the bottom of the fish's lower jaw; apparently these "feelers" help it locate the worms and shellfish on which it feeds.

Some black drums are caught commercially, mostly along the coast of Texas. Their average weight is, roughly, four pounds, but specimens weighing almost 150 are known. The fish is a bottom feeder, eating various bivalves such as clams, mussels, and oysters, and also crabs, shrimp, and worms. Large black drums crush the shells of these creatures with their strong, broad, pharyngeal (throat) teeth. Undoubtedly the numerous short barbels located on the underside of the lower jaw aid in locating this bottom-dwelling food.

Spawning takes place mainly from February to May along the Gulf

Coast. Large specimens are very prolific; a forty-four-inch female contained more than five million eggs. Young black drums are marked with five wide, dark, vertical bars. These are lost during growth. Older fish are usually a uniform dusky gray although some are coppery in color.

The Gray Squeteague or Weakfish, *Cynoscion regalis,* is a popular fish both with commercial and sports fishermen. About twenty-five million pounds are taken each year by the former alone. The range of the fish extends from Massachusetts to Florida along the Atlantic coast.

The weakfish gets its name from the character of its mouth and flesh—these are quite easily torn. Its jaws appear anything but weak, however, the lower one being quite prognathous (protruding) and the upper one having two large canine teeth, or fangs. The record weakfish ever caught by rod-and-reel weighed seventeen and one-half pounds and was nearly four feet long, but the average is considerably less than this.

Like other members of its family, the weakfish produces sounds, but only the males possess the necessary apparatus to do this. They are especially noisy around spawning areas during the reproductive season. Spawning takes place from May until September. The eggs are laid some distance offshore in certain places and inshore in others. They are buoyant and hatch in one and one-half days or a little longer. Maturity is usually attained at the age of two years. Food consists of various fishes, squid, and shrimp.

Quite extensive migrations up and down the coast are made by the gray squeteague, and during cold weather they seek deeper water. The fish generally travel in large groups although they do not seem to be a schooling fish in the strict sense of the word, as are herring and mackerel.

The Spotted Squeteague, *Cynoscion nebulosis,* can be distinguished from the gray squeteague by the presence of conspicuous, round, black spots on the body and dorsal and caudal fins, and by the absence of small scales on the anal and second dorsal fins. It ranges from New York to Texas, but is rare north of Virginia. Like its more northern relative, it is an important food and game fish. It does not grow quite as large, however.

The White Sea Bass, *Cynoscion nobilis,* is not a bass at all, but is closely related to the weakfishes of the Atlantic. It is one of the most popular of all the marine game species on the Pacific coast of the United States and is also fished commercially. It reaches a length of at least five feet and a weight of eighty pounds. The record rod-and-reel catch nearly equaled this, weighing seventy-seven pounds, four ounces.

White sea bass range from southeastern Alaska to southern California. They are uncommon north of San Francisco, however. Spawning takes place from March to August. Squid, crustaceans, and various fishes make up their food.

The Red Mullet, *Mullus surmuletus,* belongs to the group of goatfishes or surmullets, family Mullidae—it is not a true mullet. You can easily recognize these fishes by their bright golden, orange, or rose colors and by the two prominent fleshy barbels that hang down from the lower jaw. The great majority of the forty or so species range between eight and sixteen inches in length. Some are esteemed foodfishes. They inhabit the shores of all tropical seas, sometimes entering brackish or fresh water. A few species, such as the red mullet, are found in cool temperate waters.

We find red mullet from the Mediterranean Sea to Norway. They occupy the more northerly parts of their range during the warmer months. Their eggs are laid during the spring and summer to float in the open sea, and are slightly more than one thirty-second of an inch in diameter; they hatch in about one week. Like other goatfishes, the red mullet seeks its food on the bottom, apparently using its barbels to detect the mollusks, crustaceans, and worms upon which it feeds. It reaches a length of about fifteen inches.

This fish has been used for food since ancient times. The Romans sometimes paid fabulous prices for large specimens: one fish was equal to a slave in value, or even roughly equivalent to its own weight in silver. Red mullets were paraded around Roman banquet halls so that the guests might watch the beautiful play of colors over their bodies as they died. They were also kept in fishponds as pets, and it is reported that one wealthy fancier showed much more concern over the health of his fish than that of his slaves.

The Leaffish, *Monocirrhus polyacanthus,* drifts idly through the water, looking for all the world like a dead leaf. Its compressed body is roughly leaf-shaped, and is colored tan or brown with appropriate mottlings, making it an excellent mimic of a leaf that has died and fallen from some bush or tree into the water. To complete the illusion, the fish has a single stout barbel on its chin that appears exactly like the dead leaf's stem. The pectoral fins and the rear portion of the dorsal and anal fins are so transparent that they are practically invisible. By vibrating these, the fish can glide through the water, seemingly propelled by imperceptible forces.

Sometimes the leaffish lies motionless on its side, but more often it rests quietly upright with its head lower than its tail. When some likely fish strays into its vicinity, the leaffish stalks it until close enough. Then, with a sudden dart, accompanied by the opening and closing of its great mouth, the larger fish completely engulfs the smaller one.

IT MIMICS A DEAD LEAF

It is hard to tell the leaffish from a dead leaf; its brownish, leaf-sized body glides through the water much the way a leaf drifts, seemingly without effort. The smaller fish it stalks usually does not realize the enemy is at hand until escape is no longer possible.

The eggs of leaffish are attached to plants or stones by small individual stalks. They are fanned and guarded by one of the parents until they hatch, that is, for about three days. Leaffish inhabit the fresh waters of northern South America. They reach a length of about three and one-half inches.

Leaffish are members of the family Nandidae, a small group of freshwater fishes with a most peculiar geographical distribution. In India, southeastern Asia and the East Indies there are five or six species, in west Africa there is one, and in northern South America and Trinidad there are two or three species, of which one or two are leaffishes. Scientists have been puzzled as to how this group of primarily fresh-water inhabitants came to occupy three such widely isolated localities. The larger species, which are from Asia and reach a length of about eight inches, are used for food. Among these Asiatic forms, two or three are occasionally found in brackish water.

The Archer Fish, *Toxotes jaculatrix,* shoots its prey with drops of water. (It must have been named long ago, because the drops it shoots are more like bullets than arrows.) This fish cruises about the surface until it spots some likely insect resting on a leaf or bank near the water, then carefully maneuvers into position, pokes its mouth up out of the water and squirts a series of well-aimed drops of water at the intended prey, usually knocking it into the water with the first few aquatic "bullets." Up to distances of four feet archer fish are almost one hundred per cent accurate. Large specimens—they reach lengths of eight to ten inches—can propel water as far as twelve feet.

On the outside, the archer fish gives us no clue as to how it performs these remarkable feats of markmanship. Although its body shape is characteristic, it has no prolonged snout or other obvious apparatus for spitting water. Its mouth is not large and is angled downwards quite sharply, but is not very different from that of many other fishes that never expel drops of water. Its eyes are large but unspecialized.

Only when we examine the inside of the mouth do we discover the water-propelling mechanism. Running along the roof of the mouth is a narrow groove. The tongue is quite mobile and can be raised to fit against this, thus making a thin straight tube. Through this the fish forces water by quickly clapping down its gill-covers. The tip of the tongue probably acts as a valve.

The accuracy of this waterborne artillerist is truly marvelous, considering the complicating factors of refraction and distortion. The fish keeps its eyes under water while shooting and therefore must compensate for the change in direction of light rays as they pass from air into water, as well as the deformations resulting from ripples and other disturbances of the water's surface.

Archer fish eat water as well as land creatures. They live in fresh and brackish waters, usually near the coast, of southeastern Asia from India to the Philippines. Nothing is known of their reproductive habits except that they undoubtedly lay eggs and that newly hatched young are seen in May around Bangkok, Thailand. There are eight different species of archer fishes, all hailing from southeastern Asia, Australia, and the islands of the southwest Pacific. They comprise the family Toxotidae.

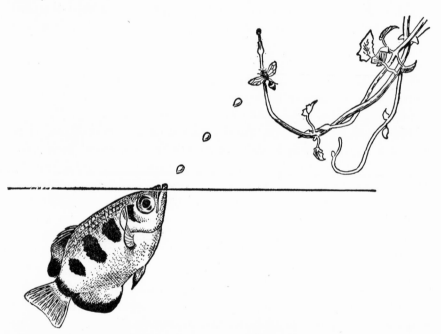

AN ARCHER OF UNUSUAL SKILL

The archer fish is one of the most extraordinary members of the animal kingdom—it actually brings down its prey with a missile. The victim, an insect on a leaf or a nearby bank, is toppled from its resting place by carefully aimed drops of water squirted from the fish's mouth. Seldom does the archer fish miss its mark.

Climbing Perch, Fighting Fishes, and Their Relatives

IF YOU NEVER KNEW IT before, by now you have observed that the fish world is far from humdrum. Its unexpected marvels startle the imagination. Once you take a close look at the fishes, you simply have to revise most of your fixed opinions about them. Even that standard symbol of helplessness, "a fish out of water," will not hold up against some of the strange realities to be told about in this chapter—fishes that are actually wayfarers on the land.

Most fishes, we have seen, are dependent on the gases dissolved in the water in which they live. They breathe by absorbing these gases into the blood stream as the water passes around their gills. But the fishes in this group often do perfectly well with the air outside the water. They possess an extra breathing device—a pair of chambers above their gills. Some of these fishes have in the chambers a labyrinth-like series of plates, and it is for these that the order was named Labyrinthici.

Because they can breathe the air directly, these fishes manage to exist in places too warm or foul for the great majority of other fishes. We often find them in swamps, small ponds, ditches, and rice paddies —in the fresh waters of tropical Africa, southeastern Asia, the East Indies, and the Philippines. Most average less than a foot in length. The larger species of the labyrinths—that is what we call the members of this order—are used for food.

The climbing perch, paradise fishes, various gouramis, and the Siamese fighting fish and other bettas belong to the family Anabantidae (this name comes from a word meaning "to go up," and most of these fishes do just that when getting a gulp of air). Some of its fifty or more species are popular tenants of the home aquarium. They are wonderful in many ways, not the least being the ritual that surrounds the laying of their eggs and the rearing of their young. Males of the Siamese fighting fish, the paradise fishes, and most of the gouramis make a floating nest of bubbles to hold the eggs. The giant gourami goes further—it builds a nest of plants. By comparison, the climbing perch appears indifferent, for it lays floating eggs and does not care for them in any way. But the Cape kurper of South Africa guards its adhesive eggs, which are laid on stones or other submerged objects. In two or three species of bettas we find an odd quirk indeed: the males carry the eggs in their mouths until hatching.

Floating eggs are the rule with the snakeheads. The males of this group (family Ophicephalidae, with about thirty different species) forsake their otherwise savage habits at breeding time to stand guard over the eggs. The snakeheads are the largest of all the labyrinths; they rather resemble the North American bowfin in appearance, and one or two species grow as long as four feet. Much smaller is the pikelike *Luciocephalus pulcher* (a single species comprises the family Luciocephalidae). It is only about seven inches long, and dwells in southeastern Asia and the East Indies. We believe it to be a mouthbreeder—that is, to carry its eggs and young in its mouth.

The Climbing Perch, *Anabas testudineus,* is often brought alive to market in a basket and can be kept alive out of water for a whole day, simply by sprinkling it with a little water from time to time. The fish breathes air by means of a pair of special cavities, located over the gill chambers and containing a series of thin, bony plates, arranged more or less in circles with a common center. These plates are covered with a membrane that is provided with a good supply of blood; through them the fish gets its oxygen. Ordinary gills are also present, but are so reduced in size that the fish drowns if kept under water. It must regularly come to the surface to take a gulp of air.

Not only can the climbing perch live out of water, but it sometimes voluntarily leaves its aquatic home to travel overland. It does this by extending its gill-covers out to the side and then flopping alternately to the left and right. The gill covers with their backwardly projecting spines prop the fish in a partly erect position and are alternately stuck into the ground, acting somewhat like a pair of short crutches as the fish hitches along. In spite of its jerky, ungraceful mode of getting about on land, the climbing perch can travel considerable distances—it has been known to cover three hundred feet in about thirty minutes.

Although its name would indicate otherwise, the climbing perch very rarely ascends the trunks of trees. Its overland trips are apparently made to find new or better bodies of water in which to live.

PORTRAIT OF A FISH OUT OF WATER

The climbing perch, a native of Asia and Africa, is a renowned land traveler. ɪᴛ possesses special breathing equipment which permits it to leave the water and journey overland in quest of a new place to live. To move about, the fish has unusual gill covers, which it uses much like crutches.

The climbing perch inhabits all sorts of fresh waters in southeastern Asia from southern China to India, and in Ceylon, the Philippines and the islands of the East Indies. Feeding principally on insects, shrimps, and snails, it grows to be a little more than nine inches long. It is an important foodfish in many parts of the Orient. Climbing perch lay floating eggs, and the parents take no care of them. Other species of climbing perches are found throughout much of Africa.

The Giant Gourami, *Osphronemus goramy,* has been widely transplanted through much of the tropical Far East. So widely, in fact, that no one is sure just where the species originated—perhaps China was its natural home or perhaps it was first found in southeastern Asia and the East Indies. At any rate it is at present one of the most important fresh-water foodfish in southern Asia from India to China, where it is extensively cultured in ponds.

Pondfish culture is an excellent way of obtaining cheap and palatable food of high protein content. This fact has only gradually been recognized and put into practice in Africa and North and South America. On the other hand, pondfish culture has been of great economic importance for some time in the Orient and in parts of the Middle East and Europe. In the United States of Indonesia alone there are at least three hundred thousand acres of fishponds, and in Poland there were perhaps two hundred thousand acres before the second World War.

The giant gourami attains a length of at least two feet and a weight of twenty pounds. It is primarily a vegetarian, but eats a good deal of animal matter if available. Being an airbreather, it can inhabit waters that are quite warm and stagnant.

Spawning may occur the year 'round. Male and female select some spot along the edge of their pool or some rocky crevice to use as a point of anchorage, and construct about it a nest made of aquatic plants. With their mouths they gather plants, carry them to the nesting area, and form them into a rather elaborate structure not unlike a bird's nest. Its shape varies, but it always has an opening on one of its lower sides. Its maximum dimensions are approximately twelve by fifteen inches, and it rests about six inches beneath the surface. Nest making occupies from a week to a month. Finally the female spawns, lying on her side while doing so. As many as two thousand lemon-yellow, buoyant eggs, a little less than one-eighth of an inch in diameter, are laid in the nest and then covered over with nesting material.

Both parents guard the nest, taking turns in watching it and circulating water around it by fanning with their fins. Hatching occurs in ten to fifteen days. The young are about three-sixteenths of an inch long when they first emerge from the eggs and float upside down at the surface. After two days they sink to the bottom, but remain belly upward. By the fourth or fifth day they are able to swim upright.

The Siamese Fighting Fish, *Betta splendens,* has been selectively bred for fighting and endurance by the Siamese for the past century. Other strains of this fish have been selectively bred by the Siamese and breeders in other nations for large fins and beautiful colors. The results of these two lines of endeavor are distinct types of fish, so different that at first glance they appear to belong to entirely separate species, although they can still interbreed.

Fighting fish that have been bred for fighting qualities are practically identical in appearance with the wild fish from which they were originally derived. Adult males, which are the fighters, reach a maximum length of about two and one-half inches. They are short-finned creatures, dull brown in color except when displaying before a female or threatening another male. Then they show the most gorgeous array of reds, golds, blues and blacks, all delicately intermixed in a subtle yet definite pattern.

Wild fighting fish are pugnacious, and if two males are placed together in a tank, they will fight for perhaps as long as fifteen minutes. Specially bred fighting males, however, often fight continuously, with only brief respites in order to breathe, for as long as three hours, and they have been known to keep up a combat for as long as six hours before one of the adversaries finally refused to carry on the battle any further. The fish attack one another with their small sharp teeth, tearing each other's fins and scales. The Siamese "fight" these fish like gamecocks; such contests have been popular sporting events in Thailand for several hundred years.

In contrast to the fighting strains, those fish bred for beautiful colors and shapely fins have lost some of their ability to do battle. Instead, the large males exhibit great, flowing dorsal, caudal, and anal fins that are sometimes longer than their bodies. Their colors include red, maroon, blue, green, and cream. Even in these showy strains, however, the females are quite uninteresting in color and fins.

Wild Siamese fighting fish are found in ponds, ditches and other sluggish waters throughout Thailand. They feed on animal life, principally small fresh-water crustaceans and insect larvae. They are said to be invaluable destroyers of larval mosquitoes. In Bangkok there are people who raise mosquitoes in order to sell the larvae to the numerous breeders of fighting fish there. Like other members of its group, the Siamese fighting fish is an air-breather and is thus capable of living in quite foul water or in very close quarters in captivity.

The male Siamese fighting fish builds a floating nest of froth by blowing innumerable small, sticky bubbles that cling together at the surface of the water. Male and female embrace under the nest, at which time a few eggs are laid. These are heavier than water, and as they sink the male swoops down, picks them up in his mouth, carries them up to the nest and places them among the bubbles. This procedure is repeated many times until two to seven hundred eggs are laid.

The male now stands guard beneath his froth raft, repairing it, driving other fish, including the female, away from it, and replacing any eggs that may fall out of it. When the young are hatched—in about 30 hours at 80° Fahrenheit—he replaces any of these, too, that tumble out of the nest. In a few days the young can swim well enough to leave their floating cradle, putting the parent's duties at an end. In captivity males are capable of breeding every three days for short periods of time; in nature they undoubtedly breed several times during a year. Occasionally in captivity, a female turns up who drives the male away from the nest after spawning and then takes charge of the eggs in truly masculine fashion—for fishes, that is.

The life span of the Siamese fighting fish in nature is about two years.

The Snakehead, *Ophicephalus striatus,* is sometimes fished with a knife. During the dry season, when the water of their pond or swamp evaporates, snakeheads go down into the mud and await the return of the rains. Siamese fishermen wade into the stiff mud and with their knives cut it away in layers in search of these fish.

Found in many places, from China and the Philippines to India and Ceylon, including the East Indies, snakeheads are among the most esteemed foodfish in the Orient. Because of their hardiness and ability to live out of the water, they are frequently brought to market in baskets. In countries where refrigeration is a rarity, such fish are a blessing. They offer plenty to eat, too—they frequently reach a length of thirty inches, more rarely three feet.

The snakehead is a tough, resourceful fish, and its undershot jaw makes it appear as tough as it really is. With its capacious, strong-jawed mouth it attacks and feeds upon a wide variety of living creatures, including fishes, frogs, snakes, and insects. Its stocky but elongated body is wriggled snake-fashion, when the fish progresses over the ground. If the skin and breathing apparatus—which consists of a pair of chambers well supplied with blood vessels and located above the gill cavities—are kept moist, snakeheads can live out of water for a number of months, depending on their stored fat for food.

In preparation for spawning, an area in shallow water is cleared of vegetation. The eggs are amber colored and about one-sixteenth of an inch in diameter. They float at the surface, hatching in about three days. The male guards both the eggs and the young fish. The latter remain at the surface for a day, then make periodic trips to the bottom for about another month before they take up life permanently at or near the bottom, coming to the top regularly to take a gulp of air and occasionally to snap up some unsuspecting animal there.

Although they are usually valuable as a source of food, snakeheads are pests in some places. Once they have gotten into a pond of fishes they proceed to destroy all of them, and having done so, move overland to another body of water. In India, fish culturists have to erect small fences around their fish ponds to keep marauding snakeheads out. A Formosan species was introduced into Japan and has proved most harmful to the native fishes.

Butterfly Fishes and Angel Fishes

THE SALT-WATER BUTTERFLY FISHES and their relatives are among the brightest, most strikingly colored of all fishes. Indeed, they seem to be aquatic copies of the lovely insects after which they were named. It is in coastal waters and around coral reefs that we are apt to encounter these fishes.

Wide from back to belly, and narrow from side to side, they are covered with small scales which extend onto the dorsal, anal, and tail fins. They have well-developed spines in the fins, and the ventral fins are located under or slightly in front of the pectorals.

These flat-bodied creatures have only a small mouth, and usually the teeth bear several cusps, being tiny and bristle-like in many instances—hence their scientific name, Order Chaetodontoidei, which means "spiny toothed." When small, the young usually pass through a peculiar stage: the head is armed with bony plates. There are well over two hundred different species; the majority dwell in the East and West Indies and around other tropical islands, one or two species venturing into brackish water.

The butterfly fishes (family Chaetodontidae) and the angel fishes (family Pomacanthidae) are the typical members of the order and include the vast majority of the species. The angel fishes are generally larger, reaching two feet in length. They are used for food in certain places.

We must travel to the far side of the world to meet some other members of this order. The scats (they make up the family Scatophagidae) regularly live in brackish and fresh water as well as salt, from the Red Sea through the Indian and western Pacific oceans as far north as Japan, as far south as Australia. The largest of the eight species attain a length of about one foot. In the more tropical part of their range we find their exotic relatives, the Moorish idols. The stout beak, the long, scimitar-shaped dorsal fin, and bold, vertical black, yellow, and white bands quickly distinguish them from all other fishes. There are only two species of these bright-hued creatures (family Zanclidae). The spadefishes (they form the family Ephippidae) occur in shallow, tropical, and warm-temperate seas, in the western Atlantic, with two or three in the eastern Pacific and one in the Indo-Pacific region. There are two or three other small families of Indo-Pacific fishes in this order.

The Foureye Butterfly Fish, *Chaetodon capistratus,* frequents coral reefs and adjacent areas from Panama to Florida and Bermuda. Strays are occasionally found as far north as Massachusetts; these are almost always young specimens that have been carried there by the Gulf Stream.

Strongly contrasted with the delicate yellow of this fish is the black band running vertically through its eye, the black eye itself, and the large black spot just beneath the rear portion of the dorsal fin. The latter, of course, is what gives the fish its name. Young individuals have a broad dusky area instead of this spot. A length of six inches is attained.

The Spadefish, *Chaetodipterus faber,* has a deep body that is quite narrow from side to side, being very similar to the angel fishes in this regard. It has, however, two dorsal fins and these immediately distinguish it from them. Its coloration ranges from almost white to almost black, but usually consists of about five black vertical bars on a silvery gray background.

Spadefish have been taken along the Atlantic coast from Cape Cod to southern Brazil. They are only summer visitors north of Florida, and north of Chesapeake Bay they are rare at any time. The only exception to this is Bermuda, into whose warm waters spadefish have been introduced by man, and where they live all year 'round. Spadefish are regularly used for food, but do not usually enter markets north of Panama. They reach a length of three feet and a weight of ten pounds.

The one-sixteenth-inch buoyant eggs are laid during late spring and summer. Hatching occurs in one day at 80° Fahrenheit, and the newly hatched young are a little less than one-eighth of an inch long. When less than an inch long, they are jet-black with completely transparent fins and they deceptively resemble the blackened pods of mangrove trees that are present in the water in some places at the same time the young spadefish are. This resemblance is greatly enhanced by the behavior of the fish, which allow themselves to be rolled in gentle surf just as the inert pods are moved about by the ebbing and flowing water.

Surgeon Fishes: Creatures with Dangerous Tails

THE SURGEON, or doctor, fishes and the tangs carry curious weapons, to which they owe their names. On each side of the base of the tail they bear a sharp spine. These spines are shaped like a surgeon's lancet, and the fish can point them forward and outward, to gash or maim other fishes as it swims by. Appropriately enough, the order is known as Acanthuroidei ("spiny tails"). However, in some species the spines are replaced by flat, bony plates.

Not quite one hundred species are known, inhabitants of tropical seas, frequently around reefs. All belong to the family Acanthuridae. Some species are brilliantly colored. A few have a grotesque horn growing straight forward out of the forehead, giving them the name "unicorn fish." In fishes of this order the body is somewhat flattened from side to side and is covered with fine scales. There are numerous spines in the fins, and the pelvic fins are located well forward. The teeth are chisel-like and the mouth small.

The Doctor Fish, *Acanthurus hepatus,* is equipped with a razor-sharp spine on either side of the base of its tail fin. These lancet-like structures can be raised and directed forward, in which position they are formidable weapons. The fish inflicts deep wounds by coming alongside another fish and sideswiping it as it passes by. Doctor fish can also badly cut the hands of an incautious fisherman ignorant of its hidden weapons.

This is a common fish in the West Indies and occurs south to Brazil. North of Florida, with the exception of Bermuda, it exists only as an occasional straggler. It reaches a length of about ten inches. It feeds almost entirely on vegetable matter, mostly marine algae, having teeth well developed for browsing. Swimming is largely accomplished by "rowing" movements of the pectoral fins, the tail being used only in times of stress.

The young are almost completely transparent and drift with the floating creatures of the surface of the sea. Depending on when they are carried inshore, these larval fish, which may be only three-eighths of an inch long at this time, leave their floating life and take up a more or less bottom existence. At the same time they start to transform into adult-like fish, completing the change in only two days.

Demoiselles and Cichlids
—Colorful and Clever

A<small>NYONE</small> who believes fish to be stupid creatures that just swim around, performing their life functions in a dull, uninteresting manner—whose only "cleverness" lies in their ability to escape the hook or net—should make the acquaintance of the remarkable demoiselles and cichlids of the order Chromides.

Here are fishes with complex and adaptable behavior patterns that are truly amazing. Many of them show a sense of proprietorship, appropriating some underwater place as their very own. Their complicated courtships and the teamwork they use in bringing up their families remind one of animals like dogs or birds, usually thought to be much higher in the evolutionary scale. A few live in partnership with deadly sea anemones. It is fortunate that some of them can easily be kept in home aquaria, where their astonishing activities may be watched firsthand.

The demoiselles (family Pomacentridae) are small, tropical, saltwater fishes, in general brightly colored, and usually inhabiting coral reefs and tide pools. So far as is known, their eggs are always guarded by at least one of the parents. The Beau-gregory, garibaldi and clownfish are demoiselles.

The cichlids (family Cichlidae) are tropical fresh-water fishes, although several species spend a good deal of time in brackish water and a few can live for extended periods in sea water. Approximately six hundred species are known. In the Western Hemisphere, they are found from Texas south through Central America and most of South America and also on some islands of the West Indies. They are most numerous in Africa; for example, there are 178 different species in Lake Nyasa alone. Only two species occur in Asia, the chromides from southern India and Ceylon. The members of this family range in size up to nearly two feet, but most species grow to be less than half as long. Nearly one hundred kinds of cichlids have been imported into Europe and North America at one time or another as aquarium fishes for fish fanciers.

Our knowledge of the intricate reproductive behavior of these fishes is based mostly on observations of captive specimens. Some kind of parental care is always in evidence. Frequently the male and female cooperate, both sharing—although sometimes unequally—in the tasks of preparing a site on which the eggs are laid, in guarding and cleaning the eggs, in transferring the hatching eggs or newly hatched young to specially prepared pits, in herding the young about, and in guarding them and putting them to bed in a pit at night. Sometimes the male alone assumes these responsibilities; in a few species, the female alone does so. A good deal of individuality is also shown, and the fish often modify their behavior to meet the different situations they encounter.

The demoiselles and cichlids are distinguished from all other perchlike fishes by having a single nasal opening on each side of the snout—all other spiny-rayed fishes have two on each side. They also have characteristics of bony structure shared only with the Holoconti (sea perches) and Pharyngognathi (wrasses and parrot fishes).

The Beau-gregory, *Eupomacentrus leucostictus,* takes possession of a bit of territory at the bottom of the shallow sea or in some tide-pool and defends it against all comers, particularly other members of the same species. When a number of Beau-gregories are kept together in an aquarium, they kill one another off until there are few enough fish that each one is able to have a territory of its own. Only then does the killing cease.

In nature each territory usually includes some shell, nook, or cranny into which the Beau-gregory retires during the night and from which the fish sallies forth in daylight to feed or to chase away some intruder. During the breeding season, which extends from late spring throughout the summer, similar or identical places are employed as nests to shelter the eggs, which the male Beau-gregory guards and cleans with constant care.

Not only natural shelters—such as the shells of conchs and bivalves, or the under surfaces of coral rocks and coral-like sea-fans—are utilized as nests, but a tin can, bottle or perhaps an abandoned shovel may provide some male with a home site. As many as four different female Beau-gregories may lay their eggs in the nest of a single male. The eggs are shaped like tiny, bright-yellow, gelatin capsules, about one thirty-second of an inch long, and are attached by one of their small ends to the shell, rock, etc., by a tuft of fine hairs. Hatching takes place in about five days, the larvae being somewhat less than one-eighth of an inch long.

Immature Beau-gregories have numerous bright blue spots on the forward part of the back; these are gradually lost as they grow up. The lower rear portion of the body is bright yellow. Adult males are generally larger than females, reaching about six inches, and they are more intensely colored. In captivity their deep bluish-black and brilliant orange-yellow coloration fades quite a bit. It has been shown that this color depends upon the fish's diet. If it does not obtain quantities of the algae upon which it naturally feeds, it loses its rich colors to some extent. Nevertheless, Beau-gregories seem to thrive on the unnatural, all-meat diet provided for them in aquariums.

An occasional Beau-gregory has straggled as far north as Maine, but the normal range of the species includes Bermuda, Florida and the West Indies.

The Garibaldi, *Hypsypops rubicunda,* has its entire body and all of its fins colored a bright orange-red, only its black-and-cream eyes being different. Young ones, however, are entirely unlike adults; up to a size of about one and one-half inches they show numerous spots of scintillating blue, contrasting strongly with an orange or scarlet background. As they get older, the spots gradually disappear and the bright, background color becomes dull and brownish, and by the time they are two inches long the fishes are quite drab in appearance. Finally, with the attainment of maturity, the characteristic bright colors develop.

Accompanying these decisive changes in color are equally radical changes in behavior. The very small, brightly colored garibaldis live on rocky reefs where grow several species of algae which shine with a similar metallic blue. The dull, half-grown fish hide most of the time, in contrast to the brilliant adults who frequently display themselves, as if advertising their presence, over their home territories, which they defend staunchly against other fish, especially other garibaldis.

In general shape, the body of the garibaldi is similar to that of the sunfish—to which it is not at all closely related, however. The species grows to a length of about fourteen inches and is probably the largest member of its family. It is found around rocky shores on the Pacific coast of North America from Point Conception to northern Baja California. It feeds upon crustaceans and seaweed. Although they do well in aquariums, captive garibaldis generally lose their bright color, and become a pale lemon-yellow.

The Clownfish, *Amphiprion percula,* lives in partnership with giant sea anemones. These creatures of the genera *Stoichactis* and *Discosoma* may have a diameter of sixteen to twenty-four inches, and are attached to the bottom by a fleshy base. At the center is the mouth and surrounding this along the edges are hundreds of tentacles, armed with thousands of stinging cells. Woe betide any small fish coming too close to these deadly arms, for it is quickly stung to death and then carried to the anemone's mouth to be eaten.

Clownfish, however, live within the area surrounded by these tentacles with impunity. Although other fishes and small animals are killed by the anemones, when a clownfish darts among these sting-bearing tentacles, they curl away and do it no harm. Even when clownfish brush up against the tentacles, they are not stung. Whenever clownfish are alarmed, they flee to the protection of their anemone; they also apparently spend their nights amidst the tentacles.

The anemones also profit by this association. Whenever a clownfish comes upon a piece of food too large to be consumed on the spot, it brings the morsel to its anemone and usually shares the food with it. According to some observers, the clownfish also cleans the anemone, aerates it by circulating water around it, and makes the anemone expand by rubbing its tentacles, presumably improving its condition. On the other hand, clownfish occasionally feed upon their anemones to a limited extent.

Clownfish are widely distributed from India through the East Indies to Queensland, the Philippines and the islands of the Pacific. In most of these regions they have been seen associated with giant anemones, as many as seven clownfish being taken from a single anemone. Clownfish can exist perfectly well, however, without an anemone partner—in captivity at least, where their peculiar pattern of brilliant colors and their engaging ways have made them most popular. They reach a length of three and one-half inches, and are bright orange, with three white bands bordered in black running vertically across the back of the head, the middle of the body, and the base of the tail. The fins are bordered with white and black.

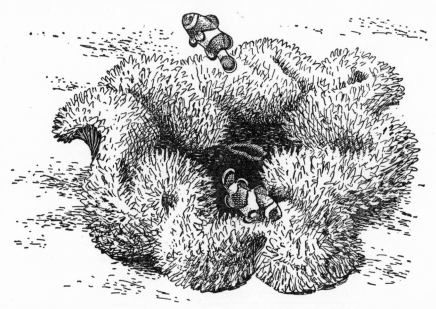

A STRANGE PARTNERSHIP

Clownfish are interesting little creatures, drolly costumed in orange, black, and white. Like the two pictured above, they make their home inside a creature known as the giant sea anemone, which looks like a plant but is actually an animal with poisonous tentacles. The clownfish share their food with the anemone in exchange for the safe shelter it affords them. Their eggs are also laid near the protecting anemone.

The nest of the clownfish is usually located very close to an anemone, and the fish may direct the stinging tentacles of its partner so that they cover the nest site. The spot is well cleaned and the peculiarly shaped eggs are attached to it in a single layer. The eggs are cylindrical in shape with rounded ends. Both parents cooperate in caring for their spawn, the male performing the greater part of the actual care of the eggs. For seven to ten days he watches over them, cleaning them with his mouth. Meanwhile the female, which may be twice as large as her mate, usually remains in the vicinity.

The newly hatched larvae travel to the water surface where they float with other creatures for about two weeks. At first they are about three-sixteenths of an inch long and gray in color. Within two weeks they have started to assume the color pattern of the adult, and at this time they drop to the bottom to search for an anemone of their own. Clownfish are quite prolific. One captive pair had sixteen broods within eight months. In nature, reproduction takes place during most of the year.

The Black-chinned Mouthbreeder, *Tilapia macrocephala,* leads a complicated home life of the kind usually associated with creatures much higher than fishes in the evolutionary scale. These fish pair off, the male and female courting each other by nodding their heads, puffing out their throats or quivering in view of each other, and by chasing, nipping, or slapping each other with their tails. The female courts more vigorously than does the male.

As time for spawning approaches a nest is constructed by scooping out a round or oval depression in the bottom and cleaning it most carefully. The female, too, is the more active nest-builder. Then the pair begins to swim over the nest, the female in front of the male, in what might for a while be called false spawning activity, and finally about fifty large eggs are laid and fertilized. These are not spherical but assume a variety of shapes, averaging somewhat more than one-sixteenth of an inch in their greatest dimension.

Soon after the eggs have been laid, the male approaches the nest and picks the eggs up with his mouth. If he delays in doing this, the female nips him violently and slaps him vigorously with her tail. In rare instances the male still refuses to take over his parental duties, and at last the female herself picks up the eggs. If the male is small, there may be too many eggs for his mouth, and the female will then take into hers those that are left over.

The eggs generally hatch in five days, but the young are carried in the parent's mouth from two to fifteen days longer. Once they have been released, the young are no longer cared for in any way. While carrying eggs or young, the parent fish does not feed, but more or less continuously churns its offspring about.

The black-chinned mouthbreeder is a native of tropical west Africa, where it inhabits both fresh and brackish waters, principally swamps and lagoons. It sometimes reaches a length of about twelve inches. Its general appearance is not indicative of any strange behavior nor is its light olive coloration very striking. A series of irregular black spots around the head, especially the lower jaw, is responsible for its name

Among the numerous species of cichlids that are mouthbreeders, several different patterns of behavior are shown. In many *Tilapia*, the baby fish are released from the female's mouth to forage under her watchful care, returning to her mouth in times of disturbance and at night. This is also true of the large genus *Haplochromis*, of which the Egyptian mouthbreeder of home aquaria is a member. In certain South American cichlids, the eggs are apparently not carried in the mouth, although the young are. Among these species the male alone does the carrying.

THE BLACK-CHINNED MOUTHBREEDER—AN AFRICAN CURIOSITY

The black-chinned mouthbreeder hatches its eggs in its mouth. After these curious fish have scooped out a nest in the bottom, the female lays her eggs in it. Like the male shown here, the father must promptly pick them up in his mouth or else the female will buffet him soundly with her tail. For the one or two weeks the father carries his eggs about, he does not eat a single morsel of food.

The Scalare or Freshwater Angel Fish, *Pterophyllum eimekei,* is, next to the guppy, the best known of all the small tropical fishes kept as pets. Its stately appearance and unusual hardiness in captivity have made it a favorite with fanciers, and its responsiveness to expert care for regular breeding under controlled conditions has kept it popular with professional fish culturists. When scalares were first imported, small ones sold for as much as ten dollars each, but they are now commercially bred in such large numbers that they are often priced as low as twenty-five cents.

Native to the Amazon Basin and the Guianas, scalares inhabit shallow, quiet streams and backwaters that are well supplied with aquatic vegetation. The fish reach lengths of five to six inches. They are quite narrow from side to side and quite deep from back to belly. The pectoral fins are each drawn out into a fine ray that may be half again as long as the fish itself, and the tail fin has a long ray at its top and bottom. These, and the high, sail-like dorsal fin, give the fish a most elegant appearance, which is not belied by its deliberate and graceful movements. The color is silvery, with four vertical black bands.

The eggs of the scalare are laid on the leaves of aquatic plants or on the more or less vertical sides of stones. Both parents care for their eggs and young.

Sea-Perch—Spectacular Live-Bearing Fish

OFF THE Pacific coast of North America dwells an interesting and important group of fishes, the sea-perch. Every year, fishermen draw over one hundred tons of them from shallow waters, from Baja California to Alaska. We also find them in fairly deep sea water, and Chinese and Japanese fishermen look for them off their coasts. One species, too, lives in streams in California. So, although sea-perch are most at home in shallow coastal waters, we see that they have adapted themselves to varying places and conditions.

The most striking thing about the sea-perch is the way it bears its young. Unlike most other fishes, it brings its offspring into the world alive, not in the form of eggs. The mother fish may carry her unborn babies in her body quite a while, and they may be remarkably mature at birth. That is why scientists named this order Holoconti ("born whole"). Such young fishes have relatively few problems of survival.

An adult sea-perch may be five to eighteen inches in length, depending on its species. (There are twenty-five in the family Embiotocidae, which makes up the order.) The lips are thick and fleshy. Pelvic fins are close behind the pectorals, and some of the fins have spines. A good help in identification is the furrow on each side of the base of the dorsal fin.

The Shiner Sea-perch, *Cymatogaster aggregatus,* brings forth its young alive—and in such an advanced condition that within two days of birth the young males are courting females and mating with them. In other words, baby male shiner sea-perch are already sexually mature when born! This has been proved not only by their obviously adult behavior, but also by microscopic examination of their sex glands, which shows that they are in a condition comparable to those in large, old males.

Shiner sea-perch are quite ordinary-appearing fish with compressed, elliptical bodies and rather fleshy lips. They are predominantly silver in color, darker on the back than on the belly. Males are almost black during the winter and spring. They are smaller than the females, reaching a length of not quite five inches, while females exceed six inches occasionally. If the anal fin of the male is examined closely, the small, masculine genital organ can be seen at the anterior edge.

From April to July, shiner sea-perch appear in shallow waters from southern California to Alaska both to deliver their young and to mate for the next year's offspring. The eggs within the female are not fertilized until midwinter, however; the male sexual secretion remains dormant within the female's reproductive tract until that time. The eggs are extremely minute, being slightly more than one one-hundredth of an inch in diameter. Yet these tiny eggs develop into baby fish that are more than one and one-fourth inches long at birth. This great increase in size is made possible by the feeding of the developing embryo within the mother's ovary. The embryonic fish at first feed through a gill-opening by means of microscopic, hair-like cilia that produce a current by rhythmically waving, and carry down into the embryo's digestive tract the more or less liquid nourishment in which the developing fish floats. This nourishment is provided by the walls of the ovary, which secrete a special substance and which also periodically shed part of themselves into the ovarian fluid. The specially produced liquid, the part of the ovarian walls shed into it, and excess sperm are all consumed by the embryonic shiner sea-perch.

For five to six months the fish grow inside their mother. As they get larger they become packed quite tightly within the ovary. A six-inch female usually has about sixteen offspring in a brood, each of which is about one-sixth as long as she is. As many as thirty-six young have been counted in a single litter, however. Newly born females are not as well developed as males; nevertheless they give birth to their first brood when just one year old.

The food of the shiner sea-perch consists principally of small crustaceans and other invertebrates.

Several other species of sea-perch are more important economically than is the shiner sea-perch. A goodly number of the latter are brought to market, however. In all, about three hundred thousand pounds of various sea-perch are caught commercially each year in the United States, while several species are popular anglers' fishes.

Wrasses and Parrot Fishes
—Dwellers of the Coral Reefs

IT IS in the warm waters of tropical seas around the world that we are most likely to find the gorgeously colored creatures known as wrasses and parrot fishes. Here they swarm around coral reefs and gather in large numbers in coastal areas. Strange, vivid fishes, they are among the most flamboyant yet beautiful of things that live in the water.

It is no easy matter to observe the ways of the wrasses and parrot fishes in these faraway places, and many of their habits still remain an unopened book to us. If we could watch these dwellers of the coral

A CORAL REEF — GARDEN OF THE SEA

Coral reefs, found in the warmer seas, are strange underwater wonderlands of incredibly varied forms of life. The corals themselves are small, primitive animals which grow attached to one another in colonies, sometimes of great size. Their stony skeletons are also joined together in a shape and pattern which varies according to the species. Over the ages these skeletal masses build up, one on top of the other, until they reach the ocean surface or above it, forming coral reefs and coral islands. The coral masses shown here *(center)* are still small, but already they form a setting in which many different kinds of creatures live together. An octopus lurks in a crevice *(bottom left)*, and a starfish *(bottom extreme right)* creeps along the bottom. Next to it there is a "brain" coral colony. In the background, the large yellow shapes are sea fans; horny, fan-shaped colonies of tiny animals, they wave gently to the flow of undersea currents. Small queen angel fish, rainbow-hued parrot fish, and trigger fish swarm about this coral reef.

reefs up close, we would see some fascinating happenings, however. For example, we might behold some of the razor fishes—a kind of wrasse—building cone-shaped mounds of coral fragments with a central crater in which they would later bury themselves to hide from enemies. Perhaps they use these retreats as nests, too, but we are not sure.

We might, too, see other wrasses patiently wedging seaweed into rocky crevices. This is no aimless activity—the fishes are actually building nests to lay their eggs in. The eggs of these species are heavier than sea water, and the nest helps to assure their safety. Some wrasses and parrot fishes lay lighter eggs, and these float buoyantly on the surface of the sea.

The fishes in this order feed on mollusks and other hard-shelled creatures, as well as the plant life they find in their native waters. Such a diet is not an easy one to swallow, but the wrasses and parrot fishes are strikingly equipped for the task. In their throats they have an efficient natural mill. The throat bones are fused together, and out of them, both at the top and bottom of the gullet, there usually grows a series of pavement-like or hemispherical teeth that serve to grind the food. (The order name—Pharyngognathi—means "throat-jaws.") The jaw teeth are also strong and prominent. In the parrot fishes they are more or less grown together, often to form a distinctly parrot-like beak, from which these fishes get their name. The fins are well spined and the pelvic fins have a rather forward position.

Some of the wrasses are at home in quite cold ocean waters, and in both tropical and temperate regions they are caught for food. Most species (there are about 450, forming the family Labridae) do not exceed one foot in size, but a few attain lengths of more than two feet and one reaches more than seven feet. Among the better-known wrasses are the tautog, cunner, hogfish, California sheepshead, pudding wife, señorita, bluehead, and razor fishes. Sometimes males and females are strikingly different in color pattern and shape. The parrot fishes (there are more than one hundred species in the family Scaridae) range in size up to about four feet.

The Tautog, *Tautoga onitis,* feeds chiefly on shellfish, especially mussels, clams, and barnacles. It has two types of teeth, conical and flat; the former are used in holding and tearing prey, the latter in crushing it. The tautog is a stocky fish with an arched forehead, thick lips and an extremely deep base to the tail fin. The single dorsal and anal fins are well spined. Its color is very dark green, gray, or black.

The range of the tautog is along the Atlantic coast of North America from New Brunswick to South Carolina. Reproduction takes place in the early summer. The small eggs are buoyant and hatch in two days at about 70 degrees. The record fish weighed 22½ pounds and was 36½ inches long, but any individual over ten pounds is unusual.

The Bluehead or King Slippery Dick, *Thalassoma bifasciatum,* undergoes a remarkable series of color changes as it grows up. How puzzling this has proved to scientists you can well imagine. Young fish less than one-half inch long have a wide dark brown band that extends from the snout through the eye to the tail fin. Above this band the slender body is generally pale green; below, it is white somewhat tinged with pink. No problem so far—but as the fish get larger, males and females become more and more unlike.

In the females, the band breaks up into a series of blotches, and the lower portion of the body becomes a pale blue with a pinkish tinge. The males pass through several stages, eventually exhibiting a deep blue or greenish head, separated from a bottle-green body by two wide, irregular, black bars that run from the dorsal to the ventral fins, just behind the pectorals. Between these two black bars the body is pale blue. The tail of the male develops an extension at its upper and lower edges, making it appear as if a semicircle had been cut out of the rear.

So different are all the various stages that they were once thought to be different species of fishes. Not until large series of specimens of successive sizes were available for study, and the actual changes had been witnessed in fish growing up in aquaria, was the confusing situation straightened out. To make things even more complicated, males sometimes assume female coloration and there are some medium-sized individuals that are predominantly yellow. At night a different color pattern is assumed, but the bluehead does not try to match its surroundings by altering its color scheme.

Blueheads are found around Florida and Bermuda and in the West Indies. During the day they actively swim about coral reefs and other underwater growths, often in small groups. Apparently they feed principally on small crustaceans. Young specimens are sometimes seen pecking at the bodies of larger fishes, which do not seem to mind this attention. It has been thought that the small blueheads were picking parasites off the other fish, but no parasite has ever been found in their stomachs.

At night blueheads hide in shells or bury themselves in the sand. Spawning takes place in the summer. The eggs are very small and float on the surface of the open sea. Blueheads reach a size of six inches.

The Blue Parrot Fish, *Scarus coeruleus,* is usually colored a robin's-egg blue and so brilliant is this pigment that the fish seems to shine through its large scales as if luminescent. Sometimes it shows darker stripes or blotches, and rarely it becomes very pale throughout. It reaches a length of about three feet.

Blue parrot fish straggle as far north as Maryland, but are not at all common north of Florida except around Bermuda. They range as far south as Panama. During the day most of their time is spent in feeding; they browse on the bottom, eating algae and other marine growths, which they remove in a dainty fashion yet with considerable force by means of their sharp, beaklike teeth. They sometimes take up mouthfuls of fine sand, swallowing it after chewing it with their throat teeth, presumably to obtain very small bits of organic material. Vegetable matter appears essential to their diet—they will not live long in captivity unless they have some to feed upon. At the New York Aquarium, they consumed sea-lettuce, *Ulva,* with seeming relish.

The Radiant Parrot Fish, *Sparisoma radians,* has a most variable coloration. In addition, the male is differently colored from the female. Consequently this fish has been described as a new species no less than seven different times by scientists who did not know that the specimen or specimens they had in hand were merely color or sexual variants.

The male also differs from the female in possessing lateral canine teeth (fangs) when only two inches long, while the female does not grow them until almost three inches long. At this size the females are mature. They lay pelagic eggs (floating on the open sea) during the summer. Specimens nine inches long have been reported. Their range includes Bermuda, Florida, and the West Indies, south to Brazil.

The Lesser Weever, *Trachinus vipera,* conceals itself in the sand in shallow waters from the Mediterranean to the British Isles, and is responsible for the sign sometimes seen on British beaches: *Ware Weevers*. These small fish, reaching a length of about five inches, are equipped with a single, long, needle-sharp spine on each gill-cover and with five smaller spines in the first dorsal fin, all of which have poison glands at their bases. Anyone unfortunate enough to tread on a lesser weever, or foolish enough to handle one carelessly, suffers agonizing pain when pricked by these poisonous spines. Such cases often require hospitalization, and recovery from the injury is a tedious, painful process.

The spawning season of the lesser weever is from May to September. Their buoyant eggs are about one-sixteenth of an inch in diameter. Hatching occurs in about ten days, and the larvae float at the surface of the sea for some time before settling to the bottom to take up an adult-like existence. They feed on small crustaceans and fishes.

The weevers, of which less than half a dozen species are known, make up the family Trachinidae which belongs to the order Trachinoidea. They are found in the eastern Atlantic Ocean and in the Mediterranean Sea. It is believed that they are related to the stargazers.

The Northern Electric Stargazer, *Astroscopus guttatus,* buries itself in sand at the bottom of coastal waters off the eastern shore of the United States, from New York to Virginia. Its eyes are located on the flattened top of its head and look directly upward. Its large mouth is practically vertical, the tip being at the same level as, and just in front of, the eyes. When the stargazer is covered with sand, only its minute eyes are visible. From this hidden position, it makes short dashes to catch unwary fishes passing by; it then settles back on the bottom, and, with a few wriggles of its body and pectoral fins, it is again perfectly concealed—all within the span of a few seconds.

Just behind each eye is an oval, bare spot; this is the site of the upper end of a column of electric tissue which extends down through the head to the roof of the mouth. The electric shock from these organs cannot compare with that of the electric eel or the torpedoes in strength, but when the fish is handled, it can be readily felt. Its voltage has not yet been measured, in fact all that seems to be known about the electric stargazer's discharge is that the top of the head is negative, the bottom positive, and that it is under the voluntary control of the fish. Whether or not the fish ever uses its electricity to obtain food is unknown, although what evidence there is indicates that it is only employed defensively. The electric organs are derived from parts of the fish's eye muscles.

Another peculiarity of the electric stargazer is that its nostrils open into the mouth, enabling it to breathe water through them while hidden under sand. (The noses of the vast majority of living fishes consist of U-shaped sacs which open only to the exterior and are used for smelling, not for breathing.) This species reaches a length of twenty-two inches and a weight of about twenty pounds. Eggs that float are laid during the late spring. At first the young also float about, but by fall, when they have grown to be somewhat more than an inch long, they have taken up life on the bottom.

Not all the stargazers, which comprise the family Uranoscopidae, possess electric organs; only a few of them are so equipped. Less than twenty-five species of stargazers are known, but they inhabit most tropical and warm-temperate seas. All of them live at the bottom; a few, in considerable depths. The largest species slightly exceed two feet in length.

The European Stargazer, *Uranoscopus scaber,* possesses a fleshy, frilled filament, which can be extended out of its mouth and wiggled about, simulating the motions of a small, red worm. Lying concealed in sand or mud, this stargazer is able to lure other fishes within reach of its capacious jaws. Like other members of its family, the European stargazer lays eggs that float on the open sea. These eggs are about one-sixteenth of an inch in diameter, and are spawned at night during the late spring and summer. This species is found in the warm parts of the eastern Atlantic and in the Mediterranean. It attains a length of about thirteen inches.

Blennies—Some Are Wolffishes

WHAT BLENNIES LACK in size and popularity, they make up in oddity and interest. The more we learn about them—and there is still a tremendous lot we do not know—the more fascinating they become. For example, some of the blennies seem as much at home on land as they do in the water! A few of these little creatures spend almost half their time hopping about on rocks and reefs. They are not washed up there by rough seas either—they leave the water of their own free will.

Most of the blennies proper (family Blenniidae) are small fishes less than six inches long. They love shallow, warm salt waters. Here, among the rocks and seaweeds of shores, tide pools, reefs and inlets, they hide from enemies on the prowl. Only relatively few dwell in cold or fresh waters.

In crevices or under shells and other submerged objects, the female blenny lays her eggs. These, so far as we know, are adhesive. In many species the male stands guard over them. Often you can tell him apart from the female—differences in the color and shape of the sexes are fairly common.

The kelpfishes or klipfishes (family Clinidae) remind us of the blennies proper in many ways. They, too, generally favor shallow salt waters, in tropical and temperate regions, and are often seen in tide pools among rocks and seaweed. Some are quite brightly hued, and males and females occasionally have a differently shaped body and fins. A number of species give birth to living young, and one kind—it is found in the West Indies—uses the inside of living sponges as a nursery. Kelpfishes are usually larger than the members of the preceding family, but seldom exceed one foot. The two groups, together, include perhaps five hundred species.

In the cold waters of the North Atlantic and Pacific live the savage-looking wolffishes (family Anarhichadidae). These blennies have powerful jaws armed with strong fangs in the front and heavy plates of rounded grinding teeth behind. Wolffishes they are in name and appearance, and their disposition seems to be fearless as well. But they use their formidable biting and chewing equipment not so much to prey upon other fish as they do to rake up and crush the hard-shelled mollusks upon which they frequently feed.

By and large, the wolffishes are giants compared to the other blennies we have been talking about. The common Atlantic wolffish averages about three feet in length. The eastern Pacific breeds a super-giant, a very elongated creature that reaches eight feet. For the way it cares for its young, the wolffish of the Atlantic is especially interesting to us. It spawns large eggs which are then formed into a ball. One of the parents stands guard over it to keep it from harm.

Of the several other families of cold-water blennies only the eel-pouts of the cold seas of the Northern and Southern Hemispheres are of any economic importance. Some species lay eggs, others give birth to live young.

As a group, the blennies and their many relatives are difficult to define. They do have one or two bony features in common, but we cannot see these from the outside. The ventral fins, if there are any, are far forward, just in front of the pectorals. These fins have either a single spine followed by up to four fin rays, or just this small number of rays without any spine. The body, rather elongated, sometimes reminds us of an eel's. The dorsal fin usually extends the full length of the back, but may be shorter. The blenny's anal fin, too, is long, extending over much of its under side. Spines may or may not be present in these two fins. Some species lack scales; none is fully scaled, and thus the blenny is a rather slippery fish. Accordingly the order to which it belongs is called Blennoidei ("slimy"). There are about eighteen families in all.

The American Eelpout, *Macrozoarces americanus,* is one of the many fishes, generally considered to be "trash" species in the commercial fisheries of the Atlantic coast of the United States, that in reality are excellent foodfish which could provide many people with nutritious, tasty, yet economical fare—if only the prejudice against their use could be overcome. Some progress in the education of the consuming public along these lines has been made: for example, four million pounds of eelpouts were marketed during the war years, 1943 and 1944. One cannot overestimate the importance of this kind of development in conserving our strained natural resources.

The appearance of the eelpout is undoubtedly the principal reason it is unpopular. It is an ugly fish with a heavy head, a large mouth surrounded by thick lips and a long, tapering body. The long dorsal fin is continuous with the tail fin, which in turn is continuous with the long anal. The coloration of the eelpout is variable but somber.

This bottom-dwelling fish ranges from Labrador and Newfoundland to Delaware, and from shallow waters to those of considerable depth. It feeds principally on crustaceans and mollusks. Maximum length is three and one-half feet and maximum weight about twelve pounds, but specimens over three feet are rare.

Reproduction is by means of large, heavy eggs about one-fourth of an inch in diameter. These are laid during the late summer and fall down into crevices or other protected places, and are there guarded by one or both parents. From two and one-half to three and one-half months elapse before hatching, depending on the temperature. A close relative of the eelpout from Europe, *Zoarces viviparus*, gives birth to living young.

Brotulids, Cusk-Eels and Pearlfishes —Little-Known Oddities

M OST OF US have never even heard of these fishes, but they deserve to be known because of their extremely curious ways of life. Some of the most remarkable of the group are the brotulids (family Brotulidae). Although the greater number are at home in the deep sea, a few strange species live out their lives in the darkness of fresh-water caves in Cuba and Yucatan. We call these cave-dwellers "blind-fish," for they have only the slightest traces of eyes. Still, they have managed to make up for their lack of sight: they have developed tiny growths or barbels on their heads to serve as "feelers." Thus the blind species are perfectly at ease in the pitch-black underground waters, where eyes would be of no use to them anyway. They give birth to living young, as do some, if not all, of their ocean-going relatives.

Equally fascinating are a group of small, eel-shaped creatures, the pearlfishes (family Fierasferidae). The pearlfish often makes its home inside the shell of the pearl oyster or some other living mollusk, or it may take up quarters in some other animal—the hind-gut of a live sea-cucumber or a starfish is not an unlikely place to find a pearlfish. From time to time it leaves this strange shelter to search for food or to lay its floating eggs. Not all pearlfishes live in other creatures, and many prefer to haunt rocky crevices. Almost every shallow, tropical sea is the dwelling place of some of these little oddities.

Because they are built on the general lines of the eel, the next family we shall turn our attention to is known as the cusk-eels (Ophidiidae). One, a five-foot giant that snakes through the waters off South Africa and Australia, is a good catch for any fisherman, being esteemed as a foodfish. Most, though, are under a foot long. They are deep-water fishes of the warm seas, as a rule.

What obvious features, then, do the fishes of this order—Ophidioidei ("snakelike")—have in common? Generally, their resemblance to the eels is the one that strikes us strongly. Their bodies are quite elongated, and the scales are tiny or absent altogether. Usually there is no tail fin, and the other fins lack spines. The ventral fins, if present at all, are located far forward and reduced to a few rays.

Mackerel, Tuna, and Their Relatives
—Mighty, Far-Ranging Swimmers

Powerful, far-ranging swimmers with streamlined bodies that cut through the ocean waters at great speeds—such are the mackerel, the tuna, the swordfish, and most of their relatives. Because their flesh is savory and rich in oil, and because they frequently travel about in schools—and therefore can be easily caught in large numbers—several species have become extremely important foodfishes. Some put up a staunch fight in the catching, and are highly prized as game-fishes.

The mackerel is typical of its family (Scombridae), which includes the bonito, tuna, albacore, and skipjack. With pointed head and spindle-shaped body, it is superbly contoured for sliding through the ocean with the ease of a torpedo. Like the rest of its family, which contains about fifty species, it makes its home in all the temperate and tropical seas of the earth. Only in warmer seas do we find the Spanish mackerel and its strangely named relative the wahoo, a dark-blue denizen of the waters off Florida and the West Indies. These belong to a separate family (Scomberomoridae) which contains about a dozen different fishes, ranging up to six feet and one hundred pounds in size.

The escolars were "scholars" to the Spaniards, who named them that because the species they pulled from the water had circles around their eyes, reminding the fishermen of glasses. These large, voracious fishes (family Gempylidae) dwell in open temperate and tropical seas, sometimes being found at considerable depths. Best known is the Barracouta, or Snoek, *Thyrsites atun,* which is one of the two most important commercial fishes of Australia, and is also widely used for food in South Africa. It lives only in the cooler ocean waters of the Southern Hemisphere, and reaches a length of three and one-half feet.

Like the great barracuda, with which it should not be confused, it can inflict terrible wounds with its fangs and numerous smaller teeth. It has never been known to attack bathers in water, however.

Another interesting group in this order includes such curiosities as cutlass fishes and scabbard fishes. These sharp-toothed creatures have elongated bodies that reach a length of at least five feet, and bear a striking resemblance to the objects for which they are named. Some species have no tail fin at all, and the end of the fish tapers to a point so fine that it looks like a hair. It is not surprising, that the scientific name given them should mean just that—"hair-tails" (family Trichiuridae). In India they are fished on a commercial scale.

We find a number of other famous fishes in this imposing order: the broadbill swordfish, the spearfish, and the various marlins and sailfishes. About some of these we shall have much to say later in this chapter. The order—Scombroidei ("mackerel-like")—has perhaps a dozen families, all told. Although related to the spiny-rayed fishes, they do not always have spines in their fins. The ventral fins, if present, are usually found well forward. A series of small fins, called finlets, frequently runs from the dorsal and from the anal to the tail fin. The attachment of the tail fin to the body is usually slender, with a horizontal keel on either side. If the fish has any scales at all, they are small and we cannot easily see or feel them. The structure of the pointed mouth, which cannot be extended, helps us to identify members of the order.

The Atlantic Mackerel, *Scomber scombrus,* provides Americans with about thirty-five million pounds of fish each year, although the amount caught varies widely, some years being "good mackerel years," others bad ones. The reason for these fluctuations is unknown, but it is suspected that excessive mortality of very young mackerel may be responsible. Unfavorable winds that blow the more or less helpless, floating baby fish into unsuitable waters, or a lack of the proper microscopic or near-microscopic plants and animals to feed them are two factors that may cause mass mortality.

In the western Atlantic, spawning of the mackerel takes place about twenty miles offshore from April into June. The numerous eggs float near the surface and hatch in about a week, but the young fish are not capable of swimming effectively for almost a month, being pretty much at the mercy of the elements during this period.

Even when lying limply on ice in a fish store, the mackerel appears graceful, but its streamlined form cannot be really appreciated save in action—when the fish courses through the water, powered by rhythmical strokes of its muscular tail, the dark network on the blue-green of its back adding to the illusion of some sort of aquatic rocket or bullet.

FISH THAT SWIM FOR THEIR LIVES
Most animals may pause and rest sometime, but not the adult Atlantic mackerel—if it stops swimming, it will suffocate, for it requires a continuous flow of fresh water to keep its blood supplied with oxygen. By day mackerel travel in schools that often number thousands, but on dark nights these schools break up.

From the time they are about two inches long and forty days old and have assumed the shape of the adult, Atlantic mackerel swim continuously until they die. In fact, if a mackerel stops swimming, it *will* die, being smothered because not enough water passes over its gills. If possible, mackerel remain in the company of thousands of their fellows, more or less of the same size and all moving at the same speed and in the same direction. These great oceanic schools break up at night unless there is a moon, and do not re-form until dawn. Experiments have shown that fish will not school unless they can see one another. Blinded mackerel in the dark pay no attention to their fellow fish, but two mackerel placed in separate tanks, close together, will school with each other, swimming side by side, back and forth along the glass sides of the tanks.

While moving about, Atlantic mackerel feed voraciously on practically all kinds of floating animals, including shrimp, worms, squid, fish eggs and fry, small adult fishes, and even small mackerel. During certain parts of the year they live on bivalves and other bottom-inhabiting creatures. The ordinary Atlantic mackerel is about one foot long and weighs about one pound. Specimens more than twice as long, weighing seven and one-half pounds, are on record, however.

In the western Atlantic, this species ranges from Labrador to North Carolina. During the spring, summer, and fall, the fish remain near the surface, but in winter they move further offshore and sink down, possibly as deep as one hundred fathoms.

The Pacific Mackerel, *Pneumatophorus diego,* is caught in larger numbers than the Atlantic mackerel, but it, too, is subject to wide fluctuations. Almost all of the Pacific mackerel caught are canned, rather than sold fresh or frozen as is the Atlantic species. It averages somewhat larger than the Atlantic species, but does not attain quite so large a maximum size. Although the Pacific mackerel looks quite like its Atlantic relative, it can be clearly separated from it by the possession of an air bladder and several other structural details. Both species have their bodies covered with very fine scales.

Spawning occurs from late April through July along the California coast. Floating on the open sea, the eggs hatch in about three days. The Pacific mackerel is a schooling species and feeds on various floating crustaceans, on squid, and on small fishes.

The Bluefin Tuna, *Thunnus thynnus,* has a sleek, spindle-shaped body that is beautifully fashioned for slipping through water with a minimum of effort. No protuberance or lack of symmetry mars its streamlined contours. The jaws fit neatly together, and the gill covers lie close against the sides. The eyes are set flush with the surface of the head. Even the paired fins and the first dorsal fit into grooves, lest they present unnecessary water resistance. The scales are very small and buried within smooth skin that is as slippery as slime can make it.

Everything about the tuna indicates aquatic speed and a life of continuous swimming, and the fish certainly lives up to its appearance. Tuna have been clocked at speeds of more than forty miles per hour and they can apparently maintain rates of about nine miles per hour indefinitely. No one has ever seen a tuna that was not swimming, unless it was dead or dying. Using the above figures, it can be estimated that a fifteen-year-old tuna must have traveled on the order of a million miles during its life. The tuna is one of the very few fish that maintain a body temperature somewhat higher than that of the surrounding water, and without doubt this is closely associated with its continuous activity.

Traveling about in schools through most of the temperate and tropical seas, tuna have been likened to packs of wolves—so relentlessly do they pursue their prey and so ravenously do they feed upon it. Squid and fishes make up the bulk of their food.

Tuna were a favorite food of the ancient Greeks and Romans. Today they are fished both commercially and for sport in many parts of the world. In commercial fisheries they are netted, harpooned, trolled, or pole-fished with two or three poles to a single hook when the fish run large. Tuna fishing is now the most profitable of all of California's fisheries. Practically all of the catch is canned, and three other species besides the bluefin are sold under the name "tuna": the Albacore, *Thunnus germo,* the Yellowfin Tuna, *Neothunnus macropterus,* and the Skipjack, *Katsuwonus pelamis.* Well over two hundred million pounds are taken each year, of which two-thirds are composed of yellowfin tuna.

The largest bluefin tuna ever landed with fishing tackle was taken off Nova Scotia. It was nine feet, eight inches long and weighed 977 pounds. Specimens weighing 1,800 pounds have been reported, but such records have not been verified.

There is still a great deal that is unknown about the life history of the tunas. The bluefin is known to spawn in the western Mediterranean and just outside Gibraltar. There is evidence that the yellowfin reproduces during the summer off the west coast of Central America and near the Philippine, Caroline, and Marshall Islands and that the skipjack spawns around the Philippines. Without doubt other areas will come to light with further study. The eggs of the bluefin tuna are small and float for about two days, when they hatch. Growth is rapid, maturity being attained in three years, at a weight of about thirty pounds.

The Broadbill Swordfish, *Xiphias gladius,* roams the tropical and temperate seas of the world, hunting the fish and squid upon which it feeds. It has no teeth, but uses its sword—a tremendous extension of its upper jaw, composed of a flat, narrow, bony prolongation of the skull—to secure its prey.

The sword makes up about one-third of the giant fish's total length. It is used like the broadsword it resembles, being slashed to the right and left, through a school of herring and mackerel, killing or maiming numbers of fish that the swordfish can then consume with ease. More rarely the swordfish has been reported to impale prey on its sharp-pointed weapon. Undoubtedly fish are also sometimes caught without the aid of the sword, the swordfish depending upon its speed and size alone in these instances.

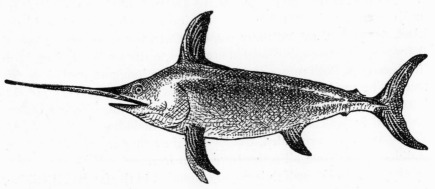

SWORDSMAN OF THE SEA
The broadbill swordfish may grow to a weight of six hundred pounds; much of this is highly palatable flesh, and the creature is much prized as a gamefish. Its famed sword is actually the upper jaw, drawn out to form a long, rigid beak. The broadbill uses this beak to cut left and right in a school of fish, and then consumes the victims.

The sword is also used in fighting. Broken-off pieces have been found imbedded in sharks and in swordfish themselves. A considerable number of boats have been rammed by swordfish, the sword penetrating well over a foot into the hardwood of the vessel's side or bottom. Many harpooned or hooked swordfish have charged into small fishing craft and have driven their swords clean through and wounded the fishermen inside. In at least one instance a man was killed when he was pierced by a swordfish's sword that came up through the bottom of the dory in which he was lying.

Such incidents have given the swordfish the reputation of pungnacity, but the truth of the matter seems that the so-called attacks are more often the distracted rushes of a tormented fish rather than the deliberate charges of a vicious one.

Swordfish steaks are a delicacy; about four and one-half million pounds are fished or imported by Americans each year. Since ancient times, fishermen have captured swordfish—with harpoons, because of their large size. They are said to reach well over one thousand pounds, and four-hundred-pound specimens are not rare. Sports fishermen catch them "the hard way" on hook-and-line; the largest that was ever landed in this fashion weighed 860 pounds and was thirteen feet, nine inches long.

The eggs of the swordfish are tiny, floating spheres about one sixteenth of an inch in diameter. The only definitely known spawning area is off northern Sicily, but there are undoubtedly several more undiscovered. Evidence that reproduction may also take place in the Black Sea and off the northern coast of Cuba has been accumulating. Baby swordfish are spiny-headed creatures, quite unlike their streamlined parents. Both upper and lower jaws are long and provided with teeth. The teeth disappear relatively early in development, and the lower jaw gradually becomes shorter and shorter until it is less than one-third as long as the upper one which includes the long sword. Young swordfish are scaled, but by the time they are are about four and a half feet long all scales have been lost.

The broadbill swordfish is the sole member of the family Xiphiidae, a name derived from the Greek word for "sword."

The Atlantic Sailfish, *Istiophorus americanus,* looks like nothing so much as a torpedo when it flashes through the water, all its fins held close to its body, its enormous dorsal fin—from which it gets its name —being folded down into a deep groove along the back. Its dark blue back and light-colored belly add to this illusion, and its sharp, cylindrical spear could well be taken as some strange sort of detonator for the sleek war head attached to it. The fish seems the very peak of streamlined form.

Like their relatives the marlins, the sailfishes are popular with big-game fishermen. There are several species, but apparently only one is found in the Atlantic. The Pacific Sailfish, *Istiophorus greyi,* is sometimes taken along the extreme southern coast of California. The Atlantic form is reported to reach 120 pounds, the Pacific species, at least 190. Their average weights are about thirty-five and one hun-

dred pounds, respectively. They are said to attain the phenomenal
speed of sixty miles per hour under water, but this is for short distances only. The record Atlantic sailfish caught with rod-and-reel
weighed 123 pounds and was ten feet, four inches long.

Available evidence indicates that the Atlantic sailfish spawns during
the summer. The very young fish have spiny heads and toothed jaws.
During development both upper and lower jaws first become elon-
ated, but only the upper one remains so, forming the spear. All spines
and teeth are lost as the fish grows larger. The enlarged dorsal fin
appears early in development, eventually becoming the enormous sail-
like structure that is found in the adult.

The Blue Marlin, *Makaira nigricans ampla,* resembles the swordfish,
but can readily be distinguished by its rounded spear, by its dorsal
fin which extends much further along the back and which can be
depressed, fitting into a groove in the skin, and by the presence of
pelvic fins and peculiar thorn-like scales—both of which are absent
in the swordfish. The shining, dark-blue back and silvery belly of the

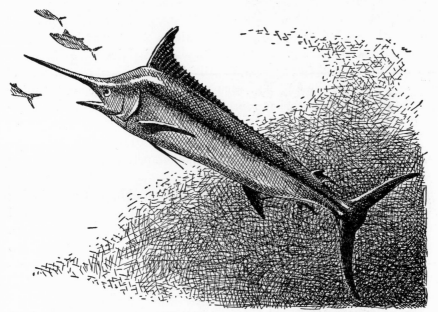

PRIZE CATCH FOR ANY FISHERMAN
The blue marlin provides a superb catch for even the most skillful of fishermen—this giant
of the deep sometimes is more than twelve feet long, and puts up a strenuous fight for
its life. On its upper jaw it carries a natural "marlinspike" which wins it its food; the
fish owes its name to this weapon.

blue marlin make it one of the most beautiful of all of the big-game fishes. Its powerful, yet streamlined, body is a delight to the artist as well as to the sportsman.

The blue marlin occurs in the Atlantic Ocean and is found from Florida and the West Indies to Montauk Point, on the tip of Long Island, New York. There is another Atlantic species, the White Marlin, *Makaira albida,* that is much smaller, its maximum size being about half that of the average size of the blue marlin. The blue marlin averages about two hundred pounds. One twelve-hundred-pound giant has been recorded as caught in a net by Cuban fishermen. The record rod-and-reel catch weighed 742 pounds and was twelve feet, ten and one-half inches long. In the Pacific, there are probably three species of marlin, the Striped Marlin, *Makaira mitsukuri,* being the one seen off southern California. The Black Marlin, *Makaira nigricans marlina,* found from Peru to New Zealand, may reach a length of fifteen feet and a weight of 1,226 pounds. It is the largest member of the group.

All of the marlins are much-sought-after game fishes. The thrill of having one of these fighting, swift-running, plunging, tail-dancing fish on the end of a line is perhaps the greatest in all sports fishing.

We know very little about the life history of any of the marlins. They all feed on fish and squid. Sometimes they occur in numbers, but more often they are solitary. They are at times found in pairs, presumably for breeding. About all that is known regarding the spawning of the blue marlin is that most probably there are breeding grounds off Cuba and that reproduction occurs during the summer and early fall. The marlin family (Istiophoridae or "sail-bearers") contains about ten different fishes, among them the spearfish and the sailfishes. All dwell in tropical and warm-temperate seas.

The Butter Fish, *Poronotus triacanthus,* lays its buoyant eggs during late June and July and August. Young specimens are often found under large jellyfish, where they apparently remain for protection. They also feed on small, swimming crustaceans close to shore—so close that they are sometimes thrown up on the beach by an unexpected wave.

Larger butter fish feed on small fishes, squid, and other creatures. They are a trim, silvery-blue fish, with a flat, deep, yet streamlined body and a strongly forked tail. They have no ventral fins, and this fact immediately distinguishes the species from the pompanos, which, at first glance, they resemble. Butter fish reach a length of a foot and a weight of one and a quarter pounds. They are found along the Atlantic coast of North America from Nova Scotia to Florida. For years this delicious table fish was discarded, or used for fertilizer or cat food. Now about twelve and one-quarter million pounds are caught annually for man's consumption.

Butter fish belong to the family Stromateidae, which is sometimes placed in the order Scombroidei, sometimes put by itself. Its members possess sacs, lined with teeth, on either side of the gullet, and have peculiar ventral fins which, when present, have a membrane connecting the inner margin with the abdomen. The California Pompano, *Palometa simillima,* is not a true pompano, but is just as highly prized for food. It is similar in appearance to the butter fish, to whose family it belongs, but is slightly smaller, attaining a length of ten to eleven inches. It ranges along the coast from southern California to Britsh Columbia.

Also included in the group is the Man-of-War Fish, *Nomeus gronovi.* This small species is found in tropical seas, often among the stinging tentacles of various jellyfishes, including the notorious Portuguese man-of-war. In times of danger, it dodges among these death-dealing filaments with apparent immunity, although merely to touch them spells death to other small fishes.

Gobies—Bottom-Dwellers

Even though the gobies are found over most of the world, you cannot blame yourself if you have overlooked them till now. They are small creatures and timid ones, and they love to hide on the bottom. That bottom may be of almost any kind—of a swift-flowing stream or a swamp, a mud flat or a tide pool, or near a sandy beach or a coral reef.

Some of the great legion of gobies (we know about seven hundred

different species, order Gobioidei, or "goby-like") can make themselves at home in both salt and fresh water. Some, when the pond or
stream dries up, can sleep away the summer in mud. Several make a
truly peculiar choice of living quarters, taking up residence in the
cavities of living sponges. There are blind gobies, too—but they
hardly need to see, for they live in places of perpetual darkness: underground rivers in Madagascar and West Australia, rocky crevices and
shrimp burrows on the California coast, and muddy waters in the
Indo-Pacific.

Still, all of those interesting creatures might seem commonplace
compared to one goby of the West Indies. This little fellow has the
curious habit of entering the mouths of large groupers, grunts, parrot
fishes, and others. What does it do there? It picks at their teeth
and gums, much the way the Egyptian plover picks the teeth of
crocodiles. Like other gobies, it is very fond of flesh.

Far and away the largest family of gobies—it outnumbers the others
in species and individuals—is the Gobiidae. We know more about
the way these gobies reproduce than we do for the rest. Their eggs
come in a great variety of shapes: from spherical, through pear-shaped
and teardrop-shaped, to those that roughly resemble a marlinspike or
belaying pin in outline. Fastened to some underwater object, the
eggs are frequently guarded by the male. In some species, the larvae,
after being hatched in fresh water, float downstream to the sea, but
return to fresh water while sti¹l quite young. The California blind
goby and the pigmy gobies—more about them in a moment—are members of this family.

Most gobies never reach six inches in length. But a few grow to be
twenty inches long, and two feet is probably the top size for any of
the order. The largest of the gobies are the sleepers (family Eleo-
tridae). Many of these live in fresh water; some, we believe, travel
downstream to spawn in the sea.

Along the tropical shores of Africa, Asia, and Australia, we come
upon the mudskippers and their relatives (family Periophthalmidae),
creatures strange both in appearance and habits. As the tide recedes
and lays great mud flats bare, the mudskippers can often be seen
right out in the open, hopping about on their powerful pectoral fins,
which they use like limbs, their protruding eyes turning from side to
side to seek their prey.

We have seen that most of the gobies are bottom-dwellers. When we examine them closely we can readily observe how well suited they are for such an existence. Except for the family of sleepers, they often have a sucking disk by means of which they can fasten themselves to rocks or other objects on the bottom. This disk is formed by the pelvic fins—they are united at the base. A goby has its pelvic fins under or just in front of the pectorals, and there are spines in its fins, but they are weak as a general rule. There are about six families, all told. The gobies are commonest in the tropics and inhabit at least some fresh waters on every continent and all but the coldest of shallow ocean waters.

The California Blind Goby, *Typhlogobius californiensis,* spends most of its life inside the burrow of a certain species of shrimp. From the age of six months or less until death—a period of perhaps ten years—it lives with a pair of these shrimp.

The blind goby shares not only their home but their fate as well. The dwelling consists of several small, connecting tunnels, with three or four very small openings. The tunnels are dug in the gravel between high- and low-water along the shores of southern California. The fish is completely dependent upon the shrimp for its shelter, since it is unable to dig or repair a burrow for itself. If both shrimp die the fish soon perishes also.

The host of the blind goby belongs to the group of ghost shrimps. It is a whitish-yellow creature, less than three inches long, shaped not unlike an ordinary crayfish. It feeds on tiny particles of organic matter that it sifts out of the water it constantly pumps through its burrow. This current also provides the blind goby with food, for the fish consumes any pieces of seaweed or animals that might be carried into the burrow and are too large for the shrimp. Although the goby thus helps keep the burrow clean, it has been shown that in captivity at least, a pair of shrimp can do very well without such guests.

The blind goby, too, usually lives in pairs, one pair to each burrow. The fish is small and pink; its color results from the blood that shows through the colorless, translucent skin. The eyes are hardly visible, being degenerate and covered with several layers of skin, but although the fish cannot see, it is somewhat sensitive to strong light. The senses of touch and smell seem fairly well developed. The pelvic fins are arranged to form a sucking pad by which the blind goby can cling to smooth objects.

The old saying about two being company and three a crowd, definitely holds for blind gobies. Should a second male put in an appearance, the original one will immediately engage it in fierce combat. The fight may last for hours, the fish biting each other and holding on with bulldog-like tenacity. The battle usually continues until one of the adversaries is killed or, less frequently, is driven from the burrow. If an extra female enters, it is the two females that battle to the death. If the interloper should win, he or she is accepted by the mate of the defeated fish without hesitation. Sex recognition has been shown to occur through chemical means.

The blind goby breeds from May until July. The ellipsoidal eggs are about one thirty-second of an inch long when first laid, but they subsequently grow to almost four times their length. From twenty-five hundred to fifteen thousand of them are deposited on the sides of the burrow. Both male and female fan the eggs and watch over them, either taking turns or working together. After ten to twelve days the eggs hatch. The young blind gobies are colored, and have well developed eyes. They are attracted to light, and this may be the reason that they soon leave the shrimps' burrow. By the time they are six months old, they have lost their dark coloration and their eyes have become distorted and partially overgrown with flesh.

The Dwarf Pigmy Goby, *Pandaka pygmaea,* is the smallest of freshwater fishes and the shortest backboned animal known. Adult females attain a length of seven-sixteenths of an inch and adult males never quite reach three-eighths of an inch. These tiny fish inhabit certain lakes on the island of Luzon in the Philippines. With the exception of their prominent black eyes, they are colorless and practically transparent.

The minute eggs of the dwarf pigmy goby are about one sixty-fourth of an inch in diameter, that is, smaller than the period at the end of this sentence. They are quite large in relation to the size of the fish, however, and each female contains only twenty to forty of them. They are tied together by means of numerous intertwined filaments; when laid, they float and become entangled with algae and other small objects at the water's surface.

Another goby from the same island, the Sinarapan, *Mistichthys luzonensis,* is almost as small as *Pandaka,* exceeding it on the average by about one-eighth inch. Perhaps the most remarkable thing about this fish is that it exists in such numbers in Lake Buhi that despite its diminutive size, it is used for food. Vast numbers are scooped or dipped up from the water to be sold in the market and eventually stewed with vegetables or made into fish cakes and fried in oil. It takes about sixteen thousand sinarapan to make up one pound. Like the dwarf pigmy goby, this fish reproduces by means of minute eggs.

Small as these gobies are, there are two fishes still smaller—if one uses weight instead of length as a standard. Both are tiny, slender, transparent fish from the Pacific Ocean. They have no common name, but belong to the genus *Schindleria*. The smaller, *Schindleria praematurus*, reaches a maximum length of slightly more than three-fourths of an inch, but most mature males do not exceed five-eighths of an inch and females with eggs eleven-sixteenths of an inch. Definitely lighter than the Philippine pigmy goby, this species weighs perhaps one twenty-five-hundredth of an ounce, and is the lightest of all backboned animals.

Schindleria lives near or at the surface of the sea, amidst many larval fishes, which it resembles in general appearance. Regardless of immature characteristics, many individuals are fully adult, as evidenced by the presence of mature sex glands. Specimens are generally found not far from land, so we believe that the fish is not an inhabitant of mid-ocean but lives in the waters surrounding the islands of the southwest Pacific and eastern Australia.

The relationship of the genus *Shindleria* to other fishes is still a mystery; some scientists have thought it related to the halfbeaks, others have placed it among the blennies, but neither arrangement seems satisfactory. Until more specimens of these rare fishes, in various stages of development, can be obtained, their exact place in the animal kingdom will remain a matter for conjecture.

The Mudskipper, *Periophthalmus koelreuteri,* combines the attributes of both fish and frog. Although it is a true fish, it behaves in a most froglike manner, regularly coming out of the water and hopping about on mud flats and mangrove swamps.

Even the mudskipper's bulbous head is rather froglike: it has puffed out "jowls," a hemispherical snout, and eyes set in sockets that project clearly above the top of the head. The eyes are quite mobile, and besides turning about, they can "wink" in a most grotesque manner.

The mudskipper's pectoral fins are mounted on movable, fleshy bases, and the fish "rows" itself along by means of them, dragging its elongated body behind. The pelvic fins also aid in this process, since they are located almost under the head and are united at the base and thus can act as a small pedestal to keep the head end of the fish off the ground. Mudskippers can leap as far as a yard, springing off the ground, mostly by means of the muscular tail, but also by using their pectoral fins. They sometimes leap from one mangrove root to another, and are said to be so agile that they can catch insects on the wing.

FISH OR FROG?

To the casual observer, the mudskippers seem to be half-frog, half-fish. What is more, these tropical oddities frequently leave the water and skip about vigorously on wet sand and mud in pursuit of insects. They must, however, make regular trips back to the water to moisten their skin and gills.

Mudskippers can remain out of water for a long time, but must periodically return to moisten their two bulging gill-chambers. By carrying a little of its native element with it, the mudskipper avoids being tied down to an aquatic life, although it never strays very far from water. It is widely distributed in shallow salt and brackish waters in the tropics, from the west coast of Africa, the Red Sea, the Indian Ocean and the western Pacific as far east as Polynesia. Experts

have not yet decided how many different species of mudskippers occupy this vast area, or whether they all belong to a single species.

Mudskippers feed on insects and small crabs and reach a maximum length of nine inches. They apparently have a well-developed
sense of proprietorship and often chase one another. At such times
they flash their dorsal fins up and down, apparently using them as a
signal device, or for bluffing. They also make burrows in the mud, in
which the eggs are supposed to be laid and carefully guarded.

Fishes with Armored Cheeks

I n the strange underwater menagerie of this group you
will find a zebra fish—a sea robin and a sea raven—scorpion fishes—
rockfishes and stonefishes—and even a miller's thumb! So beautiful
or fantastic are some of these creatures that every other domain of
nature had to be ransacked to find names for them.

But so deadly, too, are a number of these fishes that they must be
approached or handled with the greatest of care, even by experts.
Some bear sharp spines equipped with poison glands and rank among
the most poisonous fishes we know. They are capable of inflicting
wounds causing intense suffering and even death.

These fishes, by and large, have one strong, distinguishing feature—
their cheeks are armored. A bony plate or rod runs from under the eye
back into the gill cover. Some lack this plate, but the typical fish
of the group has a bony ridge that is quite apparent, and it is spiny
and rough on the outside. Sometimes we find the head completely
covered with spiny bones. These natural warriors of the seas have
pointed teeth that add to their savage appearance, and often they are
eaters of flesh.

If we were to look for living masterpieces of camouflage, we would
find an abundance of them among the scorpion fishes and their relatives (family Scorpaenidae). These rugged fishes carry numerous
spines and tabs of flesh that allow them to blend in with the weeds

among which they swim. Their color, too, makes it hard to tell them apart from underwater rocks. Some, however, vie in hue with the most gorgeous of fishes. Perhaps their bright colors serve as a warning, because their spines are frequently dangerous, the slightest prick producing agonizing pain.

The scorpion fishes are at home in all the oceans, and like shallow water as well as deep; only a few prefer streams and rivers. Generally they do not grow over a foot in length, but there are some three-foot giants. We know about 250 species, among them the rockfishes and the rosefish—we shall return to them a bit later—being important as foodfishes. Some reproduce by means of floating eggs, others bring forth their young alive.

Also equipped with extremely poisonous spines—deadly, in some instances—are the stingfishes, or stonefishes (family Synanceidae). These fishes look like the scorpions, and rarely exceed a length of one foot. They are especially adept at concealing themselves on the bottom of the tropical tide pools that they frequent. We suppose that they lay eggs, but we know little about their life history.

The sea robins and the gurnards (the latter name comes from an old word meaning "grunt," and that is just what these fishes often do) grow over two feet long and are used for food in Europe and South Africa. The common American sea robins, on the other hand, are rarely eaten. Fishes of this family (Triglidae) hatch from pelagic eggs—eggs that float on the open sea—but spend most of their life in shallow water, on the bottom of tropical and temperate seas. They give the appearance of walking across the ocean floor on the several "fingers" that make up the pectoral fin.

Anglers of the west coast of the United States—especially in the area of Puget Sound—need no introduction to the greenlings (family Hexagrammidae). Both the greenlings and the skilfishes (family Anoplopomidae) dwell in the North Pacific. Their flesh is palatable, but only the Sable Fish, *Anoplopoma fimbria,* a dark gray or green creature, is commercially fished to any extent. It reaches three feet in length and forty pounds in weight. Still, it seems puny beside the Giant Skilfish, *Erilepis zonifer*—specimens of this fish six feet long and weighing more than two hundred pounds have been caught.

It is mainly in the waters of the Indo-Pacific that we encounter a group of fishes with a humble name but great value in the larders of mankind. These are the flatheads (family Platycephalidae). Each year the fish markets of Australia sell millions of pounds of flatheads. As both scientific and popular names suggest, these creatures have broad, flattened heads. The bottom of the ocean is where they live, and they inhabit shallow as well as deeper waters. Most flatheads are under three feet long, and there are about fifty species.

The short, sharp spines of the sculpins probably serve to hold off their enemies. These fishes favor cool or cold temperatures, and the three hundred species we know of inhabit salt and fresh water, shallow and deep. Often the angler pulls them from the streams and rivers of Europe, North America and Asia and is disappointed at the small size of his catch. Freshwater sculpins—they are better known as bullheads, mudlers, or miller's thumbs—seldom reach six inches in length. Their cousins in the waters of the North Atlantic and Pacific and the Arctic oceans, however, may grow over two feet long. A number of species have broken with one of the commonest of fish habits —they fertilize the eggs *before* they are laid. Often the male stays quite close to them and drives off any fish that dares to come near. (The sculpins make up the family Cottidae.)

We see the same protective habit among those plump, ungainly creatures known as the lumpfishes or lumpsuckers (family Cyclopteridae). They are strictly ocean fishes, and they patrol much the same chill waters the sculpins do. As you might suspect from their name, the lumpsuckers possess a sucking disk that they use to fasten themselves to rocks. Some lumpsuckers reach a length of about two feet.

Earlier, we talked of the armor that covers the heads of fishes of this order, either partly or completely. (The order name, Cataphracti, means "wholly enclosed.") What other major features do they have in common? In a group that includes about twenty families we may expect great variety. Still, we do find that the fins, dorsal and anal especially, are usually well equipped with spines, although these are lacking in some species or are so modified towards the ordinary soft fin ray that we can scarcely recognize them as spines. The ventral fins are present in most species, and are located forward, close to the pectorals.

The Rosefish, *Sebastes marinus,* was once a neglected marine food resource. Until 1935 it was marketed only in limited quantities, but then new methods of filleting, scaling and quick-freezing made it more salable. By 1946, about 178 million pounds were caught in a single year for food. Since that time, however, the catch has fallen off somewhat. The fish is frequently sold as "ocean perch."

The rosefish is a bright red, varying to brownish or grayish red. It is more or less perchlike in general shape, but can be quickly distinguished from the perches by its pointed gill covers on which are located a number of spines. The single dorsal and anal fins are also strongly spined. A maximum size of at least three feet is attained. Those along the Atlantic coast of North America rarely exceed two feet, however. At this length they weigh about thirteen pounds. They are fished at depths of three hundred to seven hundred fifty feet, almost entirely by otter trawl.

Rosefish are cold water inhabitants, never being found in less than ninety feet of water during the summer even as far north as the Gulf of Maine. They are well known in the Arctic Ocean. They occur as far south as New Jersey in the western north Atlantic and as far south as the English Channel in the east.

Although the rosefish gives birth to living young, these are born in a relatively undeveloped state. They show, in fact, very little advancement over typical fishes that have just been hatched from the egg. Examination has revealed that the young are not nourished by their mother—as in the great majority of live-bearing fishes—but simply rest within her, still inside their individual eggs. They hatch out inside the mother very shortly before being expelled. About all a mother rosefish does for her brood is to protect it until hatching.

Unlike the broods of other live-bearing fishes, the size of this one's is enormous. At birth each baby is about one-fourth of an inch long, and a good-sized female may carry several thousand at one time. A thirteen-inch specimen contained approximately 20,500 young ready to be born. For some time after birth young rosefish float in the sea, pretty much at the mercy of their surroundings.

Rosefish are born from April through August, the time varying with the locality. Growth is extremely slow; it takes ten years to reach a size of eight inches. The rosefish feeds on various crustaceans, mollusks, and other invertebrates, and on small fishes, including young of its own species.

The Orange Rockfish, *Sebastodes pinniger,* is one of over fifty species of rockfishes that inhabit the shallow and deeper waters along the North American Pacific coast from California to Alaska. They are important foodfishes, more than thirteen million pounds having been taken in a single year in California. The orange rockfish is at present the most important single species of rockfish in the commercial catch of that state. The fish are taken with trawls and hook-and-line. Lines as long as one mile, carrying three thousand baited hooks, have been used.

The orange coloration of the body and fins of this fish distinguishes it from almost all other rockfishes. It has three bright orange stripes running across its spiny head, and the lining of its large mouth is pale red with dark mottling. It reaches a length of two and one-half feet.

The range of the orange rockfish extends from northern Baja California to northern British Columbia. It produces living young, apparently in the spring. The young are less than one-half inch long at birth and still carry a yolk sac. They must float helplessly in the water for quite a while after birth. Large females may carry as many as six hundred thousand young. The younger fish inhabit waters near shore; old individuals have been found in water one hundred fathoms deep.

The Zebra Fish, *Pterois volitans,* as it floats majestically through the water, its queer fins gracefully waving and undulating, looks more like an apparition than a fish. It has its very large dorsal and pectoral fins separated, each fin-ray or spine being free of the others and having its own narrow strip of fin. This, together with its large, spotted pelvic, anal, and caudal fins, the bold black and white striping on its body, and the peculiar fleshly decorations around its eyes and mouth, makes the zebra fish at once one of the most bizarre and beautiful of all the sea's inhabitants.

That this fish is a menace is quickly apparent to anyone touching its spines, however, for they are quite poisonous and can cause much pain. Its gluttonous appetite is also quite matter of fact. In nature the zebra fish preys upon other living fishes, but in captivity it can be taught to eat pieces of dead fish and clam. Care must be taken not to overfeed captive specimens, because zebra fish have been known actually to gorge themselves so much that they died of indigestion or something akin to it.

Zebra fish sometimes seem to exert a weird immobilizing effect on the small fish upon which they prey. Instead of fleeing as it ordinarily would at the approach of a large fish, the prospective prey remains as if transfixed, quivering violently until with a sudden gulp the zebra fish swallows it. This member of the family of scorpion fishes is widely distributed in the Indian Ocean and Southwest Pacific. It reaches a length of somewhat over one foot.

The Stonefish, *Synanceja verrucosa,* and its close relatives are undoubtedly the most poisonous of all fishes. Along the stonefish's back is a series of thirteen large spines. Each of these has a pair of small sacs of venom attached to it, so arranged that any pressure exerted on the spine will cause the sacs to eject their poisonous fluid along the shallow grooves on either side, and to enter any wound made by the sharp-pointed spine. The venom is a limpid, bluish, slightly acrid fluid that causes excruciating pain. Men who have received the full force of the stonefish's poison have rolled on the ground, become delirious, attacked people trying to help them and even tried to amputate the affected limb—so great was their agony. Death may result from severe shock, heart failure, or, later, infectious poisoning. The wounds heal very slowly; recovery is a matter of months.

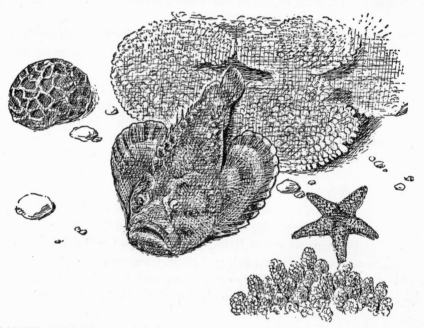

DANGER AMID THE CORAL

    The stonefish is colored like the rocks of coral among which it lives, but it is far deadlier than they. One of the scorpion fishes, this dangerous creature has on its back poison-bearing spines that can inflict a wound which is exceedingly painful, if not fatal. Fortunately the fish dwells only in some of the tropical seas.

The stonefish habitually lies on the bottom around tropical reefs and inlets. It has a flattened, short triangular body with a large mouth whose gape is almost vertical. Its whole body is covered with warty growths, and in life it looks exactly like a piece of eroded coral. It feeds on a variety of creatures that it apparently engulfs with its cavernous maw as they unsuspectingly swim by its place of concealment.

Stonefish do not retreat even when approached by a large animal, apparently depending on their camouflage and poison for protection. Thus it is very possible for them to be stepped on unwittingly. Fortunately they seem to be nowhere common, although they are found over a large part of the Indian Ocean and the waters around northern Australia, the East Indies, and the Pacific islands. They attain a length of about one foot.

The Common Sea Robin, *Prionotus carolinus,* can be quickly recognized by the bony plates covering its head, by its two dorsal fins, and by its very large, winglike pectorals at the bottom of which are

FISH THAT "WALK" AND "SING"

The common sea robins, two of which are pictured above, are sometimes reported to have been seen walking on the sea bottom. They do not have feet, but there are rays on the pectoral fins which do look like feet—with these the fish examine the ocean floor. The creatures can produce a cackling sound by means of their swim-bladder.

located three free, thickened rays. These are bent like arched fingers and seem to be walked on as the fish moves along the bottom. The chances are that any fish from the east coast of the United States, described by the uninitiated as having "feet," is one of the sea robins. These rays are undoubtedly used by the fish to explore the bottom. Common sea robins feed principally on small crustaceans that live on or near the bottom. Squid, bivalves, worms, and fishes are taken to a lesser extent.

This fish spawns during the summer. The female lays slightly yellowish, buoyant eggs, about one-thirty-second of an inch in diameter. They hatch in about sixty hours at 72° Fahrenheit. The larvae are a little less than one-sixteenth of an inch long at hatching. The maximum length is about sixteen inches.

The common sea robin is found in shallow waters from the Bay of Fundy to South Carolina, but it is rare north of Cape Cod. During the cold months it disappears from New England and New Jersey, while remaining in Chesapeake Bay and more southern waters all year 'round.

By means of special muscles that vibrate its swim-bladder, the common sea robin makes noises, described as a rhythmic squawk, squeal, or cackle, such as might be heard in a barnyard. These sounds are also said to be similar to those made by drawing one's forefinger and thumb towards each other over the dry surface of an inflated rubber balloon.

The Sea Raven, *Hemitripterus americanus,* looks extremely ragged because of the numerous fleshy tags on its head and the jagged profile of its dorsal fin—which has the individual spines separated from one another and tipped with tiny flaps as if the fish had just come through some terrible ordeal. The entire skin is prickly. Coloration ranges from blood red through reddish purple to chocolate and yellowish brown.

Sea ravens are bottom-inhabiting sculpins; they feed on various invertebrates and on other fishes, which they catch with their large sharp-toothed mouth. During the winter sea ravens come closer to shore than in the warmer months, since they quite definitely prefer cold water. They are found from Labrador, Newfoundland and the Grand Banks south to Chesapeake Bay.

Adhesive eggs, with a diameter of about five thirty-seconds of an

New York Zoological Society Photos

THE PORCUPINE FISH PUFFS ITSELF UP FOR PROTECTION

After blowing itself up with either air or water, the porcupine fish appears droll to us, but to a hungry fish it must seem a most unappealing morsel. Nevertheless, porcupine fish have been occasionally found in the stomachs of larger fishes.

SPAWNING OF THE FIGHTING FISH

Under the bubble nest that he has built, a male Siamese fighting fish (the lighter-colored individual) clasps his mate as her eggs sink slowly through the water. Quickly he turns and dashes down to pick them up in his mouth — even before some of them reach the bottom. He then swims up and places them among the bubbles of his surface nest. The male fish continues to guard the young after they hatch, which event takes place in about two days, and to replace any babies that fall out of the nest. Siamese fighting fish are noted for their pugnacity.

New York Zoological Society

MARINE HITCHHIKERS

Two shark suckers have attached themselves to this sand shark by means of the sucking plate on the top of their head. Shark suckers will attach themselves to other large fish and vessels as well.

CAMOUFLAGE ARTISTS

The gulf flounder, *Paralichthys albiguttus,* is closely related to the fluke and, like that fish, can change its colors to match the background upon which it is resting. It does this by expanding or contracting the pigment within the thousands of pigment cells in its skin. This species has its eyes and pigment on the left side, and lies on its right side, which is more or less colorless.

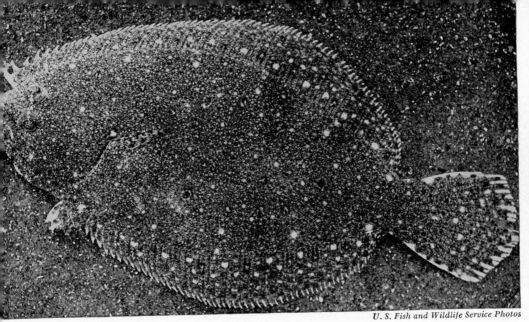

THE GULF FLOUNDER CAN VERY CLOSELY MATCH A NATURAL BACKGROUND

IT IS ABLE ONLY TO APPROXIMATE THIS ARTIFICIAL ONE, HOWEVER

A FISH THAT ACTS LIKE A FROG

In behavior, as well as appearance, the mudskipper resembles a frog, but it is a true fish. In order to demonstrate its ability to travel on land, a corrugated paper ramp was built. The mudskipper, as these striking photographs reveal, showed no hesitation in using it.

The mudskipper's head is particularly froglike with its bulging eyes, its broad, round face, and its wide mouth.

The mudskipper can use its two ventral fins, which are united at the base, as a sort of pedestal (bottom picture).

Lilo Hess—Three Lions

Lilo Hess—Three Lions

By rowing movements of its pectoral fins, the mudskipper inched itself up the ramp, resting on its ventral fins in between these strenuous efforts.

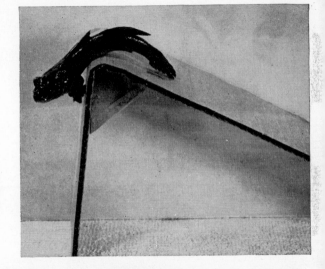

Over the top! The fish showed no hesitation at all in taking the short dive. In nature it takes much greater ones.

Not much grace, but effective nonetheless. Mudskippers are agile, and quick enough to catch insects on the wing.

A FISH WITH REMARKABLE EYES

This strange-looking creature with the bulging eyes is known as the foureye fish (why it is so named is explained below). It is found in some of the warmer waters of the New World, and is so agile that it is not easily caught. Small crustaceans, insects, and algae make up its diet.

THE FOUREYE FISH CRUISES ALONG THE SURFACE

The upper half of the eye of the foureye fish is adapted for vision in air above the water line, while the lower half is adjusted to seeing in the water. A dumbbell-shaped pupil makes simultaneous use of these parts possible. The fish spends most of its time at or close to the surface.

FATHER SEAHORSE GIVES BIRTH

It is the male seahorse that carries the young around in a pouch on his abdomen and finally, with much apparent effort, launches them into the world. Here a baby is shown just emerging while another clings to the twig on the right and a third one swims above it.

FLYING THROUGH THE WATER
These cow-nosed rays, *Rhinopter
quadriloba*, gracefully flap thei
broad pectoral fins. They ar
smaller relatives of the devil ray
not exceeding seven feet in width
On the right rises a column of ai
bubbles, which serves to aerat
the aquarium where the rays live

BIZARRE YET BEAUTIFUL
The zebra fish looks scarcely real as it slowly floats through the water. Most prominent in this view are the long rays of the pectoral fins, but those of the dorsal and
ventral fins are also apparent. Some of these rays can inflict painful wounds.

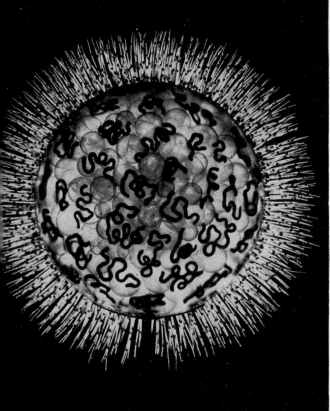

CHRISTMAS TREE ORNAMENT?

In reality it is an exquisite ball of small protozoans that floats near or on the ocean surface, supported by its many spines, which are dotted with oil. Each little **individual** in the ball has a **bright** red snakelike nucleus. The whole bubbly mass is known as a serpentine radiolarian, and is quite large for this very low form of animal life — it may be one or two inches in diameter.

ANOTHER PROTOZOAN BEAUTY

Globigerina bulloides starts life in one little ball, but with growth flows out from its main opening, secreting a new, larger ball. This process continues through life, resulting in a succession of balls of steadily increasing size. They belong to a primitive form of life known as foraminifera, and live in oceans all around the world, sometimes at the surface and sometimes on the bottom.

INCHES   1   2   3

Photos on this and next page: Lilo Hess—Three Lions

A SNAIL DEMONSTRATES HOW SLOWLY IT TRAVELS

The slow pace of the snail is a byword the world over, but these remarkable photographs present it as a measurable fact. Note that, at the start of its travels along the ruler, the animal has deposited some slime; it oils its path with this as it moves along. In one respect at least the snail is more fortunate than many other living things — it does not have to return home, for it carries its house wherever it goes. Shown here is the common pale brown land snail.

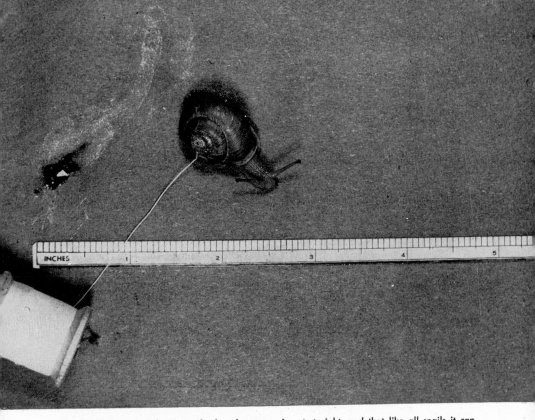

This snail has proved that its path, though narrow, is not straight, and that like all snails it can travel about three inches a minute. Such a rate is hardly fast enough to help it to escape its enemies — birds, mice, shrews, and other animals.

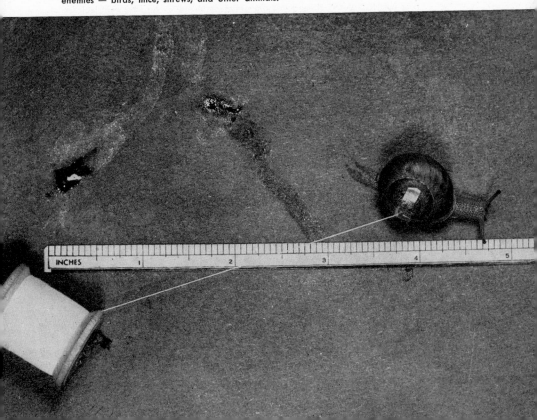

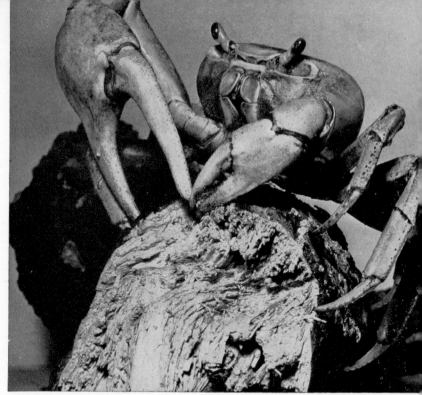

LARGEST OF THE LAND CRABS
This big crab, common in the West Indies, occasionally comes ashore in Texas.

THE WOLF SPIDER HAS EIGHT EYES
Four eyes look down; above them, two eyes look ahead; on top, two eyes look up.

SHE LOVES HIM
AND EATS HIM

Immediately after mating, the female praying mantis cuts her husband in two just behind the forelegs, and devours the softer portions of his body, discarding the dry wings, legs, and head. Only a few other insects have this husband-eating habit, but several of the spiders do.

MR. WALKING STICK
DANCES FOR HIS LADY

The common northern walking stick appears very awkward to us, with its long (four-inch) twiglike body and legs, and its stiff, jerky movements. Nevertheless, the male usually courts the female by dancing before her, and she seems to appreciate it.

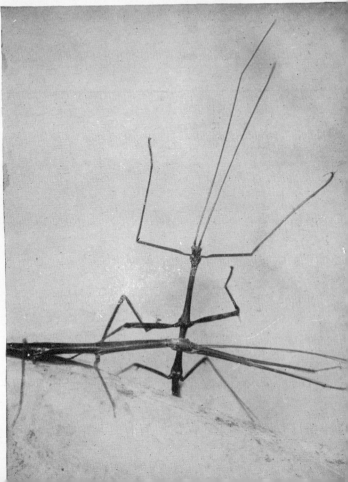

Lilo Hess
Three Lions Photos

American Museum of Natural History

**DRAGONFLY NYMPH
SEIZES MOSQUITO LARVA**
The dragonfly nymph does not
need to use its feet to seize its
victim. It has an extendible
mouth part (labium) which it
can quickly shoot out. At the
end of the labium two small
claws grasp and hold the prey.

**MR AND MRS. DRAGONFLY
FLY TANDEM**
They fly together over ponds
and streams, looking for suitable homes for their progeny.
Sometimes they pause just at the
surface of the water, where,
furiously fanning his wings, the
male can keep his mate safe
while she deposits her eggs.

*Lilo Hess
Three Lions*

MR. KATYDID FIDDLES
TO HIS LOVE

He stands on his head before her and rubs his forewings together, making the familiar rasping "Katydid, Katy didn't" noise that we associate with late summer. Not all species of katydid use this courting technique; each kind has its special method.

A GIANT KATYDID FROM NEW GUINEA

It may grow up to be four inches long. See how the prothorax (behind the head) is enlarged to a serrated shield. The wings look like leaves. The dark spot you can see on the front leg of the katydid is a kind of hearing organ.

A CICADA READY FOR WINGS

After two years spent underground this cicada has dug its way to the surface and is now looking for a tree or stout plant to climb. There it will break out of its ugly shell. Other species of cicadas spend thirteen or seventeen years below.

THIS IS A NIGHT JOB

Holding fast to the bark of a tree, the cicada is ready to split its nymphal case down the back and push itself out. It does this at night, when there are no birds around to take advantage of its helplessness.

ITS BACK HAS SPLIT OPEN

Now the insect has begun to push its head and part of its back out of the case. It is almost white as it emerges from the brown shell, but will soon change to subdued tones of brownish or greenish gray.

THE NEW CICADA EMERGES

After a few minutes most of the body has emerged and the cicada is struggling to get its legs out. Below, you can now see the tightly folded wings on each side of the body. Finally the cicada manages to free the last segments of its abdomen and ovipositor, or egg-laying apparatus (this is a female).

Photos on this and facing page:
Gerard (Monkmeyer)

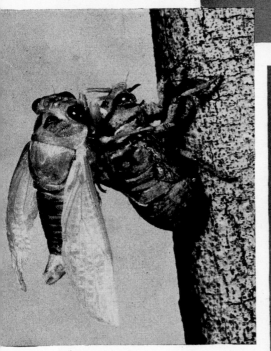

WINGS!

Perched on the husk of her former self, the cicada rests while her body fluids flow into her wings, which unfold, expand, and dry. The emergence has taken about one hour. At last, adult and lovely, she wanders off a few feet and waits to hear some male cicada drumming upon his abdomen. She herself is silent.

CHANGA FROM PUERTO RICO

This nightmarish apparition consists of nothing more fearful than the solemn face and sharp claws of a West Indian mole cricket, called a "changa" by Puerto Ricans. We call it a mole cricket because the insect burrows in the ground.

HEAD OF A COMMON CORN EARWORM — A MOTH IN THE MAKING

The ten beady dots forming a semicircle are the simple eyes or ocelli of this larva, which is greatly magnified here. Above the ocelli you can see the outline of the undeveloped large compound eyes the moth will have. These do not function in the larva. Living in the dark, surrounded by its food, it does not require sharp vision.

MORMON CRICKET

About two inches long and wingless, the Morman cricket is popeyed and bland of face. In color it varies from pale yellow to dark brown, black, and sometimes green. This cricket feeds on almost everything edible — vegetation, dead animals, and its fellows. It is common in Utah.

AMERICAN COCKROACH

Compare its large, oddly shaped eyes with the Morman cricket's smaller ones. Cockroaches work at night, so they need larger eyes than the daylight-loving cricket. A native of Florida, this cockroach has emigrated north and south, and has even reached Europe, traveling as a ship's stowaway.

A BIG-GAME HUNTER OF THE INSECT WORLD AND ITS PREY

The robber fly, which feeds on other insects, is so audacious that it thinks nothing of seizing a victim much heavier than itself. With its two front legs it clings desperately to the twig while it grasps the prey, a dragonfly, with its middle and hind legs. It will not drop the dragonfly.

American Museum of Natural History

MAGNIFIED FACE OF THE COMMON HOUSEFLY

It looks like a marvelously engraved and jeweled brooch; the design is intricate and the crafts-manship perfect. Those huge, beaded mounds at the left and right are the compound eyes of the insect. They are set with thousands of tiny lenses, giving the fly remarkably good vision. The object at the bottom is the tongue. It is fitted, at the tip, with a rasp or grater. This scrapes the food into small portions, serving the housefly the way teeth do the higher animals.

Lilo Hess—Three L

A STAG BEETLE TOURNAMENT

Two male stag beetles are dueling for the favor of the lady, seen watching amid shadows at the
bottom. The combatants do not necessarily fight to the death; usually it is enough for the victor
if he can overthrow his rival, as he has done in this instance. With his cumbersome build, the
vanquished one will be unable to get himself right side up again for some time.

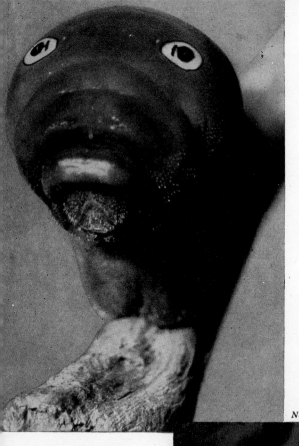

WHAT GREAT BIG EYES!

But this caterpillar is fooling you. Those alarming "eyes" are only spots placed far back behind the head; perhaps they serve to scare away hungry birds. This is the caterpillar of the tiger swallowtail butterfly. Some other species of swallowtails go further — they have two sets of false eyes.

New York Zoological Society

ECROPIA CATERPILLAR

is caterpillar of the Cecropia
oth eats and eats and eats,
r it is going to be a very large
oth. It is pale green, decor-
ed on the back with red and
llow horns. Its true legs are
ose together up near its head.
e false, fat legs you notice are
ere extensions of the abdom-
al segments of this larva.

John C. Pallister

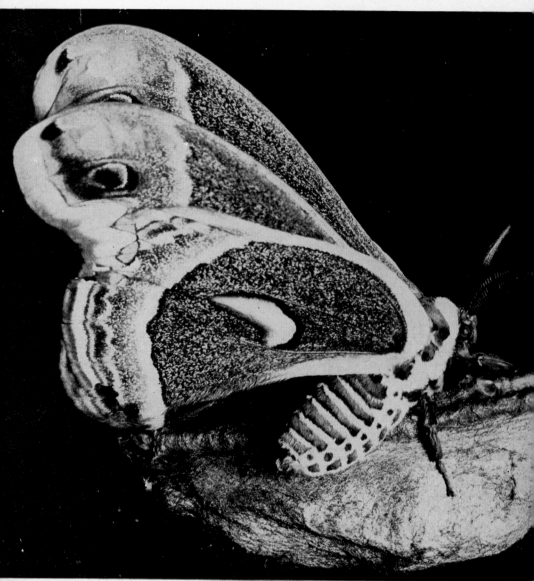

THE CECROPIA — LARGEST MOTH OF THE EASTERN UNITED STATES

This gorgeous creature has just come out of its cocoon and is resting on top of it. Its wings are not yet fully developed. From its heavy abdomen you might think this moth to be a female; but the abdomen will decrease in size within the next few minutes as the body fluids flow into the veins of the expanding wings. The large feather-like antennae tell us this insect is a male.

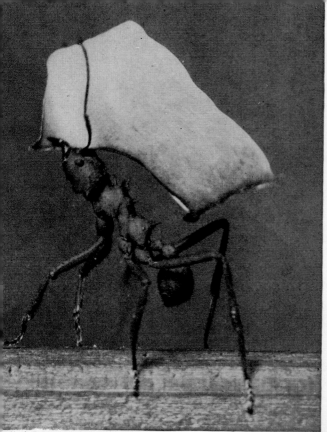

A LEAF-CUTTING OR PARASOL ANT
This ant is carrying part of a green leaf to its nest underground, where the leaf will be used in a bed to grow fungi for food. Parasol ants live in huge colonies sometimes thirty feet across and ten feet deep. The nest is mostly below the surface of the ground; only a small mound at the top shows its location.

AN ANT EMERGING FROM ITS PUPAL CASE
Nurse ants will clean up this young one, and may feed it its first few meals. Soon it will start work; first it will serve as a nurse ant, but later it will graduate to a field ant job. Notice that the ant's eyes are not so large as those of some other insects — living in burrows and close to the ground, it has little need for keen vision. Ant pupal cases are sold as "ant eggs," a bird food.

Lilo Hess—Three L

A WORKER WASP GOES ABOUT ITS HOUSEWORK

This wasp appears to be busily examining a larva, to see how it is developing; later, when it emerges as an adult, it too will take over some of the duties of the wasp colony. All around the worker you can see empty cells, some still with ragged edges. These the worker will clean up, so that the queen may lay more eggs in them. Unlike bees, wasps feed mainly on insects.

inch and ranging in color from bright orange to pale yellow, are laid among the fingers of sponges from mid-October to late December at the latitude of New York. Hatching probably does not take place until after several months. The larvae are not quite half an inch long when they first emerge from the egg. At the age of one and one-half years, young sea ravens are about six inches long. A maximum length of twenty-one and three-fourths inches and a weight of five pounds, five ounces, has been reported.

The Miller's Thumb, *Cottus bairdi,* is a small, grotesque fish from the streams and lakes of eastern North America. It prefers cool, clear water with a rocky or gravelly bottom. It often hides under stones, rarely swimming in midwater. Its large head is bony and flattened, with the eyes located high on the sides. The body sharply tapers down towards the tail and is practically naked. The pectoral fins are large. A length of seven inches may be attained, although most adult specimens range between three and five inches.

During spring and early summer, masses of adhesive eggs are laid, usually attached to the underside of stones or, more rarely, on aquatic plants. The male prepares the nesting site and generally guards the eggs. Two or three females may lay in a single nest. The salmon-colored eggs are large, being about one-eighth inch in diameter. Miller's thumbs principally eat algae, small fishes, and crustaceans, and aquatic insects and their larvae. They consume the eggs of other fishes, when they can get them, but have been cleared of the charge of destroying significant quantities of trout eggs.

The Lumpfish, *Cyclopterus lumpus,* is just that—a lump of a fish. It is short from head to tail and deep from back to belly. The belly is wide and flattened while the back is narrow and rigid, giving the fish a triangular cross section. The back is also strongly arched from head to tail, and the skin is covered with wartlike tubercles in place of scales. The ventral fins are modified into a sucker, located just behind the throat. The fish may be gray, brown, yellow-green, or slate-blue in color. During the spawning season the lower portions of the male's body become bright red.

As many as a hundred thirty-six thousand adhesive eggs are laid by a single female in large spongelike clumps during late winter and spring. These are faithfully guarded and cared for by the male, who blows water through the egg mass, fans it with his pectoral fins and drives away all intruders, including fishes larger than himself. If the water temperature is low, hatching may take two months, at the end of which time the father fish appears quite worn out. The eggs are pink when first laid but change color as they develop. They are about one-eighth of an inch in diameter.

Newly hatched lumpfish are about one-fourth of an inch long and fully equipped with a tiny sucker which they use to fasten themselves to seaweed and other drifting objects.

Adult lumpfish inhabit cool waters off the coast of North America from Hudson Bay and Greenland south to New Jersey and, exceptionally, Maryland. To the east they are found along the coast of Europe south to the Bay of Biscay. Although lengths of two feet and weights of twenty pounds may be reached, most specimens are considerably smaller.

Flatfishes—They Swim on Their Side

No DOUBT you have met the halibut, the flounder, and the sole so many times at the dinner table that you consider them among the most commonplace of fishes. Yet people who see them alive—who watch the strange way they grow—feel that they are entitled to a place in the front rank of nature's wonders!

These ordinary-seeming creatures go by the name of flatfishes, and flat they are. But that is not what is really curious about them. The odd fact is that after having passed their babyhood swimming like other fishes, they make a remarkable change—they turn on their sides, and spend the rest of their lives swimming that way.

Even more noteworthy than all this is what happens to the fish's eyes. Earlier in normal position, they make the change, too: they move to the top side of the head. Now we call this the "eyed side"; the other, on which the fish lies, is the "blind side." The skull and jaws, gill-covers, paired fins, lateral line, and other organs alter as part of this extraordinary shift, so that they may best serve the flatfish in its new, one-sided way of life. (The flatfishes belong in the order Heterosomata, which means "different bodies.")

At the same time, the color changes in most of the flatfishes. Just one side—the side bearing the eyes—has pigment in it. The "blind side" becomes plain white. You may expect exceptions here as else-where, and we find some abnormal fishes with color on top and bot-tom, others with no color at all.

When the flatfishes swim they keep their whole body in a plane, more or less parallel to the ocean floor. As a rule, they make their home on the bottom of the sea, most of them staying rather near shore. Sometimes a number may venture up rivers, and there are members of the sole and tonguefish families that live entirely in fresh water. By and large the six hundred or so different kinds of flatfishes lay eggs that float in mid-water or at the surface. The winter flounder, whose ways we shall soon examine more closely, is a notable exception.

One sure way of recognizing the flatfishes, we have seen, is by the eyes, which are always on one side of the head. But which side? That depends on the species. The turbot, European brill, summer flounder, and sundial (family Bothidae)—found widely scattered through tem-perate and tropical seas, mainly—have eyes on their left side. The op-posite is true of the halibuts, winter flounder, plaice, lemon sole, yellow-tail, and starry flounder (family Pleuronectidae). However, driving home again the great truth that nature is variable and that it is a rare generalization that fits all the facts, a few species regularly show individuals with eyes on the left. The fishes of this family are salt-water-dwellers, and we encounter them practically all over the world, from the Arctic almost to the Antarctic.

North Americans are fond of fillet of sole, but many have learned by now that it comes from other fishes masquerading under that title for the chef's convenience. The true soles (family Soleidae), includ-ing the hogchoker, do dwell in North American waters, but those of economic importance are found around Europe and South Africa. It is in warm-temperate and tropical seas that they are most numerous, and the same are also the home of the tonguefishs (family Cynoglos-sidae). But though the tonguefishes and the soles may meet, they cannot see eye to eye: the first have their vision on the left side, the second on the right.

The Pacific Halibut, *Hippoglossus stenolepis,* has had the distinction of being studied by an International Fisheries Commission set up by Canada and the United States especially for that purpose. Alarmed by the decline of the fishery, these countries in 1924 ratified a treaty that created a body of scientific experts to find out the essential facts in the life history and fishing of the Pacific halibut. No idle business, this. Proper regulations were needed to place the fishery on a sound basis for the years to come, but first there had to be sound knowledge.

In 1930 the recommendations of this group of scientists were accepted by both governments and a new treaty was signed, giving the Commission power to regulate the fishery. Although the efficacy of its rule has been argued both pro and con, the fact remains that Pacific halibut fishing has improved in recent years.

Approximately fifty million pounds of Pacific halibut are now taken annually. The fish are caught by hook-and-line in waters ranging from ten to five hundred fathoms deep. The fish is marketed fresh or frozen and the liver and other viscera are treated to yield valuable, vitamin-rich oil. As an example of international cooperation for the purpose of advancing the cause of conservation and the intelligent, long-term utilization of a natural resource, the case of the Pacific halibut is classic.

Pacific halibut reach a weight of at least 470 pounds and an age of thirty-five years or more. Like all the flatfish, they lie upon their sides as they rest upon the bottom.

The story of how the Pacific halibut grows and develops is more curious than any you can find in fiction. When first hatched out of its egg, a baby Pacific halibut is not unlike many other larval fishes—has an eye on either side of its head, and it soon grows normally located fins. It stays this way from a size of about five-sixteenths of an inch (the size at hatching) until the baby is about nine-sixteenths of an inch, but at this time peculiar changes start to take place.

Little by little, the baby's left eye becomes elevated above the right one and shortly afterward the right eye begins to move down on its side of the skull. The left eye now makes an amazing migration from the left to the right side of the head of the fish. Meanwhile the pigment on the left side has not developed as much as that on the right. The body broadens—from back to belly—and by the time the fish is about one and a quarter inches long, the baby Pacific halibut looks very much like a miniature adult, with both eyes on the right side of its head and with the left or "blind side" practically devoid of pigment. The right or "eyed side" is colored a dark brown or gray. The fish thus lies on its left side on the bottom, and when it swims, it keeps its eyed side uppermost, its blind side facing the bottom.

As a result of the investigations of the International Commission, we know a great deal about the Pacific halibut. There are still, however, many things about the fish we should know but do not. On the average, females mature when twelve years old, but males do so when considerably younger. Spawning occurs from November to January. A female weighing 140 pounds may produce as many as 2,700,000 eggs. These eggs are relatively large, being more than one-eighth of an inch in diameter. They float freely in deep water until hatching, after which the larvae, too, continue to live in mid-water. When four or five months have passed, they rise toward the surface to be carried inshore by winds and currents. Here the young change into small halibut, and take up their life on the bottom. During this long period the eggs and young are at the mercy of the elements and their predatory enemies, consequently the death rate is very heavy.

Unlike many flatfishes, halibut not only feed upon fishes, crabs, clams, and worms that live on the bottom, but actively pursue prey, such as squid and fast-moving fishes.

The Pacific halibut ranges from the Bering and Okhotsk Seas south to California. The fishing regions or banks run along the coast of North America from the southwestern tip of Alaska to Washington.

The Atlantic Halibut, *Hippoglossus hippoglossus,* can be distinguished from the Pacific species by its somewhat differently shaped body and by its scales and the way they are set in the skin. Said to attain weights of seven hundred pounds, this is the largest of all the flatfishes. These giants may live as long as forty years. The Atlantic halibut is found in the North Atlantic as far south as New York and the Bay of Biscay.

The Summer Flounder or Northern Fluke, *Paralichthys dentatus,* possesses two distinct means of concealing itself as it rests on the bottom. One is by "bedding." As the fish comes to rest on a muddy or sandy bottom, it vibrates its body, fins, and tail in such a way that water currents are set up carrying the loose material composing the bottom out from under it. The fish then quickly stops moving and drops to the bottom. The material stirred up settles on top of it, covering most of its body or, if the material is coarse, its edges.

The second method is "concealing coloration." The fish comes to match the background upon which it rests. It accomplishes this by changes in the various kinds of pigment cells that color the eyed side. The summer flounder has remarkable powers of duplicating the visual effect of a muddy, sandy, gravelly, stony, or shell-covered bottom. On a very dark background the fish will become practically black, on a very light one, almost white. Blue, green, yellow, orange, pink, and various shades of brown are all excellently matched, but red is not. It takes several months, however, for the fish to assume a green or blue coloration, while yellows and brown can be duplicated in much less time. On the other hand, many changes in pattern, rather than hue, can be effected in a matter of minutes.

As startling as these color and pattern changes are, the summer flounder cannot assume the appearance of a Scotch plaid, no matter how long it may be forced to live upon one!

All flatfishes apparently possess the power of matching their background to some degree; in the summer flounder it is especially well developed. Experiments have shown that the pigment cells are controlled by nerves, and that the fish must see its background to be able to match it. Blind summer flounders do not match their environment at all. It has also been demonstrated, however, that hormones influence the color and pattern of the fish. Finally, we know that light, acting directly on the individual pigment cell, can also bring about pigmentation, because summer flounders that have their right, colorless and eyeless sides exposed to light—by being kept in a glass-bottom tank over electric lights—develop some pigment on that side, whether they are blind or not. Control of coloration in these fishes is therefore a complicated process.

As indicated above, the summer flounder rests on its right side, both of its eyes being on the left, in contrast to the halibut and winter flounder. Occasionally, a flatfish is *reversed*, that is, an individual belonging to a species normally having its eyes on its left side will have them on its right side instead and vice versa. At least one reversed summer flounder is on record; it had its eyes on the right side but was colored on both sides.

Although there is little definite information on the reproductive habits of the summer flounder, all indications are that it spawns during the early winter and that the eggs are buoyant. It feeds on a variety of animal life, often rising to the surface in its efforts to catch fish. The maximum weight is twenty-six pounds but it usually does not exceed five. It is an excellent foodfish and a popular gamefish; well over eleven million pounds are caught yearly. It ranges along the Atlantic coast of the United States from Massachusetts to Florida.

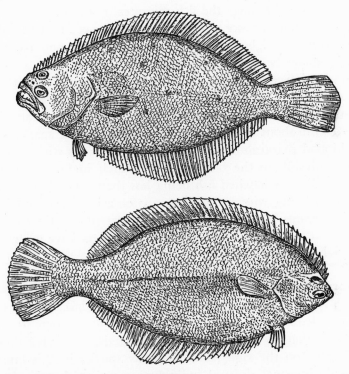

FLOUNDERS AND THEIR CURIOUS EYES
Flounders, or flatfishes have two eyes, all right—but both are on the same side; the fish lie on the other side, which is blind. The chief difference between the summer flounder (top) and the winter flounder (bottom) is that the eyes of the first are on the left, while the eyes of the second are on the right.

The Winter Flounder, *Pseudopleuronectes americanus,* lies on the bottom, and when some shrimp or crab appears, it rapidly pursues it, snaps it up, and again settles down to rest. It undoubtedly also roots out some of its food, because bivalves and worms that live beneath the surface have been found in its stomach. Occasionally it catches small fish, but cannot eat large ones, as its mouth is rather small.

This species is a dextral or right-handed flatfish, that is, its eyes are both on the right side, and it lies on its colorless left side when resting. Sinistral, or left-handed, winter flounders, having eyes and pigment on the left side and no pigment on the right, are very rare.

A popular food and game fish, the winter flounder is well known to both commercial and sports fishermen. It is found along the Atlantic coast of North America from Labrador to Georgia. In the warmer parts of its range the fish migrates offshore during the summer. A specimen of more than five pounds is very unusual; the record individual weighed slightly more than five pounds, thirteen ounces, and was twenty-two inches long.

Reproduction takes place from mid-December to May in the vicinity of southern New England. In water from one to three fathoms deep, small groups of fish swim rapidly in tight circles, scattering the eggs and milt about in a manner reminiscent of the sparks from an old fashioned pyrotechnic pinwheel. The tiny eggs stick together in clusters and sink to the bottom. They hatch in fifteen days at 69 degrees, the newly hatched fish being less than three-sixteenths of an inch long. Young winter flounders are occasionally found in fresh water in streams but never far from the sea. By the time they have become two to three years old, winter flounders have grown to between eight and ten inches in length.

The Starry Flounder, *Platichthys stellatus,* ranges along the West Coast of North America from southern California to Alaska and in the Far East north from Japan and Korea. This species belongs to a family of flatfishes that are normally dextral; that is, they have their eyes and pigment on the right side. In many species in this family, an occasional abnormal sinistral individual turns up, but in the starry flounder a large percentage of these reversed fish, with color and eyes on the left side, occurs. In California about half the starry flounders are reversed, in Alaska about two-thirds, and in Japan the great ma· jority of individuals are sinistral.

The body of the starry flounder is covered with small, spinelike, star-shaped plates, from whence it gets its name. It grows to a size of twenty pounds but averages considerably less. The eggs are laid from early winter to early spring. A variety of invertebrates, including crabs, shrimps, worms, and bivalves, make up its food.

Adults usually live in shallow salt water, along the shore, sometimes venturing into deeper areas, but the young are often found in the fresh or brackish waters of the lower reaches of streams. Of the several species of flatfishes on the Pacific coast of North America, the starry flounder is the most important for sports fishing. It is also an important commercial foodfish.

The Common European Sole, *Solea solea,* provided the original filet of sole, a great delicacy supposed by some epicures to be the most tasty of piscine dishes. Those foodfishes in North America called soles are not true soles. The true soles are characterized by their very flat, leaflike or tonguelike appearance, with dorsal, tail, and anal fins often continuous with one another, making a complete fringe around the body. The mouth, as well as the pair of eyes, is completely reoriented, being twisted almost completely onto the under side of the head; that is, to the left side of the fish, while the eyes are located on the right side. The true soles found in North America, such as the hogchoker, are of practically no commercial value.

The common European sole is found from the North Sea to and throughout the Mediterranean. The usual size at which it is marketed is about eight inches. During the day soles hide most of the time, doing their feeding at night. They eat bottom-inhabiting forms like worms and shrimp, which they apparently detect by means of tiny filaments on the under side of the head. Spawning occurs from April to August. The eggs float in mid-water, hatching in about ten days. Young soles frequent shallow water but move further offshore as they grow larger.

Shark Suckers—Other Fishes Carry Them

THE SHARK SUCKER or remora has a "free ticket" to journey almost anywhere it wishes in the great watery world of our tropical and temperate seas. The vehicle it travels on may be a shark, a barracuda, a marlin, a swordfish, a whale, or even a ship. It carries its ticket with it always: a sucking disk on top of its head, enabling the remora to attach itself to these carriers and leave them at will.

For creatures that travel free of charge, the shark suckers are difficult to please when it comes to selecting their transportation. Of the ten species or so, some have a marked preference for one type of carrier, some for another. Usually, however, they show a certain amount of latitude in their choice.

Remoras attach themselves in some peculiar spots. Favorite places are inside the gill-cavities or mouths of large fishes like sharks, marine sunfishes, and the swordfish, for instance.

The largest of the remoras reach a length of three to four feet. All those alive today are placed in a single family (Echeneidae) in the order Discocephali—"disk-headed" is a literal translation.

The Shark Sucker, *Echeneis naucrates,* regularly takes free rides on large fishes and turtles, and sometimes on porpoises and ships, by fastening itself to them by means of a powerful sucker. This organ is located on the top of its head, and is a flat, oval plate with raised edges, having twenty or more narrow slats in its center. These can be raised, thus creating a vacuum. They are also provided with tiny backward-pointing spines; when pressure is applied from the front, they prevent the shark sucker from sliding off the surface to which it is attached. Once a shark sucker has fastened itself, it cannot be removed by pulling on its tail, but must be slid off forwards or sideways, or the edge of the plate must be lifted to destroy the vacuum.

The shark sucker sometimes uses a shark only as a means of transportation, leaving its carrier in order to feed on small fishes. At other times it also shares the shark's food, picking up scraps from its table so to speak. Despite its "hitchhiking" habits, the shark sucker can swim very well and rapidly on its own. It has to, in order to catch a ride on a swiftly moving fish.

This species is somewhat elongated with a rather long second dorsal and anal fin, and a squared-off tail fin. Its first dorsal fin is lacking since it has become modified to form the sucker. The shark sucker has an undershot jaw, and it is provided with many small teeth.

Color changes are very rapid; the fish may be almost black or almost entirely white or marked with broad, longitudinal black and white stripes, changing pattern from one minute to the next. The shark sucker reaches a length of about two feet. It is found in all tropical seas, and during the warm months ventures into temperate zones. It has been reported as far north as Massachusetts on the east coast of North America and San Francisco on the west.

At one time in northern Australia, southeastern Asia, western Africa, northern South America and the West Indies, the larger species of remoras were used in fishing. A line was attached to the fish's tail and it was allowed to swim about until it attached itself to some large fish or turtle. Then by slow, steady pulling both remora and the creature to which it was attached were brought to the fisherman's hands. As we have already suggested, the remora is unable to free itself if a pull directly backwards is exerted on it. This peculiar kind of fishing is still carried on with the shark sucker in some parts of the West Indies.

The feasibility of this method of fishing was once tested at the New York Aquarium. After placing a large shark sucker in a bucket filled with sea water, it was found that the whole bucket could be lifted off the ground by grasping the fish's tail. So strong was the suction developed that the two shark suckers tested supported buckets filled with water that weighed twenty-one and twenty-four pounds respectively.

So far as known, the remoras lay pelagic eggs. The larvae, up to a size of about one-third of an inch, have no sucker and float in the open sea.

Trigger Fishes, Trunkfishes, Puffers, and Their Relatives

In THE TROPICS, in ocean waters of little depth, dwell the trigger fishes, the trunkfishes, the puffers, and their equally strange relatives. Often they throng the waters around coral reefs. They lack a streamlined body, and, when danger approaches, you might expect them to be somewhat at a loss.

Many of these fishes, however, are ready to meet all comers. They have an array of spectacular defense mechanisms they can depend upon. Some bristle with spines; some can turn a hard, bony shell to bear the brunt of the onslaught; others can blow themselves up like a balloon to foil the attacker. A number possess sharp teeth, capable of inflicting painful wounds.

Large, rough scales cover the bodies of the trigger fishes (family Balistidae), creatures that actually have a trigger mechanism in their dorsal fin. We shall see later in this chapter how they use it. For most of this large group, the central and western Pacific is home. Many are extravagantly colored, but the few that occur in warmer temperate waters or offshore tend to be dull. The maximum size of practically all lies between six inches and two feet. With their powerful teeth they are able to cut into shells to get at the living animal inside.

Because their leathery skin is covered with tiny prickles making it rough to the touch, another family is known as the filefishes (Monacanthidae). They are shaped like their cousins the trigger fishes but the body is narrower and the first dorsal fin is just a single long spine. On the whole, they are small creatures—most are less than a foot long. In tropical and warm-temperate seas they form a numerous tribe.

Heavy armor is the hallmark of the trunkfishes (family Ostraciidae). It does indeed form a kind of trunk to protect these creatures, but a quite unusual one—it may have three, four, or five sides of hard bone. There are about a score of these brightly colored species dwelling in tropical seas, the largest being twenty inches in length or longer. One notable kind has hornlike spines projecting above the eyes; these creatures are known as cowfishes.

The puffers, blowfishes, or swellfishes (family Tetraodontidae) are aptly named. Most of them can blow themselves up with air or water and assume a globelike shape. At such times, their mouths, eyes, and fins seem dwarfed by comparison, so that the puffers appear to be more a part of an underwater fantasy than creatures of flesh and blood. In the bargain some are poisonous. The largest species attain a length of three feet, but most are less than half this size. After laying their heavy eggs in the warm waters they inhabit, the ocean puffers give them no further care; in sharp contrast, the fresh-water puffers of the tropics guard their adhesive eggs and keep a parental eye on the newly hatched young.

Also at home in tropical and warm-temperate seas are the porcupine fishes and burr fishes or spiny box fishes (family Diodontidae). They resemble the puffers in size and can inflate themselves the same way. But their numerous spines provide a clear means of telling them apart, and the beak is made up of two teeth instead of four as in the puffers. When they are puffed up, with their sharp prickles thrust out in every direction, the porcupine fishes look more like curious marine plants than fishes. There are some fifteen species.

To round out our picture of the strange forms of life that make up this group, we should take a glance at the headfishes (family Molidae). As they swim about in the water, they seem to be all head! Their deep bodies appear to be cut off behind the high dorsal and anal fins. But they actually do have a short fringe of a tail. Their skin is tough and leathery, and those who have tasted them say the same of the flesh. The ocean sunfish, reaching eleven feet, is the largest of the three species, the smallest being about three feet long. Sometimes they are seen sunning themselves in mid-ocean, but they may go down to great depths in their native tropical and temperate waters.

The members of this order are most closely related to the surgeon fishes, and there are seven to ten families in all. Because of certain peculiar features of the skull they are called Plectognathi ("joined jaws"). All species have small mouths, which they cannot extend. The outer openings of the gill cavities are small, and ventral fins are usually lacking; when present, they are little, and located near the pectorals. As we have seen, these fishes may be very unlike each other in appearance, some being covered with rough scales, others with prickly or leathery skin, or with a hard, bony shell.

The Common Trigger Fish, *Balistes carolinensis,* is known from both shores of the warmer parts of the Atlantic and also from the Indian Ocean. During the late summer and fall it is a fairly regular visitor as far north as Massachusetts. Young specimens are common in floating seaweed and are undoubtedly carried north with these plants by the Gulf Stream.

A length of slightly more than two feet is attained by the common trigger fish. Like most members of its family, its body is compressed and somewhat rhomboid in profile, with the mouth, the trigger mechanism, the tail and ventral flap each located at one "corner." The anal and second dorsal fins extend along most of two of the "sides." In contrast to many other trigger fishes, which are armored with enlarged bony scales, it has a leathery, yet rough, scaly skin. It is capable of color changes, ranging from pale white to dusky brown, decorated with blotches or reticulations. The strong jaws and teeth are used to obtain both animal and vegetable food.

The fish's trigger mechanism is made up of the first three spines of the dorsal fin. The front one is quite stout and can be made to stand up by the fish, at will. The second spine fits into a groove at the back of the first, and when the two are erected, it slips snugly against the first and locks it in the erect position. Once locked, the strong first spine will break off before it can be depressed. The trigger is the still smaller third spine. This is connected to the second by a "ligament" so that depressing the third spine pulls the second away from the first and allows these two to move freely and fall backwards. The fish is able to move its third spine and thus can unlock its fin at will.

What practical purpose this arrangement serves we are not entirely sure. Perhaps the spines, when locked in an erect position, prevent the trigger fish from being eaten. They can also be employed, together with the ventral flap (that replaces the ordinary ventral or pelvic fins), to wedge the fish securely in crevices between rocks or coral formations, so that it cannot be removed. At the New York Aquarium trigger fishes frequently wedged themselves in the rockwork of their tanks, and many a visitor informed us that these fish were stuck there, not realizing that they could release themselves whenever they wanted.

The common trigger fish is frequently used for food, but many of the more brightly colored species of trigger fishes of the tropical Pacific are reputed to have poisonous flesh. Some of these are members of the genus *Balistapus* that go by the musical Hawaiian name of *Humu-humu Nuku-nuku Apua-a*, which means "a spined fish with the snout or grunt of a pig."

The Orange Filefish, *Ceratacanthus schoepfi,* always looks as if it were half starved. Its flat, angular, bony body gives it the appearance of being chronically underfed. As it slowly pokes along, swimming by means of undulation of its dorsal and anal fins, with its little protruding mouth, small but prominent eyes, and single, coarse spine located just above them, it exhibits a gravely comic deportment.

Its skin is hard and rough and was used as sandpaper at times in the past. It is variously mottled with orange, brown and black. The range of the orange filefish extends from Maine to Brazil. The fish feeds mostly on sedentary or fixed animals and plants which it nips off from their place of attachment by means of its sharp teeth. It attains a length of about two feet.

We know practically nothing about the spawning of the orange filefish. Undoubtedly it lays buoyant eggs during the warmer months. Young specimens are frequently found along the east coast of North America during summer and early fall. They frequently take up a position with their head pointed almost straight down. When in close association with underwater plants, young orange filefish at first glance seem to be plants themselves, both their color and shape helping to create this illusion.

The Cowfish, *Acanthostracion quadricornis,* lives inside its own suit of armor which it carries around with it at all times. The scales on the fish's head and body have become modified into hexagonal plates, securely cemented together to form a hard, immovable case, covering the entire fish save where its fins, eyes, jaws, and tail project through. Just in front of the eyes a pair of small, sharp horns point forward, and at the rear of the body there are three pairs of spines pointing backwards.

Like a tortoise the cowfish is encased in a rigid shell, and like a tortoise it cannot move very fast. Depending entirely on its dorsal and anal fins and, to a lesser extent, on its caudal and pectorals, the cowfish must "scull" or "row" itself through the water. Since it feeds upon worms and other small creatures ensconced in coral reef formations, by breaking down the sheltering stone with its powerful, sharp teeth, it need not swim fast in pursuit of prey.

Although they have lost the mobility of their bodies, cowfish have not lost the ability to alter their colors. Sometimes they are pure white, other times tan or brown with networks of light blue markings. Probably because their shell retains water around the gills, these fish can survive for two hours or more out of water.

The cowfish lays buoyant eggs about one thirty-second of an inch in diameter. In about two days they hatch into larvae that within a week have begun to develop the hard covering so characteristic of their parents. Adults reach a length of about one foot. They range on both sides of the tropical Atlantic, being fairly common as far north as the Carolinas. Cowfish may not look appetizing, but their flesh is delicious and is often cooked in the fish's own shell.

FISH THAT RESEMBLE COWS
The cowfish gets its name from two curious hornlike projections above its eyes. This fanciful-seeming creature is encased in a rigid sheath; it is not able to maneuver very well and is incapable of speed. Worms are among the cowfish's favorite foods, and it bites them out of coral reefs in the tropical Atlantic, its home.

The Northern Puffer, *Sphoeroides maculatus,* blows itself up with either air or water until its whole body is spherical, like a balloon, with only its fins and tail projecting. The water or air is pumped directly into the stomach, part of which is modified into a special, inflatable sac. The mouth cavity acts as the pump, its floor being capable of considerable expansion and contraction. Strong muscles at each end of the stomach prevent the escape of the fluid or gas from that organ until the puffer wishes to release it. An eight-inch specimen engulfs a little more than a quart of water in becoming fully inflated.

When blown up with water, the puffer is a difficult or impossible morsel for hungry predators to handle, and inflation with air can make it impossible for fish-eating birds to hold a puffer in their claws.

Puffers themselves are savage predators, however, and are provided with four very strong, sharp, nipping teeth. They feed on crabs, bivalves, snails, barnacles, and a variety of other invertebrates. When tackling a large crab, puffers gang up on it and take turns in attacking it from all sides, harassing it like a pack of wolves until one member can deliver a bite to the crab's vital nerve center to paralyze it. Then they all quickly tear it to pieces.

Whether the northern puffer lays its sticky, heavy eggs on the bottom or whether it simply broadcasts them through the water, allowing them to sink by their own weight, is not definitely known. At any rate, spawning takes place during the late spring and summer, and the tiny spherical eggs hatch about four to five days after being laid. Baby puffers only one-fourth of an inch long can inflate themselves, practically turning inside out to do so. Female northern puffers attain a length of almost nine and one-half inches, while males rarely exceed eight and one-half. The species ranges from Maine to Florida in shallow salt waters.

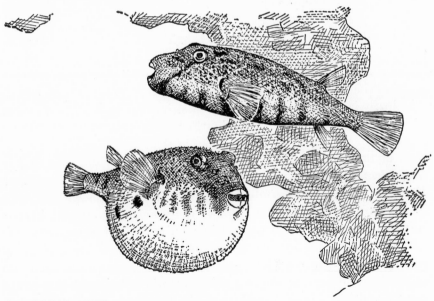

SEA SQUAB ALIVE

On our tables the tail muscles of the northern puffer make a succulent dish known as sea squab. Alive, in its home waters along the Atlantic coast of the United States, this fish is capable of inflating itself with air or water until it assumes a globelike shape. Its foes find it a difficult prey to take hold of.

For many years it was realized that the tail muscles of the puffer make delicious eating, but it was not until World War II that the fish was utilized to any extent for food. Now so-called "sea-squab" is a regular item in many markets, and consists of puffers' tail muscles removed from the fish.

Reluctance to use the fish commercially arose partly from the knowledge that some of its Pacific relatives are known to be deadly poisonous. It has been shown, in some of them at least, that their poison resides in the internal organs and that if these are removed soon enough after catching, the poison does not diffuse into the muscle meat—which then can be eaten with impunity. There is only a mild poison at some seasons in the ovaries of the northern puffer, and it apparently does not diffuse out into the fish's muscles. Moreover, puffers are stripped of their meat very soon after catching so that there is never even the slightest danger from eating tasty sea-squab.

The Deadly Death Puffer, *Tetraodon hispidus,* is fatal to anyone who eats it; the unfortunate victim usually dies within five hours. The flesh of this fish contains a poisonous substance called tetrodotoxin, which causes great pain, nausea, vomiting, and diarrhea, often accompanied by paralysis and convulsions. The toxic material seems to be concentrated in the reproductive organs, but enough of it is present in the muscles to make eating the flesh almost invariably fatal.

Fishes that cannot be eaten because they are poisonous are found principally in tropical seas. It has been estimated that there are about three hundred species of such fishes in the central Pacific, for example. Most of these are not as dangerous as the deadly death puffer and some of its relatives. Other closely related puffers from that region are perfectly edible, however; in fact they are considered delicacies! To make matters more confusing, certain kinds of fishes seem to be poisonous only at definite seasons of the year, and some species are deadly in one area, but harmless in another. The latter fact might indicate that the food consumed by the fish imparts some poisonous quality to its flesh.

But the deadly death puffer is poisonous whenever or wherever it is found—and it is widespread through the warmer parts of the Indian and Pacific Oceans from the Red Sea to the Hawaiian Islands. It also occurs in brackish or fresh waters. The deadly death puffer is a brightly and variably colored fish, covered with yellowish or whitish spots on its back and sides and with yellow or light olive streaks on its belly. Like most other puffers it can inflate itself with air or water. It may grow to a length of twenty inches.

The Porcupine Fish, *Diodon hystrix,* is covered with numerous long spines. Ordinarily these lie close to the body, but when the fish inflates itself—like its relative the puffer—it looks like a spherical pin cushion, all of its spines sticking straight out. These can inflict painful wounds, for they are both sharp and long—more than two inches in large specimens. Porcupine fish grow to a length of more than three feet and then appear like basketballs studded with nails, when they are blown up.

Found all over the world in tropical seas, the porcupine fish is well known to many peoples, but its life history is pretty much of a mystery. The Japanese use it for food, although it is considered poisonous in most countries. People have died from eating its flesh, which is believed to become toxic by absorbing poison from the fish's vital organs after its death. South Sea Islanders employed the spiny skins of porcupine fish in making helmets for their war dress.

The Ocean Sunfish, *Mola mola,* has a peculiar oval body, flattened from side to side, with a long narrow dorsal and anal fin projecting up and down from the posterior part of it. At first glance it seems to have no tail at all, but close examination reveals that an abbreviated, crescent-shaped one covers the whole back of the body. The fish gives the appearance of having had the rear half of its body chopped off. It swims by swinging its dorsal and anal fins back and forth, both together, and by undulating them at the same time.

Large specimens of the ocean sunfish are seen swimming or floating lazily at the surface of all the tropical seas or in temperate ones during the warmer months. They attain weights of over a ton and lengths of perhaps eleven feet. Their grayish brown skin is leathery in texture, very tough, and averages more than two inches in thickness. The interior of the fish shows specializations as peculiar as those manifested externally. For example, it has lost the usual trunk muscles present in ordinary fish, and its skeleton is so soft that it can be cut with a knife.

Ocean sunfish feed on small crustaceans, jellyfish, the larvae of other fishes, and perhaps algae. Reproduction is by means of tiny, floating eggs. Larval sunfish look entirely different from adults, bearing a number of variously shaped spines. The species is not generally considered edible, although the Japanese are said to relish its liver.

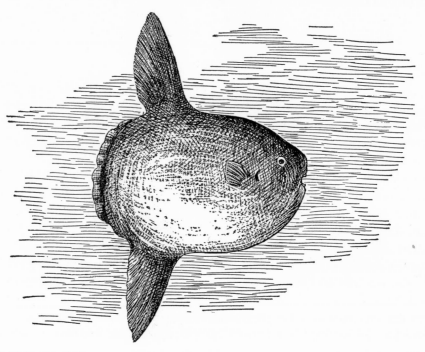

A TON OF FISH

The ocean sunfish loves to take the sun, swimming lazily along the surface of warm and temperate seas. This remarkable fish may weigh as much as a ton and measure eleven feet in length, but it is of scant value to the larders of mankind, for its flesh is leathery.

Toadfishes—Some Can Sing

THE TOADFISHES—ugly, battling scavengers—live on the bottom of tropical and temperate seas from shallow to deep water. Some haunt inlets; a few tropical species enter rivers. Colored like the rocks and weeds amid which they dwell, they often stay in ambush till their prey draws near.

The largest toadfishes reach a length of about one and one-half feet, but the majority are less than one foot long. Some of them, because they have, on the belly, rows of luminous organs rather like shining buttons, are known as midshipmen. Many are able to produce noises by vibrating their swim bladder. Those species whose habits we know, lay adhesive eggs over which the male keeps watch.

On the east and west coasts of tropical South America and in the Caribbean Sea there are a few toadfishes (genus *Thalassophryne*) which are notorious for their poisonous spines. Two of these spines are located in the front part of the first dorsal fin, and one projects backward from each gill cover. The dorsal ones at least are hollow, with an opening near the tip, and are connected to sacs in which poisonous material is stored. The resemblance to the fangs of venomous snakes is striking.

The toadfishes and their relatives (order Haplodoci) are generally stout-bodied, with naked skins or with small scales thoroughly embedded in slime. The mouth looks savage; it is large and armed with curved canine teeth. Pelvic fins are located well forward. There is only one family (Batrachoididae, or "froglike"), and it has about thirty species in it.

The Toadfish, *Opsanus tau,* acts as tough as it looks. Its stocky, scaleless, darkly mottled body and large, flattened, tab-covered head give it a somewhat repulsive appearance, while its capacious mouth and strong jaws, well armed with numerous blunt teeth, is set at the correct angle to make it appear most pugnacious.

1631

Toadfish can and do inflict nasty wounds when incautiously handled; they are especially full of fight while guarding their nest. Moreover, they can survive under adverse living conditions shunned by most fishes. For example, they can withstand severe shortages of oxygen, particularly in the younger stages. They can also live out of water for several hours. If annoyed by sticks or shells, toadfish will often bite the object so hard that they can be lifted out of the water still tenaciously hanging on.

Toadfish often live in very shallow water along the shore from Maine to Florida. Such places may become very warm in summer, hence the usefulness of the fish's ability to withstand poor breathing conditions. They feed voraciously on a great variety of animals, including worms, shrimps, crabs, snails, bivalves, squid, fishes of all sorts, and offal resulting from the activities of man.

Toadfish have even turned to good account man's proclivity to litter

UGLY IN APPEARANCE AND DISPOSITION
The mouth of the toadfish is armed with many teeth, and this unpleasant-looking, mottled creature has been known to inflict extremely painful bites with them. Toadfish live close to shore, and will often use a tin can or some other man-made object as a nest; the male guards the eggs, and will fight off any intruders with great ferocity.

the world with his trash. Among their favorite nesting sites appear to be broken bottles, jugs, tin cans, boards, and old shoes—apparently anything that provides a large enough cavity—as well as more natural objects like shells and stones. These nests are diligently guarded, each by a male fish. During June and July the large, three-sixteenth-inch, amber eggs are spawned. They are spherical and adhesive and are usually laid in a single layer on the floor or roof of the nest.

As many as seven hundred eggs may occupy one nest, such a large number being the product of more than one female. They hatch in ten to twenty-six days depending on the temperature. All this while the male carefully cleans his nest and eggs and from time to time fans them with his large pectoral fins. The young remain within the nest under the protection of their father for some time after hatching.

Toadfish spend the winter hibernating in mud. By the time they are one year old, young toadfish are about three and one-half inches long. They may grow to be fifteen inches in length, but rarely exceed one foot. In captivity toadfish sometimes become quite tame, learning not to resist handling and to be fed by hand.

The Pacific Midshipman, *Porichthys notatus,* is best known for the noises it makes, giving it the name of "singing fish." These sounds have variously been described as a humming, a resonant croak or bark, or a grunting noise that sounds like "oonk." It is agreed, however, that the fish can make itself heard for remarkable distances—at least forty to fifty feet. The sounds are produced by vibrating the swim bladder by means of special muscles.

The midshipman is an elongated fish with a rather large head, mouth, and pair of eyes. It is a dirty brown or green, and its scaleless body and head show numerous small, round luminous organs, arranged in rows. Each of these tiny light-producing regions is equipped with a minute lens. Midshipmen grow to be about fifteen inches long. During most of the year they inhabit moderately deep water along the west coast of North America from southeastern Alaska to the southern end of Baja California. North of Point Conception they migrate into shallow water to spawn during the late spring.

Cavities underneath stones are used as nests. Sometimes these are scooped out by means of the fish's pectoral fins. Large, adhesive, pinkish eggs are laid in a single layer on the roof of the nest. Sometimes several females will spawn in a single cavity. Usually there are from two hundred to five hundred eggs, guarded faithfully by the male midshipman, who never leaves even to feed. He cleans the eggs by rubbing them, and if the nest is so located that the eggs are exposed to air during low tide, he remains below splashing them by means of his fins. Midshipmen can live as long as eight hours out of water if kept moist.

Hatching occurs in two to three weeks, and for a month afterwards the larvae remain attached to the roof of the nest by the yolk sac. Finally, when they are about one and one-fourth inches long, the young fish become free-swimming. They burrow in the sand during the day, and feed on small invertebrates at night. Adults consume larger crustaceans and other fishes.

Anglers and Batfishes—Fish That Fish for Other Fish

THE VARIOUS KINDS of angler fishes and their relatives are especially interesting, because they are not only fish, but fishermen. Many of them have a spine of the first dorsal fin modified to form a lure and use it to attract prey. Usually, their bodies are stout and clumsy, with a head and mouth that are relatively enormous.

The frogfishes or fishing-frogs and their cousin, the sargassum fish, (family Antennariidae) are found in shallow, tropical salt waters around coral reefs and among seaweed, or in mid-ocean living in floating seaweed. Many of them show bizarre color patterns and threadlike "decorations," but in all instances these seem to aid in camouflaging the fish. The largest species reaches a length of about eighteen inches and a weight of several pounds, but few antennarids are ever one foot long at maximum size, many being less than six inches.

The anglers (family Lophiidae, with perhaps a dozen species) are large, bottom-inhabiting fishes found most frequently in fairly deep water. Some species enter shallow water during the colder parts of the year. Anglers are known from the Atlantic, Pacific, and Indian Oceans. The largest species become four or more feet long.

The deep-sea anglers belong to nearly a dozen families. Approximately one hundred twenty species are known from the depths of oceans all over the world. Most of them are small, but a few reach lengths of about three and a half feet. Unlike the members of the family Lophiidae, the deep-sea anglers do not habitually lie on the bottom, but do their fishing in mid-water, fifteen hundred to fifteen thousand feet below the surface. Females are equipped with a lure, which is believed to be luminous in all cases—as indeed it would have to be in order to operate effectively in those regions of total darkness. It has been shown in a number of cases that the light is not produced by the fish itself, but by special bacteria living inside the bait.

There is a fantastic variety of styles among the fishing apparatus of deep-sea anglers. Some are short, in others the "fishing rod" is as much as three times as long as the total length of the fish. Some are tipped with simple, bulbous lures, others with weirdly branched or shaped ones, often bearing peculiar tentacles or buds. So little is known about these fish that it would be foolhardy to try to explain just what is the significance of this great variability.

Deep-sea angler males are very much smaller than females, and they never possess a lure. So entirely different are they from the females that for years they were considered to belong to entirely separate species, even different families.

In the north Atlantic, spawning occurs mostly during the summer. After hatching, the young fish live mainly in the upper layer of the ocean, feeding on small floating creatures, until they become adult-like in form and sink down into deep water.

The batfishes (family Ogcocephalidae) are among the most peculiarly shaped of all fishes. They are much depressed, that is, flattened from back to belly, and the pectoral fins extend out at an angle from broad triangular bases on either side of the head. With these two fins and the sturdy pair of pelvics underneath, a batfish can walk about the bottom, moving alternate forelimbs (pelvics) and hind limbs (pectorals) together. This "four-footed" gait, unique in fish, may be replaced by rabbitlike hops. When the fish jumps, the pectorals provide the power for the leap, and the fish lands on the pelvic fins.

At least one species of batfish has been seen to angle for prey. The knoblike bait is affixed to a short stem that moves in and out like a plunger. When not in use, the mechanism is hidden inside the "forehead" of the fish. The various batfishes inhabit the bottom of tropical seas, often in deep water. They seldom exceed one foot in length.

WALKER ON THE OCEAN FLOOR

The batfish is a fish with "feet"—its lower fins are long and sturdy, and the creature is able to walk about on them on the ocean floor, or even hop, after a fashion.

All told, there are about sixteen families in this group of salt-water fishes (order Pediculati—"little feet"). We have already had a brief picture of some of their peculiar features: these include strange pectoral fins, ribs, tail, and bony structure of the skull. The gill openings are small and are located behind the pectoral fins, not in front of them as in other fishes. In a few of the anglers, however, these openings extend in front of the base of the pectorals. Each pectoral fin is attached to a fleshy base with an elbow-like joint. This structure is so well developed in some of the antennarids (frogfishes and the like) that the fin acts somewhat like a limb, complete with "arm," "wrist," "hand," and "fingers." When present, the pelvic fins are located in front of the pectorals. Scales are present only as prickles in the skin or are absent altogether.

The Sargassum Fish, *Histrio gibba,* lives among sargassum weed and climbs about this floating ocean plant by means of peculiar pectoral fins, so constructed that the fish can actually grasp a branch with its "fingers" and hold onto it. At the same time the pelvic fins are also employed somewhat like feet, in a shuffling manner, to aid in moving about. So well do the many fringes and tabs on the sargassum fish's head and body break up its outline, and so perfectly does its color and pattern match that of the sargassum weed, that an individual can disappear before one's eyes as it deliberately moves about in a clump of this seaweed.

Although they rarely exceed four inches in length, sargassum fish have huge appetites and, if given the chance, will eat considerably more than their own weight in food at one time. They can swallow a fish larger than themselves because of their relatively enormous mouths and the fact that their stomachs can be stretched out of all proportion to their size. Prey is stalked—sometimes for hours on end— until approached near enough, when with a sudden dart and widely opened mouth the sargassum fish engulfs it. The fish is capable of making relatively great flying leaps, and it can also swim slowly in mid-water by utilizing the jets of water emitted from its gill openings together with the pectoral fins.

The eggs are laid in floating, gelatinous rafts that are many times as large as the fish that spawned them. They lie tightly rolled up within the ovaries, but once laid the jelly-like sheet enveloping them swells tremendously. The sargassum fish has been found in practically all tropical seas. It occasionally drifts north along with the seaweed in which it habitually lives.

The Goosefish, *Lophius americanus,* uses one of its spines as a fishing rod, complete with bait, to lure prey within reach of its great mouth. The first three spines of its dorsal fin stand apart, separated from one another; the most forward of these is located just behind the upper lip of the mouth and is equipped with an irregular, leaflike flap of skin at its tip. This lure is jerked back and forth over the mouth in a way that apparently successfully imitates the movement of small, edible creatures, because several kinds of fishes have been seen to be attracted by it—and abruptly to end their lives within the goose-fish's maw.

At first glance the goosefish appears to be "all head," and its head seems to be "all mouth." Almost one-half of the entire fish is composed of the very wide, flat head, and the body so sharply tapers down to the tail and is relatively so small that the goosefish looks like a tadpole at first glance. The enormous mouth is directed upwards, and the lower jaw projects far beyond the upper. Both jaws are lined with numerous sharp, fanglike teeth which may be an inch long in large specimens. The eyes are located on top of the head and are directed upwards. The pectoral fins arise from thick, fleshy arms instead of directly out of the body as they do in most fishes. No gill covers are present, but instead there is a small opening from the gill chamber behind each pectoral fin. Rows of fleshy tabs decorate the scaleless, slimy head and body. The color is dark brown or black on top and dirty white underneath.

Goosefish reach lengths of three to four feet. They actively stalk their prey and also lie passively on the bottom, luring it within reach by means of their rod and bait. In either case, the creature is suddenly and completely engulfed (if not too large) by the goosefish's tremendous mouth, the mere sudden opening of which causes a strong flow of water, helping to draw the prey to its fate.

The appetite of the goosefish is enormous, if not insatiable. Not only are fishes and invertebrates of all sorts consumed, but many species of sea-birds and now and then a sea-turtle are captured and eaten. One goosefish's stomach contained twenty-one flounders and a dogfish, all of marketable size; another had seventy-five herring, and a third had seven ducks! The mass of food frequently weighs half as much as the whole fish, that is, twenty pounds or more. Sometimes goosefish swallow, or try to swallow, too large an animal and die as a result.

The range of the goosefish is along the eastern coast of North America from Newfoundland to North Carolina in shallow water and to Barbados and the Gulf of Mexico in deep water. The fish tends to come closer inshore during cold weather.

The eggs are laid in late spring and summer. They appear in floating ribbon-shaped veils of mucus that may be twenty to thirty feet long and two to three feet wide, containing hundreds of thousands of eggs about three thirty-seconds of an inch in diameter. They hatch

in about four or five days; the young swim at the surface of the open
sea until about an inch and a quarter long, when they take up a life
among floating seaweed. Later they sink to the bottom, near or upon
which they spend the rest of their lives.

The Deep-Sea Angler, *Borophryne apogon,* is one of a number of
fishes that inhabit the depths of the ocean. It has a baglike body that
is capable of great expansion, well-developed fins, and enormous jaws
lined with many sharp teeth, some of them fanglike. These teeth are
so long that the creature apparently cannot close its mouth completely.
The eyes appear to be well developed. Just over the mouth is located a short, flexible projection at the tip of which is a bulbous structure carrying a complicated mass of hairlike threads. This bulb is
bluish-purple, and the filaments are white, while the rest of the fish
is jet black. The bulb is capable of emitting purplish light.

This small species of deep-sea angler reaches a length of somewhat
more than three inches. Nevertheless it is capable of swallowing a

AFTER THE DEEP-SEA ANGLER HAS DINED
The female deep-sea angler, only three inches long, is able to swallow another fish fully
her own size, after which her belly swells up enormously. The tiny fish below her is the
inch-long male. He becomes permanently attached to his mate's body, a mere appendage
serving to fertilize her eggs.

fish almost as long as itself or as many as three specimens, each measuring two-thirds of its length—after which its belly swells out like a balloon. So far as known, it inhabits the icy depths of the tropical eastern Pacific, but may of course be much more widely distributed, since we know so very little about the geography of deep sea fishes. Experts believe that it uses its glowing lure to attract fishes within reach of the fearsome jaws. Since it is capable of swimming strongly, even when its stomach is bulging with food, the possibility cannot be overlooked that it also actively pursues prey, or moves about in search of suitable fish on which to use its lure.

What we have said applies only to females, for the adult males of this species start out as free-swimming fish less than an inch long with no mechanism for angling but possessing well-developed eyes, noses, and jaws. When a male comes upon a suitable female, he attaches himself to her by means of his mouth. Any part of her body seems to be satisfactory, and eventually his jaws become fused with the skin of the relatively gigantic female, only enough space remaining between the two partners for a small amount of water to enter the male's mouth, presumably to bathe the gills. Experts believe that the male's blood stream becomes connected with that of the female, and that she supplies him with nourishment through this means. For the rest of his life the male remains attached to his mate, a mere parasitic tab on her body. His only function is to fertilize the numerous eggs, about a sixty-fourth of an inch in diameter, when they are laid.

BOOK V: Insects and Other Invertebrates

JOHN C. PALLISTER

THE ORIENTAL PRAYING MANTIS GOES HUNTING IN THE GARDEN

Here it destroys all kinds of insects, not only those we do not like, such as grasshoppers, but also the valuable bee and lovely butterfly. In a day of good hunting the praying mantis will consume several times its own weight in insects. (Like most other insect-eaters, it leaves the Japanese beetle alone.) The Oriental praying mantis is beautifully colored in varying shades of green brushed over with bronze or copper; in a favorable season and location it will grow to four and even five inches in length. In China, the insect's native land, the people like to cage two males or two females for fighting bouts. It will be a fight to the death; the champion dines on the loser. (Kodachrome by Edwin Way Teale, courtesy of the American Museum of Natural History.)

The Great World of the Animals
Without Backbones

HOW WE CLASSIFY ANIMALS

IF A MODERN Noah were to assemble specimens of all the kinds of animals, from the least to the greatest, and to try to allot them berths so that each would be surrounded by its next of kin, he might first try to arrange them according to size. But he would not like the resulting groups. Placing the ostrich between the kangaroo and the tuna fish just wouldn't do, nor would it seem right to place the hummingbird between the tarantula and the field mouse.

Our twentieth-century Noah would soon decide that all creatures with wings and feathers must be more closely related to one another than to any other animals. He might then try to separate all animals into large categories, such as animals that live in the water and animals that live on land. That division would seem valid as far as birds and fishes are concerned; but Noah would quickly observe that some shelled animals live in the ocean and some climb trees, while some six-legged animals, such as mosquitoes, spend the first part of their lives wriggling in the water and the last part flying in the air.

Sooner or later, he would observe that many animals have backbones, and that many more have none. If he put all creatures with backbones in one division, he would see that all of them have very complex bodies, and that they can be subdivided easily into five distinct groups: fishes, amphibians (consisting of frogs, toads, and their relatives), snakes and lizards, birds, and finally the mammals. If he looked, then, at all the animals without backbones, he would be facing a tremendous number of creatures, of such differing body formation that they have almost no points in common except that they are animals and they are spineless.

This problem that we have given our imagined Noah is a very real one to the zoologist who wants to look at animal life as a whole, and to study the habits, origins, and relationships of living creatures. Most of our methods of arranging and studying living forms have been developed within the last two hundred years. It was only about 150 years ago that the great zoologist Lamarck first classified all animals into two divisions. All those with backbones he called vertebrates; all the spineless, invertebrates.

A few years before Lamarck's work, the Swedish botanist Linnaeus had devised a set of terms for the divisions and subdivisions among both plants and animals. Let us review them here. The term for the largest division is phylum (plural, phyla). The vertebrates are considered a phylum. A phylum may be subdivided into classes. Birds form one class of the vertebrate phylum. Classes are further subdivided into orders. For example, all the perching birds are placed in one order. Each order consists of a number of families. The thrush family belongs to the perching-bird order. Families are divided into genera (singular, genus). Bluebirds form one genus of the thrush family. Finally, genera are divided into species, a classification by which, for example, we separate the Eastern from the Western bluebird.

To take an example from the invertebrates: The Arthropoda (lobsters, spiders, insects, etc.) is a phylum, of which the insects are one class, and in this class moths and butterflies together form the Lepidoptera order. One of the largest of its 160 families is the Nymphalidae, and in this family *Vanessa* is a genus, and the Painted Lady, *Vanessa cardui,* is a species that almost everyone in Europe and the United States has seen.

THE INNUMERABLE INVERTEBRATES

In the following chapters we will consider some of the odd, interesting, or beautiful animals that make up the invertebrates. Unlike the vertebrates, these do not consist of just one phylum but of several, possibly eleven, each possessing characteristics as distinct from those of the others as from those of the vertebrates.

"Innumerable" is the word to stress in trying to think of these animals en masse. Not only do the invertebrates outnumber the vertebrates in phyla, they also exceed all mammals, birds, reptiles, amphibians, and fishes in species by about twenty-eight to one. They range in structure from a simple, microscopic globule of protoplasm, like the amoeba, to creatures of such complex and specialized formation as the lobster, the seventeen-year cicada, the sponges, the chambered nautilus, the mosquito, and the octopus.

Some of these creatures live simple, uneventful lives from beginning to end. Some live parasitically on, or in, other animals; and some of these, like the malarial parasite, may become seasoned travelers, living for a time in one kind of animal, then moving to another kind, and then to still another. Some live the early part of their lives as alarming caterpillars, and the latter part as beautiful butterflies. Obviously, only a very few species can be discussed in these pages. You will find descriptions here of those that are typical, or lead especially exciting lives, or have some known relation to man. All of the phyla will be discussed to some extent.

The First Animals

ANIMALS OF BUT A SINGLE CELL

Protozoa are the first or earliest creatures in the animal kingdom in the sense that they have the simplest kinds of bodies. These minute animals do not have a head, heart, stomach, legs, or any of the other parts we usually find in an animal. The protozoan's entire body consists of just one cell. With this single cell, the protozoan absorbs its food, moves about, divides itself to form new individuals, and may even develop a covering.

Protozoa are everywhere, on land, in the sea, and in the air, but chiefly near the surface of shallow water, either salt or fresh. Stagnant water teems with them. Most of the species are too small to be visible to the naked eye, and only a few can be seen without a hand lens. They are so transparent that you look right through them, seeing only a speck of jelly-like material, called protoplasm. It takes a medium-powered, compound or binocular microscope to reveal these beautiful little creatures belonging to the phylum Protozoa.

The Amoeba. One-celled though they may be, the animals belonging to the genus *Amoeba* are unique in that they are constantly changing shape. The best way to observe some of them is to place a drop of stagnant water on a glass slide. If naturally stagnant water is not easily available to you, soak a little grass in a jar of water at room temperature for a few days. Place a thin cover glass over the water to compress it into a thin layer. This is necessary because the focal depth of a microscope is extremely shallow, and gets rapidly shallower as the magnification is increased. However, in order to gain a little more room for activity in the water, you will find it helpful to support the cover glass by a few fibers of cotton or some hairs from your head placed beside the drop of water.

Adjust the focus and the light to get the clearest possible view, and you will soon be gazing at the strange and intriguing world known only to the microscopist. If you are fortunate, a disk of transparent jelly on the slide will start to bulge on one side. You will see the bulge extend farther and farther, until, suddenly, the entire blob will seemingly flow into this extended arm, or pseudopod. Meanwhile, other pseudopods will have reached out from the blob. The main mass will finally flow into one of these, as it did before. This is the amoeba's method of travel.

You may notice a darker spot somewhere near the center of the mass. It is the all-important nucleus, the spot of essential life within the protoplasm. And, somewhere, you should observe one or more oily spots known as the contractile vacuoles, small cavities which contract and expand at more or less rhythmical or regular intervals. There may be other roundish spots, the food vacuoles; these are fragments of food which the amoeba has surrounded and is assimilating. When the edible parts have been dissolved, the animal discards the remainder by the simple process of flowing on and leaving it behind.

——How Amoebae Separate and Unite. There comes a time when two pseudopods form, seemingly of equal importance, and usually on opposite sides of the animal. The protoplasm is now flowing into both of these arms. The amoeba is increasing in length and is beginning to shrink in the middle. The nucleus has divided, one-half to each part. Soon, the two parts separate and flow off in opposite directions. This method of reproduction, known as binary fission, is followed by the Protozoa.

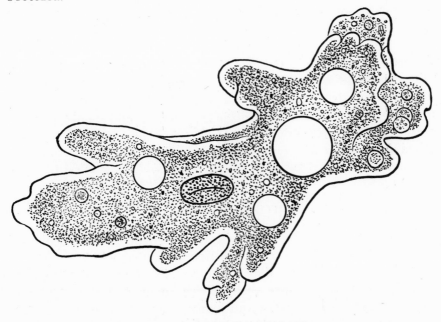

THE LOWLY AMOEBA, MOST PRIMITIVE OF ANIMALS
This tiny speck of protoplasm, endowed with the spark of life, flows slowly through its little world. It moves by pushing out a part of itself and pulling the rest along. In its travels, it engulfs everything smaller than itself. As it passes on, it absorbs whatever is food; whatever is not food it leaves behind.

Sometimes two amoebae unite. They meet and, after a moment of hesitation, either slide along past each other or flow into each other.

For all its apparent fragility, the amoeba is a durable animal. When it finds conditions unfavorable for an active life, it prepares for hard times. First, it assumes a spherical shape by pulling in all its pseudopods. Then, it thickens and toughens the wall which surrounds its one-celled self. In this condition, when the pool in which it has been living dries up, the amoeba is picked up by the wind and carried away, to lodge, perhaps on a mountain peak, or perhaps on the side of a shed. There it can linger until rains come to carry it to another stream, pond, or puddle. Then, its cystlike wall is broken, and the amoeba resumes activity once again.

If the amoeba we have been watching has pseudopods that are rounded at the ends, it is probably *Amoeba proteus. Amoeba quarta* has short, sharp pseudopods. Another amoeba that you might find in your drop of stagnant water has pseudopods so short and round that the creature appears to have a roughly scalloped edge. It is called *Amoeba verrucosa.*

Amoebae That Live in Other Animals. Most amoebae live in water, salt or fresh; a few live in damp earth. One whole family, comprising many species, lives in the digestive tracts of other animals. Of these, one species makes its home in cockroaches. Another species, *Entamoeba coli,* lives harmlessly in the human colon; but the species called *Entamoeba histolytica* causes the dangerous illness, amoebic dysentery.

FORAMINIFERA

This large group of protozoans with the long name is interesting for two reasons. Their first claim to distinction is that within the limits of their one-celled bodies these creatures have developed strange or beautiful shapes. There are about twelve hundred species of Foraminifera, each as queer or as exquisite as the others. They are so tiny that you can study them only under a microscope, but you will find them well worth all the time you spend on them. Secondly, they have lived through so many geological ages that today, in many parts of the world, their tiny skeletons form important parts of our landscape. They compose the chalk cliffs of England, and they are present in many of the limestone ridges of North America. They are also a large part of the soft muck that we find at the water's edge at low tide.

It is hard to believe that the great city of Paris is indebted to these obscure animals. In the region of the city, there is a large bed of limestone. It is composed almost entirely of the shells of the Foraminifera genus *Miliolina,* and is hundreds of millions years old. Many of the buildings of Paris are made of this stone; in it you can see the minute remains of Miliolinas with the aid of a lens.

Most of the Foraminifera build shells of lime or silica. These shells are perforated with many small and some larger holes (called foramen, from which we get the name Foraminifera). Through these holes stream the pseudopods, not lumpy or clubbed like those of the amoebae, but long, slender, very delicate, sometimes branching, and often interlaced into a net or web. And yet, for all this extraordinary outward form, within its shell the tiny creature remains a simple, one-celled mass of protoplasm.

Most Foraminifera are ocean dwellers. A few live in fresh water; a very few species have been found in damp earth. Certain species live on, or near, the surface of the ocean and are called "pelagic" forms. Many of these create complicated and spiny shells. In the *Globigerina* species, the individual, while growing, builds a series of adjoining shell-chambers, all connected by a passage through which the protoplasm is united in a single cell. As these pelagic Foraminifera die, their shells sink to the bottom of the ocean, forming a layer of gray mud there. This mud is called "globigerina ooze," although it might be more accurate to call it "foraminifera ooze."

Most of these creatures live only on the beds of deep seas, and these are called "abyssal." Those at the greatest depths have shells of silica, more durable stuff than the lime used by their surface relatives.

Foraminifera have been living on this earth for some 500,000,000 years, ever since the days geologists describe as the Cambrian period, the earliest subdivision of the Paleozoic era. Their fossils have been found all over the world, but chiefly in the North Temperate Zone. Many of the ancient species were much larger than any of those living today; others were only about the size of a quarter.

It is not their size, however, that is significant, but their great numbers. The stupendous quantities of Foraminifera that compose our familiar limestone ridges and chalkcliffs are beyond human comprehension. Those living today are almost equally numberless.

SOME COMMON FRESH-WATER PROTOZOA

Euglena. Often enough, as you stand beside a small pond or walk beside a roadside ditch, you will notice that the water appears greenish. A drop of that water examined under a microscope is almost sure to show, among many other things, a specimen of the protozoan *Euglena viridis*. It does not look at all like the amoebae that are likely to be living in the same drop of water. It is greenish and spindle-shaped, and at its blunt end you can distinguish what looks like a short, wavy hair. This hairlike tail is called a flagellum (plural, flagella). Its tiny possessor lashes it back and forth to propel itself through the water.

Inside the body of *Euglena viridis,* and not far from the base of the flagellum, you will notice a bright-red spot, called a stigma. This is believed to be a light-detecting organ, the very simplest suggestion of a primitive eye.

The green coloring of this animal is caused by the vegetable pigment, chlorophyll, together with a starchlike material called paramylum. This little green creature has the plantlike ability to decompose the carbon dioxide in water, assimilating the carbon and releasing the oxygen. However, it also possesses the animal characteristic of sweeping food into a mouthlike opening with its flagellum.

Volvox globator, found in ponds, looks like a small, green jellyball, but is actually composed of thousands of individuals. As the ball ages, subcolonies, called daughter colonies, form inside it. Eventually, the ball breaks, the daughter colonies separate, grow, and develop daughter colonies of their own. The ball appears to move through the water by the coordinated action of the flagella of its members, a faint presage of the beginning of many-celled life.

PROTOZOA THAT MAKE THEIR HOMES
IN OTHER ANIMALS

Quite a number of protozoan species live as parasites in the bodies of other animals, both vertebrate and invertebrate. We have already mentioned two *Amoeba* species parasitic on man, one dangerous and one harmless. The majority of the protozoa parasites apparently do their hosts no harm, but a few are deadly, at least to some of their hosts.

Among these deadly parasites are the species of *Trypanosoma,* one of which, *Trypanosoma gambiense,* causes the fatal African sleeping sickness in man. A slender little creature, it lives harmlessly in the blood of African antelopes. When the tsetse fly sucks the blood of an infested antelope, the trypanosome is transferred to the insect's body, where it multiplies rapidly and peacefully in the insect's salivary juices. When the fly bites a man the trypanosomes enter his blood stream with the fly's saliva. There they wreak great havoc, first poisoning the victim's blood with their waste products, causing fever, then entering the cerebrospinal fluid, causing loss of consciousness and death.

Other species of *Trypanosoma* cause sickness and death in horses and cattle in Africa and Asia. They all lead complicated lives in a series of hosts and are conveyed to the domestic animals by flies. Species of a related genus, *Leishmania,* also cause some damage to man and other vertebrate animals. "Kala azar," a human disease common in Asia Minor, is inflicted by *Leishmania donovani.*

The three malarial Protozoa, *Plasmodium malariae, Plasmodium vivax,* and *Plasmodium falciparum,* are credited with destroying as large a population as the atomic bomb now threatens. Fortunately, man has been able, with the help of science, to arrest these deadly malaria Protozoa.

THE HIGHEST TYPE OF PROTOZOA—CILIOPHORA

This large group of some three thousand species presents an amazing variety of shapes and forms. Some are ball-shaped; some look like fishes, or eels. Some resemble bells; some, flowers or seed pods. Some look like miniature monsters. But all have one characteristic in common—each one wears tiny, fine, hairlike structures, called cilia. Some are so thoroughly covered with cilia that they present a furry appearance. Ciliophora cannot push parts of themselves out to make pseudopods as the amoebae do, but some of the species can vibrate their cilia rapidly enough to propel themselves through the water. A very few lose their cilia when they mature, but most species retain them throughout their lives.

Ciliophora are the most highly organized of the Protozoa, for they possess a definite place for taking in food, and an exit for excrement. Their cilia may be highly specialized: some providing locomotion, some bringing food to the mouth, some protecting the animals from attack. Ciliophora live in salt and fresh water, in stagnant pools, and sluggish streams. At certain times most of them encase themselves in a horny covering, so that they can live in dry places or be carried by the winds to new locations.

The Protozoan That Looks Like a Slipper: *Paramecium.* Another protozoan that you are almost sure to see in a drop of stagnant water is one of the slipper animalcules, probably *Paramecium caudatum.* It is

larger than most of its companions, being about a quarter of a millimeter in length, and shaped somewhat like a heel-less slipper,
rounded at the front end and pointed at the back. Along the under
surface it has a groove, called the buccal groove, corresponding to the
mouth of higher animals. This leads to an opening, called the gullet,
which ends within the protoplasmic interior of the animal.

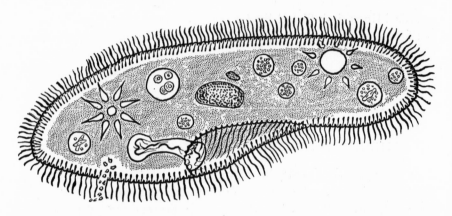

THE ROLLICKING PARAMECIUM

Unlike the plodding amoeba, the paramecium dashes about its microscopic world, propelled
by vibrating cilia (hairlike growths) which cover its entire body. On one side it has a small
depression, which is a primitive mouth. The cilia around this depression sweep in food.
The paramecium is sometimes called the slipper animalcule.

The surface of this *Paramecium* is covered with lengthwise rows
of tiny cilia. By vibrating these, the creature is not only able to travel,
but also to use those along the buccal groove for bringing a constant
supply of food to the gullet.

When the animal is disturbed, it suddenly shoots out long, delicate
threads. When it is at rest, these threads lie coiled, each in its own
sac, a great many such sacs being imbedded in the animal's surface.

The Cone-shaped Protozoan: *Stentor*. From plants in your aquarium,
or from small, still ponds, you may be able to collect samples of the
interesting *Stentor polymorphus*. This cone-shaped animal lives with
its small end firmly fastened to the underwater stem or leaf of a
plant. You may be able to see a *Stentor* with your unaided eye, for
they often grow to be more than one millimeter in length. Sometimes
they are green with the plants called algae, but usually they are colorless.

Under a microscope you will be able to see a row of very fine cilia growing around the edge of the animal's wide upper end. The vibrations of these cilia bring to the mouth of the gullet, which is near one side of the upper end, all sorts of other animals small enough for *Stentor* to eat.

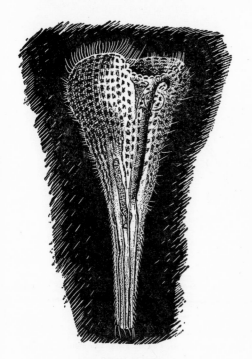

STENTOR—A VASE-SHAPED ANIMALCULE

Stiff-stemmed stentor stands at attention in its little drop of water. Some stentors are blue and some are green, but many are colorless; a number are large enough to be seen by the naked eye. Stentors usually live in colonies, attached to some solid object. But many of them can swim and, when one does, it contracts its funnel-shaped body into an oval lump.

The Cell with a Stem: *Vorticella. Vorticella campanula* is even more astounding than *Stentor*. It fastens its short, bell-shaped body to a water plant by means of a long, slender stem, which it is able to stretch or contract. When the creature is feeding, this stem is extended to its utmost, and the body sways like a flower in the breeze. The animal vibrates the cilia around its thickened edge rapidly in order to sweep the food within reach of its gullet.

Perhaps you may see more than one of these long-stemmed beauties, a garden of them, under the lens of your microscope, with cilia vibrating as they sway. They do not move in unison; each individual sways to its own rhythm. But jar the microscope or tap the slide, and fear invades the little group. All activity ceases instantly. The stems are retracted, the cilia are stilled, and the *Vorticellae* lie close to the bottom. Not for long, however. First one extends its stem to resume operations, then another, followed closely by the others, each anxious to share in the food floating by.

VORTICELLA—A LONG-STEMMED ANIMAL VASE

A microscopic cup, fringed with cilia, waves on a long, slender stem. The stem is fastened to a rock or a piece of wood in the water. The vibrating cilia sweep food into the cup. When disturbed, the little animal stops waving its cilia, retracts its stem closer to its base, and rests motionless until the danger has passed.

The Sociable Cell: *Zoothamnium.* Some of the Ciliophora live in true colonies. Instead of each animal's attaching its stem separately to some plant or other object, a number of individuals may be attached together as a branched, treelike structure, often of striking form. *Zoothamnium* exhibits this neighborly habit very beautifully. From a central trunk numerous branches fork out, sometimes dividing again. Dozens of little creatures nod and sway from the ends of these branches.

They live in fresh and in salt water, fastened to plants or to animals. *Zoothamnium arbuscula* is one that you may find on plants in fresh water. Its colonies are sometimes a quarter of an inch high.

Protozoan with a Snout: *Didinium*. A violent little Ciliophora, familiarly known as the "water bear," is *Didinium nasutum*. It has a small, snoutlike apparatus which it can push out or pull in, and which is surrounded by a fringe of whisker-like cilia. It is not too common, but occasionally you may see one on your slide, rushing madly about, seeking a *Paramecium*. Finding one, it fastens its snout upon the victim and pulls it bodily into itself.

THE MANY-CELLED ANIMALS

All the one-celled animals in the world are contained in the one phylum, the Protozoa. The many-celled animals, having much more material with which to work, developed in widely different directions, so that they form several phyla. Nevertheless, they all start life in the same fashion, as a single-celled egg. This cell divides again and again to form other cells, amounting to many millions in the higher animals. The new cells specialize, and in this way form the various organs and tissues that make up a body.

An essential physical requirement for every animal is a place where it can hold and assimilate its food. So, from the lowest to the highest types, the many-celled animal is basically a tube into which food can be taken and digested, and from which waste can be discharged. This tube must have at least two layers, or coats, of cells, an inner layer to do the digestive work and an outer coat for protection.

Between these two layers are the cells from which all the other activities of the animal will develop—the muscular system, the reproductive organs, systems for obtaining oxygen and circulating blood, the organs of nervous control, and the organs of sense. The lower the animal, the less specialization in its cell composition and function, and the fewer and simpler its organs.

We will examine the invertebrates in the order of their complexity, as nearly as possible, beginning with the simplest. Many of the phyla show an approximately equal degree of organization, however.

The Sponges—
Animals That Grow Like Plants

THE HUMBLE SPONGE with which you clean yourself or your car is the skeleton, or part of the skeleton, of a member of the odd and isolated Porifera phylum. Many phyla have members that resemble some in a lower group, but the sponges have no close relatives. It is supposed that they have developed from a group of Protozoa of which we know no examples; and none of the higher phyla appear to have evolved from the Porifera.

Sponges are water animals and, except for one small, fresh-water family, are found in the sea. They tend to live fused together in colonies, where they look very much like plants or many-branched trees.

The immature, or larval, sponge can swim about. In the course of its swimming, it soon finds a rock, shell, or other firm base to which it can attach itself. After it becomes adult it cannot move. An adult sponge has no tentacles or legs, no muscles, no respiratory organs, no sense organs.

Most sponges have a cylindrical body. Pores or openings in the body wall admit water, which brings food and oxygen to a central cavity. In fact, Porifera, the name of the phylum, means "pore bearers." A large opening at one end of the body lets out the water and the waste the animal has picked up. The sponge feeds on minute animals and plants. Between its cavity and its body wall lie gelatinous cells that are able to abstract minerals from the sea water and to build up the skeletons with which we are familiar.

Sponges are classified according to the composition of their skeletons. Some create skeletons of calcium carbonate; some of a beautiful, glassy silicate. Some use a nonglassy silicate combined with a

1656

horny, fibrous material called spongin. Others compose their skeletons entirely of the elastic spongin, and furnish the commercial sponges that are so useful.

Some sponges, instead of being cylindrical or vase-shaped, are more or less flattened. These spread out on a supporting rock, much as the plants called lichens might spread on a tree trunk. Others are hemispherical in shape.

All are alike in that they take water in through the pores of the outer surface, circulate it through the tubular structure of the sponge, and pass it out through one or more openings after the food has been absorbed from it.

Scientists have described about three thousand species of sponges. The few that we find in fresh water are rather small and insignificant. They have no commercial value, but are interesting to the student.

Look at the underside of a floating log or plank that has been in the water for some time, and you will probably see masses of the greenish *Spongilla* species. Turn the log back again after the short

SPONGES—NATURAL WASHCLOTHS
From prehistoric days the skeletons of some sponges have been used by people as washcloths. Not all sponges, however, have the right kind of skeleton for this purpose. These animals grow in many different shapes, colors, and sizes; all but one small family of sponges live in salt water.

time needed for your observations, for the sponge cannot live out of water. Other fresh-water sponges live on sunken logs, stones, and even on leaves lying on the bottom of some shallow pool.

We find most of the species, however, in the warmer sea waters, where the rocky bottom, providing firm bases, comes near to the surface, and where the ocean currents sweep over these rocks, bringing food.

HOW WE USE SPONGES

From the beginning of history, man has used sponges for many purposes. Undoubtedly, prehistoric man used them too.

Tribes living close to the sea collected specimens that had drifted ashore and used their surplus for barter with friendly inland tribes. The ancient Greeks used sponges not only for bathing and for scrubbing their floors and furniture, but as padding in their shields and armor. The Romans used them as mops and as paint brushes. One of the unusual uses to which sponges were put in ancient times was as drinking cups. The sponge was dipped into liquid and then squeezed into the drinker's upturned mouth. Today, we use sponges in many ways, washing cars, cleaning our homes, applying shoe polish, and even for patting on face cream (the tough spongin fibers wear better and feel better on the skin than rubber or plastic applicators).

SPONGE FISHING, A FASCINATING INDUSTRY AND SPORT

Millions of sponges are sold annually, making sponge fishing a great industry in many places that border on the sea. One of the world's finest sponge-fishing grounds lies off the Florida coast, in the Gulf of Mexico. The gathering of the high-quality bath sponges found here furnishes a livelihood to many people. In this area, Tarpon Springs, Fla., is the main port for the sponge-fishing boats from which divers descend to cut the sponges from their rocky bases.

The living bath sponge, when brought up from the bottom of the sea, has a dark, leathery covering. When cut open, it looks like a piece of raw liver. The spongin fibers are invisible in this mass of slimy protoplasm that bears not the slightest resemblance to the finished bath sponge.

As soon as the sponges are received on board, they are given a preliminary cleaning to remove rough dirt, then hung from the boat's rigging until the protoplasm decays. A sponge boat upwind can be smelled for a considerable distance beyond its visibility. The exploring scientist who goes out with a sponge fleet to study fresh specimens is likely to find the odor of the decaying ones unbearable.

When the boat docks, the sponges are washed and sorted according to their size and quality. Then they are strung on a cord for inspection by the wholesaler. Before they are sold to the trade, the sponges are pounded with mallets to break up any solid material, such as shellfish, that may be buried inside. After a second washing, they are trimmed to attractive shapes. Since the sponges are highly elastic, quantities of them can be pressed into compact bales for economy in shipping.

Sponge fishing is sometimes carried on in shallow waters, usually by two men, one who rows, and another who watches the bottom of the ocean through a water telescope. This contrivance is simply a bucket with the bottom replaced by a sheet of glass, or a tube of metal or wood with glass cemented in one end. When the fisherman spots a sponge that looks marketable, he pulls it from its support with a hook fastened to a long stick.

HORNY SPONGES

The bath sponges and most others of commercial value belong in a group called horny sponges because of the horny consistency of their spongin skeleton. One of these, called the Elephant-ear Sponge, although it is shaped more like a broad-mouthed urn, makes its home in the Mediterranean Sea. A very large sponge, it is cut into several pieces for marketing. It is used for many purposes, but particularly in the pottery trades.

CALCAREOUS SPONGES

Of the three thousand species of sponges, the majority have no commercial value because their skeletons are of hard consistency, being made up of calcareous or silicious little spikes instead of the elastic spongin. Calcareous sponges, which might be best defined as hard-shelled, limey sponges, are of various shapes and are often attached to piles or wharves. Frequently, several species will be found growing together. Many are small and bristle with calcareous deposits. They are the most common sponges in temperate sea waters.

Sycon ciliatum, which makes its home in cooler waters, consists of stubby, finger-like protuberances standing erect on a heavier base. Older specimens frequently look like a cluster of hands, with the fingers all pointing upward. There are many other species of *Sycon* scattered throughout the salt waters of the world.

SILICIOUS SPONGES

The silicious sponges, which we might in everyday language call sandy sponges, are also numerous in species. They are not useful, but many are breath-taking to see. Perhaps the most beautiful are the Venus Flower Baskets of the genus *Euplectella.* These are cylindrical tubes, six to twelve inches long, and about one to two inches in diameter. Beautiful to look at, they are unpleasant to handle, for, even through the surrounding protoplasmic material, the supporting spikelets can be felt, slightly pricking the fingers.

The remarkable beauty of this sponge is revealed only when the protoplasmic material has been removed and the skeleton washed. Gleaming white, the delicate filigree tracery appears so fragile that one fears to touch it. These sponges are extraordinarily strong, however, for nearly perfect ones are sometimes washed up on the beaches, although one would think they might be pounded to bits by the waves before reaching shore.

Another genus of the glassy silicious spicules, *Staurocalyptus,* is usually urn-shaped. Protruding through the protoplasmic substance in some species are long, fine filaments of glass. The genus *Microciona* has numerous, finger-like elongations arising from one or more trunk-like bases.

Hydras, Jellyfishes, Sea Anemones, and Corals—Weird and Beautiful

THE COELENTERATA are a colorful group of water-dwelling animals. Of the ten thousand species, some live in colonies, some as free-swimming individuals. In all species, the mouth is in the center, and the body is arranged symmetrically around the mouth.

The coelenterates differ from the sponges in having no pores in their bodies. They do, however, possess a central body cavity of some sort, and it is from this cavity that the phylum receives its name. Coelenterata comes from two meaningful words of ancient origin, *coel*, meaning "hollow," and *enteron*, meaning "intestine," and referring to the central cavity. This cavity, which serves as the stomach, has only one opening to the outside. Through this opening the animal takes in water bearing food. The water is circulated, so that the food may be gathered, not as in the sponges by means of ciliated cells, but usually through the pulsating action, or the waving, of the tentacles surrounding the mouth.

The species vary in size from organisms so tiny they are scarcely visible, to some larger organisms of considerable size. Some of the groups secrete carbonate of lime, a hard substance, which forms a supporting skeleton. These are the Stony Corals. Others have a horny secretion and are sometimes called the Black Corals. When the animal dies, its skeleton is left as a rocklike mass on which other coral animals continue to live and build.

Four classes make up the Coelenterata: fresh-water polyps, or Hydrariae, and some of the jellyfishes (Hydrozoa), large jellyfishes (Scyphozoa), sea anemones and stony corals (Anthozoa), and the jellyfishes known as comb jellies (Ctenophora).

1661

HYDRAS AND A FEW JELLYFISHES

The Fresh-water Hydra, *Hydra,* is one of the simplest forms of the class called Hydrozoa. You will sometimes find it in abundance in roadside ditches and small stagnant pools. Sometimes, however, you can look in all the usual places without finding any.

The hydra is a little creature about half an inch high. It consists of a tiny stem from the top of which reach out six tentacles, which can be extended for a moderate distance or pulled in close to the stem at the will of the animal. An opening, centrally located at the bases of these tentacles, and leading into the interior of the stem, serves as the mouth. The stem is attached to a firm base by means of a sticky substance. The attachment is not permanent, for the hydra frequently wishes to move, and does so by simply detaching itself and floating off.

The hydra has an amusing way of traveling. It goes places by means of a series of somersaults, and looks very much like a small boy turning handsprings. It is aided in these somersaults by its tentacles, which act like hands. Reaching a favorable new location, the hydra again attaches itself to a base, expands its tentacles, and waits for a passing morsel in the shape of a smaller animal. The unsuspecting victim, touching one of the tentacles, is stunned by the tiny, poisonous threads which shoot out from cells along these tentacles. The hydra then closes its tentacles upon the helpless victim, using them to work the animal toward its waiting mouth.

If you watch a hydra with the aid of a lens, and happen to be fortunate, you will see a bulge forming on the side of its stem. The bulge develops, becoming larger and larger, until it appears to be a little hydra. And that is exactly what this growth is. The bud soon separates from its parent and swims off on its own, an entirely new creature. This fascinating little drama is called reproduction by budding. The hydra also reproduces by means of eggs, which, when ripe, are expelled from the side of its stem. When fertilized by a swimming sperm from another hydra, the egg develops into a new creature.

The name hydra, which is actually no more than the old Greek word for "water serpent," was given to this animal because of its ability to replace parts which may become injured. This name goes all the way back to the ancient Greek myth about a great serpentine monster, the Hydra, which had nine heads. When one of its heads was cut off, two new ones immediately grew in its place. Eventually, the monster was slain by Hercules.

The little fresh-water hydras of our real-life world come in several colors. Green ones usually belong to the genus *Chlorohydra.* Their green color is largely caused by algae in the outer part of the body. Brown hydras belong to the genus *Pelmatohydra,* and the pinkish species to *Hydra* proper.

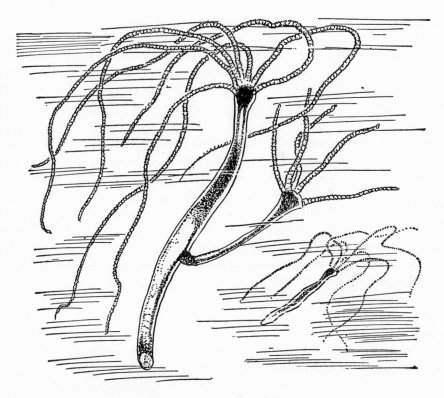

FRESH-WATER HYDRAS TRAVEL BY SOMERSAULTS

Yellowish or brownish little fellows, fresh-water hydras are rarely more than half an inch long. Their slender tentacles act as legs to carry them about in a tumbling fashion, or as arms to bring food to the mouth in the center. They possess a stinging organ with which they can kill or paralyze their prey.

Obelia is a close relative of the hydra. It is, in fact, a hydroid colony, or group of hydra-like animals living together and forming minute treelike structures. They appear as a filmy, oceanic growth on old logs or debris, branching and spreading and reaching heights of less than an inch in some species, while in others, a foot may be the maximum size. *Obelia* reproduces mainly by budding.

The Portuguese Man-of-war, *Physalia pelagica,* or one of its close relatives, is a startling sight for the ocean traveler who visits the warmer seas or the Gulf Stream for the first time. To see a flotilla of these purple balloons sailing on the sea far from land is an experience long to be remembered. Suddenly, at the approach of a ship, they may sink below the waves and disappear, to arise again at a later time. The animal, or perhaps we should say animals, for the Portuguese man-of-war is also a hydroid colony, can deflate the balloon apparatus through a valve in the top, or inflate it by means of a self-generated gas.

This six-inch balloon, or bladder, as it may be called, is only part of this colorful animal, for streaming down from its underside are masses of fine tentacles. Some are quite short, others may reach a length of forty feet or more. They may stretch out straight or retract and coil up like a wire spring. Situated along the tentacles are stinging cells which can hurt you as badly as the sting of any bee or wasp. Swimmers coming in contact with even a single thread of these trailing streamers suffer indescribable agony. Wherever a tentacle touches human flesh, a red welt is raised like that left by the lash of a whip.

The animal secures its food by means of these paralyzing, stinging cells, easily killing fish of considerable size. Strange to say, a few sea-dwelling animals have been able to adapt themselves to the stinging cells, and live happily amid the tentacles, protected from their enemies.

Portuguese men-of-war are carried north by the Gulf Stream and are frequently washed ashore along the Atlantic coast of the United States. The beaches of Florida are often covered with them. The gas-filled balloons quickly dry in the hot sun, and, if stepped on when dry, explode with a loud pop, much to the delight of small boys, as well as some of the larger ones. But beware of the purplish tentacles along the sands, for even after the animal is dead the tentacles retain their nettling properties for a considerable time. There are a number of other Coelenterata that have inflatable bladders, but none as spectacular as the Portuguese man-of-war.

Velella lata is a close relative. It is much smaller, and its tentacles are much shorter. Unlike the Portuguese man-of-war, it does not have a large bladder. It looks very much like a small, dark-blue boat with a clear, transparent sail to drive it along before the wind, over the wide waters of the Pacific, from Vancouver, Canada, to Central America.

Velella mutica, another near relative, makes its home along the

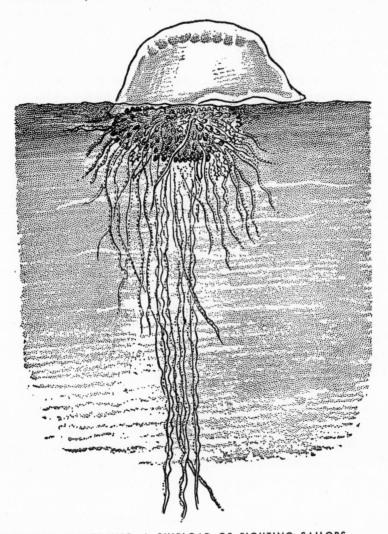

PORTUGUESE MAN-OF-WAR—A SHIPLOAD OF FIGHTING SAILORS

This exquisitely colored balloon belongs not to just one animal but to a whole colony. The tentacles, sometimes thirty to forty feet long, have stinging organs with which the colony captures its food and defeats its enemies. You see Portuguese men-of-war at their loveliest when you are out in a boat. Those on shore are dead and have lost some of their iridescent colors; however, for a while they may retain their ability to sting.

Atlantic coast. Nautical folk frequently refer to the members of this genus as "by-the-wind sailors," because they are always sailing before the wind.

JELLYFISHES

The Many-tentacled Jellyfish, *Zygodactyla groenlandica,* is one of the familiar jellyfishes seen along the Atlantic coast. It ranges from Greenland to the Carolinas. The circular mass of jelly-like material reaches a maximum diameter of about five inches. The mass is slightly depressed in the center. About the edge and trailing downward are approximately one hundred tentacles ready to bring food into the animal's stomach. The stomach itself is a large tube, frilled around the edge, and extending downward from the center of the medusa, or jelly cap. This mouth can be seen distinctly through the transparent jelly from above and serves as a quick means for identifying this species.

The genus comprises only one species. Northern specimens are transparent, but those in southern waters are tinted pink. Because of its numerous tentacles, some authors have named this animal the many-tentacled jellyfish.

The Flat Jellyfish, *Aequorea tenuis,* is a small species, scarcely two inches in diameter, with a flat umbrella. It also has many tentacles, eighty or more in number, but, since they are very fine, and the creature is small, they are hardly discernible. Although not common, this jellyfish may be seen in late summer along Long Island Sound.

Aequorea albida is found along the New England coast, also around Alaska and western Canada. Other species of the genus occur in the Mediterranean and Japanese seas, as well as in other waters of the world. When disturbed, many species of *Aequorea* show a luminescence from the base of their tentacles.

LARGE JELLYFISHES

Most abundant of the jellyfishes are those belonging to class Scyphozoa. This class, although rich in individuals, contains only about two hundred species. They are generally larger in size than those of the preceding class. Each one has four large reproductive organs, called gonads, arranged like a four-leaf clover in the center of its umbrella. These are very conspicuous, and often brightly colored.

The Common, or Moon, Jellyfish, *Aurelia aurita,* is undoubtedly the most abundant and widely distributed of the jellyfishes. That is why it is so popularly known as the common jellyfish. Its other name, moon jellyfish, it owes to its round, moonlike shape. From May to July, swarms of these jellyfishes float just below the surface in almost any backwater arm of the Atlantic and Pacific coasts. In early spring, they start life as tiny blobs of jelly. By midsummer, they have reached their maximum size of eight or ten inches. At this time, when mature, the gonads turn pink. Earlier, they are black, and are conspicuous as four circles sharply outlined in the white or blue-white of the jelly umbrella. These jellyfishes move laboriously by jerking pulsations as they alternately expand and contract this umbrella.

The Sea Blubber, *Cyanea capillata,* is our largest jellyfish. Although it is usually a foot or less in diameter, some are six or seven feet across. From its underside eight groups of tentacles stream out. In the larger sea blubbers, these may reach a length of thirty or forty feet, and are capable of paralyzing a swimmer. Widely distributed up and down the Atlantic and Pacific coasts of America, this jellyfish can be a serious menace to bathers. It is frequently washed ashore, or left stranded by the retreating tide, remaining on the sand as a mass of jelly. Its jelly is thicker and more resistant than that of most jellyfishes and, thus, persists longer. The color of its umbrella varies from light yellow to brown. Individuals are sometimes bright pink or purplish. This bright coloring has caused the name sun jelly to be applied to the species.

Other Large Jellyfishes. *Stomolophus meleagris,* a small species about six or seven inches in diameter, is quite hemispherical in form. Brown in color, it resembles a large, cone-capped mushroom that has come to life and is swimming in the water. It lives in the warmer waters of our Atlantic and Pacific coasts.

Rhopilema verrilli is also hemispherical and much larger in size. It frequently reaches a diameter of a foot or more. Although not common, it flaunts a yellow color that makes it easily seen. It ranges from Long Island Sound southward into the warmer seas. *Rhopilema es-*

culenta, of eastern Asiatic waters, is the edible jellyfish highly prized by the Chinese and Japanese.

SEA ANEMONES AND STONY CORALS

Unlike other Coelenterata, the sea anemones and stony corals (class Anthozoa) have no medusa form. They exist only as polyps which make up the colony formation of the complete animal. The six thousand species all agree in being ocean-dwelling animals, but many of them differ so radically in shape that they would scarcely seem to be related. Most of them are fixed in place, and most have a skeleton composed either of lime or of a hornlike material called ceratine. Most of the species are found in the warmer waters of the world.

The Sea Fan, *Gorgonia flabellum,* is a colony secreting a skeleton of horny material, flat or fanlike in shape, with a single main stem. The blade, perforated with numerous openings, may be as much as two feet in height. Sea fans are common in the shallow waters of the West Indies and the warmer Atlantic Ocean regions. Yellow or reddish in color, they were much sought after at one time as curiosities, or for decorative purposes. There are many other closely related species, all of them having their characteristic forms. One, *Gorgonia acerosa,* has tall, slender stems which are sometimes slightly branching.

The Red Coral, *Corallium nobile,* of the central and western Mediterranean Sea, is the commercial red coral used so extensively for jewelry a number of years ago, and now back in fashion. The colony, which reaches a height of about one foot, is profusely branching, and forms the very hard, slender twigs which, when broken, make the beads that are so familiar to everyone. Other species occur in the Atlantic Ocean and in Japanese waters. These, however, are not used as extensively for jewelry as the typical red coral.

The Yellowish Red Coral, *Alcyonium carneum,* is a curious relative of the red corals. Its grayish, limey skeleton is frequently cast up on the shores from New York to the Gulf of St. Lawrence, where it lives in waters ranging from low tide to several hundred feet in depth. It looks like a tiny, but heavy, treelike growth, three to four inches tall. When alive, these animals vary in color from yellow to red. The little yellow polyps that build up the skeleton are like tiny stars on the stubby branches of the colony. The skeleton is too coarse in grain and dull in color, however, to have any commercial value.

Pennatula aculeata is the most common of the Sea Feathers, which get their name from their feather-like shape. They are seldom seen, for they inhabit the deeper waters, five hundred to three thousand feet off the eastern coast of North America. Only about four inches high, they are a deep red in color. Living in about the same depth of water off Nantucket and Newfoundland is *Pennatula grandis*. It reaches a height of fourteen inches, and its color is a beautiful orange.

SEA ANEMONES

We now come to the sea anemones, which number about a thousand species. Looking like a beautiful underwater flower, the sea anemone has numerous outspread tentacles, usually brilliant in color, which radiate from the top of a supporting stalk. When disturbed, the animal pulls in its tentacles and becomes a lumpy stump.

The Brown Anemone, *Metridium dianthus,* is the most common of the sea anemones and the largest among those found off the Atlantic coast between North Carolina and Labrador. It is also found in European waters. Four inches high, with a stalk nearly two and a half inches across, it spreads its yellowish tentacles like welcoming arms to any passing victim, in waters ranging from low tide to five hundred feet in depth. This species has won its common name, brown anemone, because of the brownish color of the larger specimens.

Sagartia luciae is a tiny, but beautifully colored, species. A slender creature, only half an inch high, it is light green, with about twelve vertical orange stripes on its body. From the top of its body radiate eighty-four tentacles arranged in four rows. This pretty creature is common in shallow water among rocks or in tidal pools from Florida to the Gulf of St. Lawrence, and also on the Pacific coast of the United States. Other species of *Sagartia,* equally beautiful, are found in all the waters of the world.

STONY CORALS

The stony corals are polyps which, sometimes singly, but usually in colonies, secrete a skeleton of calcareous material in the form of a cell into which the polyp can withdraw itself. The massing of these hard, stony skeletons forms the corals with which we are familiar. Those of the more temperate waters seldom result in the massive structures, whole islands of coral rising above the surface of the sea, which species in the tropical waters build up.

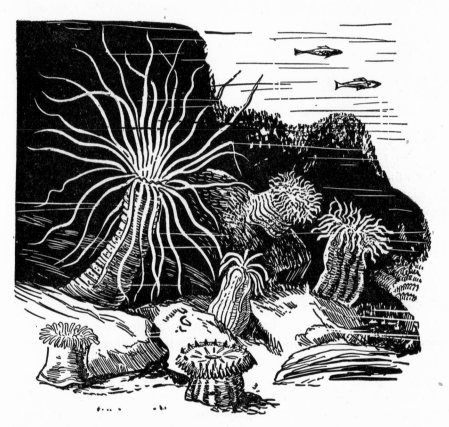

SEA ANEMONES—ANIMAL FLOWERS IN THE TIDAL POOLS

These little creatures are very lovely when they are waving their fringe of tentacles just below the surface of sunlit waters. Frighten them, and they huddle in unattractive stumps. A sea anemone usually has a broad, sucker-like foot for attaching itself to wharf posts, rocks, or even shells. But some live in sand, just below low water mark, and some can swim. Those along the Atlantic coast come in shades of brown, green, or yellow; those in tropical waters are more brightly colored.

The Star Coral, *Astrangia danae,* develops a small, encrusting coral colony, of ten to thirty individuals, covering stones or other submerged objects. The little polyps, looking like tiny stars, are conspicuous as they lie imbedded in the calcareous material. The coral patch may be four or five inches in diameter and about one-quarter of an inch thick, and is generally of a whitish color. This creature is often washed ashore from the shallow waters, where it is common from Florida to New England. Another species is found on the Pacific coast. The encrusting corals are widely distributed and invade the colder waters of the world.

The genus *Porites* includes some of the more conspicuous branching corals. These are warm-water species, and are frequently reef-builders. Several species are common around Florida and in the West Indies.

Other corals are the fungus, or mushroom, corals, which get their name from their rounded or mushroom-like shape. Although the individuals are small, the resulting mass may be tremendous in size.

COMB JELLYFISHES

The Ctenophora are very soft jellyfishes, usually spherical or cylindrical in shape. They get their common name from their eight lengthwise rows of platelike cilia, or "combs." These are the organs of locomotion, which, through their waving, propel the organism through the surface waters of the seas. Although treated here as a class of the Coelenterata, the Ctenophora are considered a separate phylum by many zoologists.

The Common Comb Jellyfish, *Mnemiopsis leidyi,* is a colorless, nearly transparent jellyfish, three inches long and one inch in diameter. It is abundant from the New England coast southward to the Carolinas. Late in the summer, these jellyfishes sometimes become so numerous in the back bays and inlets along the coast that the water feels thick and gelatinous to swimmers who venture in at this time. At night they glow beautifully with a phosphorescent blue light as they swim slowly and sedately along. This is especially true when the water is agitated by a passing boat or even by a hand swept through the water. A smaller species, *Mnemiopsis gardeni,* one and a half inches long, and a translucent blue in color, is found from Chesapeake Bay to Florida.

The Sea Walnut, *Pleurobrachia pileus,* is a small sphere of transparent jelly less than one inch in diameter. Its notable features are two six-inch tentacles, white or bright rose in color, which stream out into the water. These tentacles are extremely beautiful when observed closely, for each is feathered along one side with very fine, long threads. The sea walnut is common, during August and September, from Long Island to Greenland, as well as in European waters, and along the American Pacific coast. Other species occur elsewhere.

Beroë ovata, about four inches in length, is a common and nearly cosmopolitan species. Along the Atlantic coast, it ranges from Chesapeake Bay southward. The more northern forms are pink, while those in the south are milky white. *Beroë cucumis* is found in great abundance from Long Island Sound north to Labrador, and also on the Pacific coast. It is about the same size as *ovata,* but has a slight neck behind its mouth. Its color is a beautiful rose. This species is frequently called the northern comb jelly; but the more appropriate name of sea mitre or mitre jellyfish is often used because of its resemblance to a mitre. *Beroë forskali* is twice as long, or nearly eight inches. More conical in shape, it tapers from its mouth to a blunt point. This species is found along the Pacific coast and in the Mediterranean Sea.

Moss Animals and Lamp Shells

MOSS ANIMALS OR BRYOZOANS

LIKE THE SPONGES and the corals, the moss animals (phylum Bryozoa) usually live in colonies.

The individual animal is small and roundish, or cylindrical, with a bunch of waving tentacles protruding from its limey covering. After the death of the animal or colony, the covering remains, like coral or the shell of a mollusk.

The colonies of some species form mosslike patches on stones, logs, and even on other sea animals, such as corals and sponges. Some of the larger colony-making species, consisting of thousands of individuals, branch and re-branch until they take on the appearance of miniature, leafless trees. So plantlike in appearance are the bryozoans that early naturalists regarded them as seaweeds.

All bryozoans are water animals. Of the known species, over three thousand make their homes in the ocean, while less than fifty live in fresh water. While all of them are interesting to study, many of them are especially so, for they are colored, or iridescent, with yellow, orange, pink, or red. Examine carefully any submerged object, such as seaweeds, stones, logs, piles, and floating wharves, and you will surely find one or more bryozoan colonies.

The Seaweed Crust, genus *Flustrella,* is commonly seen on many of the seaweeds. It forms a small patch, gauzy or lacy in appearance. The Hyaline Encrusting Bryozoan, *Schizoporella hyalina,* is a glossy-appearing species. It builds successive layers of translucent material, usually on submerged stones or logs.

Another, the Silvery Encrusting Bryozoan, genus *Membranipora,* is easily recognized by its somewhat circular patches of gleaming silver on small submerged stones.

The *Lichenopora* form small, lichen-like spots, one-half inch or less in diameter, on stones or shells. The spots are usually gray or yellow in color.

The genus *Crisia* contains a number of small species commonly found on stones, shells, or other submerged objects. Only ten inches or so tall, they look like tiny, branching plants, with miniature leaves covering the stems. Yellow or yellow-brown is their usual color. The Bushy Gray Bryozoan, *Crisia eburnea,* is a common species along the Atlantic coast.

We find the giants of the group in the genus *Bugula,* for some of its species actually reach a height of one foot or more. They occur throughout the waters of the world, and may be found on submerged objects, from low-tide mark to one hundred or more feet below the surface. Each is a colony of thousands of individual animals, all of which wave their tentacles and feed independently.

The Fern Bryozoan, *Bugula turrita,* is the species commonly found along the Atlantic coast, from Maine to the Carolinas. So called because of its delicate, fernlike growth, it has a lower stem of orange, and upper parts of yellow. A number of years ago there was considerable commercial activity in dredging up these growths, drying them, then spraying them a bright green, and selling them as Christmas decorations. In this form they acquired the name of "air fern."

LAMP SHELLS

While wandering along the coastal beaches of America, you frequently see, washed up on the sand, what appear to be tiny clam shells, about one-half inch long. A delicate yellow in color, they are thin and translucent, so thin and fragile that it is difficult to find a perfect example. Because of their shell-like appearance (and they have fooled many experts), they have been given the name "lamp shell." Most of them belong to the genus *Terebratulina*. Closely related to the Bryozoa, the lamp shells are put in a separate phylum called Brachiopoda ("having arms and feet").

Starfishes, Sea Urchins, and Their Kin

ANYONE who can walk along a sea beach, or at least any sea beach not too close to the filth of our cities, has a fine opportunity to observe some members of the phylum Echinodermata, the "spiny-skinned" animals. Starfishes and sea urchins glide imperceptibly over the sands at low tide. Occasionally, you can see a brittle star walking stiltlike on the tips of its points. Storms, especially along the warmer coasts, are sure to toss up on the beach for your amazement feather stars, sea lilies, and sea cucumbers, from their deep-water homes.

If you live inland, you can see collections of these animals in most museums, for their calcareous shells or skeletons are easily preserved,

rome by Ruth Bernhard   *American Museum of Natural History*

THE LION'S PAW SHELL IS SELDOM SEEN ASHORE
One of the most striking members of a large and colorful family, the lion's paw shell is noteworthy because its prominent radiating ribs are adorned with large stubby projections. About
four and one-half inches long, the shell grows in water fifty to one hundred feet deep, from
North Carolina and around the coast of Florida to the Gulf of Mexico. Perfect specimens are
rarely washed ashore, but are often brought up by divers. They are also called knobbed scallops.

and a large collection is highly interesting from many points of view.

Indeed, to get any over-all picture of the Echinodermata phylum, you will need to see a large collection of its members. If you do, you will notice an important feature that the casual beach-walker would miss, namely, that the five-sidedness, which is so obvious in the starfish, is also present in a camouflaged, or imperfect, manner throughout the whole phylum.

Labels and charts in the museum will inform you of the great geological age of the Echinodermata, and of the great number of extinct species that have been found. This is a group that at an early period diverged markedly from the other groups, and then evolved along a line all its own. In having few connecting links with other animal life, the Echinodermata are like the sponges.

The phylum readily divides into five main divisions or classes: Asteroidea, comprising the starfishes; Echinoidea, the sea urchins; Ophiuroidea, the brittle stars; Crinoidea, the feather stars and sea lilies; and Holothurioidea, the sea cucumbers.

Over five thousand species are known. They inhabit all of our seas and oceans, except the very coldest, with most of the species preferring the warmer waters.

STARFISHES—NOT FISHES AT ALL

Some persons have labored to establish the term "sea stars" for these creatures, and there is no doubt that it is an apter name. But, although they are not fishes in any sense of the word, the term "starfishes" has been used so long that it is impossible to change it now.

Most of the many species of this group (class Asteroidea) are plentiful along the coast of the United States and Europe. During high tide, they travel up the beach and then are left stranded, to die in the sun as the tide retreats. Rocky tidal pools are good places to observe them, for, frequently, dozens, representing a number of species, will be left in one of these miniature seas. If they are fortunate and the pool does not dry up, the returning tide will allow them to travel on and perhaps get back into deeper water.

The five-pointed body is characteristic of most of the starfishes. A few have six points, however, and others have as many as ten, or more, points. In some, the space between the points is filled in, making a nearly perfect pentagon. The upper surface of a starfish is covered with blunt spines. Near the junction of two of the points, or arms, as they are called, is a porous plate called the sieve plate. Through this plate, water enters the ring canal, then flows into the five, or more, radial canals that extend out into the arms. The underside of each arm is fitted with sucker-like processes, called ampullae, or tube-feet, which are moved by the hydraulic action of the circulating water.

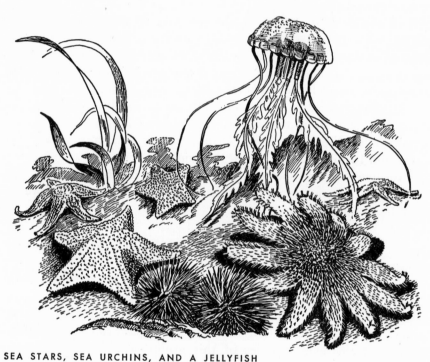

SEA STARS, SEA URCHINS, AND A JELLYFISH

Most sea stars, or starfishes, are five-pointed, but a few, like the sunburst sea star pictured at the lower right, have from eight to fourteen points (the huge Alaskan sea star, not shown here, may have as many as twenty-four points). The burrlike creatures are sea urchins, or sea porcupines. One of the Florida jellyfishes is shown at the upper right.

HOW STARFISHES MOVE

Starfishes walk in any direction, with the arm on the direction side taking the lead, a process which makes them amusing to watch. The tip of one arm curls up, then pushes out. Slowly, the animal slides forward as this lead arm contracts. If turned on its back, the starfish will lie quietly, as if it had no idea what to do. Then, with scarcely any perceptible movement, one arm, sometimes more, will curve backward until the tip touches the ground. Curving more and more, it presses flatter and flatter to the ground. Another arm follows in a similar manner. Meanwhile, the arms on the other side are curving higher and higher. The creature is now almost on edge. A little more now, the balance swings to the other side, and the starfish flops over, right side up.

This ability to turn over is not the only accomplishment of the starfish, for it is a remarkably versatile creature. It is able to squeeze through a crevice no wider than one of its arms. With one arm leading the way, the creature will elongate the remainder of its body and drag itself through the narrow opening. The starfish also has the peculiar habit of raising its body from the ground and standing on the tips of its arms, as if preparing to trip off to a dance.

IMPATIENT EATERS

The mouth of the starfish is on its ventral, or bottom, side, in the center, at the spot where the arms meet. A starfish feeds largely on shellfish, and it shows a special preference for clams and oysters. Although the starfish moves slowly, the clam is much slower in plowing through the mud, and the starfish soon overtakes it.

The starfish is an impatient eater and swallows small shellfish and mollusks whole. Absorbing the edible parts, it evacuates the hard, indigestible remains through its mouth. It uses its arms to deal with larger clams, encircling them and attaching its sucker-like ampullae firmly to the smooth surface of the clamshell. Then, with steadily increasing force, the starfish begins to pull the two shells apart. Eventually, even the biggest mussels, which can resist larger and stronger creatures, give way before this continuous pressure and slowly open. The starfish then literally turns its stomach inside out and extends it into the shell, surrounding and devouring the body of the clam.

When starfishes invade oyster beds, they cause a tremendous amount of destruction. The oyster fishermen of a few generations back thought they were wreaking vengeance on their enemy when they tore a captured starfish in two and tossed the parts back into the ocean. It remained for the research scientist to discover that, instead of destroying this pest, the fishermen were helping to increase its numbers, for a starfish can regenerate all its missing parts, and may even regenerate an entire animal from a single arm.

The Common Starfish, *Asterias vulgaris,* is also called the purple starfish because of its deep violet color. The sieve plate, or madreporite, is yellow or gray. This species is common along the New England coast. Some grow to the diameter of a foot or more.

Forbes's Starfish, *Asterias forbesi,* replaces *vulgaris* farther south along the Atlantic seaboard. It is greenish, with a bright-orange sieve plate. At the tip of each arm is a red eyespot. Its arms and body are more convex, or arched, than those of *vulgaris,* which tends to be flattish. A full-grown adult is seldom over six inches across.

The Scarlet Starfish, *Hippasteria pharygiana,* is bright scarlet in color when alive. Although not much over eight inches in diameter, it is a very convex and heavy species, for it has short, stocky arms and a large central region. This species lives in rather deep water, and is seldom seen along the beach, except after a violent storm which has stirred the ocean to its depths.

The Common Sun Star, *Crossaster papposus,* is quickly identified bv its many short, thick arms. These arms may vary in number from eight to fourteen. Nearly six inches in diameter, it is of a rich, purple color that becomes lighter toward the center. It lives in shallow water, as well as in the deeper parts of the sea. The Pacific coast is the home of a number of similar species, such as the sunflower star and Dawson's sun star.

Other Starfish. From the thick-armed species we go to the slender-armed. The Common Slender Starfish, *Leptasterias tenera,* is one of these. Only about three inches across, it varies in color from gray to violet. The Red Slender Starfish, *Henricia sanguinolenta,* is also a common species in shallow waters and varies from yellow to a reddish color. It has a smoother surface than that of *Leptasterias tenera.* A very similar species, *Henricia laeviuscula,* is common on the Pacific coast. This slenderness of the arms reaches its maximum in the Ophiuroidea, or brittle stars, which we will meet later.

SEA URCHINS, SAND DOLLARS, AND SEA EGGS

Quite different in shape from the starfishes are the members of this group (class Echinoidea). They are without arms, and they are round, disk-like, or hemispherical. Their surface is thickly covered with numerous rather sharp spines. They look much like pin cushions, except that their pins are pointed outward. In some species, the spines are quite small; in others, very large. The spines are movable, being hinged on a sort of ball-and-socket base in the skinlike covering of the calcareous plates which make up the skeleton. They are concentrated in the five areas that compose the five-part arrangement so notable in the starfish. In some species, the spines are poisonous.

The Common Sea Urchin, *Arbacia punctulata,* is also called the purple urchin, because of its purplish or violet color. In some, it may be a deep purplish-red. The sea urchin is about one and three-quarters inches in diameter, and thickly covered with three-quarter-inch spines. When the animal dies, its spines soon drop off. This occurs because of the disintegration of the outer skin, in which they are imbedded. It is for this reason that you rarely find a perfect shell or skeleton of a sea urchin on the beach. Living members of this species may be found on the shore from the low-tide mark to depths of six hundred or seven hundred feet. The sea urchin ranges along the Atlantic coast, from the New England states to Yucatan. Other species are found in all the waters of the world. In many places, sea urchins are eaten and considered quite a delicacy. In European countries, particularly those along the Mediterranean, hundreds of thousands of these sea animals are consumed annually. They are also sold in many of the fish markets of New York, as well as in other cities that contain immigrants from southern Europe. Naturally, they are a common food of many oceanic animals.

The Sand Dollar, *Echinarachnius parma,* is a familiar object along the sea coasts of the United States. The specimens cast up on beaches are usually only the lime skeleton, a gray-white disk, three inches, or less, in diameter. The softer coat and very minute spines with which the sand dollar is covered have all been worn away. Alive, it is purplish, mottled with gray. This mottling gives it the appearance of a five-petaled flower on a mosaic of tiles. Because of its lack of flesh and considerable quantity of calcareous material, very few marine animals feed upon it.

On the Atlantic coast, the sand dollar is found from Delaware northward, and on the Pacific, from Vancouver Island southward for a considerable distance. Other species replace it on the various beaches of the world. The sand dollars are also referred to as "sea cookies."

BRITTLE STARS

The brittle stars (class Ophiuroidea) look like strange starfishes. They have a very small central, or body region, but exceedingly long, slender arms. More than a thousand species are known, and some of these occur in all the waters of the world, except the very coldest ones. Most of the species prefer the deeper waters, although a few are always found in the shallower places.

The Green Serpent Star, *Ophioderma brevispinum,* is the most common species of brittle star along the Atlantic seaboard, ranging from the New England states southward nearly to Florida. It varies in color from green to brown.

FEATHER STARS

The feather star (class Crinoidea) is like a starfish or a brittle star turned upside down. Its mouth is in the center, and its five arms reach out into the surrounding water ready to grasp any passing prey. Each arm divides near the base, so that the animal actually appears to have ten arms. The arms are feather-like and very flexible. By alternately flexing and extending these feathery arms, the animal swims through the water. When it wishes to rest, it anchors itself by coils of slender appendages located on the side opposite the mouth. Some feather stars possess a distinct stalk, making them appear like beautiful, white flowers waving in the water. The name "sea lily" has been applied to these.

SEA CUCUMBERS

Sea cucumbers differ from all the other echinoderms in that their bodies are very large in proportion to the length of their tentacles.

The sea cucumber's body is occasionally roundish, but is more frequently elongated and curved, being much like a cucumber in shape.

Although sea cucumbers are not eaten as a substitute for cucumbers, many do serve as an important article of food. The well-known *bêche-de-mer* of eastern Asia, the Malay Archipelago, Australia, and a few other places is made from sea cucumbers, or, as they are also sometimes called, sea caterpillars. The sea cucumbers are cooked in sea water and then dried. Before being eaten, they are boiled again; they are frequently used in soup. The Chinese call the dried product "trepang." Other specimens of sea cucumbers could be used as food by the people of various countries, for some of them would make excellent chowders, and a number are good substitutes for lobster.

At one end of its body the sea cucumber has a rosette, or whorl, of short, fleshy tentacles which clasp any passing food. This animal is usually more selective in its choice of morsels than the starfish, or some of the other echinoderms. Sea cucumbers move slowly along the bottom of the ocean, aided by their tentacles. Most of the time, however, they lie buried in the mud, with only the branching tentacles exposed. They are members of class Holothurioidea.

Cucumaria frondosa, a very common sea cucumber along the New England coast, also appears along parts of the European coast. It occurs from the low-water mark to the depth of a thousand or more feet. The color of its body varies from reddish-brown to dark-violet, and is somewhat lighter along one side. Although occasionally rounded in shape, this species is usually elongated and may reach a length of ten inches and a diameter of five inches.

Stichopus and *Leptosynapta* are two genera that have more elongated species. These various species range in size from a few inches to two feet or more. Some are so transparent that they resemble fragile blown glass. Others are colored a brilliant red or brown.

Roundworms — Some Are
Man's Deadly Enemies

T HE ROUNDWORMS, or threadworms, comprise some three thousand species. Members of phylum Nemathelminthes ("thread worms"), they are slender, unsegmented animals without cilia or paired appendages, and, therefore, cannot be confused with the true worms or annelids. Most of them are parasites on many species of higher animals. Some destroy plants or plant products; the Golden Nematode, for example, is a pest to potatoes, but many other roundworms are valuable in reducing dead animal and plant material to a condition suitable for re-use by plants and animals.

The Hair Snake, *Gordius lineatus,* is familiar to almost every farm boy and to others who have looked into shallow pools for what they might find. Hairworms, as these creatures are also sometimes called, are two feet or over in length, and very, very slender. Reddish, or dark brown, in color, they suggest a hair, and for a long time it was a popular superstition (which, in many places, still persists) that these slender animals were snakes or worms transformed from horse hairs that had fallen into water.

So widespread and so firmly fixed in the popular imagination was this idea, that every summer horses would have to sacrifice some tail hairs to small boys, who put them into a bottle of water and exposed them to the sun, hoping to see them transformed into hair snakes. Perhaps one reason for the universal acceptance of this idea was the fact that hair snakes were frequently found in the water of horses' drinking troughs.

Hair snakes may also be found in the bodies of insects, mainly grasshoppers and some of the water insects, the last-named being the favorite hosts. One wonders how one of these long hair snakes could possibly be contained in the body of a grasshopper, but there it is, tightly coiled like the "Gordian knot," from which it gets its generic name. In the grasshopper's body it develops from one of the tiny larvae which the insect has swallowed. When full grown, it leaves the insect to get back into the water to lay its eggs, and hair snakes are most frequently seen at this time.

The author has often collected grasshoppers which had one or more inches of a hair snake trailing out from a tiny opening in the abdomen. Taking hold of this projecting portion with tweezers and pulling slowly and steadily, he has been able to extract the entire hair snake. After the hair snake leaves it, the host dies, although it may have been quite active up to a few minutes earlier.

If the hair snake is fortunate and leaves its host at, or near, water, it then deposits its eggs in the water or a damp place. The eggs are in fine strings, sometimes six to eight feet long, and number into the millions. Their tremendous number accounts for the survival of the species, since perhaps only one or two of the little larvae developing from one string will ever be swallowed by an insect. Should the infested insect be eaten by fish, bird, or other insect, *Gordius* will develop in this new host.

ROUNDWORMS THAT CARRY DISEASE

Roundworms are everywhere. *Trichinae,* which are parasitic in the flesh of numerous animals (including man), cause the sometimes fatal disease of trichinosis. The Whipworm, *Trichocephalus,* is thought sometimes to complicate appendicitis and even typhoid fever. The Hookworm, *Necator americanus,* is perhaps the most serious parasite menace facing man in North America. Probably two million people in the southern states of the United States suffer from the effects of this nematode, and even greater numbers in other parts of the world are attacked by it. Trouble from hookworms is most prevalent in the warmer climates, where the poor do not wear shoes.

An animal infected with hookworms evacuates the hookworm eggs with its own excretions. These eggs hatch into little larvae which live in damp earth or water until they can meet another host. They accomplish this meeting in several ways. They are swallowed with dirty water, with food that has been handled by dirty hands, or on vegetables grown in contaminated soil. They also enter through the skin.

This last method is the most common, and happens when bare feet or other parts of the body rest in infested soil. From the skin, the little larvae follow the blood stream, traveling to the heart, lungs, throat, and the small intestine.

Many species of nematodes attack useful or ornamental plants, sometimes causing great destruction. Others, like the Vinegar Worm, wiggle about in the food we eat. Fortunately for our appetites, they are small, and we cannot see them without a strong microscope.

Tapeworms and Other Flatworms

A LITTLE HIGHER UP the scale of animal development comes the group known as the Platyhelminthes ("flat worms"). Flatworm is a good name for these creatures, because they are all more or less flat. The more than 6,500 species in this phylum are widely distributed throughout the world.

The phylum is divided into three classes: free-living, or true, flatworms (Turbellaria); flukes, which are parasitic animals (Trematoda); and tapeworms, which are also parasitic (Cestoda).

PLANARIANS—THEY HAVE TRACES OF EYES

One of the most common and familiar of the true flatworms is *Planaria,* a little wormlike creature that every student of invertebrate zoology has met face to face. It is a flat, brownish worm about half an inch long. A distinct head, forming the front, or anterior, end, and a tail, or posterior, end distinguish it as being more advanced than any of the invertebrates we have met so far. As it moves, one surface of its body remains upward and is the back, or dorsal, surface, while the other, usually somewhat lighter in color, remains downward and is the belly, or ventral, part.

Two dark spots on this creature's head are sensitive to light. The two spots are among the first traces of eyes to appear in the lower animals.

We notice also that one side of the animal is similar to the other side. This is the first example of "bilateral symmetry" in the evolution of animal forms.

The *Planaria* gets about on the large number of cilia that cover its ventral side. As the cilia vibrate, a mucous material is discharged from the body, forming a slimy pathway along which the planarian glides. Disturb the creature, however, and it swims hurriedly away, giving a series of flapping waves of its body.

Planaria are seldom seen, although there are many species and they are found in most streams and waterways, crawling among the vegetation. If a piece of meat is placed in the water, however, they will soon gather in numbers from all the surrounding regions to enjoy the banquet. At such a time it is easy to see how they received their class name Turbellaria, a name composed principally of a Latin word *turbella,* meaning "little crowd," for when planarians are abundant the water takes on a disturbed appearance because of the mucous secretions which they give off.

TREMATODES OR FLUKES

The Trematoda, or flukes, are parasitic, either internally or externally, on many different species of higher animals. Flattened, they are much like the planarians, except that they possess two or more suckers for attaching and feeding upon their hosts. The name fluke, another name for the flounder, has been given them on the basis of this flattened appearance and their slight resemblance to the bottom-feeding flounder.

These creatures comprise a large group, whose members you will seldom see unless you look for them.

THE TAPEWORMS

Perhaps the most important members of the Platyhelminthes are the cestodes, or tapeworms. They, too, are seldom seen but are present everywhere. Tapeworms are internally parasitic upon vertebrate animals. Sectional animals, with a distinct head, they possess a sucker-like process by means of which they acquire their food and cling to their hosts. The sectional pieces frequently break off and pass out of the host animals. These sections are capable of reproducing; therefore, any parts swallowed by an unwitting animal may readily start a new infestation of the worms.

A number of species of tapeworms are parasitic in man. Most common of these are *Taenia saginata* and *Taenia solium*. Both occur in Europe and North America. The first is called the Beef, or Ox, Tapeworm because it develops in the flesh of cattle, from which man acquires it by eating raw, or poorly cooked, meat. Although the presence of the tapeworm seldom proves fatal, the animal will reduce its host to a condition in which other diseases or troubles will develop. This species frequently reaches a length of thirty feet or more, with over a thousand sections. *Solium*, a somewhat similar species, occurs in the muscles of swine, and is acquired by man largely through eating badly cooked pork.

The True Worms — Among Earth's Most Important Creatures

Worms are simple, commonplace creatures to most of us, and we think of them mainly in connection with fishing, as a rule. Such an impression is grossly unfair to the true worms or annelids, including the humble earthworm. Small they certainly are, but they play an enormous role in the natural scheme of things. Our earth would be a far different place without them.

Examine a true worm closely and you will see it is a long, segmented animal having a head and digestive tract, and, sometimes, paired, unjointed appendages. It is this lack of jointed appendages that at once differentiates this phylum (Annelida, meaning "ring worms") from the phylum Arthropoda, whose members have seg-mented bodies with jointed appendages. The familiar Fishworm is a typical representative of the annelids.

There are about seven thousand known, present-day species of an-nelid worms, belonging in five different classes. Some are land ani-mals, but most prefer the water, some living in fresh water, others in the sea. We are going to discuss only those few species that are commonly met.

EARTHWORMS—NATURE'S PLOWMEN

The earthworm is unusually talented in being able to stretch or shrink itself to an almost unbelievable extent. This capacity is the result of a ringlike structure joined together with softer membra-nous material. Minute bristles on the underside, with the aid of a mu-cous secretion, enable the animal to crawl, even to ascend very smooth surfaces. The head end of an earthworm is pointed; the tail end more or less flattened. The animal is usually pink or reddish in color. It often reaches a length of ten inches, a species found in Australia measuring as much as ten feet.

Many of the earthworms belong in the genus *Lumbricus,* the spe-cies *terrestris* being one of the most common.

THE USEFUL EARTHWORM
Fishes can be caught without earthworm bait, even by small boys; but farms and gardens would not do nearly so well if earthworms did not constantly plough up and pulverize the soil. In the United States a ten-inch-long earthworm is a big fellow, but in Australia there is a kind of earthworm that grows to be ten feet long.

Earthworms burrow in the ground, but come to the surface at night to feed on decaying plant, or other organic, material. The worms frequently drag the food below the surface to devour it at their leisure. It is this constant dragging below of debris, and bringing to the surface pellets of earth and digested material that have given to the earthworms the name of "Nature's plowmen."

The tremendous value of these animals was brought to our attention by Darwin, who estimated that each acre of land contained up to fifty thousand earthworms. In the course of a year, more than fifteen tons of soil per acre might be brought to the surface by these little cultivators, and in twenty years this might amount to a layer of two or three inches.

Earthworms live in any part of the world where they find conditions suitable. They prefer a slightly damp soil. Some species can stand considerable moisture, but most of them are seriously bothered by too much water. This is particularly noticeable after a heavy rain, when a great many earthworms of several species may be seen crawling on the ground. The old superstition, which still exists in a few places, was that the worms had "rained down." The opposite, that they "rained up," is more nearly correct, for the heavy rains flood them out of their burrows.

TANGLEWORMS AND SOME OTHERS

The Tangleworm, *Cirratulus grandis.* If, while wandering along the seashore from Massachusetts to Virginia, you find a yellow-green, earthworm-like creature about five or six inches long, it will almost certainly be one of these tangleworms. The front end of the worm has a great mass of long, red, hairlike filaments, called cirri, extending out in all directions. These are respiratory tubes or gills. As it works its way through the sand at the low-tide mark, the worm appears to be in a tangle of threads. Similar species are found on the west coast.

The Amphitrite, *Amphitrite ornata,* is frequently confused with the tangleworm. It is somewhat larger but has red, feather-like gills and yellow, threadlike filaments.

The Lugworm, *Arenicola marina,* is found at lowtide mark and in about the same regions as the tangleworm. You will not see the lugworm unless you dig for it, for lugworms burrow deeply in the sand. The burrows can be located by the small piles of castings surrounding the entrances. When dug out, the lugworm is discovered to be nearly ten inches long, with a large, bulbous head end. Its color is olive green or brownish. A number of species of *Arenicola* are found in various parts of the world. One is widely distributed on the Pacific coast of the United States.

The Jointworm, *Clymenella torquata,* also can be found in the sand at low-tide mark. It has, however, a much greater range, extending from Nova Scotia to the Carolinas. Its reddish body outlined in dark or brilliant orange at each segment makes it a conspicuous object, long to be remembered. It builds a straight little tube of sand to accommodate its three or four inches of length.

BLOODWORMS—DWELLERS IN THE SAND

The Smooth Bloodworm, *Glycera.* Almost any red worm that makes its home in the sea is called a bloodworm. They are all much sought after for fish bait. Those of the genus *Glycera* are called the smooth bloodworms because of their generally smooth bodies. They are more quickly recognized by the long, tubelike extension of the head. It is with this apparatus that they make the sand tunnels in which they live. When full grown they may reach a length of eight or ten inches. They are common worms along the Atlantic coast.

The Fringed Bloodworm, *Polycirrus eximius,* is a tiny worm not over two inches long. Bright red, or orange, becoming paler toward the tail, it has a mass of tiny filaments (each with a small knob at its tip), extending out in all directions from the head. At low tide, along muddy shores, it can be found burrowing just below the surface.

The Slender Bloodworm, *Lumbrinereis tenuis,* is also called "red thread," because it looks like a piece of red yarn. At low tide, these foot-long, slender worms can be found curled up under stones, masses of seaweed, or buried wreckage. They always prefer a muddy area.

THE BEAUTIFUL AND THE ODD IN THE WORLD OF WORMS

Nereis is a genus containing a number of interesting sea-dwelling worms. They all make excellent fish bait. One of the most common species is *virens,* unusually beautiful because of its iridescent coloring. The male is bluish, becoming green along the sides. The female is light green, with yellow, orange, and sometimes red, mottling.

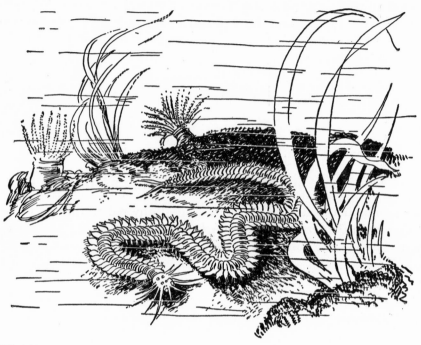

THE SAND WORM OR CLAM WORM
You can find this beautifully colored worm burrowing in the sand at low tide almost anywhere along the Atlantic or Pacific coast of the United States. There are many different sizes and colors among these creatures. The large green clam worm found on the New England coast is ten inches long; like others of its kind, it is of considerable value to the fisherman, who finds it makes excellent bait.

These creatures are known to the fishermen as clam worms or sand worms. When full grown they reach a length of ten inches. When the tide is out, look for them as they burrow in the wet sand or in a sand-mud mixture. Worms of this genus are common subjects for study in elementary zoology courses.

The Green Paddle Worm, *Phyllodoce catenula,* is a beautiful, iridescent green, spotted with brown. Much smaller than many other oceanic worms, reaching only two inches in length, it is found burrowing in the sand of tidal pools along the New England coast.

A number of other ocean-dwelling worms build cases in which they live. Almost any shell picked up along a beach will have fastened to it masses of the entwined tubes of lime made by the tube worms of the genus *Hydroides*. Or they may be the coiled tubes, looking almost like snail shells, of the genus *Spirorbis*. Sandy shores may have hundreds of the tubes of the Little Sandworm, *Pectinaria,* imbedded in them. About two inches long, these tubes are made of sand grains cemented together.

LEECHES, THE BLOOD-SUCKING ANNELIDS

Leeches form an important group of the annelids because of their blood-sucking habits. Over 250 species are known, coming from all parts of the world. Most of them occur in muddy pools, or moist, swampy areas. The commonest North American species is *Placobdella parasitica*. Although only about two inches long, it can stretch itself to twice this length. Greenish-black mottled with darker spots, it is equipped with a sucker at both ends. It feels its way with one, taking hold with the other. This leech normally preys on water animals, such as fishes, turtles, or snails, but will not hesitate to attach itself to dogs, cows, and man.

Not too many years ago, and even today in some sections of the United States, a European species of leech was used for bloodletting. This medicinal leech sometimes grew as long as eight inches.

The Mollusks—Animals with Shells

EVERYBODY who has walked along sea beaches is familiar with shells. Many people have collected them, arranged them, and know their names, but have never given a thought to the animals that have lived in them. The shells are easier to examine than the living mollusks, but every pool of sea water, every beach at ebb tide, and, to a lesser extent, every pond, lake, and stream contains some member of this group that you will find interesting to watch.

The Mollusca phylum contains a large variety of animals. Most of us are familiar with only two of its five classes, the snails, with their single shell, and the bivalves, with their double shell. Even here we have seen only a few of the animals—a few slugs, a few living snails, some oysters, clams, and scallops.

Most of the mollusks have a shell, a protective covering of calcareous (lime) material, which has been secreted in the muscular body covering that is called the mantle. Each Mollusca species possessing a shell creates its own particular shape and marking, and can be identified by its shell alone. Since these shells are often amazingly beautiful and since they are easily preserved, it is not surprising that the collection and study of shells have been going on since the beginning of learning, and that this pursuit even has its own name, conchology. It makes a delightful hobby.

In addition to the shell and the mantle, most mollusks have a foot. It may be a simple fleshy organ for pushing the animal along, as in the clams; or it may be a flat structure used for creeping, as in the snails. There is, however, considerable variation among these animals, for oysters have no such foot. Mollusks with double shells have no distinct head. Octopuses have very large heads, but no shell.

More than seventy thousand species of mollusks have been described. In numbers of individuals some species, like the oysters, run into uncountable billions, while others are quite rare and limited in numbers.

The phylum divides readily into five classes: chitons and their relatives (Amphineura); the tooth shells (Scaphopoda); slugs and snails (Gastropoda); clams and oysters (Pelecypoda); squids, octopuses, and their relatives (Cephalopoda).

CHITONS AND THEIR RELATIVES

Small, inconspicuous, and bug- or grub-like, these creatures (class Amphineura) all live in salt water. They make their homes all over the world, except in polar waters. A very few of them (about fifty species) have no shells. These look like small, fat grubs, and they burrow in the mud, sometimes under deep water.

All other Amphineura (about six hundred species) are provided with a kind of shell, consisting of eight overlapping plates. Our everyday name for these armored creatures is chiton. Most of them live in shallow water, and you may often find them, looking like large sow bugs, crawling at the water's edge at low tide, clinging to rocks or seaweed.

CHITONS OF THE NEW ENGLAND COAST

Chitons of one sort or another are found along every coast in the world; the animal illustrated is a kind very common along New England. This creature's inch-long shell is yellowish-brown, just about the color of the wet sand where it crawls on its one broad foot. The chiton has never been given an English nickname; its many-plated shell reminded the ancient Greeks of their garment, the chiton, and a chiton it has been called ever since.

Chaetopleura apiculata is the most common chiton along the east coast of the United States from New England to Florida. It can be seen at low tide, clinging to the rocks as it feeds upon the plant life of the sea. Oval in shape, it reaches a maximum size of nearly three-quarters of an inch long, with a width of three-eighths of an inch. Its shell is light yellow or brownish, and there are twenty-four gills on each side.

Amicula vestita, a two-inch species, is much more restricted in distribution, for it is limited to the New England coast from Cape Cod northward.

On the west coast of the United States there are a number of species ranging up to three or four inches in length. In the early days of the nation's history these were eaten by the Indians, as well as by the first white settlers. Most of the larger chitons make rather good eating, so much so that they are commonly called "sea beef."

TOOTH SHELLS

The tooth shells comprise a small group of mollusks numbering about two hundred species. They are long, slender animals (class Scaphopoda), living in tapering shells which are open at both ends. The shell is curved and looks like the tusk tooth of a hog. Some of the tooth shells burrow in clean sand in shallow water. Other species descend into the very deep water.

THE TOOTH-SHELLED SNAIL AT HOME

The snail-like creature that builds this curious, glossy, ivory-colored shell lives in deeper waters off the coasts of the world, so you are unlikely to see the live animal, although you can often find the empty shells along the beach after a storm. The kind pictured is about one inch long and is at home in the Atlantic, along New England coasts.

The Common Tooth Shell, *Dentalium entale,* is found from Long Island Sound to the Arctic Sea. Nearly two inches long, it is ivory white. Although it lives under rather deep water, its shells are frequently washed ashore. A similar, but slightly larger, species, *pretiosum,* is found on the Pacific coast, from Alaska to Lower California. *Dentalium* shells are slender and not as curved as some others in their class. Their common name, elephant tusk shells, is vividly descriptive.

SLUGS AND SNAILS—A VAST HORDE

Numbering nearly fifty thousand known species, snails and slugs compose the largest class (Gastropoda) of the mollusks. You can easily recognize any of the snails by the spiral, or conical, shells that protect most of the species. A few have only a trace of a shell, and a very few (the slugs) have no shell at all. The spiral shell in most cases twists to the right, and when the tip of the shell points upward, the opening will be on the right. A few species normally twist to the left, however.

There are some rugged individuals that do not follow the regular rules, for occasionally members of right-handed species will spiral to the left, and those that should be left-handed will spiral to the right.

Snails are found everywhere. By far the greatest number live in the ocean. Some live in fresh water, and streams, rivers, ponds, and lakes all have their respective species. Others like to live on land, even ascending to high altitudes. In general, these land species like the moist conditions of the jungle (where they climb trees), damp woods, or humid mountain valleys. The species are most numerous in tropical waters, but some species are at home in the colder waters, and some are found in polar waters, avoiding only the very coldest regions.

SLUGS THAT LIVE IN THE SEA

The Yellow Sea Slug, *Ancula sulphurea,* is an extremely interesting creature, as are most of the sea slugs. On turning over a stone at low-tide mark along the New England coast, you may be surprised to see this slug of rather startling appearance wallowing in the sediment. Nearly one and a half inches long, it is tan or brown in color, and its head and back are decorated with bright-yellow tentacles and appendages. When eaten raw, it tastes very much like an oyster.

Dendronotus frondosus is a sea slug even more startling to see. Nearly three and a half inches long, it is pale red, with light-brown, or white, spots. On its back it wears a double row of five to seven branching, transparent appendages called cerata. You will find this bright-colored creature crawling on the rocks or in seaweed along the coasts of nothern North America, Europe, and Asia, but rarely south of Long Island Sound in the United States, for it is a species frequenting polar waters.

THE GREEN SEA SLUG

Sea slugs, like land slugs, are simply snails that have no shells. The little one shown is about one inch long, and is bright green with red and white spots. Here the creature is pictured swimming; when it is at rest the leaflike sides fold over the back. The green sea slug is very common in coastal pools from New Jersey to Maine.

The Papillate Sea Slug, *Aeolis papillosa,* is two inches long. Its orange body, spotted with brown, is covered with cerata arranged in fifteen or twenty slanting rows, each row containing ten. It makes its home in the waters from the Arctic Ocean south to New York, and is also common along the coast of Europe.

SLUGS THAT LIVE ON LAND

Limax flavus is a large yellowish or brownish land slug, native to Europe, but introduced into the eastern United States, where it appears to have become established in many places. When full grown it may reach a length of three and a half inches. Its head is usually bluish. Land slugs are not too closely related to the sea slugs, but rather to the land snails. *Limax maximus* is also a European species now established in many places in the eastern United States, as well as in California. Reaching a length of six or more inches, it is gray, mottled with black spots or blotches.

LITTLE TRAVELER ON THE SEAWEED
Although the papillate sea slug is nearly three inches long, this odd little orange-colored creature is not as easy to see as the smaller green sea slug, for it matches very closely its sand and rock background. When it crawls on seaweed, it becomes more visible. The tiny, soft protuberances that cover its back are called cerata. The animal has two pairs of tentacles on its head.

Land slugs native to North America are few in species and much smaller than the European slugs, seldom reaching a length of two and a half inches. Normally, they live on damp or molding vegetation, but sometimes invade our gardens to feed upon lettuce and other tender, leafy plants. The best way to control them is to place poisoned bran mash in small piles, each pile covered with an upturned flower pot or small box to keep away other foragers.

LAND-DWELLING SNAILS

The land snails of the temperate regions are mostly small. They are generally found in moist places under loose bark or decaying leaves or vegetation, but after a rainy period both slugs and snails may be seen in more exposed places. Dr. John Oughton, of the Royal Ontario Museum, Toronto, Canada, tells of finding 3,100 land snails, representing thirty species, in a small paper bag of debris he had scooped up along a flooding river. Most of the shells were less than an eighth of an inch long.

In some of the species, the shell may be flattened, in others the spiral may be very conical. All land snails are more or less thin-shelled and quite fragile. In the tropics, the land snails reach a much larger size. There are several species in the Amazon basin with shells that are a beautiful red in color and four or five inches in length.

The Edible Snail, *Helix pomatia,* is a European species that has been introduced into the region around New Orleans. It has a rather thin shell about one and a half inches long and yellowish, with several broad brown bands. It is sold in the markets of New York and in

THE COMMON EDIBLE SNAIL

The large yellow-and-brown snail pictured at the left is a native of Europe, but has been brought to the United States, where it thrives amid decaying leaves and wood around ponds and marshy places. Europeans consider it a great food delicacy. The large slug pictured beside the snail is also an immigrant from Europe.

other cities where there is a large European population with a taste for such delicacies.

The fresh-water snails of the temperate regions have species looking so much like the land species that only a specialist can identify them.

LIMPETS

The limpets are easily recognized by a rounded or oval shell that rises to a central point like a miniature volcanic cone. In fact, some, known as keyhole limpets, have a small opening at the top of the shells that is much like a little volcanic crater. The limpets are oceanic snails, and, although not numerous in species, are found in practically all the waters of the world, except the extreme polar regions. Limpets feed on seaweed and other vegetation of the sea.

ABALONES

Closely related to the limpets are the abalones or ear shells. The shell of an abalone looks like one of the halves of a clam shell, and many people think there should be another shell adjoining. Actually, it is a spiral snail shell with the apex, or spire, very much flattened and the opening very much expanded. There are usually a number of perforations along the left margin. The outer surface of the shell is rough and coarse, the inner smooth and with iridescent colors. When the calcareous material on the outer surface is ground away, and the shell is polished, the exterior becomes as beautiful as the interior. The abalone is gathered wherever it occurs. The shell is used in Europe and the United States for making decorative buttons and for inlay work. The flesh, which formerly was exported to China and Japan, is now being eaten in many American cities along the Pacific coast.

The Red Abalone, *Haliotis rufescens,* is rather common along the California coast southward from Cape Mendocino. One of the larger species, frequently measuring ten inches or more across, its shell is coarse and thick, brick red on the outside, and green and pink inside. There are three or four perforations along the margin.

The Blue Abalone, *Haliotis fulgens,* found along the California coast south of Monterey, is thin-shelled and much smaller. Its maximum size is about six inches, and there are six perforations. The inside coloring of the shell is a beautiful blue. The Black Abalone, *Haliotis cracherodii,* is five inches long, black outside, and white inside. There are eight perforations. It is common south of the Farallone Islands that lie off the coast of California.

IMPORTANT NAMES AMONG THE SEA SNAILS

The sea snails are so numerous and so varied in size, shape, and color that it is possible to mention only a few of the outstanding examples. The author hopes that these short notes on a few of the species may stimulate the reader to continue the study of these intriguing creatures of the sea.

The Green Snail, *Turbo marmoratus,* is one of the turban snails from the Indian Ocean. Its large shell, four or five inches long, and about the same width, is green outside and pinkish or pearly inside. The lip of the opening turns out widely. Above the opening, the body spreads to resemble an East Indian turban. The shell of this snail is used extensively for ornamental and manufacturing purposes.

The Giant, or Queen, Conch, *Strombus gigas,* is the largest snail on the Atlantic coast. It may be as long as ten inches and weigh nearly five pounds. Its outer surface is rough, with numerous protuberances; the inside, pink. It is common on the Florida coast, particularly along the Keys. Its flesh is used as food and is quite delicious. The shell is used for ornamental purposes, as well as in the making of cameos. *Strombus pugilis,* common in the shallow water from North Carolina to Panama, is smaller than the giant conch, ranging in size from four to seven inches. Its spire is longer and is sharper at the end. The outside of the shell is reddish brown; the interior, pink.

The Finger Shell, *Pterocera lambis,* is so called because of the six or seven long, finger-like processes on the outer lip of the shell. A large shell, about five or six inches long, and found in the Indian Ocean, it is used for ornamental purposes.

THE BEAUTIFUL COWRIES

More than two hundred species of these exquisite shells of gastropods belonging to the genus *Cypraea* are known. Most of them are found in the warmer parts of the Indian and Pacific oceans. The shell is oval, rounded on top, and flat on the underside. The opening is long and narrow, and toothed on both sides. Cowries are much used for ornaments, and highly prized by collectors. Some species are quite small; others are as much as four inches long. In Africa and the Pacific islands, the *moneta* species is used as money.

THE FIGHTING CONCH IS NAMED FOR ITS COLOR

Conches are large, snail-like animals with heavy, spiny shells usually beautifully colored on the inside in rose and orange tints. Beaches from Georgia to Panama are strewn with their usually imperfect shells. The conch pictured has been named "fighting" because of the blood-colored stain at the mouth of the shell; the outside is colored reddish-brown. Conches make very good chowder.

Cypraea exanthema is four-inch species found in shallow water along the Atlantic coast from North Carolina to Panama. It is brown in color, with round, white spots; sometimes each spot has a center of brown. Down the middle of the shell runs a yellow band. The inside of the lip is violet.

CLAMS AND THEIR RELATIVES

Like the three preceding classes, this group of the mollusks we can easily recognize by the style of their shells. Instead of the one-piece shell of the snails and tooth shells, or the many pieces of the chitons, the Pelecypoda have a two-piece shell. This accounts for the name bivalve that is used to describe them. The two pieces are very similar and are joined together with an elastic joint called the ligament; they are guided into a perfect fit by interlocking teeth, the whole making up the hinge.

The animal is enclosed between the two shell halves, surrounded by the mantle. A powerful muscle joins the two halves and controls the opening or closing of the shell at the will of its owner. The creature has no head, but a foot of muscular material can be extended from between the two valves. With the aid of this foot, the animal pushes itself along, plowing through the mud in search of food.

The bivalves form the second largest class of the Mollusca, numbering about eleven thousand species. All are water animals, and partial to the ocean, living generally in the shallower waters along the margins of our islands and continents. They range from the tropical seas well into the colder waters, but do not get quite as far north as the snails. A few are fresh-water species, found in the streams and rivers, the ponds and lakes of the world. A few, and these are usually very small species, are to be found only in the wet, mucky soil of swamps or bogs.

The bivalves furnish some of the most delicious and nutritious foods that man has discovered. Indeed, man now cultivates beds of clams and oysters with almost as much care as he cultivates corn and cattle. The shells of many bivalves are used in making buttons, knife handles, and ornamental inlay, while the pearls that are obtained from the clams and pearl oysters are among the most beautiful and valuable of our jewels.

FRESH-WATER CLAMS

North America is extremely rich in fresh-water clams, for out of about a thousand known species of the world, five hundred occur in the streams and ponds of North America. In fact, most of these are in the Mississippi River or its tributaries. The rest are scattered throughout the Great Lakes and other inland lakes, and the rivers of the Atlantic and Pacific coasts. Fresh-water clams belong to the family Unionidae.

Most of the clam shells are oval sometimes as much as five inches long. Others are more nearly round, and only about three or four inches long. Most are dark colored or greenish on the outside, while the inside is pearly white. It is in the mantle of many of these clams that the fresh-water pearls are found. Sometimes they lie so close to the shell as to become attached to it. When this occurs, the pearl is usually distorted in shape and practically valueless. Excellent pearl buttons are made from the shells of these fresh-water clams. This pearl-button industry is valued at hundreds of thousands of dollars, and employs thousands of individuals. Most of them are the "clammers," that shifting population that moves up and down the Mississippi Valley eking out a meager existence from the shells, but always hopeful of finding the pearl of all pearls that will yield a fortune. They may come close to starvation, but they would never leave their "clamming" for what they consider the dull security of a job in a button factory.

OYSTERS

The oyster family, Ostreidae, differs in certain respects from many of the other families of its class, particularly from that of the clams. The oyster has no foot, leads a sedentary life, and needs just one muscle, instead of the usual two, to open and close its shell. The two parts of the shell are unequal in size and shape. The left side is large, round, and thick and is securely fastened to some larger object, such as a stone or another shell. The right side is flattened, and is smaller and thinner than the left. The exterior is coarse, irregular, and ruffled.

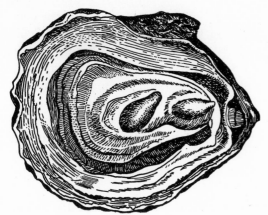

THE COMMON OYSTER—NOT USUALLY A PEARL-BEARER
Basis of a leading United States industry, the oyster is one marine product that man cultivates or raises as he does chickens or corn. The oyster has no foot and never moves after it becomes adult. Although clams, common oysters, and other two-shelled mollusks all may sometimes grow pearls, most of our gem pearls come from "pearl oysters," which are found mainly on America's Pacific coast, off northern Australia, in the East Indies, and in the Persian Gulf.

In past geological ages the oyster family was much larger than it is today. About five hundred fossil species have been found, but there are only a hundred living species. They live in all the temperate and tropical seas. Only four species are important to the fishing industry: the European oyster, *Ostrea edulis;* the Portuguese, *Ostrea angulata;* the Japanese, *Ostrea gigantea;* and the American, *Ostrea virginica.* While pearls are to be found in the shells of many bivalves, including the Ostreidae, the so-called "pearl oysters" belong to another family, the Pteriidae.

Fishing for Oysters. Oyster fishing is one of the important food industries in the United States. It employs thousands of persons and is valued at several million dollars a year. The oyster gathered is *Ostrea virginica,* a native of our entire Atlantic coast and recently introduced on our Pacific coast. This oyster is capable of reaching a maximum length of eighteen inches, but the fishing is too intensive to permit one to grow that large today. You may occasionally see an oyster ten inches long, but the average size for commercial use is four or five inches.

An adult oyster may lay as many as nine million eggs. These are so tiny that five hundred of them side by side will measure only one inch. The eggs hatch in about five hours into transparent little larvae. They swim about freely for a time, but in about thirty-two hours they start to secrete a shell, and within six days the little oyster is completely enclosed. In three weeks they begin to settle to the bottom, attach their left sides to some firm base, and thereafter remain fixed.

These little oysters have many handicaps and enemies; consequently, few out of the millions of eggs ever reach maturity. Sediment in the water or on the bottom causes one of their greatest troubles, since they are unable to move out of it. For this reason, fishermen scatter tons of old shells on the oyster beds, knowing that these will rest on top of the mud and provide a new, hard base. In the harbors of many of our coastal cities you may often see barges of shells being towed out to the oyster beds. The oysters may be dredged from these beds when they are one or two years old and taken to deeper water or other favorable spots to establish new beds. When four years old they are ready for market.

The finest oysters are usually produced in sounds and bays that are fed by streams. It is here that a plentiful supply of minute plant and animal matter is swept along to keep the growing oysters well fed. Oysters from areas that may have been contaminated with city sewage should always be thoroughly cooked, otherwise they can transmit typhoid and dysentery. The best oyster beds are still, as they have been in the past, Chesapeake Bay, Narragansett Bay, Long Island Sound, and the Gulf coast.

Oysters are frequently found with a small crustacean, one-half inch long, living peacefully with them. This is the Oyster Crab, *Pinnotheres ostreum.*

SCALLOPS—JUMPERS WITH SHELLS

The Common Scallop, *Pecten irradians,* is also a very valuable, delicious shellfish that is found in abundance along the Atlantic coast, from the New England states to Texas, making scallop fishing a very important industry. Other species occur along the Pacific coast, providing employment to hundreds in that region.

SCALLOPS ARE REALLY SHELLFISH

The many different kinds of scallops that live along our coasts are as dainty to look at as they are good to eat. The big muscle that holds the two shells together is the only part of the animal that is eaten. Scallops move in a series of leaps by snapping their shells open and shut. The common scallop, pictured above, is common on mud flats and in eel grass. It is about three inches long, and the upper shell is darker than the lower.

Scallop shells are easily recognized by their radiating ribs, the two wings forming a broad base, and the numerous concentric darker and lighter lines that follow the curvature of the margin. The edge of the shell is generally wavy. This scallop reaches a diameter of about three inches. The Giant Scallop, *Pecten magellanicus,* found from New Jersey to Labrador, has a diameter of five or six inches.

Scallops propel themselves in a series of leaps and bounds, over a zigzag course, by opening and shutting the two parts of their shells. They are frequently abundant in shallow waters over mud flats, and particularly where the eel grass grows well. They used to be common up and down the Atlantic coast, but they have decreased enormously as the result of intensive netting, for tons are taken every year.

The big muscle connecting the two shells is generally the only part of the scallop eaten. It consists more or less of a disk, five-eighths of an inch to one inch in diameter and about one-half to five-eighths of an inch thick, of white, fibrous, muscular flesh, the fibers running the short way of the muscle, or from flat surface to flat surface. By observing this structure you can tell if the next scallops you have are real or a substitute product (such as pieces of stingray).

SALT-WATER CLAMS

Salt-water clams are undoubtedly the best for eating, but they seldom yield a good pearl, and the shells do not make the best buttons.

The Hard-shelled Clam, *Venus mercenaria,* also called the littleneck clam, and quahog, is found along the Atlantic coast from the Gulf of St. Lawrence to Texas. It is one of our most common clams and is equally at home on muddy or sandy bottoms, boring through the soil to a depth ranging from a few inches to a foot or more. You will find these clams in water from a little above the low-tide mark down to fifty-foot depths. Those in deep water escape their enemies, but those in ground exposed at low tide are in constant danger from "clammers" and small boys who dig them for food or for fish bait.

It is interesting to walk along the shore through a clam bed as the tide is receding. At this time, the clams are closing their shells until the water returns. They do this with a sharp snap, forcing the water out of their bodies and shells. It rises like a miniature geyser from a little opening in the ground. Be careful where you step and be ready to jump, for this little fountain can give you a very wet foot.

The hard-shelled clam may reach a size of five and a half inches by four and a half inches and two and a half inches thick. The shell is a dirty white on the outside, with distinct concentric rings. The inside is dull white, turning purplish along the margin. It is this purple part that was most highly prized by the coast Indians of early America for making their wampum.

The Soft-shelled or Long-necked Clam, *Mya arenaria,* is the one most frequently used for food. It is widely distributed on mud flats, under stones and logs in shallow water, between tide lines from the arctic to the Carolinas, in Europe, and along the Pacific coast southward to California.

The Giant Clam, *Tridacna gigas,* is the largest bivalve known. It is a native of the seas in the region of East India, where the animal is eaten and greatly relished. One of these will provide a meal for a large gathering of people, for a medium-to-large clam will produce twenty or more pounds of meat. The shells are frequently more than three feet long and weigh over five hundred pounds. The margin of each shell is deeply waved and indented, each shell fitting closely into the opposite shell.

The shells of the giant clam have been used for various purposes, such as baptismal fonts, holy-water receptacles, and, of course, babies' bathtubs. This genus has a number of other species, all much smaller, including *Tridacna squamosa* and *crocea. Hippopus maculatus,* known as the "bear's claw," is a closely related species of considerable size.

SQUIDS, DEVILFISHES, AND THEIR RELATIVES

It is hard to believe that the animals in this group (class Cephalopoda) have any affinity to the rest of the mollusks. For one thing, the external shell, which we ordinarily consider an essential mollusk characteristic, is missing in most of the cephalopods. But zoologists, studying the internal structure of the cephalopods, have placed them in the Mollusca phylum, nevertheless. Through the ages these animals have evolved to fit changing conditions, becoming highly organized and specialized.

The Cephalopoda are all marine mollusks that make their homes in the sea. Many have a large head, and large eyes, with a circle of eight or ten tentacles around the mouth. Some of these tentacles are armed with suckers or hooks, or both. Some cephalopods have as many as ninety tentacles. All members of this group except the genus *Nautilus,* secrete an inky fluid which they store in an ink sac, and which they can shoot into the water to befog an enemy or a victim. Since this is a highly specialized group, there are only about four hundred species.

The Pearly, or Chambered, Nautilus, *Nautilus pompilius,* lives in rather deep waters of the Pacific and Indian oceans. Consequently, very few people have ever seen the living creature. The shell, however, is sometimes washed ashore on the Pacific islands or on the coasts bordering these oceans. It is white, porcelain-like in texture, and banded in brown. The interior is pearly white.

This shell looks like a gigantic snail shell for it is coiled and curved and large in size, some examples reaching a diameter of ten inches. The animal lives in a large chamber at the aperture, or opening. Behind this area numerous partitions cross the shell, dividing it into other chambers, all empty. These can be seen only in a broken shell or in one that has been sawed in two. The empty chambers are the animal's earlier coverings, onto which it has built successively larger hoods.

The body of the nautilus may be six or seven inches long. The head, which protrudes from the shell, has about ninety tentacles arranged about the mouth. The tentacles are intricately arranged. There are four groups of twelve to thirteen; two groups of seventeen larger tentacles; two very large tentacles that loop over the animal's head; and two small ones, located on each side of the eye. The tentacles of the pearly nautilus have no suckers. They bring food to the animal and assist it in traveling along the bottom. The animal itself makes excellent food for man, although difficult to obtain, and is much prized by Pacific islanders.

THE PAPER NAUTILUS, OR ARGONAUT

Fishermen in Mediterranean waters often see a lovely shell scudding before the wind. Five arms, very much dilated at their ends, seem to act as sails. Several other arms, which hang over the shell, can be compared to oars. You can see from this description that it was reasonable enough for ancient mariners to call this exquisite creature the argonaut, after the famous ship in their mythology, or simply nautilus, meaning "the sailor." The term "paper" refers to the extreme thinness and fragility of the shell when dry.

Actually, it is not a boat or ship that the fishermen see sailing across the sea, but a baby carriage, and the apparent sails are maternal arms protecting the precious contents. Only the female argonaut carries a shell. This shell is a loose egg case which she has created from secretions from her two expanded arms. It is spirally coiled and symmetrical and looks like the shell of the pearly nautilus or like a snail shell, but it contains only the eggs, not the body of the animal, and she can drop it at will.

ONLY THE FEMALE PAPER NAUTILUS HAS A SHELL
This looks like a large, exquisite snail shell, but the creature that builds it is much more like an octopus. Only the female builds a shell, and she is much larger than the male. The paper nautilus lives in deep water along the southern coasts, and expels a jet of water to make itself move.

Only about a dozen species of the argonaut are known. The common species in Atlantic waters is *Argonauta argo*. The female of this species is some eight inches long and carries a white shell of about the same length. The shell is decorated with two rows of protuberances. The male is only one-eighth as long as his mate and resembles a small squid or octopus.

The Common Sepia, or Cuttlefish, *Sepia officinalis,* has a calcareous, shell-like body, which is the cuttlebone of the commercial world. It is used as a polishing agent and as a lime-supplying food for cage birds. The cuttlefish is common in European waters and particularly in the Mediterranean Sea, where large quantities are used as food. The living animal is brown in color, with whitish spots or stripes and purple fins.

SQUIDS—SOME ARE "SEA SERPENTS"

The Common Squid, *Loligo pealei,* is a common sight along the Atlantic coast from Nova Scotia to Florida. Built like a torpedo, it is also called the "sea arrow." About eight inches long and two inches in diameter, it has a head at one end, and a tapering tail, with two fins, at the other. Its body is dark gray, with red spots. Squids frequently swim in large schools and are netted in great quantities, for they make excellent bait, particularly for cod. *Loligo opalescens* is

THE COMMON SQUID OR SEA ARROW

It does not seem right to call anything as odd as this creature "common." But fishermen often see great schools of these small torpedoes, and net quantities of them to use as bait for cod. However, people along Mediterranean and Oriental waters find their squid make excellent food. This sea squid is about eight inches long, and is dark gray with red spots.

very similar, but is found in the Pacific Ocean. The Chinese consider this squid an excellent food.

The Giant Squid, *Architeuthis princeps,* is not only the largest mollusk, but also the largest invertebrate animal. Its body may reach a length of nineteen feet; the tentacular arms, thirty-five feet; making the total length over fifty feet. The sessile arms are nine feet; the beak, five inches; and individual suckers on the tentacles, nearly one and a quarter inches across. The tentacular arms are covered with smooth-rimmed suckers, used for grasping prey, mingled with rounded projections known as tubercles. The sessile arms are much smaller and are armed with toothed suckers which the squid uses to feed itself once the tentacular arms have brought the food in close.

The giant squid lives in the open sea, descending rather deeply, and few live ones have ever been seen. We are familiar with it largely through the occasional dead ones cast ashore on some beach. The beaches of Newfoundland seem to be those most frequently favored in this respect. Undoubtedly, this tremendous creature is the basis for some of the tales of sea serpents that occasionally liven our radio broadcasts and newspapers.

OCTOPUSES—FRIENDS OR ENEMIES?

Is the octopus a terrible, man-eating monster, lurking in sea caves, waiting to dart out and seize a diver in its eight-armed grasp? Or is it a shy and timid dragon, changing color in fright or hiding behind an inky smoke screen?

The first characterization has been the basis for many an exciting tale in the past, and will be, doubtless, for many still to come. The second opinion is held by marine zoologists who have studied these odd creatures. The author knows of a marine laboratory which had in an aquarium an octopus so tame that it would take food out of the hand, actually leaving the hand intact for another feeding! While there is little evidence to support stories of octupuses attacking human beings, there is no doubt that a man attacking an octopus might be grasped by one or more of its tentacles and drown before he could free himself.

There are only about fifty species of octopus, but they range in size from one inch to twenty-eight feet. Whatever its size, an octopus appears to be chiefly head and arms. Its eyes are large and prominent. The jaws are sharp and beaklike and seem to be used chiefly when octopuses fight each other. The octopus can creep about on its arms, but it also has an arrangement that sucks water into the body and then pushes the water out, shooting the octopus forward like a torpedo.

THE OCTOPUS—A RELUCTANT DRAGON

Possibly the octopus owes its bad reputation to its ugly appearance. Scientists say it never starts a fight with a human being, although, if attacked, it has eight arms to fight with. Only a few kinds of octopus are over two feet long; however, one in the North Pacific Ocean is twenty-eight feet long. The common little octopus of the North Atlantic Ocean, pictured here, is only three or four inches long.

The animal's outer surface is dotted with a number of pigment cells, one set yellow, one brown, and one black. Normally these colors do not show, but if the animal is alarmed it changes colors rapidly by opening first one set and then another of its color cells. Most octopuses are creatures of the night, spending the daylight hours in rocky crevices or in burrows dug in the sand.

Octopus bimaculatus, one of the common octopuses along the Pacific coast, has a small, oval body about four inches long. Usually gray in color, it varies, however, from white to black. It has two short, hornlike processes between its eyes. It prefers a diet of scallops and clams, but sometimes eats fishes or crabs.

Octopus bairdi is the common Atlantic species, both in European and North American waters. Its body, about three inches long and one and a half inches wide, is bluish, with brown spots, and covered with small warts. The arms, about five inches long, are connected to each other at the base by a thin membrane.

Animals with Jointed Legs— Lobsters, Barnacles, Spiders, Scorpions, Insects, and Their Relatives

THE LAST and largest group of the animals without backbones includes those small creatures that have jointed bodies, jointed legs, jointed antennae, and sometimes jointed tails or stingers. This phylum is called Arthropoda, which means quite appropriately, "having jointed feet." We found in an earlier chapter that the true worms have segmented or jointed bodies, but never any trace of segmented appendages. If you compare an earthworm, which is a true worm, with any of the baby insects so often called "worms," such as an appleworm, a mealworm, a caterpillar, or a grub, you will see that all but the earthworm have segmented legs.

Arthropods have no internal skeleton. Their body wall is made up of alternate thin and thicker rings of a tough material called chitin. This tough covering takes the place of a skeleton, and the muscles are fastened to it. The thicker parts are hard and horny, and the thicker they are, the less flexible. Joining these hard rings is a thinner material which is flexible and allows the creature to bend.

The arthropod's body cavity is filled with fluids which are circulated by a pumping organ called the heart; it is shaped like a tube that is open at the front end. Along the sides of the tube, or heart, are several openings through which the body fluids enter. A pulsing action forces the fluids out of the front end, setting up a circulation. Along the outside of the body a number of small openings admit air into finely branched tubes within the body, permitting the body fluid, or blood, to get its necessary oxygen. This is the early form of the circulatory system that evolves into such a complex function in the vertebrate animals.

To the observer of the external appearances of the arthropods, the general impression is of much jointedness and many appendages. Jointed legs are a major distinguishing feature, three pairs on insects, four pairs on spiders, up to one hundred fifteen pairs on some of the many-legged classes. You will also see one or two pairs of jointed antennae, often much longer than the creatures sporting them. You will usually note one pair of eyes. Sometimes, as in the case of the grasshopper, there are auxiliary eyes, known as ocelli. Other arthropods have their eyes on stilts, as in some of the crabs. Others have as many as four pairs of eyes.

Of course, in such a very large phylum there are always a few exceptions that never seem to fit any rule.

The phylum Arthropoda, with nearly a million known species, is the largest group in the animal kingdom, outnumbering all the rest by six to one. Insects make up the bulk of these, comprising about nine hundred thousand species. (We shall learn more about them in following chapters.) Since there are so many species in the group, it is only natural that there should be considerable diversity in their body formations. However, they drop into about thirteen well-differentiated classes. Here is the list: Onychophora, composed of the unusual little animal called the peripatus; Crustacea, comprising crabs, lobsters, shrimps, and barnacles; Palaeostracha, the king, or horseshoe, crabs; Arachnida, scorpions, spiders, mites, and ticks; Pycnogonida, pycnogonids; Tardigrada, bear animalcules; Pentastomida, pentastomids; Diplopoda, millepedes; Pauropoda, pauropods; Chilopoda, centipedes; Symphyla, symphylids; Myrientomata, myrientomata; and Insecta, insects.

Out of this vast assemblage, we are going to consider a few of the arthropods that are most conspicuous in appearance or are most commonly seen.

THE MYSTERIOUS PERIPATUS

Every so often a strange creature is discovered which does not seem to fit into any recognized group. The peripatus, genus *Peripatus,* is one of these. It is a caterpillar-like creature, two or three inches in length, which lives in deep leaf mold, under logs, or stones, or under the bark of rotting stumps in humid, tropical forests.

At first glance the explorer might, because of its fifteen or more pairs of short, wedge-shaped legs, mistake peripatus for an odd-looking centipede. Its velvety body is not distinctly segmented. Its legs are not jointed, but they are armed with chitinous claws, very much like those found in some insects. The class name Onychophora means "claw bearer." The animal's head is adorned with a pair of ringed antennae.

The zoologist finds the peripatus fascinating because it has some of the characteristics of the phylum Annelida, the true worms, and some of the characteristics of the Arthropoda. Some zoologists believe this odd animal should be set up in a phylum all its own. However, most students in the field retain it in the Arthropoda. It undoubtedly represents an ancient form, a living connecting link between the two phyla. Its wide distribution also suggests that peripatus has lived on this earth through many geological ages. The fifty or so species are scattered throughout the hot, forested regions of South America, West Indies, Africa, Malay Archipelago, Australia, and New Zealand.

The group as a whole is unable to cope with the changing conditions and keen competition of today's physical world, and is rapidly approaching extinction. It is surprising that it has persisted up to the present day. All of the species are quite rare.

LOBSTERS, CRABS, SHRIMPS, BARNACLES,
AND OTHER CRUSTACEANS

The crustaceans (class Crustacea) include the lobsters, crabs, shrimps, water fleas, barnacles, and many other familiar creatures. Most are water animals and breathe by means of gills. Millions of minute crustaceans dwell on the surface of the open ocean, where they make the principal food of the larger animals of the sea. Others live in rather deep salt water. Many are found on coasts and beaches. A few live in fresh water. The so-called "land crabs," or crayfishes, live in soggy clay soil where the water comes close to the surface. Others climb the steep slopes of high mountains. They vary in size from the Water Flea's one-hundredth of an inch to the ten-foot span of the Japanese Crab.

Two pairs of antennae and at least five pairs of legs are the crustaceans' principal characteristics. The head and thorax are fused into one piece, called the cephalothorax, which forms a protecting sheath over the animal. It is this sheath, or crust, which suggested the name Crustacea for these animals.

CRAYFISHES

Anyone who has poked around streams, ponds, or swampy places knows the crayfishes, although he may call them "crawfishes," or simply "fresh-water crabs." There are a number of species (all belonging to genus *Cambarus*), all of which look pretty much alike to the casual observer. Any fresh-water pool or shallow brook should have a number of crayfishes lurking under flattish stones or in shallow burrows in the gravelly bottom. Approach a likely spot quietly, and you can often see their heads protruding from their hiding places. The two pairs of waving antennae, one pair short, the other long and slender, the two large pincher claws, and the bulging eyes will attract your attention.

In this sheltered position, the crayfish can grab at small fishes or other passing creatures without exposing itself to its enemies. However, the crayfish is also a scavenger, feeding upon decaying animal and vegetable matter, and you will frequently see the pond forms crawling around submerged plants.

When engaged in their ordinary pursuits, crayfishes walk forward slowly and jerkily. But if disturbed, they shoot backward, out of harm's way, by contracting their abdominal muscles. It is to this ability to retreat with rapidity that we refer when we say that someone has "crawfished," meaning that the person in question has backed out of an undertaking or retreated from a position. This unflattering mention has associated the crayfish with an unpleasantness it does not deserve.

The female carries her eggs on the underside of her abdomen. Hundreds of little round eggs are attached to small flaps, called swimmerets, along the under edge of the abdomen. These eggs hatch into midget crayfishes that are exact replicas of the mother, and cling to her abdomen for some time. Although the species vary in size, crayfishes average about three inches in length.

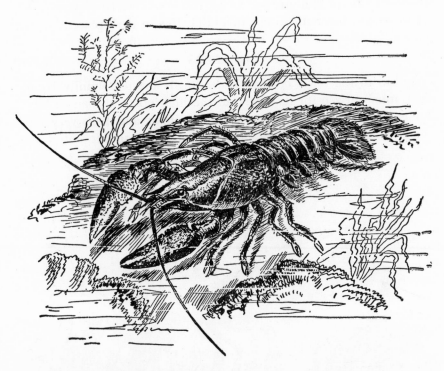

THE CRAYFISH LIKES FRESH WATER

Many different kinds of crayfish live in the streams and ponds of the United States. Some hide under flat rocks with just their heads and front claws protruding, waiting for some small fish to pass within reach. Others dig holes in swampy land down to water level, and stack the excavated soil in rounded turrets above their holes. You can sometimes see quite a village of these small towers or chimneys on the slope of a pond or marsh.

Crayfishes that do not live in ponds or streams but prefer swampy ground are also very common throughout the central and southern United States. These crayfishes dig burrows one to three feet deep, excavating a chamber in the bottom in which water collects. It is here in this chamber that the swamp crayfish is at home. The excavated dirt is carried to the surface and piled around the mouth of the burrow like a turret or chimney. These piles of dirt may be eight or ten inches high, but are usually only from four to six. The swamp crayfish may sometimes be brought to the surface by poking a weed stalk down the burrow. The crayfish will seize the weed, and if the weed is then gently withdrawn the crayfish may be pulled out before it lets go. These swamp species are much lighter in color than their relatives of pond and stream, being straw yellow. In general, paler colors are characteristic of creatures that live in dark places.

LOBSTERS

Close kin to the lowly crayfish is the lordly lobster (family Homaridae), much prized for its meat and the high point of many a "shore dinner." All lobsters are sea-dwelling animals and look very much like glorified crayfishes. The American lobster, *Homarus americanus*,

THE LOBSTER TAKES A STROLL

Marine cousin to the crayfish, the American lobster was once very abundant along the North Atlantic coast, and grew to a very large size. Lobster fishermen have nearly killed their industry with overfishing, and now coastal states have very strict laws to try to conserve what is left. The spiny lobsters, relatives of the American lobster, are well-known in Europe and South Africa, as well as in the United States.

can grow to a large size, as much as twenty-four inches in length and twenty-eight pounds in weight, although the activities of the lobster fishermen rarely permit such attainments. In life it is dark green, mottled with still darker spots, and yellowish underneath. When boiled, the only way most of us ever see it, it turns a brilliant red.

Lobster fishing is a great national industry, in the United States, particularly along the northern Atlantic coasts. The lobsters are lured, with clams or fish as bait, into traps made of lath and shaped somewhat like bushel baskets, with funnels of cord at each end. The lobsters enter through these funnels and then find it impossible to get out. As with some of our other natural resources, no thought was given to conserving or developing the supply of lobsters until it was too late. Not long ago the annual catch for Canada and the New England states amounted to over one hundred million. Today it does not reach twenty million. In an attempt to save the industry from itself, most states now have stringent laws prohibiting the sale of small-sized lobsters.

In the warmer waters off Florida and southern California lives a lobster without any pincher claws. Instead, it is armed with spines. Even its antennae are covered with long spines. With these, it can deliver a vicious blow to an enemy or stun a victim. This lobster makes excellent eating and is, therefore, much sought after. It belongs to the genus *Panulirus*.

CRABS

The Blue Crab, *Callinectes sapidus,* one of the most important food crabs, ranges along the Atlantic seaboard from New England to Brazil. It sometimes follows the rivers up into brackish, and even fresh, water. It does this possibly because it prefers muddy bottoms, particularly where vegetation is plentiful, for this type of growth forms a large part of its diet. It also feeds on dead and decaying animal matter.

In the winter, the blue crab travels out to sea into deeper water, away from ice. In the summer, it returns to shallow places, where it may be seen clinging to piles and wharves, easily recognized by the bluish coloring of its legs. The body of the blue crab is a dull, dark-green, and might make the crab invisible against a dark background, but the flashing blue legs betray its whereabouts.

The blue crab lays several hundred orange-colored eggs, and in a week or ten days they develop into free-swimming animals. The young crabs at first molt every week, later at much longer intervals. After each molt they remain quiet and hidden, if possible, for this is their soft-shelled stage. Males will reach a size of three by six inches; the females are usually smaller.

THE BLUE CRAB OFTEN CHANGES ITS SHELL

This is the common crab of the American fish markets; it lives around docks or in the mud of brackish waters from Maine to the Mississippi delta. It molts or casts its shell quite frequently, and each time remains soft for some days until the new shell can harden. In this newly molted condition the animal is called the "soft-shelled crab."

A somewhat similar species occurs on the west coast of the United States.

The Fiddler Crab, *Uca.* This crab is delightful to watch. Everything about it is grotesque. The male has one claw that is extraordinarily larger than the other and looks as if it belonged by right to a much larger crab. Usually this is the right claw, but the fiddler is equally adept at manipulating the left claw, if it should prove the larger.

The fiddler's eyes are set on long, slender stalks that protrude way out above its head. Its colors are tame enough, a light-brown, mottled with purple and dark-brown, providing excellent camouflage against the dark sand of the salt marshes where the fiddler spends its very active life.

The fiddler makes its home in burrows, which may be over a foot deep, but it loves to sit at the mouth of its burrow, slowly waving its large claw. It seems to be beckoning you to come on, but this friendly gesture is not meant for you. The fiddler is trying to attract one of the near-by females. If a female responds to some particularly irresistible male, she is led into the tunnel, with elaborate gestures, also with some prodding if she fails to respond quickly. If you should approach in answer to the beckoning, however, all dash sideways for their burrows and are soon out of sight.

The fiddler crab lives in colonies at the edge of the water. It feeds on small pieces of organic matter which it has rolled into little pel-

THE FIDDLER CRAB AND HIS "FIDDLE"

This odd and amusing crab wears its eyes at the ends of long stalks, and the male has one claw enormously enlarged. He likes to sit at the mouth of his burrow, moving his great claw in a manner that reminds us of a musician playing his fiddle. Actually he is trying to lure some passing female into his den. There are a great many kinds of fiddler crabs all over the world, usually about the same color as the sand or mud they live on.

lets. The female, whose claws are of equal size, uses both to roll her pellets; the male has to roll his with one small claw. There are many species of fiddler crabs, all belonging in the genus *Uca*.

Hermit Crabs. Hermit crabs comprise a large group of creatures which, from the front look like crabs, with the pincher claws, the long antennae, and the stalked eyes that we associate with crabs. The abdomen of a hermit crab, however, instead of being protected with a hard covering, as in most crabs, is soft and, usually, tapering. To provide a covering for its unprotected body, and a home into which it can retreat from danger, the hermit crab moves into an empty snail shell. Outgrowing one shell, it crawls out of it and hunts for a larger one. If it sees many shells available and no enemy approaching, the hermit crab will spend considerable time trying out several shells for size, balance, and feel, twirling the shell around with its feet, and

THE HERMIT CRAB IS A PERENNIAL TENANT
The large family of hermit crabs (there are several hundred different kinds) never dig a burrow or build a shell for themselves but live always in some marine snail shell. When they outgrow one shell, they move to a larger one. Most hermit crabs are very small, but some Pacific coast species grow as large as three inches.

probing the recesses with its antennae. Finally, when a satisfactory home has been found, the hermit crab pushes its tail into the opening and settles down for another term.

Pagurus longicarpus, a common small species, lives in the small snail shells found in shallow backwaters or tidal pools along the Atlantic coast. Larger species live in the deeper waters along the same coast. Some very large hermit crabs, twelve to eighteen inches long, are extremely common along the Pacific coast.

Spider Crabs. The spider crab is so called because of its small, round body and long, gangling legs. Like some of the tarantulas, its body is covered with a dense growth of hairs. This crab has the curious ability to draw its eyes back into its head and thus conceal them.

A very common spider crab is *Libinia emarginata,* which occurs on both the Atlantic and the Pacific coasts. Its rough, brown body is from two and a half to three inches long; its legs are much longer. It is often called the sea spider. These crabs are sluggish and crawl about on the bottoms of harbors and bays. Lobstermen and all fishermen detest them because they swarm into the traps and eat the bait.

Rock-dwelling Crabs. If you search among the rocks along the New England coast between high and low water you are almost certain to find the Rock Crab, *Cancer irroratus.* If you don't find it among the rocks you may discover it buried in some sandy spot with only its eyes showing. The rock crab is rarely seen south of New Jersey. It is tan or light brown, thickly mottled with dark brown, and measures two to three inches in length and three to four inches in breadth. It is often eaten, although it is not so highly prized for food as some other crabs.

The Jonah Crab, *Cancer borealis* is extremely similar in shape, but is red above and yellowish beneath. It, too, makes very acceptable food.

The Ghost Crab, *Ocypode albicans,* a well-known citizen of our eastern sandy beaches, digs its long burrows in the loose, dry sand that is just out of reach of high tide. It is partial to the sand dunes, and you can often see hundreds of burrows opening on the seashore face of dunes. Pale blue-gray in color, it blends nicely with the white sand on a cloudy afternoon or evening. It avoids sunny weather, if possible, for then its shadow betrays it, as do the funny black eyes it wears on stilts.

Walk along a beach that has only a few ghost crabs, and you will never be aware of them, unless you are very sharp-eyed, so quickly will they fade away from you. If you should happen to walk past a large colony, however, their numerous dodgings will attract you, and you will be able to see them as individuals scurrying along ahead of you. One by one they will duck into their burrows. Sometimes, the little crab will find the burrow he chooses already occupied. In that case the late-comer pops out of the burrow and is off immediately in search of another.

GREEN CRAB AND ROCK CRAB

The green crab shown at the left is a pretty little fellow; its shell, about two inches across, displays varying shades of green mottled with yellow. The animal lives on both sides of the Atlantic, but in the United States is found mostly north of New Jersey, where it is very common. Shown at the right is the rock crab, usually much larger than the green crab. It is mottled in pinkish and reddish brown. Mediterranean cousins of the rock crab gave their family name, Cancer, to the astronomical constellation and the Zodiac sign.

At night, these crabs come out in numbers in search of food, chiefly smaller crustaceans and other arthropods. One night, some years ago, the author tried to sleep on a beach near the mouth of the Chesapeake. All night long, he could hear the ghost crabs prowling around him, making a very ghostlike, scraping noise, but never touching him. Next morning there was a well-worn path all around the depression where his body had lain. Apparently they had been curious about the strange object on their beach, but not brave enough actually to examine it.

THE GHOST CRAB PROWLS THE SANDS AT NIGHT
Ghost crabs are land crabs, living on dunes or sandy beaches just beyond high tide; they are whitish, like the sand they scamper across. Ghost crabs stay indoors in the daytime, coming out in large numbers to hunt at night, and are very common from New Jersey to Florida. One claw is a little larger than the other, but usually not so much so as shown. Mostly, crabs travel sideways, but can move in any direction without turning.

Crabs That Spend Most of Their Time on Land. Not all crabs are sea animals. A number of species spend their adult lives on land, although their early days are spent in the sea, and they return to the sea to deposit their eggs. Land crabs spend the day under some convenient stone or log, and prowl about at night. One species that is rather common in the West Indies is occasionally found in Mexico and Texas, all the individuals presumably having spent their youth in the Gulf.

BARNACLES—THEY SWIM WHEN YOUNG

At first glance you would not believe that the common barnacles could possibly be related to the crustaceans. Their thick, calcareous shells are more suggestive of mollusks, and, indeed, early zoologists did consider them to be mollusks. It was only a little more than one hundred years ago that barnacle larvae were discovered to have the same characteristics as other crustacean larvae.

The young barnacle starts as a free-swimming creature. It soon attaches itself to some solid object, such as a rock, ship bottom, pile, or even the back of another sea-going animal. Here, it develops into a jelly-like creature, slightly smaller than a marble, sometimes referred to as a "grape barnacle." It then begins to secrete, as a shelter for itself, a cup-shaped shell of lime, with a little cap to fill the opening. From the top of this shell, the barnacle's legs protrude like tentacles and sweep smaller animals out of the water into its mouth.

The Common Barnacle, *Balanus balanoides,* is a familiar sight all along the North Atlantic coast, where we see it closely massed on wharves, rocks, old shells, and boat bottoms. The shells vary in color from white, through gray, to brown. They are from a quarter to half an inch long, and just about as wide. The freely swimming young look like tiny lobsters. This species is replaced on the Pacific coast by a very similar species, *Balanus glandula.*

The Purple Barnacle, *Balanus tintinnabulum,* has a shell about two inches across when full grown. It is usually a rich purple, but is sometimes red, blue, or even yellow. It is frequently found on the bottoms of sea-going vessels, for it is at home in all the seas of the world. You may often see it in a home as a mantel or desk decoration, for a number of them often cluster in an unusually attractive arrangement. In some countries, it is valued as food.

The Ivory Barnacle, *Balanus eburneus,* is widely distributed throughout the waters of the world. It is about three-quarters of an inch across, and is ivory-like both in color and in texture. It is unusual among the barnacles in that it can live in brackish, and even fresh, water, whereas all the other barnacles die after a few days or even a few hours of exposure to fresh water.

Ocean-going vessels are often piloted into fresh water to kill the barnacles and other life adhering to their bottoms. Unfortunately, the ivory barnacle cannot be so easily killed. Furthermore, the shells of these barnacles, which retard a ship's speed, continue to adhere to the bottom long after the animals that made them have died.

SAND AND BEACH FLEAS AND RELATED CREATURES

The Sand Flea, or Scud, *Gammarus locusta,* is not a flea at all but a small crustacean found on beaches under stones, logs, piles of seaweed, or other debris. The male is about one-half inch long; the female, somewhat longer. They vary in color from greenish to dark-brown. When their cover is disturbed, they go sliding, or scudding, along on their sides or backs. They are distributed all through the Northern Hemisphere.

The Common Beach Flea, *Orchestia agilis,* is similar in appearance to the scud, or sand flea, but somewhat smaller and yellower in color. Like the scud, it hides under wet seaweed and other beach debris. When disturbed, however, it goes leaping off.

The Mole Beach Flea, *Chiridotea caeca,* burrows in the wet sand between high and low water, throwing up a little ridge of sand much like a miniature mole tunnel. About three-quarters of an inch long and nearly as broad, it varies in color from white or yellow to green or brown.

The Green Seaweed Flea, *Idothea metallica,* can be found far at sea on floating seaweed. Only a quarter of an inch long, this tiny, greenish crustacean is typical of creatures that have learned to adapt themselves to unusual environments.

The Sand Bugs, *Emerita talpoida,* are familiar to most bathers along our sandy Atlantic beaches. A moderate surf will hurl hundreds of them onto the shore. Scurrying through the receding water, they immediately begin to burrow in the wet sand. So rapidly do they disappear that one does not have a chance to see what they look like. Grab one, or dig it out of the sand before it burrows in too deep, and you will be holding a funny little bug about one and a quarter inches long, if it is full grown.

The shining, purplish body of the sand bug is hard and egg-shaped. It has two feathery antennae, which it uses to strain food from sea water as the surf races down the beach. Its hard, round body is admirably shaped to withstand the buffeting it receives as the waves roll it over and over. You can easily understand the reason for one of its common names, the Humpty-Dumpty bug; but it is difficult to see how another common name, tadpole bug, originated.

THE GRIBBLE, A CREATURE WITH
A TASTE FOR WOOD

Limnoria lignorum, commonly called the gribble, is a destructive little creature, less than a quarter of an inch long. To the naked eye, the gribble looks like a small, white seed. Under the lens it is worm-like, with six pairs of legs and two pairs of antennae. Alone, it could do very little; but, accompanied by millions of companions, it destroys floating or submerged wood by boring tunnels in it. If the wood happens to be a ship's bottom, a floating wharf, or a pile, the gribble proves a very dangerous enemy. If the wood is floating wreckage, the gribble is a friend and benefactor, cleaning up the sea for us.

SHRIMPS AND PRAWNS

High on the list of our delicious sea foods is the shrimp, a small relative of the crayfish, lobster, and crab. Most shrimps have long, cylindrical bodies and very long antennae. They are all good swimmers, but like the crayfishes, they swim backwards by jerking their broad, finlike tails beneath them. Very large shrimps are usually called prawns.

The shrimps comprise several families, most of them edible. Most of the commercial shrimps of the eastern United States belong to two species, *Peneus setiferus* and *brasiliensis.* The industry thrives best in Louisiana, but flourishes from North Carolina to Texas.

The Common Sand Shrimp, *Crago septemspinosus,* is easily seen if you hunt for it along the seashore, where the water is shallow and the bottom is sandy. It loves to hide under seaweed, along the edges of rocks, or to snuggle into the sand, where its grassy color makes it almost invisible. When fully grown it is about two inches long and makes a delicious food.

Not all shrimps are sand- or glass-colored. Some are mud-colored, live in shallow pools or ditches with muddy bottoms, and are appropriately called mud shrimps. They can live in brackish and fresh water, as well as in salt. The Common Mud Shrimp of our Atlantic coast is *Palaemonetes vulgaris.* It is little more than an inch in length.

THE KING OR HORSESHOE CRAB

King, or horseshoe, crabs are familiar creatures to all who have gone crabbing or clamming along the Atlantic Coast, especially along the wharves and floating docks near the moorings of small craft. In a spot close to a bank, where the water is only a few feet deep, you will sometimes see dozens of these large crabs (class Palaeostracha) crawling about on the sandy or muddy bottom.

They are called king crabs because of their size, which may reach two feet, and horseshoe crabs because their arched back has a horseshoe outline. The abdomen ends with a long, spinelike tail. The sluggish creatures plow slowly through the sand and mud looking for

KING CRABS ARE KING-SIZED
Fully grown king crabs are a foot or more across, and have a body like a spider, a heavy brown shell like an enormous crab. In early summer you can sometimes observe large groups of them in shallow water. At the lower right you see one of their neighbors, the sand dollar or sea cookie, a purplish little relative of the starfish. If you find a sand dollar shell on the beach and examine it, you will see that it is divided into five parts like a starfish, but there is no space between the parts.

oceanic worms or other animal food. In late summer, the females lay their eggs in shallow depressions in the sand. When hatched, the young resemble the adults, except that they have no tails.

King crabs are an ancient group, now nearly extinct. They are not closely related to any creature living today. In some respects they are like the crustaceans; they are water animals and breathe by means of gills, and they have compound eyes. In other respects they are like spiders, for they have four pairs of walking legs, a pair of pinchers (called chelicerae), and no antennae. Zoologists are now inclined to place them in a class by themselves.

There are only five species of king crabs. One, *Limulus polyphemus,* is found along the Atlantic coast from Maine to Yucatan. It is not used for human food, although it is sometimes fed to chickens and pigs. The other four species all make their homes in the East Indies and southern Japan, where they are a common food.

SPIDERS, SCORPIONS, TICKS AND MITES

Most of the invertebrates that we have considered so far live in the water; the great majority of those yet to be discussed are land dwellers. We are all familiar with spiders, ticks, and mites, and many of us have seen scorpions, and we know that they are all land animals. A few members of this class, Arachnida, are water animals, however, including two families of mites.

Arachnids differ from all other arthropods by having four pairs of legs. Remembering this, you will never mistake an eight-legged spider for a six-legged insect. Usually arachnids have no antennae. Their eyes are the simple, primitive organs, called ocelli, rather than the large, compound eyes commonly found in other Arthropoda. Scorpions bear live offspring; the other arachnids deposit eggs. Members of this class feed largely upon insects or upon each other, but a few feed on the blood of higher animals.

They inhabit all land areas, large or small, from the tropics to the polar regions. Even the arid deserts of the world offer little hindrance to their progress. They push up mountainsides until they reach the very limits of perpetual snow. A few, as we said before, have invaded the water. However, like all other forms of life, they reach their greatest development in the temperate and warm regions.

The class is an ancient one, dating back to the Silurian era, roughly four hundred million years ago. It is still a large class, containing more than seventy thousand species. Despite its size, it is a homogeneous class, in which the various members have a considerable physical resemblance, and what differences arise are distinctive enough to divide it into readily identifiable orders.

TRUE SCORPIONS

Scorpions form a very distinct order (Scorpionida). Once you are acquainted with one species you will be able to recognize the others, for all scorpions are essentially alike. From the shining, black, eight-inch species that infest the tropical jungles to the thin, pale, one-inch fellows that live in sandy wastes, all have an abdomen ending in a tail-like section that is armed with a curved stinger at the tip. Arching over the back, this tail waves in all directions.

THE SCORPION KNOWS HOW TO DEFEND ITS FREEDOM

True scorpions of various kinds live in warm, dry countries around the globe. In North America they are plentiful in the southwestern United States and in Mexico. They hunt at night for spiders and insects; days they spend under stones or loose bark, away from the light and heat. A scorpion kills its prey with a poison sting at the end of its tail. It will also defend itself with this sting, and can give a painful wound to anyone who attacks it.

With its poisonous stinger, the scorpion not only defends itself from its enemies but delivers a lethal jab to quiet struggling victims on which it intends to feed. On large animals, including man, the poison generally has no serious effect other than to cause a very painful wound. In addition to having its stinger, the scorpion has a front end armed with two enormous pinchers, called pedipalpi, which grab, hold, and mash its prey.

Unless you deliberately hunt for it, you will seldom see a scorpion. It is a nocturnal creature, coming out at night from its den in the sand, under a stone, log, loose bark, or other debris on the ground, in order to hunt.

Scorpions produce living young which immediately climb on the mother's back. Here, they ride about until after the first molt, when they go off to shift for themselves. During this early period they eat nothing, living on the energy stored up in their bodies. The belief was once common that the young fed upon the body of the mother; but the facts are that the mother's back is hard and without perforations, and the babies' jaws are weak.

About four hundred species are known. They are common in southern Europe and northern Africa and in Mexico. Of the thirty-five species found in the United States, most are in the West and Southwest.

From the days of the ancient Greeks and Egyptians to the cowboy era of our own Southwest, the scorpion has been much feared and much discussed, but not very closely observed. Thus, there are many strange stories and superstitions regarding it. One of the oddest and commonest declares that a scorpion, when cornered or surrounded by a ring of fire, will sting itself to death rather than be captured or burned.

WHIP SCORPIONS

Whip scorpions, unlike the true scorpions, have no stinger. The whip scorpions also differ in that their pinchers are much thicker and are armed along the inner edge with numerous spines and teeth which aid greatly in breaking and mashing their prey. They use only their three pairs of legs for walking; the first pair are very long, held forward, somewhat like antennae, and probably serve as feelers. The one hundred and fifty known species live in caves or rocky crevices.

Although the whip scorpions are quite as evil-looking as the true scorpions, they are not poisonous, although they might be able to give you a severe nip with their spiny pinchers. When collecting them, the author prefers to take no chances, but picks them up carefully with long forceps.

The order (Pedipalpi) divides into two easily recognized suborders, the Tailed Whip Scorpions, in which the end of the abdomen is equipped with a slender, jointed, whiplike tail; and the Tail-less Whip Scorpions, in which the end of the abdomen is rounded, with no trace of a tail.

The most familiar example of the tailed group is *Mastigoproctus giganteus,* the Vinegaroon of the southwestern states and Mexico. It gets its English name from its vinegar-like odor. A dark-brown, some-

WOULD YOU LIKE A WHIP SCORPION FOR A PET?

Unlike the true scorpion, the whip scorpion carries no poison in its tail. But it does have spiny pincers which can nip a careless finger. Note how long the first pair of legs are; the whip scorpion uses them as antennae, or feelers. Some people make pets of the large rust-colored whip scorpion, or vinegaroon, which lives in the southwestern United States.

what hairy creature, it may grow as long as three inches and flaunt a tail almost the same length. It is easily kept in captivity, for it quickly learns to take food from your fingers. Almost any kind of insect is acceptable as food.

The tail-less whip scorpion has much longer legs. It is rarely seen because it lives in dark caves or deep crevices in rocky cliffs. Those in the United States are very small and may be mistaken for spiders. In a limestone cave in eastern Peru, the author once captured a species that had a body about two inches long, but the outstretched legs more than covered a dinner plate. The front legs, in particular, were long and slender, each measuring about nine inches. These front legs served much the same purpose as antennae or feelers. The pinchers were well developed and armed with numerous heavy spines or teeth, making them very efficient clasping organs.

FALSE SCORPIONS

Tiny little creatures, the largest scarcely a quarter of an inch long, the false scorpions (order Chelonethida) look like miniature scorpions. Little is known about their habits, but they are believed to feed upon mites, springtails, psocids, and other small insects. They delight in damp places, and you can almost certainly find a few under slightly loose bark on trees or under stones, leaves, or debris on the ground. They frequently invade the nests of bees, ants, and termites. They like to travel and do so by attaching themselves to bees, flies, and beetles, and in this way hitchhiking from one locality to another.

Some have long been associated with man, living in the out-of-the-way corners of his dwellings. They pay for their lodging by destroying other tiny tenants. The house scorpion, *Chelifer cancroides,* one of the larger and better-known species, has accompanied man to all parts of the world.

HARVESTMEN, OR DADDY LONGLEGS

As summer ripens into fall, the daddy longlegs assemble in our gardens and fields. Suddenly, they are everywhere, clambering over hay, up and down old apple trees, over the woodpile, on the ground. They are unattractive creatures, but for some reason are not so much feared as their near relatives the spiders. In Europe, where they are called harvestmen, their appearance in large numbers is said to presage a good harvest, and it is considered unlucky to kill one. In the United States of the author's boyhood, a daddy longlegs, by pointing with one of its long legs, could be depended on to inform any youngster the direction in which his dog had gone.

The daddy longlegs (order Phalangiidae) differs from the spider in that it has no constriction, or waist, between the front part (called the cephalothorax) and the abdomen; and in that its abdomen is segmented, while that of the spider is not. The two front pairs of appendages are very long. The two eyes are set on short projections atop the cephalothorax. The legs, as everyone knows, are extremely long, enabling the creature to move rapidly, if awkwardly, over wet ground or loose vegetation. A pair of glands on the abdomen can throw out a disagreeable odor if you are careless in handling the daddy longlegs.

The daddy longlegs does not spin a web or make a nest. It feeds on spiders, mites, and small insects, and perhaps on decaying matter. Before the arrival of the first frost, the female deposits her eggs in some damp earth. Winter cold kills all the adults but the eggs live and hatch in the following spring.

Some of the tropical species grow quite large. Many of these tend to live together in fairly large swarms. In Jalapa, Mexico, the author once saw nearly a hundred large daddy longlegs hanging, huddled together, on the underside of the huge leaves of a castor oil plant. The legs of this species were three or four inches long.

There are some sixty species in the United States, of which four species of the genus *Leiobunum* are the most common. They have small, yellowish to dark-brown bodies and very long, slender legs.

OUR ALLIES, THE SPIDERS

To many, the word "spider" brings to mind a horrendous creature, sitting in the middle of a web, ready to pounce out and bite them. This picture is wrong in most of its details.

Spiders pounce only on something they want to eat, that is, flies and other insects; they do not feed on human beings, as do the more dangerous but less feared fleas and mosquitoes. Of course, if you hurt or frighten a spider, it will bite you if it can. The skin on a man's hand is usually much too tough for a spider to pierce, but it can get through in softer areas, and when a large one finds itself squeezed between you and your clothes it may try to sink its fangs in you.

Nearly all spiders have fangs and poison glands. In some the venom is more potent than in others. Strange to say, some of the medium- and small-sized spiders are more venomous than some of the larger ones. But even the larger ones have fangs, although they may be small and feeble. In general, spiders use their fangs and poison only to quiet their prey so that they can eat it. Since their prey includes many of the insects that are a pest to man, it is more realistic to consider spiders our allies rather than our enemies.

Not all spiders create webs. While all can produce silken strands of one kind or another, only a few spin the complicated and beautiful orb webs that we tend to associate with all spiders. Some use their silk to build a flat, or sheet, web. Some make funnel webs or silken tunnels, and others simply string a jumble of crisscross threads. Still other spiders hunt their prey, disdaining any trap, but letting out a "drag line" as they move about. Some of the largest spiders dig burrows and line them with silk. Each species or group of species spins its silk and makes its nest in a manner characteristic of itself. The web spinners, even those using crisscross threads, can be identified by the types of webs they construct.

Most persons recognize a spider when they see one, even those who call it an "insect." A spider has four pairs of legs, however; the insect has only three. A spider's head and thorax are fused together; its abdomen is unsegmented, round, and soft. It spins its silk out through spinnerets on the underside of its abdomen. Usually there are six spinnerets, but some species have eight, and some have four. Most spiders have four pairs of simple eyes on the top of the head, but there may be fewer, or none at all. The male is smaller than the female. The spider belongs to the order Araneae.

Nearly thirty thousand species of spiders have been described, over two thousand of them in the United States. They can live anywhere in the world where they are able to find living food. They have reached their wide distribution without wings and without hitchhiking on other animals. Since ages ago, and long before man was exploring the air, spiders have been ballooning. A young spider climbs a weed stalk, a fence, or other elevated object and lets out a few strands of silk. Very soon the buoyancy of these silk threads in the rising air currents equals the weight of the spider, which is lifted and carried away. Increasing the length of the silk, the spider ascends. The spider can descend by reeling in the silk.

TRAP-DOOR SPIDERS

One of the finest examples of silk spinning is exhibited by the trap-door spider, *Cteniza californica*. This large, dark spider digs a burrow in the ground, about six inches deep and three-quarters of an inch in diameter, and lines it carefully with silk. It bevels the top edge evenly, makes a lid, or trap door, of webbed silk and earth, which fits the burrow opening exactly, and which is hinged to it with more silk threads. The top of the lid is covered with the same material as the surrounding soil, so that when closed it is invisible.

The young stay with the mother in her burrow until they are fairly well grown. This may be as long as eight months. Leaving the home burrow, they go out and build small burrows for themselves, enlarging or reconstructing them to fit their size as they grow. They

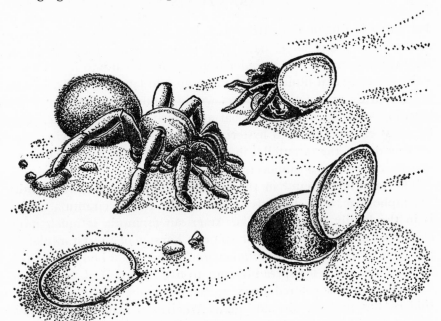

TRAP-DOOR SPIDERS HAVE CURIOUS DENS
This spider digs its burrow about six inches into the ground, lines it with silk, and covers it with a hinged lid that fits exactly. The young stay home with mother, sometimes for several months, until old enough to build their own nests. They build small burrows at first, and enlarge them or make new ones as they grow older and bigger.

spend all their lives in their burrows, only popping out to capture some unwary insect that has wandered too close.

For all their skill in home building, and their speed in capturing food, life is not too easy for the trap-door spiders. Parasitic wasps are always waiting to dash in and capture any spider that is the least bit slow in closing its trap door.

There are several other species of trap-door spiders in the United States, all having much the same habits. Some are not as careful about the interiors of their burrows, and some make only a simple flap for a door.

All are harmless and may be handled gently. They make interesting pets around a southwestern garden, for it is in this region that many of the species live. Specimens kept in a terrarium, free from their natural enemies, have been known to live for six or seven years.

TARANTULAS

Tarantula is a name that strikes fear into most persons. Now a common name for any large, hairy spider in any part of the world, it was originally applied to a spider found around Taranto in southern Italy. Here, several hundred years ago, an odd fancy arose that a person bitten by one of these spiders would surely die unless cured by listening and dancing to a special and spirited type of music. This harmless example of mass hysteria has long since died, leaving only a lively dance, the tarantella, in southern Italy, and a bad name everywhere for many an innocent spider.

The tarantulas found in the United States belong to the family Theraphosidae, only distantly related to the Italian tarantula, which is in the family Lycosidae. The American tarantula is much more closely related to the trap-door spiders. Largest of the tarantulas in this country is *Eurypelma californicum*, which has a body about two inches long, and a leg spread of four to five inches. Dark brown and covered with rust-colored hairs, it is one of the most harmless of spiders, but its large size and general hairiness make it a fearsome object. It will bite in self-defense if handled roughly, and sometimes inflicts a painful wound. Outside infection, the same sort that gets into the pin pricks and other minor wounds, is doubtless the cause of the fatal spider bite about which we read occasionally.

Eurypelma californicum is found only in our warm southwestern states, where it digs deep burrows in the sand. The female lays four or five hundred eggs and guards them carefully. It takes the young four or five years to reach full size, and individuals have been known to live for fifteen or sixteen years. They make entertaining pets, learn to recognize their keeper, and seem to show considerable intelligence. Their greatest enemy is a large, orange and blue wasp, of the genus *Pepsis,* called the tarantula hawk, which is expert in seizing and paralyzing the tarantula, and carrying it off to feed its young.

The tropical Americas contain a number of very large tarantulas. One in South America has a leg spread of eight inches. Another has a large body, three and a half to four inches long, but very short legs. Many of these tropical species make their homes in trees. Here in the treetops they actually catch and kill small birds. Our North American species are ground lovers, hiding in their burrows during the day and hunting at night.

FUNNEL-WEB SPIDERS

Early mornings, in late summer, the sun will light up hundreds of small, dew-laden webs scattered like handkerchiefs over the lawn, the bushes, everywhere. Before noon the dew has evaporated, and the webs, stripped of their spotlight, have seemingly disappeared. They are the homes of the funnel-web, or grass, spiders, *Agelena naevia.*

The web is a silken sheet, dipping in the center to a tube which leads down into the leaves or grass. Somewhere in that tube the spider is usually hiding, ready to rush out and seize any insect that may have landed on the sheet.

There are some forty American species in the genus *Agelena,* but they are among the commonest spiders in our region. Two long spinnerets protruding from near the tip of the abdomen usually distinguish this genus. *Agelena naevia* is tan colored, with a gray line bordered by a black line running down each side of the abdomen. It dies at the end of one season. Its eggs, laid in a flattish cocoon under a board or stone, hatch in the spring.

WOLF SPIDERS

Wolf, or hunting, spiders build no web but pursue their prey on the ground. They are usually medium-to-large spiders, hairy, and dark colored. Their eight eyes are arranged in three rows, four small eyes in the front row, and two large eyes each in the second and third rows. The female carries the young spiders on her back for a short time. Wolf spiders are usually more active at night, when the insects on which they feed are out, and when the wasps that prey on the spiders are asleep.

THE WOLF SPIDER RUNS DOWN ITS VICTIMS

A large, hairy, active spider with strong legs, the wolf spider does not spin a web, but catches its prey on the run. It usually hunts at night, when the insects it likes are active and the wasps that prey upon it are not. By day this spider hides under stones or wood or matted grass. The mother carries her young on her back until they are big enough to care for themselves; one hundred tiny babies may travel on her at one time.

Lycosa helluo, one of the common wolf spiders in the United States, has an olive-colored body about three-quarters of an inch long and inch-long legs. You will find it under flat stones or pieces of wood in damp fields and woods.

THE COMMON HOUSE SPIDERS

Theridion is the genus name of the house spiders, those familiar little gray spiders, marked with darker spots and lines, that spin their loose cobwebs in all the dark, out-of-the-way places in our homes, barns, and garages. More than three hundred species have been described, of which fifty are found in the United States. Although most housewives consider them a nuisance, and some are fearful that the spiders might bite them (which, of course, they will not), they are in reality excellent little helpers; for they consume quantities of flies, moths, and mosquitoes.

THE BLACK WIDOW SPIDER

The Black Widow Spider, *Latrodectus mactans,* is certainly poisonous, but her bite is not nearly as bad as her reputation. Of authentic black widow bites, less than ten per cent have been fatal, and these have all been cases with unusual complications. A healthy adult need have no fear of serious consequences resulting from a bite, or, indeed, of being bitten at all. This spider is an especially shy creature, not in the least aggressive, and usually must be forced to bite. If you are bitten, you should apply a ligature or tourniquet above the wound, which should then be opened by cutting. Try to make it bleed as much as possible. If a snake-bite suction-pump is available, it should be used. If not, apply dilute ammonia, if available.

The black widow spider is shining, velvety black, with a red, hourglass-shaped mark on the underside of its abdomen. Sometimes it has tiny red spots along the middle of the back. The abdomen is round. The female when full grown is seldom more than half an inch long. The male is very much smaller. The web is of loose, crisscross threads and is provided with a short tunnel in the center, where the spider waits for insects. The black widow lives in cool, dark places, under boards and debris, under doorsteps and porches, in cellars and sheds, in stone walls, and in deserted buildings.

Although rarely seen, these spiders are extremely common over an enormous area. They are found from the New England states and

Canada southward almost to the tip of South America, and from the Atlantic to the Pacific. They appear to be most plentiful in the southern part of the United States.

THE BLACK WIDOW SPIDER—NOT SO DANGEROUS AS SHE IS SAID TO BE

Black widows are shining black little spiders found in cool, dark places all over North and South America, but are most common in the southern United States. As a rule they are too small to inject enough poison into an adult person to make him seriously ill. The name, originally applied to the female, refers to her practice of eating the male; the young also devour one another. These habits are shared by other spiders.

THE GARDEN OR ORB-WEB SPIDER

The Orange, Garden, or Orb-web, Spider, *Argiope aurantia*, is one of our largest and showiest spiders. Its inch-long abdomen is black, with yellow or orange markings. The front part of its body is gray above and yellow beneath. Its legs are long and velvety. It spins its beautiful orb web across our garden paths, and then rests head-down in the center.

The webs are large and strong, usually three or four feet in diameter, although the author has occasionally seen them six or eight feet across. A zigzag band of silk runs vertically through the center. This is the final touch put upon the web, and looks as if it might be a title or signature. For this reason the spider is sometimes called the "writing spider." The damaged web is usually repaired or rebuilt each evening.

In the fall, the female places her eggs in a silken, parchment-like cocoon, about the size of a hickory nut. You will find the cocoons in the winter time, hanging from the tops of old weed stalks. It is at

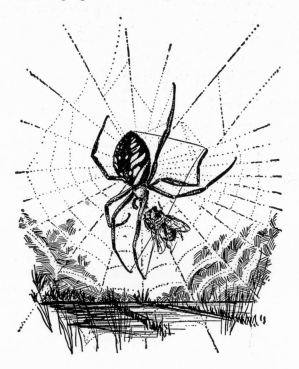

THE BEAUTIFUL GARDEN SPIDER WORKS HARD FOR A LIVING
The garden spider works hard to build a large, strong web, but it is often destroyed or damaged, and must be built again. You will find the webs—they are often several feet across—in almost any garden or meadow path in late summer. The silk from the egg case of the garden spider is used as cross hairs in finer telescopes and optical instruments.

this time that the eggs are hatching, as you will quickly discover if you open one of the cocoons. The young remain in their cocoon until settled weather arrives, usually in May in the northern states.

CRAB SPIDERS

A large-bodied, flattish spider, the crab spider has two pairs of legs much shorter than the others, a fact which gives it a crablike appearance. It even walks sideways, as the crab does. It builds no web but makes its home on walls and fences and in flowers.

There are over one hundred species in the United States. One genus, *Misumena,* with about fifteen American species, is interesting for its brightly colored members who tend to wear the same colors as the flowers in which they live. Many of them are yellowish, and these live in the yellow Compositae, the *Rudbeckia,* goldenrod, and sunflowers. You may find white crab spiders in cosmos, boneset, or joe-pye weed.

JUMPING SPIDERS

If you look on the outside of any building you are almost certain to see a jumping spider at its hunting. Backwards, forwards, or sideways it leaps and jumps. There are hundreds of jumping-spider species, but one of the commonest, here and in Europe, is *Salticus scenicus,* a little, dark-gray spider, about a quarter of an inch long. Across the abdomen it has three transverse bands of lighter gray.

MITES, TICKS, CHIGGERS, AND THEIR RELATIVES

Some of the members of this order (Acarina) are among man's most irritating pests; a few are helpful in destroying insect pests, but most of them are strictly neutral. Many of the tropical species are brilliantly colored, and many North American Acarina are some shade of red. All of the Acarina are small: the largest is barely half an inch long; the smallest is microscopic. They have spherical or egg-shaped bodies, usually unsegmented. The pinchers that many arachnids use to break and mash their prey are often used by the Acarina for piercing and sucking.

About half of the species are parasitic, some upon man, some upon man's domesticated animals, and some upon insects. The free-living species feed upon small animals, including each other, and also upon plants, and on decaying matter. They live everywhere, on land and water (salt or fresh), wherever there is the slightest amount of vegetable or animal food for them.

Fifteen thousand species have been described in all, 1,500 of them in the United States. Since much of the study of Acarina has been directed to those species with economic importance, there are doubtless a great many species with no relation to our lives that are still to be described.

The Itch Mite, *Sarcoptes scabiei,* annoys hogs as well as man. Tiny, and whitish, it is almost too small to be seen without the aid of a good lens. The female burrows under the skin to lay her two dozen eggs. These hatch in about seven days, and the little ones add to the intense itching caused by the parent. In favorable weather, the life cycle averages about four weeks.

The Water Mite, *Hydryphantes ruber,* once seen is easily remembered; for it is usually a bright-red in color, although individuals may be brown or almost black. Any woodland pool in spring or early summer should have a few of these mites, half swimming, half crawling on the bottom. These are adult mites, and they have gone into the water to breed. In the late summer or fall, if you catch a grasshopper and spread its wings, you may find some mites firmly fastened to it. These mites also attack other insects, particularly large beetles. It is only the immature mite that is parasitic on insects. In this stage it has only six legs, causing you to wonder if it is some insect.

Among the other mites that annoy us are the Clover Mites that are sometimes bothersome about our houses in early spring. Another, called the Red Spider, sometimes is a pest on greenhouse plants. Kerosene emulsion or sulfur spray are the common controls used.

The True Chigger, or Red Bug, *Trombicula irritans,* sometimes called the United States Jigger, should not be confused with the Chigoe, or Jigger Flea, *Dermatophilus penetrans,* belonging to the true fleas or order Siphonaptera. The chigger is a minute, stout, fuzzy, rust-colored mite, widely distributed from Canada to central Mexico, but much more plentiful in the South. It prefers a grassy or weedy field, but is almost equally at home in scrub or second-growth timber.

In Central and South America and in the countries of the Eastern Hemisphere, this species is replaced by other species of similar appearance and habits. Some of the species are thought to be carriers of the Rickettsia organisms that cause Rocky Mountain spotted fever and other human diseases. However, little is known of this at the present time.

It is the larvae of the chigger that are parasitic on man and animals. So tiny that they can crawl through the meshes of most cloth, they do not burrow under the skin, but cause intense itching wherever they are attached. Persons severely attacked, or particularly allergic to the chiggers, may suffer high fever and nervous disturbances.

HOW TO REMOVE TICKS FROM YOUR BODY

Ticks are usually much larger than mites. A tick's body is protected by a tough covering which can be enormously stretched. When well fed, the body of a female may be as large as a marble. She deposits an enormous number of eggs, sometimes four thousand or five thousand, on the ground. Crawling up the vegetation, the young larvae can easily attach themselves to the legs of some passing animal or human being.

When you find a tick attached to you, do not try to pick it off with your fingers. You will get only part of it. Apply alcohol or the hot end of a match or cigarette to the tick and it will be forced to free itself.

MILLEPEDES—THE MANY-LEGGED CREATURES

These crawlers are called Thousand-legged Worms (class Myriopoda and order Diplopoda), but if you should take the trouble to count their legs, you would not find anywhere near that many on any known species. It is true that they have quite a few legs. Two pairs are attached to each of most of their segments, and since they have from thirty to seventy or more segments, according to species, they are certainly well supplied with legs. One wonders how they can travel without stepping on their own toes.

Millepedes like dark, damp places, well supplied with the decaying vegetable matter upon which they usually feed. A few will attack living roots if plenty of moisture is present. When disturbed, a millepede will curl up into a circle which leaves the hard upper surface exposed, but protects the legs and soft underside. Most species have stink glands along the sides; in some, these are charged with prussic acid, making them very unpalatable to their enemies.

Nearly 150 species are known in North America. Very little is known about the species making their homes in tropical countries.

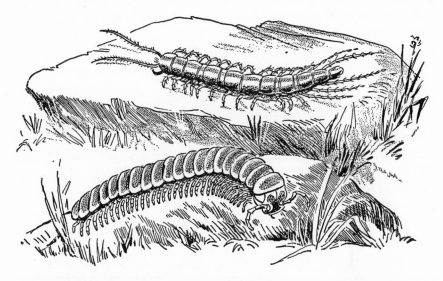

MILLEPEDE AND CENTIPEDE—HOW MANY LEGS?

A millepede (*bottom*) never has as many as a thousand legs, and a centipede (*top*) may have more than a hundred; the house centipede that we see in cellars and bathrooms has only thirty legs. Millepedes live on damp ground and feed on decaying vegetation, but centipedes feed on insects and spiders, which they kill with poison. Some tropical centipedes can inflict a painful wound on a person, but those we commonly find in the United States are not large enough to be dangerous.

CENTIPEDES—EATERS OF FLESH

Fear seems to be the reaction of the average person when centipedes are mentioned. Countless stories and legends deal with centipede poisoning. It is true that some of the larger species in the tropics are dangerous and to be avoided. There seems to be some basis for the claim that when one of these big fellows walks across your bare skin it leaves a welt as a result of the irritation caused by its scratchy feet, for some of these feet have special poison-bearing claws. Better as a story than advice is the American cowboys' claim that a centipede when disturbed is so fast to strike that shooting it off is the only way to keep it from biting you.

The centipedes belong to the order Chilopoda. They differ from the millepedes in having only one pair of legs to each segment. They also differ in being carnivorous, or flesh eating, feeding upon insects and even upon small animals. There are about two hundred species in the United States. Those found in damp places in houses, especially in cellars and sometimes in bathrooms, belong to the family Scutigeridae. They feed on cockroaches, flies, and mosquitoes, and, therefore, are not only harmless but distinctly helpful to the householder.

The Insects—Little Miracles of Life

WHAT IS AN INSECT?

Do you think of insects only as enemies to be destroyed? The author believes just the opposite. If, after reading these pages, you have not been persuaded to share his opinion, it will not be because of lack of effort on his part.

It is true that many insect species compete with man for food. Several annoy and irritate him. A very few endanger his life or health. But the credit side offers at least twice as many items.

Innumerable species collaborate with man by pollinizing flowers, a service in which they are irreplaceable. Without insects we would be without many of our fruits, vegetables, and garden flowers. Some species aid the farmer by reducing weeds. Many save our crops by feeding on the crop-eating insects. The adults and larvae of most species are food, sometimes the only food, for birds and fishes that serve as food for us. In a few countries, certain insects are themselves a staple or occasional food for human beings.

The honeybee, the various insects whose bodies are used in making dyes, the lac insects (from whose secretions shellac is made), and the silkworm are only a few of the insects whose work has made life richer and easier for man. Thousands of insects which the majority of us never see keep this old world sanitary and productive by reducing dead animal and vegetable material back to the soil. Above all, however, insects can enchant us with their beauty or strangeness, and the more we study them the more beauty and enchantment we find.

Whether we like them or dislike them, insects (class Insecta) are our most important neighbors. It is estimated that they total 85 per cent of all living creatures. Most versatile of any of the classes, they have adapted themselves to life on land, in the water, and in the air. They can and do eat everything. Some insects hold onto life very stubbornly. Others that die quickly or easily can, nevertheless, reproduce themselves in astounding numbers.

Through millions of years insects have developed a great variety of highly efficient body shapes. Compared with another dominant class, the mammals, for instance, the insects have small bodies which can fit into very small places and which require very little food. Instead of a skeleton covered with vulnerable flesh, the insect wears a coat of mail, tough enough to protect its vital organs, yet jointed and hinged for freedom of movement. The wings that many insects have developed are so useful that it is surprising that only one other class possesses them. Wings carry their owners to new locations, to better food supplies, to their mates, and away from their enemies.

HOW TO RECOGNIZE AN INSECT

Why are insects called "insects"? The word originally meant "cut in," and was used to describe these creatures because their bodies appear almost to be "divided" into several different parts—the head, thorax (chest), and abdomen.

Although the name insect is loosely used, often in reference to animals that are not insects, insects have certain distinctive characteristics which help you to distinguish them from their relatives. They differ from other arthropods in having only three pairs of legs. (Spiders, for example, have four, crustaceans have five, centipedes and millepedes have from eleven to seventy pairs of legs.) Many insects have wings during their adult life, usually two pairs, but there is much variation in this matter. Flies, for example, have just one pair of true wings; in place of the hind pair they have small, knobby stumps, called halteres. Beetles use only their hind wings for flying, their front wings having developed into a pair of curved, leathery shields, called elytra, which protect the true wings and the abdomen, but are useless for flying. Some insects never have any wings at all; some ants lose their wings; some butterflies seem to be mostly wings.

Insects always have one, and only one, pair of antennae, the feelers that project from the head and are usually located between the eyes. The antennae may be threadlike, pointed, or clubbed or knobbed at the ends; then again, they may resemble feathers or combs. In attempting to identify any insect, you should always look closely at its antennae for distinctive characteristics.

As is the case with many everyday things, such as radios and automobiles, an insect has various parts described by technical names which are not too difficult to learn. The few we have to use here are thoroughly explained so that you will have no trouble in remembering them.

THREE PAIRS OF JAWS

Every insect has three pairs of jaws, placed one before the other. Insects that live on fluids have these jaws fused to make piercing and sucking organs. Biting insects, naturally, have well-developed jaws. The big back jaws are the mandibles. They vary in size and shape, according to the species and the kind of food it eats. Sometimes they are greatly enlarged and may be used in fighting.

Located just in front of the mandibles, the second pair of jaws, called maxillae, help chew the food and carry it into the mouth. These jaws end in feelers, called palpi, which examine and hold the food. Sometimes they are so long that they look like antennae. The third pair of jaws, the second maxillae, are usually fused into one piece, the lower lip, or labium; these jaws also have feelers, called labial palpi.

The central part of the insect is the thorax, and to it the wings and legs are attached. The part of the thorax holding the first pair of legs is called the prothorax. The middle pair of legs and the front wings are attached to the mesothorax. The third pair of legs and the hind wings are attached to the metathorax.

Each leg is divided into five parts. The piece that joins the thorax is the coxa. Then comes the trochanter, usually just a small joint; then the femur (plural, femora), or thigh, sometimes greatly enlarged; followed by the tibia, or shank; and last, the tarsus (plural, tarsi), or foot. The tarsi, which vary enormously among the different insects, are composed of one to five segments, usually have claws at the tip, and may be padded on the underside, as in some flies.

The largest division of an insect's body is the abdomen. It is made up of a varying number of ringlike segments. The insect breathes through spiracles, or breathing pores, usually on the sides of the abdomen. Many insects have two or three feelers, or tails, called cerci, at the end of the abdomen. May flies have extremely long cerci. In earwigs, the cerci are shaped, not like antennae, but like pinchers.

HOW THE FEMALE LAYS HER EGGS

Female insects usually carry an ovipositor, or egg-laying organ, between the eighth and ninth abdominal segments. This may be extremely long, and needle-like, as in the ichneumon flies, or broad and knifelike, as in some grasshoppers, or it may be invisible when not in use. Some ants, bees, and wasps use their ovipositors not for egg-laying but for stinging.

All insects develop from eggs. Female aphids and some flies carry their eggs within their bodies until the eggs hatch. But most insects deposit their eggs in some suitable place, often taking great pains to find or build a proper nursery. The eggs vary in size from a microscopic $\frac{1}{250}$ of an inch to a quarter of an inch. They are often beautifully shaped and sculptured, and many of our classical art forms in pottery and in decoration have been modeled after them.

THE WONDERFUL STORY OF HOW INSECTS GROW

From the egg to the adult, an insect goes through a series of dramatic changes, called its metamorphosis. There are two types of metamorphosis. Insects undergoing incomplete metamorphosis make three changes in form, graduating from the egg to the young insect, and from the young insect to the adult. In complete metamorphosis there are four changes, from the egg to the young, to the pupa, and to the adult.

Among insects experiencing incomplete metamorphosis, the young, or nymphs, resemble the adults in general body formation, except that they are usually wingless. The young insects of the grasshopper are a good example.

The young of insects going through complete metamorphosis do not at all resemble the adults. We call the young of these groups larvae (singular, larva), although the young of moths and butterflies are commonly called caterpillars, and the young of flies and beetles are usually called grubs, or even worms.

The shedding of the skin of an immature insect is called its molt, and the stages between the molts of nymph and larva are called instars. Each species of insect requires a definite number of instars to complete its development, and the nymphs, particularly, may show considerable change in form between the first and the last instars.

When the larva is fully developed it stops eating and pupates, or changes into a pupa. Just before this change a great many of them spin some kind of silken covering for themselves, called a cocoon. In others the outer skin grows hard and parchment-like, and is called a chrysalis. Many others spend all their lives deep within the tissue of some plant or animal and pupate in the cell in which they lived as larvae. While its body is changing to the adult form, the pupating insect remains inactive. When it emerges from its pupal skin and cocoon, it is a mature insect.

Silverfishes or Bristletails—
Most Primitive of All Insects

THE MOST PRIMITIVE of all the insects, the silverfishes or bristletails (order Thysanura) resemble what must have been the very earliest insect life. This type of insect is wingless but has a segmented body and the jointed legs of the typical insect. Two rather long and slender antennae extend from the head, while from the tip of the abdomen, three, or occasionally two, tail-like appendages (cerci), looking very much like antennae, are directed backward. Because of these cerci, one has to look closely to make sure which is the head and which the tail.

Most of the Thysanura are covered with scales, giving them a slick and silvery appearance, and they feel quite slippery when you attempt to catch them in your fingers. As they run swiftly for cover, they look very much like small fishes. One of their common names, silverfish, comes from this resemblance. The other common name, bristletail, is a tribute to their long cerci.

Two common species in this order long ago deserted their outdoor homes under logs, debris, or rotting vegetation, where most of the Thysanura live, to take up residence with man. Here, if numerous enough, they may do considerable damage to any product containing starch or glue. They have been known to eat the bindings of books, and have loosened wallpaper by eating the starchy paste that held it to the walls. Since they usually feed at night, hiding during the day in crevices or under anything loose, we rarely see them.

FISH MOTH AND FIREBRAT

One of these species, *Lepisma saccharina,* also called the Fish Moth, is pale gray or silvery in color and lives among books or papers. The name "saccharina" suggests that they feed on sugar, but this is doubtful. They are sometimes found in sugar bowls, but the explanation given for this is that they have fallen in and cannot get out.

The other common species, *Lepisma domestica,* is silvery gray, mottled with blackish specks. A common name for this species is Firebrat, because it likes to live around stoves and ovens, but particularly among the stones of the old-fashioned hearths once used for cooking.

GREAT MOLTERS

Most of the Thysanura are rather small, seldom growing beyond three-eighths of an inch in length; but the two species mentioned, when full grown, may be from one-half to five-eighths of an inch long. Although about three hundred species have been identified, we still know very little about the life histories of any of them. The female lays many minute eggs in the dust of cracks and dark corners. The metamorphosis of these insects is incomplete; that is, the young resembles the adult and does not need a pupa in which to change to the mature form. However, they do have a great many more molts or instars than most insects, and some species may spend two years or more as nymphs.

THE SILVERFISH—A COMMON HOUSEHOLD PEST

This slick and slippery little creature is a primitive insect; it is wingless and covered with powdery scales. Most silverfishes live out of doors under logs or in brush piles; a few kinds have moved inside to eat the paste from our bookbindings and wallpaper. The one shown here is called the "firebrat" because it loves to make its home around old-fashioned cooking hearths. Once established, the insect is hard to eradicate.

Springtails — Wingless Insects That Can Fly

THE SPRINGTAILS are also primitive, wingless insects, but you can see them go flying through the air. To accomplish this flight, they make use of a pair of short, abdominal appendages which can be coiled up and held by another pair of abdominal appendages. When this spring is released, the little creature is catapulted into space, landing about a foot away. The name of the order (Collembola, meaning "glue wedge") refers to a sucker-like appendage on the abdomen.

Collembola are all very small, usually pale in color, although some of them are dark gray, blue, or even red. Like the Thysanura, and unlike most other insects, they show no change in body formation between youth and adulthood. They live in hiding, under leaves or decaying vegetation, or around old logs and wood. One species, which lives under leaves in the woods, does come into the sunlight. The winter hiker trudging through the snow on a bright day may be startled to see tiny, dark specks hopping about. Warmed by the winter sun, these little springtails have ventured up through the crevices in the snow to skip around on the bright surface for a few hours.

The Earwigs—Insects with
Many-Jointed Antennae

No ONE KNOWS why that odd-looking insect, the earwig, was ever accused of entering the human ear. It probably never does; it does not look as if it could. We wonder why our ancestors did not choose a more probable villain for one of their horror stories. But untrue as this story is, people all over Europe have believed the charge, as testified by the earwig's German, French, Spanish, and Swedish names, and similar terms in half a dozen other languages, all implying that the insect enters the ear.

ODD FEATURES OF THE EARWIGS

Earwigs are rather unattractive, small, brownish crawlers, rarely more than an inch in length. The first thing you notice about them is a large pair of pinchers at the end of the abdomen.

Observe them more closely and you will see other odd characteristics. Their heads are quite large, their antennae long and many-jointed. Some species are wingless, but most of those in Europe and North America have thick forewings somewhat like the wing covers of a beetle, and these are so short that when laid back over the body, they leave most of it exposed. The rear wings, in contrast, are extremely thin and transparent and when not in use are folded fanwise under the heavy forewings. The earwigs belong to the order Dermaptera, "skin wings."

Earwigs use their wings very little, preferring to chase about on the ground. However, you will sometimes see one species, *Labia minor*, flying about lights at night.

1756

INSECTS OF THE NIGHT

Most earwigs are night animals and apparently eat anything. They kill other insects, slugs, and caterpillars. They also act as scavengers, eating decaying animal and vegetable material. Some of them have been seen to capture insects or other prey in their forceps, or pinchers.

THE EARWIG WAS ONCE GREATLY FEARED

It was once believed that the little earwig would enter a person's ear and kill him, but, so far as we can observe, this unattractive little insect restricts its murders to caterpillars and the like. Earwigs have four wings. The upper pair are very short, dark and stiff, something like a beetle's upper wings; the lower pair are large, thin and transparent, and can be folded up under the upper pair. Some species watch over their eggs and look after their young. In the illustration, the earwig is greatly enlarged.

The female earwig deposits a small number of white eggs in a hollowed damp spot and broods over them until they are hatched. The young resemble the adults, much as young grasshoppers resemble the adults of their group.

Most of the thousand or so Dermáptera species live in the hotter countries. There are about a dozen native species in North America, but probably the most common is *Forficula auricularia,* a European immigrant which has spread all over the civilized world.

The "Straight Wings"—The Mantids, Walking Sticks, Cockroaches, Grasshoppers, Katydids, and Crickets

THE NAME of this order (Orthoptera, or "straight wings") refers to the long, straight or parallel edges of the front wings of most members. Some of the order, however, have front wings that are rather broad at the middle. The hind wings are folded, like a folding fan, into numerous pleats and disappear, when at rest, under the front pair. Not all of the Orthoptera have wings. Practically every family in it has some species which, having possessed wings in earlier geological eras, have lost them after ages of disuse. A familiar example of a wingless orthopteron is the walking stick.

This order is an ancient one, dating from before the Carboniferous period, which is set by geologists as having occurred some 280,000,-000 years ago. Fossil Orthoptera, particularly cockroaches, have been found in the coal dating from this period. The Orthoptera are primitive insects, but, unlike the very primitive Thysanura or Collembola, go through a gradual change from the egg to the adult. The wings are complete in the adult, but just before this stage, in the last instar, they are useless pads. Since there is no quiet, or pupal, stage, the transformation of the Orthoptera is called an incomplete metamorphosis.

Members of this order vary in size from crickets less than half an inch long to walking sticks that are six, eight, and even twelve, inches in length. The various families differ so much in shape that their essential relationships are not easily recognized. As a matter of fact, many species are not easily recognized as insects, for they are masters of the art of camouflage and may simulate the appearance of green leaves, dead leaves, sticks, twigs, sand, or stones. By all standards, the Orthoptera are a highly successful group. Of ancient lineage, they have not decayed in strength or numbers, but have used the many geological ages to develop a great diversity of body formation, of such a practical nature as to insure their survival. Now, their species have invaded all the regions of the earth, adapting themselves to hot and cold climates, to low and high altitudes, to swamps and deserts.

COCKROACHES—MOST DO NOT LIVE WITH MAN

The word cockroach brings horridly to mind the familiar examples of this family (Blattidae) which have invaded our homes. Actually, most cockroaches are self-respecting individuals that still live in their ancestral homes under stones, logs, or the loose bark of trees, and in or about decaying vegetable material.

All of the cockroaches are scavengers, feeding largely upon vegetable food, but they frequently like to vary their diet by feeding upon the remains of some dead animal. In general they are night-loving creatures, avoiding the bright daylight as much as possible. All are soft-bodied and flattened, and have wings that fold flat upon the body. This compact shape is a distinct advantage, enabling them to slip into narrow openings.

They vary considerably in size, ranging from a quarter of an inch to a four-inch South American species. The largest native species in the United States measures slightly more than two inches.

Although the family is still strong in number of species (some 1,200 have been described), it reached its greatest development during the coal ages. The number of fossil cockroaches that have been discovered leads one to believe that the insect was much more numerous then than it is in the present age. The average size was also somewhat larger, for fossil roaches measuring nearly eight inches have been found.

The black sheep of the family, from man's point of view, are those that have moved into our houses. They long ago learned of the advantages human dwellings offered in the way of food and safety from their enemies and the weather, and have so completely adapted themselves to this mode of living as to be now almost incapable of existing elsewhere.

The German Cockroach, *Blattella germanica,* is the species you most frequently meet. It is about one-half inch long, straw colored, and darts swiftly for the nearest crevice when discovered. It originally made its home in Central Europe, but has now spread to all parts of the world.

The Oriental Cockroach, *Blatta orientalis,* is black and nearly one inch long. It likes damp locations, such as the vicinity of sinks, drains, and similar places. For this reason, it is sometimes called "water bug," or "black water beetle," although it is neither a bug nor a beetle. The female has greatly reduced wings and cannot fly. This species, originally from Asia, has also traveled with man to all parts of the world.

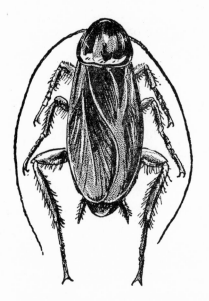

THE COCKROACH IS A GREAT TRAVELER

The medium-sized black cockroach which sometimes gets established in city kitchens came originally from the Orient, but now is at home around the world. The one pictured here is the giant American cockroach, which has left its early home in southern forests for more luxurious quarters in warehouses and bakeries. It can fly better than our other common domestic cockroaches, and often wings its way along city streets on a warm summer evening. Cockroaches are very swift runners.

An Australian species has likewise started hitchhiking its way around the world. A Florida species, *Periplaneta americana,* recently developed the wanderlust and has set out to spread into all suitable places, adapting itself to many unusual situations. Having originally lived under loose bark of trees throughout Florida and the other southern states, it has now invaded buildings, largely warehouses, bakeries, and stores, as far north as Canada, as far west as the Rocky Mountains, and southward into Central America and parts of South America.

THE MANTIDS—THEY AMBUSH THEIR PREY

Although not too common, the mantids (family Mantidae) have, during the last generation, become quite well known and even popular in the eastern part of the United States. This is doubtless the result of the large size and striking appearance of the Oriental species that has migrated to our shores.

Mantids are flesh eaters. Among the outer leaves of plants or along flower stems, they lie in wait for passing insects. The better to capture and hold their victims, the front legs of the mantids are modified into two powerful pinchers, or claspers, armed with sharp spines along the edges. As it waits for an insect, the mantid holds these pincher legs up before it in a praying attitude, from which we get the common name, praying mantis. Naturally, the term is sometimes written "preying mantis," and this is equally applicable. The insect is also often called a "soothsayer."

THE ORIENTAL MANTIS—AN INTERESTING PET

There are a number of native species in the United States, most of them living in the South. Only two species range as far north as New Jersey and Ohio, and they are not common.

The most common mantid in this country is an introduced species, the Oriental Mantis, *Paratenodera sinensis*. Brought here about 1896, it was liberated near Philadelphia. From there, it was carried to many parts of the country, and quickly became established. Because of its flesh-eating habits, it has been regarded as a beneficial insect. This is doubtful, however, because the Oriental mantis probably destroys just as many valuable insects, such as honeybees or lady beetles, as it does harmful insects.

So firmly and generally fixed is this idea of the usefulness of the Oriental mantis that a great many people believe that it is protected by law, and that anyone destroying one will be fined. Actually, no such law has ever been made.

The Oriental mantis makes an interesting pet. Each one requires a private cage, however, for if two are housed together the weaker one will be devoured. A mantis can be fed on insects, such as meal worms, on pieces of raw beef, apple, and potato and other raw vegetables, which it will learn to take from your fingers. It will eagerly sip water from a spoon. You will enjoy watching it cock its little head to one side as it observes you approaching, looking expectantly for what you may be bringing it.

THE PRAYING MANTIS—IMMIGRANT AID FOR THE GARDENER
Because the praying mantis eats other insects, it was brought to the United States from China about fifty years ago to help gardeners. Unfortunately, it does not limit its appetite to harmful insects; it eats a honeybee or a lady bug as readily as a grasshopper. Mantids are beautifully green, or green and brown, move slowly, and hold their pose, making good subjects for photographers. The native species of the United States are more plentiful in the South; they are smaller than the Oriental mantids.

In the fall, the adult female lays her two hundred, or more, eggs in a frothy mass which quickly hardens into a waterproof egg case. This case, about the size of a walnut, is attached to a weed stem. In late April or May, the eggs all hatch at once; the little mantids drop down and scamper off. Their one idea seems to be to get away from the egg case as soon as possible. An excellent idea, for any slow ones are instantly pounced upon and eaten by their more rapid brothers. From the time that they are hatched, each mantid is entirely on its own, and starts to make a living at once by capturing other insects.

The full-grown mantids are heavy in body; looking at one you would think it unable to fly very well. However, the author has grown accustomed to hearing an excited voice over the telephone, inquiring about the strange and startling creature that has suddenly appeared at a window of a towering office building in New York City. Mantids have been reported from the twentieth floor of the Hotel Statler. The observation platform of the Empire State Building has also had its quota of these visitors. Since these insects frequently fly at night, it is likely that they are attracted by the bright lights in the buildings.

WALKING STICKS AND LEAF INSECTS

Walking sticks (family Phasmidae) are seldom seen, and when they are it is usually by accident. One may be looking at a small oak tree or any shrub or tree that appears to be stripped of its foliage, wondering what may have caused the damage. Suddenly, what appears to be a bare twig starts to move off in a sedate but ludicrous manner. Only the movement of the insect reveals its presence, so exactly does it resemble the twigs among which it lives. This "look-alike" capacity is called protective resemblance, and undoubtedly does help to protect the walking stick from its enemies.

There are several species of walking-stick insects in the United States, most of them in the South. The most common and widely distributed is *Diapheromera femorata*, which ranges over the entire eastern part of the country. In general it seems to prefer oak foliage, particularly patches of young, second-growth oak. In the fall, when the insects are full grown, the female drops her eggs, letting them fall where they may. They are dropped one after another at short intervals until three or four hundred eggs are laid. As one walks through autumn woods where a great number of these insects occur, the constant dropping of the eggs on the dry leaves sounds like the patter of raindrops. The eggs lie among the leaves until spring, when little green walking sticks hatch out and start off for a summer of feeding.

All of our walking sticks have smooth bodies, but in the tropics there are some equipped with knobs and spines to afford them a better disguise in the thorny vegetation in which they live. Some of these tropical species are eight, ten, and even twelve, inches long, and some of them are winged.

THE WALKING STICK DOES NOT DO MUCH WALKING

This curious insect resembles a twig, and by day may lie as still as any of the twigs around it for hours at a time. When it does move, its gait can only be called "wooden." America's northern walking sticks have no wings and are colored to suit the bark they rest on; they carry their front legs in front of their heads, like antennae. Giant walking sticks of fourteen to sixteen inches live in the East Indies, and some of them have wings.

INSECTS LIKE LEAVES

One of the largest members of this family lives in the East Indies. It is one of the winged species. Its general color is tan, with the wings beautifully mottled with dark-brown. In the same region live some of the most curious of the phasmids. They are known as leaf insects,

POISED FOR FLIGHT
In the hot countries of India and the East Indies there are relatives of the walking stick that look like leaves—some like green leaves, some like dried leaves. Not only do their wings resemble leaves; the insects also have leaflike outgrowths on their legs. The one pictured lives in India and is shown in a flying position, when its camouflage does not serve it so well.

because their bodies, wings, and even leg joints, are broadly dilated. Usually colored bright green, although a few are brown, they blend so well with the foliage on which they feed that they are practically invisible. Indeed, to add to the deception, the wings are veined like leaves. The most common and most extremely camouflaged of these insects is *Phyllium scythe,* which is found in India.

GRASSHOPPERS AND LOCUSTS

The familiar grasshoppers of many species are found throughout the United States in fields and roadways and along streams; a few species have moved into the forests. Ordinarily, they like the dry and warm locations. Preferring to feed on grass, they will not hesitate to eat all sorts of vegetation when their regular food plants become scarce. They are known as the Short-horned Orthoptera because of their short, rather stout antennae. Their family name is Locustidae.

Although most of the species have wings, there are some that have no wings at all, and there are others whose wings are merely pads and entirely useless for flight. The posterior, or hind, legs of most are enlarged or well developed for hopping.

The female deposits great masses of eggs in the ground by inserting the tip of her abdomen into the soil. Many of these eggs do not hatch, either because of unfavorable weather or because other insects have parasitized them. Given favorable conditions, however, enormous numbers of certain species will sometimes develop. Soon, they will have depleted their food supply and will start off for other fields. Eventually, great numbers of them will be on the move, and we have what is known as a locust invasion or migration or plague. In some countries where these migrations occur yearly, the natives, making up for their ruined crops, collect the grasshoppers, pull off the inedible wings and legs, then dry the bodies in the sun for future food. They also eat the grasshoppers alive. Holding the insect by the hind legs, they pull off the wings, and then bite off the body.

Grasshoppers are active during the day. They produce their familiar scratchy, rasping call, by rubbing the hind femora, the thickened part of the hind legs, over the edges and stout veins of the wings. The male makes more noise than the female, and it is believed that this is a means of attracting the female. Since a noise is produced, one must conclude that the insect bears some structure which receives these vibrations, and it does. At the base of the abdomen, just under the wings, on each side, there is a round membrane, or earlike structure. These membranes are the ears of the locusts.

There are too many species of grasshoppers in the United States to permit any adequate discussion of them in this book. We will look at only two.

The Carolina Locust, *Dissosteira carolina,* is one of the most familiar in the eastern United States. It measures two to two and a half inches in length as it walks sedately across a dusty road during late summer days. Approached too closely, it leaps into the air, spreads its yellow-margined wings, and flies rapidly away.

The Lubber Grasshopper, *Romalea microptera,* is the largest in the country and inhabits the southern states. It is a heavy-bodied, flightless creature, three and a half inches long. The wings are simple pads. The adults and the nearly full-grown stalk along singly and in a ludicrous manner. The young are gregarious, wandering around like a small, straggling army of twelve to fifteen. If one becomes separated from its crew, it will enlist in the next group that comes along.

GROUSE, OR PYGMY, LOCUSTS

These are small, short-horned grasshoppers (family Tettigidae), somewhat triangular in shape, and quickly distinguished from the other grasshoppers by their curious prothorax (that part of the body holding the first pair of legs), which extends backward in a long projection nearly covering the wings and frequently longer than the abdomen. They are seldom over an inch long and are usually mottled in color.

These locusts frequent the margins of streams and ponds, and can swim rather well when a misdirected hop lands them in water. Their coloring matches well the wet sand and mud which they like so well. A few species are found in dry, sandy places. These do not have the dark, mottled shades, but are tan and even a light-straw color. Like the other grasshoppers, these are plant feeders, but they have never become plentiful enough to be pests.

KATYDIDS AND OTHERS

Almost everyone has heard these broad-winged gossips of the autumn. Only at night, however, do we hear their constantly repeated, rasping "Katy did—Katy did—Katy did," occasionally varied with a "Katy didn't," for the katydids (family Tettigoniidae) are night animals. During the day they sit quietly among the leaves, their green color effectively disguising them. They do not depend too far upon their disguise; for if you spot one and attempt to catch it, it will permit your fingers to come only so far before it has launched itself on its broad wings and is sailing off to a distant tree.

Katydids do not feed to any extent on grass or cereals, preferring the leaves of trees, shrubs, and weeds. The eggs are laid in the fall, inserted by the mother into the tissue of soft twigs or the stems of plants. Here they remain until the warmth of the early spring causes them to hatch. The little ones are long-legged, ungainly replicas of the adults, but, of course, have no wings.

SOME LARGE KATYDIDS

In the tropics there are truly giant katydids, some species reaching a length of five or six inches, with their forewings one and a half inches wide. When they fly one might think that they were small birds, except that their flight is somewhat misdirected and not nearly as rapid as that of birds.

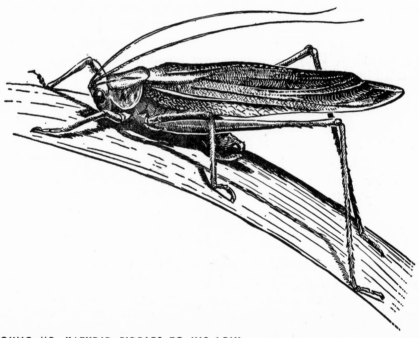

YOUNG MR. KATYDID FIDDLES TO HIS LOVE
By day the bright green katydid sits silent and almost invisible in the leafy tops of trees and bushes. In the evening the male rubs his wings together to make his familiar rasping noise. Each different kind of katydid produces a different sound. The female does not fiddle; she just sits still and listens through a hearing device in her front legs.

The largest katydid in the United States is *Amblycorypha oblongifolia*. It has longer wings than those of a close relative, *rotundifolia*, in which the forewings are more oval. The first-named species

in certain localities develops a curious differentiation in color. Instead of the usual bright-green of most members of the species, some
individuals are pink. This pink may range from a solid, bright hue
to a dull, mottled straw color. These unusual individuals are called
simply pink katydids. A tendency toward this pink condition is found
in a few other species, as well as in some of the homopterous insects
of the families Membracidae and Cicadellidae. Just what causes the
color change is not known.

Not all of the Tettigoniidae are broad-winged, nor are they all
green. They do have one characteristic in common, and that is the
possession of long, slender, almost threadlike antennae. For this reason, the family is known as the Long-horned Grasshoppers (or Long-
horned Orthoptera). Those that are not green vary in color from
light-gray to tan to very dark shades. Most of them feed on broad-
leaved trees or on weeds. One group is called the cone-headed grasshoppers, because the top of the head is prolonged forward into a
sharp cone shape.

MALES AND FEMALES

Female long-horned grasshoppers are recognized by their conspicuous
ovipositors (egg-laying organs), which in some may be short, and
in other species actually longer than the body itself. The place in
which the eggs are laid depends upon the length of the ovipositor.
Some species place their eggs in the soft tissues of plants, others in
the deep crevices of tree bark, still others in deep humus.

The males are the singers of the family. The songs of the different
species vary from a slight "zipp" to a rasping screech. If you have a
good ear, you can learn to recognize the various species by their
calls, for each has a distinctive note, rhythm, and timing. The timing, however, is somewhat dependent upon the temperature. The
higher the temperature, the more rapid the calls. So invariable is
this that formulae for the relation of temperature and timing that
are accurate to a very small percentage have been worked out for a
number of species.

HOW KATYDIDS SING

The males make the calls by slightly opening and closing the forewings in alternation. On the dorsal, or inner, part of the wings, near

the base, where the two wings overlap, is a flattened area. On the upper wing is a row of small teeth, and on the lower wing is a strong vein. The membranous part of the wing acts as a sounding board. Since the long-horned grasshoppers have this elaborate sound apparatus, it seems they should have equally good ears, and so they do. But where do you suppose their ears are located? Their ears are on their front legs just below the elbows, and are directed forward. This location is extremely convenient, especially for the female, who, picking up the call of the male, orients herself in the direction from which the call is coming, and follows down the beam. Here we have the earliest example of a direction finder.

THE CRICKET

The most common cricket in this country is the Black Cricket, *Gryllus assimilis.* Entomologists have recognized at least eight subspecies, each restricted to a particular geographical or local area. To the layman, these subspecies look pretty much alike, and we will let the taxonomist (the scientist who classifies plants and animals) worry about fine points of this sort.

In the fall, in turning over old boards that have been lying on loose, sandy soil, one is certain to see a dozen of these inch-long, black creatures rushing pell-mell in all directions, some leaping, others running, but all in a hurry to get to some other hiding place. There will also be other, smaller crickets under these boards. Most of these are less than half an inch in length and of a brownish color. They are some of the many species belonging to the genus *Nemobius.* The cricket family is called Gryllidae.

The Common European Cricket, *Gryllus domesticus,* made famous by Dickens' Christmas tale, *The Cricket on the Hearth,* has immigrated to this country, where it has become a resident in a number of widely scattered localities. At first it showed a preference for greenhouses, but later established itself in country estates, and now is invading apartment buildings in some of our larger cities, where, long into the winter months, it regales the inhabitants with its song. When it confines itself to singing it is generally tolerated, but when it has chewed a few holes in the clothing of its hosts, its lease is pretty sure to be terminated.

However, the European cricket is not as bad in this respect as our native black cricket, which sometimes does considerable damage to clothing in farmhouses or woodland cabins. Many a summer camper going reluctantly at vacation's end to the nail on the wall for his city clothes has found that what the crickets had left would not cover him as well as the shorts he was wearing. The author remembers with affection a certain tailor in Alabama who mended all night long so that the writer could return in decency to Ohio. The native crickets remain rustic; modern dwellings, apartment houses, and city life do not appeal to them.

THE CAMEL OR CAVE CRICKET OF THE WESTERN UNITED STATES
This odd-looking creature is common enough, but is not often seen because it hides in caves and under stones in the daytime, coming out to hunt only at night. Camel crickets have no wings, and their humped bodies are about the color of the soil or stones where they live. They have no noise-making or hearing organs.

Not all crickets live on or near the ground; a large group lives in trees and shrubs. Many of these are called, naturally, "tree crickets." In general, they belong to the genus *Oecanthus*.

Like their relatives the long-horned grasshoppers, the crickets all have very long, slender antennae, and produce their pleasant chirps in the same manner. They also have the same kind of ears. Of these musical insects, the tree cricket's song seems the most pleasant to human ears, and its soft chirping can be very soothing on a warm summer night. Most cricket activities are carried on at night. In a number of countries, particularly in the Orient, crickets are kept in cages to amuse the householder with their chirpings. In China, male crickets are kept, like gamecocks, for fighting purposes.

MOLE CRICKETS—THEY BOTH BURROW AND FLY

As the name implies, these crickets burrow in the ground. Their front legs are well adapted for digging, being broad scoops armed with sharp claws. In soft soil, they can dig themselves out of sight in a few seconds, while a minute is enough for them to disappear in harder soils. They are at home not only in the ground, but in the air as well, for they can fly long distances and very swiftly. Flying usually at night, they are frequently attracted by bright lights, and so may often be collected around street lights.

Mole crickets (family Gryllotalpidae) sometimes do considerable

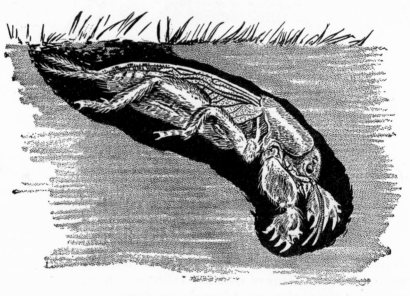

THE MOLE CRICKET—AT HOME IN THE AIR OR IN THE GROUND
Look at the enormous claws on the front legs of this mole cricket. With them it can burrow into the ground among plant roots, sometimes doing considerable damage. Its dark brown, two-inch-long body is covered with hairs, increasing its mammal-like appearance. This insect has strong wings and can fly long distances.

damage to cultivated crops. This is especially true in the tropics and in the warmer regions of our country, where the insects as well as the species are more numerous. Of the approximately ten species known in the United States, *Gryllotalpa borealis* is most commonly seen.

The Wood Eaters—Termites, or White Ants

So FAR and deep has the fear of termites spread among home owners that a constant stream of people, letters, and telephone calls passes through the author's office, all wanting to know whether they have termites, and, if so, what to do about it. This fear is well founded, for once these little creatures become established in a building, they are bound to do considerable damage unless quickly eliminated. And eliminating them is difficult, for termites usually start their attack in some little-seen and inaccessible place. In fact, they usually have been well established for a number of years before the householder even suspects their presence.

Termites (order Isoptera, "equal wings") destroy buildings and eat the roots of trees and plants. They do millions of dollars worth of damage every year. Yet they do very useful work in helping to keep our forests alive and growing. Trees that fall to the ground are quickly reduced to humus by the action of fungi, ants, and other insects. On the other hand, dead trees that do not fall but are exposed to air become dry and hard, or cured. In this condition, they do not disintegrate under insect attack, and can clutter up the forest for years, preventing new growth. Here, the termite proves its worth. It can eat the hard, dry wood and digest it, with the aid of some intestinal protozoans which it always carries along. It tunnels back and forth through the tree until it finally brings it down to earth.

HOW TO DISCOURAGE TERMITES

Apparently the wooden structures that man erects are just so many dead trees to the termites, and they attack them with equal appetite. However, since the wood they eat is dry, the termites must have water, which they get from the ground. If we can prevent them from getting water, either from the ground, a leaky tap, or sweating pipes, they will soon die and leave the building. Creosoting timbers or injecting mineral oil into timbers already attacked will also discourage their activities.

TERMITES HATE LIGHT

The most common and widely distributed termite in the United States is *Reticulitermes flavipes*. It ranges over the entire country and into southern Canada. It is, in fact, the only species occurring in the northern United States. It prefers sandy or gravelly soils to the heavy or clay soils. Termites hate light, and if it becomes necessary for them to cross an exposed area through which they cannot tunnel, they set about building a covered passage of wood fiber cemented together with their gluelike saliva. Because they have little or no coloring, they are sometimes called "white ants."

QUEENS, SOLDIERS AND OTHER CASTES

Like the ants, they are social insects and have a somewhat similar society, although they are a more primitive and ancient group. They have many castes, the number differing in different species to fit the particular activities of the colony. Principal castes include the males and females, winged for their marriage flight, but later wingless; the enormous queen, her wings torn off, laying eggs for her colony; the soldiers, with their large heads armed with powerful jaws, ready to seize any invader; and the workers of the colony.

TERMITE HOUSES IN THE TROPICS

Termites reach their greatest development in the tropics, both in activity and in number of species. Indeed, our present temperate species migrated not too long ago from the tropics. In the warm climates, many species build very large houses. Some of the termitaries, as these houses are called, in Africa and in Australia are as much as twenty feet high and several square feet in area. They are usually built of sand grains cemented together, and may become so hard as to defy onslaught with axe and crowbar.

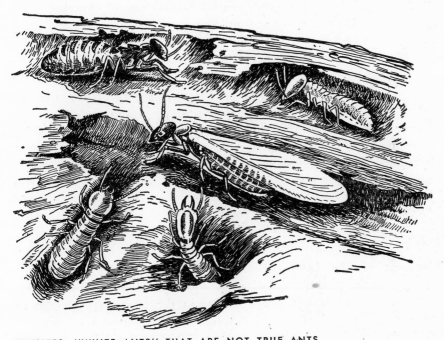

TERMITES—"WHITE ANTS" THAT ARE NOT TRUE ANTS

Like the ants, bees, and wasps, termites live in colonies and have a caste system. Some species build large and sturdy homes of their own, but the species that is becoming common in eastern North America makes its nests in wood which the termites eat as they tunnel it. Is it their fault that the best wood they can find is in the houses erected by man? Pentachlorophenol is used to kill a colony established in a house.

Many primitive peoples use termites as a staple article of food. They dry them, roast them, and even eat them raw. Accomplishing the last is quite a trick. The insect must be crushed by a quick little bite while still held in the fingers, for once let the termite's sharp jaws fasten on cheek or tongue and it will be next to impossible to disengage them.

Net-Winged Insects and Lacewings
– Including Some Insect Lions

W HEN the great botanist Linnaeus set up his seven insect orders, based on wing structure, he called one of them Neuroptera ("nerve wings"), including in it the insects whose wings had an intricate network of veins. Many of the groups of insects that he included in this order have since been established in orders of their own, so that today only a few well-marked families remain in the Neuroptera.

APHIS LIONS—A HUNGRY FAMILY

Members of the beautiful family Chrysopidae are distributed throughout the world, and look much alike, wherever they are found. Of some 425 species, only twelve live in the United States. There are fourteen species in Great Britain, and a few more in Europe.

All species have oval-shaped wings, thickly crossed by numerous veins. Although most are green, some are yellow, others are tan, and still others are dark brown. All are shimmering and transparent, well described by the order's common name of lacewing. The name Chrysopidae, from the Greek words for "golden" and "eye," refers to the golden eyes of the adult, which are large, compound, and set far apart. The name aphis lion refers to the immature, or larva, which feeds upon aphids and other small insects.

MOTHERS AND BABIES

In general, all species have the same habits. When her eggs are ready, the mother, poising over a suitable leaf surface, exudes a bit of secretion which hardens instantly in the air, to form a fine, hair-

1776

like stalk. On top of this stalk, she places one egg; then she makes another stalk for another egg, until there are several eggs on the leaf.

THE BEAUTIFUL LACEWING WAS ONCE AN APHIS LION

The young of this lovely creature is a spiny, sticky little monster which earns the gratitude of mankind by crawling along plant stems and eating every aphid (plant louse) it can find. When the aphis lion has eaten all it can, it spins a beautiful, round, shining white cocoon about itself, from which it will later emerge with large, fragile wings and brilliant golden eyes. The lacewing also eats aphids, but not so many as when it was an aphis lion.

One can imagine two possible reasons for this procedure, the first being to prevent other insects from eating the eggs, and the second to prevent the first-hatched from eating all the remaining eggs. If you ever watch infant aphis lions in action, you will accept the second theory as most plausible. They seem to have just one desire in life, to sink their jaws into the first object they meet. All too often the author has had these tiny creatures drop out of a tree on to the back of his neck. Sinking their jaws in, they inflicted bites that hurt for hours.

MOST VORACIOUS OF INSECTS

As their name suggests, the larvae feed upon plant lice, which they devour by dozens. Drinking in the juices through grooves inside their jaws, they proceed from aphid to aphid, casting aside the drained bodies when finished. They never stop, or even hesitate, until the branch they are on is swept clean. No other insect is as voracious as these aphis lions, not even the larvae of lady beetles, which feed in much the same way.

When full grown, the aphis lion spins a rough cocoon in which it remains until ready to emerge as a winged adult. When handled, the Chrysopidae, both adults and larvae, give off a disagreeable and lasting odor, and for this reason are sometimes called stink flies.

ANT LIONS—TRAPPERS OF INSECTS

Like the aphis lion, the ant lion (family Myrmeleonidae) owns a powerful pair of jaws with which to seize its victims. Unlike the aphis lion, it does not go out hunting for its prey, but lies in wait at the bottom of a trap constructed in loose, dry sand.

THE FIERCE AND UGLY ANT LION IS MEEK AND LOVELY
AFTER IT GETS ITS WINGS

The ant lion (*bottom right*) digs a funnel an inch or two deep in loose sand, and lies in it waiting for an ant to tumble in. (You can often find a small colony of ant-lion holes along a sandy stretch.) In its pit, only the ant lion's jaws are exposed, normally. When the ant lion has eaten enough ants, it spins itself a rough cocoon from which it will later emerge (*left*) as an exquisite creature with four long, delicate wings (*top*).

The ant lion excavates its pit by crawling backward in a small circle, tossing the sand out by means of a flipping motion of its head. Eventually, it has a pit one or two inches in diameter and just as deep as the shifting sand will remain stationary. Buried in the bottom of the pit with only its large jaws exposed, the lion waits— a most unlionlike method of attack.

An ant or other small insect wandering over the edge of the pit starts an avalanche of sand and bug rolling to the bottom, where the jaws are waiting for it. The ant lion now goes into action.

Tossing sand up from the base, to confuse the victim, and also to keep the avalanche rolling, the ant lion grabs at its prey, and usually is successful in seizing and dragging it in to be eaten. The remains are then cast out of the pit, and repairs are made in preparation for the next adventure.

When full grown, the larva pupates in a rough cocoon and emerges as a winged insect looking very much like a damsel fly. It differs from the latter in having its wings, when at rest, folded rooflike over its abdomen, and in having slightly longer antennae, which are usually distinctly knobbed.

ANT LIONS OF YOUR OWN

Sandy places are sure to contain little colonies of ant-lion pits where you can watch their trapping tactics. However, it is quite easy to keep two or three ant lions in a shallow dish of sand where you can observe them undisturbed. Ants and other small insects steered toward the trap will provide food for your hungry pets.

Ephemerids, May Flies, or Dayflies

To those who live inland, near a small, muddy stream or pond, the May fly is an exquisitely graceful insect, with ethereal, glistening wings, a slender, curved, beige-colored body, and two or three long, thin filaments streaming out behind. They can get a clear view of an individual May fly as it rests on a tree trunk or wall. Occasionally, they are fortunate enough to see a number of the lovely things in their leisurely mating dance.

But to those whose business takes them through the lake-shore streets of Cleveland, Ohio, on a late spring day when the May flies are swarming, one insect is about as noticeable as a snowflake in a blizzard. For three or four days each season clouds of them fall on lake-shore streets and pelt against auto windshields, making driving as hazardous as in a sleet storm. They cover walls and windows, pedestrians, and street lights. They are a nuisance, and no one appreciates them, not even the commercial fishermen, whose livelihood depends on the quantity that falls a few hundred feet north of these streets, in the waters of Lake Erie, to supply the principal food for its fish.

Cleveland's experience is shared more or less by all the cities and towns along the Great Lakes, and sometimes by those along the Mississippi. Indeed, the Ephemerida thrive wherever there is fresh water, except in the very cold regions. The slow-moving rivers of western Europe produce heavy storms of them, usually in August. A few years ago large swarms appeared in New York City's Central Park.

MATING DANCE OF THE MAY FLIES

The swarming of May flies is largely the mating dance, and properly takes place over streams and ponds instead of futilely over city streets.

1780

Then, the female can drop her eggs into the water, usually in two clusters totaling sometimes as many as four thousand eggs.

These clusters sink to the bottom, and after a time odd little creatures called naiads hatch out, ready to start their underwater life. They have fringed antennae, fringed legs, several feather-shaped gills

THE MAY FLY BEFORE AND AFTER
The May fly spends up to three years of its life as a larva (*bottom*) and only a few days as an adult (*top*). As a feathery brown creature it feeds on plants on the bottom of a stream or lake, and is itself one of the principal foods for fresh-water fish. The larvae finally rise to the water surface, break out of their brown skins, and fly to nearby vegetation. In a few hours they molt again, and emerge as shining insects with gauzelike wings. Now they live only long enough to mate and drop eggs in the water.

along each side, and two or three feathery tails. A few of the Mayfly species pass through the naiad stage in a few weeks, but most of them require one, two, or even three, years. During their underwater life they are very active, feeding voraciously on decaying plant material, stems and leaves of aquatic plants, and seaweeds.

BEAUTIFUL CREATURES WITH GLISTENING WINGS

When fully grown, the insects come to the surface, molt, and fly away for just a short distance, for their wings are not yet fully developed. This stage of their life is called the subimago, and is peculiar to the ephemerids. In a few hours they molt again, this time emerging as shining, beautiful creatures with glistening, tissue wings.

You can always recognize May flies by their rear wings, which are quite small in comparison with their front wings. Another noticeable characteristic in most species is the set of two or three long, slender filaments, called cerci, extending from the tip of the abdomen.

These insects belong to the order Ephemerida ("lasting but a day"), and in Europe they are called dayflies, for it was formerly believed that adult May flies lived only one day. This is not entirely correct, because individuals have been kept alive for as long as two weeks. Outdoors, however, their fragile bodies are unable to cope with the elements, and few survive more than two or three days. They are attracted to bright lights, and a great number are killed beneath the wheels of traffic. Other countless hordes fall back into the water and are devoured by fish.

THE MAY FLY IS A VALUABLE FISH FOOD

May flies, both adult and naiad, are among the most important of the fish foods. Without them, in our waters, fish cannot live in any numbers. Unthinking persons, annoyed by the annual swarms along the Great Lakes, frequently ask how May flies can be exterminated. They do not realize that to destroy this fish food would practically eliminate a valuable food of man. As a matter of fact, the May-fly population along Lake Erie has been greatly reduced in the past thirty-five years, owing to sewage and mill dumping and other hazards of civilization, and the fish catch during those years has decreased accordingly.

The sports fisherman is well acquainted with the fact that fish are fond of May flies. He has modeled several of his flies after these insects, the Green and the Gray Drake being typical examples. In France, fishermen call the hordes of Ephemerida that fall into the Seine and the Marne "fish manna."

YANKEE OR CANADIAN SOLDIERS?

In the Great Lakes region, May flies are given another colloquial name, with variations. Along the American shores they are called "Canadian soldiers," because the vast hordes seem to come out of the north. Given a southerly wind, the helpless insects are carried out over Canada, where, of course, they are called "Yankee soldiers."

The Mosquito Eaters —
Dragonflies and Damsel Flies

UNTIL RECENTLY the dragonfly was better known as the devil's-darning-needle, snake feeder, and horse stinger. So general was the idea that the dragonflies coursing back and forth over some waterway were looking for victims in order to sew their ears back, that these valuable creatures were shunned by many persons. It was also supposed that if there were no ears to practice on, they must be looking for a hungry snake to feed. If both of these supposed activities appeared implausible, dragonflies must have those long abdomens in order to sting. Since they never sting man, it was supposed that they attacked horses.

As agricultural communities became more observant and better educated, these ill-founded names died, and three more appropriate terms (dragonfly, bee butcher, and mosquito hawk) gained usage. All three refer to the voracity and fierceness with which these insects attack and devour other insects. The second title is angrily bestowed upon them by beekeepers, especially those who make a business of rearing queen bees. Mosquito hawk is also a good name, for mosquitoes, both adult and larval, are the principal food of these insects.

Members of this order (Odonata) may be easily recognized by their long, straight abdomens, their two pairs of long, thickly net-veined, membranous wings, and their large, compound eyes. All of our species are contained in two easily differentiated suborders. In the Zygoptera, or damsel flies, the wings at rest are held straight up over the body. In the other, the Anisoptera, or dragonflies, rest with their wings stretched out flat from the sides of their bodies.

The damsel flies are dainty little creatures, usually delicately colored with reds, yellows, and blues or compounds of these colors. The abdomen is slender, and the eyes are great globular bumps set far apart on the sides of the head. Damsel flies are not strong of wing and are usually found fluttering among the weeds and grasses bordering a stream or pond.

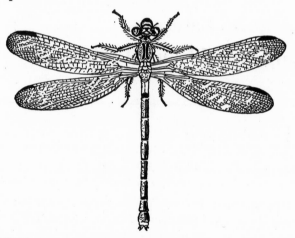

DAINTY CREATURE OF THE STREAMS AND PONDS

Smaller, weaker cousin of the dragonfly, the damsel fly is equally fierce and beautiful. Some species of damsel flies fly tandem, the male using pincers at the end of his body to grasp the front of his mate's body. When she is ready to drop her eggs, the pair descend together into the water and out again along a weed stem. Damsel flies always rest with their dainty wings held upright over their bodies.

True dragonflies make up the other suborder, the Anisoptera. They are larger, stronger, and fiercer than the damsel flies. Their two huge, compound eyes occupy most of the head. Their long, strong wings are not as slender as those of the damsel flies. They love to patrol selected districts, back and forth, chasing out any intruder, returning from time to time to rest at a favorite observation post.

SKILLFUL HUNTERS

Damsel flies slip quietly through the grass and weeds to seize their prey with their feet. They feed upon mosquitoes, midges, and other small insects. The dragonfly pursues, and, by its speed and dexterity, overtakes and grabs its victim out of the air with its six feet. Quickly killing its catch with its powerful jaws, it retires to a near-by perch to devour it. If disturbed at this time the dragonfly rarely abandons its meal, almost always carrying it away to another perch. Not only do the dragonflies feed upon mosquitoes, which provide them with a mere mouthful, usually eaten on the wing; they also capture honeybees, robber flies, butterflies, and other large insects.

INTERESTING WAYS OF THE NYMPHS

The nymphs, as the immature Odonata are called, live under water. The damsel-fly nymphs breathe by means of three long, slender, leaf-shaped processes, called gill plates, extending from the end of the abdomen, which extract oxygen from the water. Dragonfly nymphs employ a unique method which serves a dual purpose. They suck water into a chamber lined with oxygen-extracting gills, situated at the rear of the abdomen. This water is then suddenly expelled by muscular contraction. The expelled water propels the nymph for a considerable distance, providing a convenient means of travel.

Most nymphs crawl or shoot themselves along on the bottom. A few species plow through the silt in search of live food. Still others climb up and down the stalks of the water vegetation. They all have very peculiar, though efficient, mouth parts, and it is interesting to keep a few nymphs in an aquarium in order to watch them at their feeding. A nymph may lie quietly in wait for a mosquito larva or any other possible food, or it may approach its victim slowly. Suddenly, its lower lip, armed with a pair of claspers, shoots forward on an extendable, armlike process, seizes the unlucky prey, and pulls it back to the real jaws.

IMPORTANT DESTROYERS OF INSECTS

The Odonata are undoubtedly a tremendous factor in controlling the balance of insect life. So valuable are they in mosquito control, that a few years ago a bill was introduced into the legislature of one of our large states to build houses in which dragonflies could roost at night. This measure was defeated. A much more useful piece of legislation would have been one against the wholesale draining of our ponds and swamps, and especially against the straightening of our little streams, which has been carried on so extensively and thoughtlessly by politicians who know more about the relation of money to votes than about the relation of insects to man.

GIANT DRAGONFLIES OF YESTERDAY

The Odonata are an ancient group, dating back to that geological period when our coal beds were being laid. Perhaps at that time it was a larger order in number of species. Certainly in the rich, dank days of that age some of its members grew to tremendous size. A fossil forerunner of the present-day dragonflies has been discovered with a wingspread of twenty-nine inches. It may have fed on the giant cockroaches of those days. Did the forerunners of the mosquito exist at that time? And were they also giants? We do not know as yet.

THEIR COLORFUL DESCENDANTS

Present-day species of Odonata are distributed all over the world. About 4,500 have been described, with 650 of them occurring in North America. Let us look at a few that an amateur might be able to recognize.

The Common Damsel Fly, *Agrion maculatum,* called *Calopteryx maculata* in many books, is the only easily identified damsel fly. The all-black wings (smoky in the female) and the metallic-green abdomen will at once place this insect.

The common damsel fly likes the margins of quiet brooks and small streams that flow through wooded areas, preferring those overshadowed by willows or drooping vines. The males love to rest on a leafy spray in the sun, slowly opening their wings, and then quickly snapping them shut, as if proudly displaying their lovely, iridescent colors. They can be found throughout the eastern United States, from Canada to Florida, and westward as far as Texas.

The Green Darner, *Anax junius,* is probably the most common of the dragonflies. Its shining, olive-green thorax and brown abdomen, neatly trimmed with blue, make this one a handsome creature. Throughout the Western Hemisphere, from Alaska to Panama, you can see it flashing by on its clear wings on almost any bright day from early spring until frost.

The warmer the day, the greater this dragonfly's activity. Tirelessly, it ranges far afield from the pond or stream where it developed, skimming over an upland meadow or down a country lane. Early in the morning and late at night it searches for food. Sometimes it joins its fellows in a great swirling mosquito-hunting party.

A close relative, *walsinghami,* the Giant Green Darner, lives in California. Probably the largest dragonfly in the United States, it measures over five inches across the wings.

OTHER DRAGONFLIES

Epiaeschna heros is probably the largest species found in the eastern part of the United States. Although a handsome species, with its brown body and smoky wings, it is not as striking as *Anax junius.* It ranges from Maine to the Dakotas, and southward to Florida and Texas. In its hunting it frequently blunders into houses, much to the confusion of the residents and itself, for it tries again and again to get out through the ceiling or anywhere except the place where it came in.

The genus *Libellula* contains a number of common species. They are called skimmers because they fly close to the surface of the water. The Ten-spot, *Libellula pulchella,* is a familiar dragonfly near almost any quiet pond, from Maine to the Dakotas and south to Texas and Florida. It has three brownish-black spots or bands on each wing. These three spots are very distinct, and nobody now knows why the insect is called a ten-spot. A western species, *Libellula forensis,* takes the place of the ten-spot in British Columbia and from Montana south to Arizona and California. It lacks the brown spot on the tips of its wings. *Libellula semifasciata* is similar, but its spots are smaller and browner.

Plathemis trimaculata looks very much like a small ten-spot, but its basal spots are very much smaller. It is a long-season flier, appearing early in the spring and continuing until frost. It ranges from southern Canada to North Carolina, Arizona, and California.

The Amber-wing, *Perithemis domita,* is one of the smaller species. Only the male has entirely amber wings; the female's wings are clear, except for two amber spots or bands across each wing. You will find them flying in early summer.

THE DRAGONFLY IS A REAL DRAGON TO OTHER INSECTS

Immature dragonflies live under water. They have powerful mouth parts for seizing and eating other insect young. The adults are equally fierce in chasing and eating adult mosquitoes, robber flies, and even bees and butterflies. Dragonflies usually rest with their wings outspread, like an airplane's, except when newly emerged from the nymph stage.

The genus *Celithemis* also contains a number of rather small but beautiful species. *Celithemis ornata* has a brown patch at the base of the rear wing, *eponina* sports many small spots on its yellowish wings, while *elisa* restricts its decoration, besides the basal area, to a single brown spot toward the tip of each wing.

Toward fall, red-bodied dragonflies are noticed, resting on the tips of thick-growing weeds. These all belong to the genus *Sympetrum.* All have clear wings, except *semicinctum,* which has amber wings.

Stone Flies—Great Producers of Eggs

HAVE YOU EVER, as you walked along a rocky stream, noticed odd, squat little creatures clinging to, or crawling over, the stones under the water? If you have, you are observant, for they are so drably mud colored as to be easily overlooked. They are the larvae, or nymphs, of the stone flies (order Plecoptera).

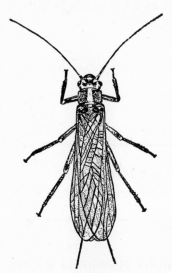

THE STONE FLY IS THE TROUT'S DELIGHT

Young stone flies, called nymphs, live on the rocky beds of rushing streams, where they eat the young of May flies and are themselves eagerly eaten by trout. The grayish-green adults vary from half an inch to two inches in length. You will sometimes see a great many of them collected on suburban lamp posts, to windward of the stream where they grew up.

Pull one of them out of the water, and you will see the two tail filaments that are among their identifying characteristics. Examine your catch with a hand lens, and you will see that there are two claws on each foot, and at the base of the legs there are short, hairlike gills. Because of this limited gill structure, stone-fly nymphs must live in well-aerated water, such as rushing streams and the wave-washed shores of lakes. Most of them feed upon the minute creatures called animalcules; a few are plant eaters.

1789

Wherever the nymphs are found, the adults, which look very much like the nymphs, except that they have wings, will be found resting on the foliage along the water's edge. They are not strong fliers, but are often carried far from their nymphal homes by heavy winds. Bright lights attract them, so that on warm summer evenings you can see them flying around, or clinging to, street-light poles that are not too far from their regular haunts. They vary in length from one-half inch to two inches.

In the Northwest they are frequently called salmon flies. As this name would indicate, the nymphs of this insect are an important fish food. Fishermen use both adults and nymphs for bait, and several trout flies are made in imitation of the adult.

Since the stone fly has such formidable enemies, Nature has compensated it in several ways, principally by making it capable of enormous egg production. A female may lay as many as six thousand eggs.

Cicadas, Leaf Hoppers, Aphids, and Scale Insects — Clowns of Insectdom

THE INSECTS belonging to the order Homoptera display a greater diversity of form than those found in any other order of insects. All of them, large or small, parade the most fantastic, grotesque, and clownlike bodies in all insectdom. All are vegetarians, equipped with strong, segmented beaks for the piercing of a plant and the sucking of its juices.

Many are very small, and so inconspicuous that we are scarcely conscious of their presence. And the smaller they come, the more numerous they are and the more troublesome to man, as, for example, the aphids and the scale insects.

In contrast, there are the husky cicadas, the smallest of which is about three-quarters of an inch long, and the weird Lantern Fly, which reaches three inches or more. Many are wingless; others have excellent wings and know how to use them. Some watch us silently from the bushes; others inform us of their presence in loud and rasping voices.

Although most of the Homoptera are a nuisance to man because they feed on the same plants that he wants, there are a few species that he has been able to exploit. Shellac and the red pigment called lake are the products of some Asiatic scale insects. Another of the Homoptera secretes a honeydew in such quantity that it can be eaten by human beings; it formed the manna described in the Old Testament. A Mexican species produces the famous cochineal dye.

THE CICADAS AND THE SEVENTEEN-YEAR LOCUSTS

Is there anyone so city-bound that he has not heard the voice of the cicadas (family Cicadidae) rattling out of shrubs and trees in the late summer and early fall? Some of you, hearing them, might enjoy knowing one little piece of cicada biology, the fact that only the males sing. An old Greek wisecrack declares:

> "Happy be the cicadas' lives,
> For they have voiceless wives."

The cicada is not always too happy, however, for his voice is his undoing. English sparrows, and other birds, too, have learned to connect this raucous singing with a nice, large, juicy morsel of food. Hearing the racket, the sparrow will fly to the spot from which the sound comes, and, if quick enough, will seize the cicada, tear off its wings, and devour the body. The singing also attracts another enemy, the two-footed human collector, or cicadaist, for cicadas make a most attractive collection.

COLLECTING CICADAS

Since the average human collector is clumsier than an English sparrow, he will need to use all his equipment of vision, dexterity, and patience, especially patience. You will find it very exasperating, for instance, to see a fine example of a cicada casually drumming overhead, just out of reach of your net. Wait patiently; the cicada after repeating his routine several times is likely to take wing for another station. If you are fortunate, you will be able to net him on the wing. It is also very possible that the cicada may alight on a more reachable spot. While collecting in Guatemala, the author was intrigued by a giant cicada that made a voluminous racket, but found it impossible to capture a single one, in spite of all his efforts. Even an offer of the equivalent of a United States nickel to the quick, keen-eyed Mayan children of the locality for each cicada they caught brought in only one. The insects were just too hard to catch.

On another occasion, in Peru, on the headwaters of the Amazon, the author had great difficulty in collecting specimens of a large species with a call like a distant locomotive whistle. This call was a most elusive sound, heard just at dusk, and then only for a short period, for twilight is very brief in these equatorial regions. The natives fear this sound, believing that it foretells the imminent death of someone in the vicinity, and will have nothing to do with these insects. Only by accident was it possible to secure a few samples of this interesting insect, as when one blundered into the collecting lamp, or hit the reflecting sheet and tumbled to the ground.

THE VOICE OF THE CICADA

Male cicadas possess a pair of sound chambers, one on each side, on the under, or ventral, surface at the base of the abdomen. Over each of these is stretched a membranous plate which the insect vibrates in order to produce his characteristic call. The body walls and the wings probably aid as sounding boards. Different species produce different calls, those in the United States usually having shrill or rackety voices. One in Ceylon is well named the "knife grinder." Some of them are even musical: harplike in Greece, bell-like in Egypt.

The female cicada has no apparent ears, as have some of the Orthoptera. If, as is thought, however, the cicada song is a sexual call, she must be able to receive the vibrations somehow. This could be accomplished by means of her body walls, although not as well as by a specialized part of the body.

The Seventeen-year Cicada, *Magicicada septendecim,* is the most remarkable species in the United States. It is frequently, but incorrectly, called the seventeen-year locust. Among the longest-lived of the insects, it requires seventeen years for its life cycle.

——How the Eggs Are Laid. The eggs are inserted by the mother, with the aid of her sharp ovipositor, in the twigs of trees or shrubs. She then partially severs the twig near the base by repeatedly puncturing it with her beak in order to check the growth of the plant tissue. You can pick out these twigs very easily in the late summer by the browning of the leaves and the drooping of the branch. If the mother did not do this, the healthy growth of the plant would seal in the eggs so effectively as to prevent the escape of the little nymphs.

——The Nymph Burrows for Food. When hatched a few weeks later, the nymph leaps or drops to the ground and immediately starts to burrow in. Locating a tree rootlet, it sinks its beak into the tissue and starts its seventeen years' existence underground. Burrowing by means of its powerful, shovel-like, front feet, it travels from root to root, stopping to feed in favorable places until it is full grown, seventeen years old, and ready to "come out."

——Out of the Ground at Last. Now fat and about an inch long, looking very much like a brownish cicada without wings, but with functionless wing pads, the insect works its way to the surface. Once in the open air, it ascends the nearest tree trunk for a short distance, fastens its claws firmly in the bark, and awaits the change into a winged adult. Its skin splits down its back, and out wriggles a pale, anemic-looking creature with shriveled wings. Soon, however, the wings begin to expand as the lifeblood flows through their veins. The pale color darkens, and the brilliant reds, yellows, browns, and greens blossom out.

The complete transformation requires several hours. During this period the insect is helpless, and many succumb to plundering animals. Even the weather takes its toll. Sharp rains and heavy winds dash many to the ground, while very dry weather will dry out the wings before they are properly spread. During such a dry season, you will often see helpless individuals with shriveled wings crawling on the ground.

——Where Seventeen-Year Cicadas Are Found. Scattered over the eastern part of the United States are a number of broods of the seventeen-year cicada which entomologists, the scientists who study insects, have carefully plotted as to location and tabulated as to year of emergence. Naturally, there are some years when many broods emerge, and some years with few or none. If you live in the East, your nearest entomologist or naturalist can tell you where and when to look for the coming-out party of these extraordinary creatures.

THE SEVENTEEN-YEAR CICADA AND ITS TWO LIVES

For seventeen years this cicada lives as a queer, pale grub, burrowing in the soil and feeding on plant roots. Then it comes out of the ground, climbs part way up a tree, sheds its skin, and emerges with wings that rapidly grow strong and beautiful. The male cicada has at the base of his abdomen a drumlike apparatus on which he produces a vibrating call. Large broods of cicadas are a pest in suburban yards, some years.

If you live in the South, you will find the same cicadas, and plenty of them; but here they cannot be called seventeen-year cicadas, because in the warmer climate they require only thirteen years to complete their life cycle.

OTHER CICADAS

About 1,500 species of cicada are known in the world, about two hundred of them in North America. Among these are several species all looking pretty much alike, and all familiar to us under the common name of dog-day harvest flies, cicadas, or, incorrectly, locusts. The adults of some species are much larger than those of the seventeen-year species and appear much later, in late summer and fall. Their habits and life histories are much the same as those of the seventeen-year cicadas, except that they require only two years for their development.

In the southwestern United States live a number of species, many much smaller, some having a wingspread of less than two inches. As if to match their smaller size, their voices are weaker, many producing nothing louder than a faint "z-z-zip-p-p," very much like a grasshopper's rasp, or the rattle of a distant rattlesnake.

LANTERN FLIES—QUEEREST OF ALL BUGS

This family (Fulgoridae) contains some of the queerest of all of the bugs. Tops in the family is undoubtedly *Fulgora lanternaria,* which, together with several closely related and very similar species, is widely distributed throughout the American tropics. The lantern fly is also called the alligator bug and the peanut bug, because of the curious prolongation of its head, which resembles an alligator head, or a peanut. This head is a hollow, shell-like structure which seems to have no purpose at all. None of the many suggested purposes seem to have any authentic basis.

Besides being the most grotesque, the lantern fly is also the largest in the order. It is about three inches long and has a wing expanse double its length.

HOW THEY WERE NAMED

The first of these insects known came to the early Swiss entomologist, Maria Sibylla de Merian, in a little box, which she placed on her study table. During the night, she heard a great commotion in the box. Fearing that the insects might escape, she leaped out of bed to look after them. When she opened the box she was astonished to see the heads of these curious creatures all aglow. The next day, when she described the insects, she gave them the name *Fulgora lanternaria,* from *Fulgora,* the Roman goddess of lightning, and *lanternaria,* meaning "a lantern." Since then no other observer has ever seen a lantern fly with a luminous head.

THE GREAT LANTERN-FLY MYSTERY

There is no questioning the accuracy of this scholar's observations, for she was always meticulous in her writing. The insects she had were undoubtedly actually luminous. Why they were so we can only guess. While collecting in the tropics, the author often kept lantern flies alive for a few days, to see if a glow could be detected on them at night, but none was ever seen. This is just another of those unsolved problems that await some careful observer who will examine a great many lantern flies under many different conditions.

Another question about these insects that needs investigation is whether they bite human beings, and, if so, how serious the wound

THE LANTERN FLY—DREADED BY SOUTH AMERICA'S INDIANS

That horrid-looking snout is not really dangerous, but natives of the South American tropics, where this curious insect lives, are very much afraid of its bite. No one knows much about the lantern fly; it is truly a creature of mystery.

is. All through the tropical parts of South America, and particularly along the headwaters of the Amazon, the natives are positive that the bite of a lantern fly means certain death within hours. The author has been shown and has brought back from the jungles of Peru individuals that were supposed to have bitten people, all of whom died within a short time.

It is true that lantern flies, like the cicadas, have strong beaks, fitted for puncturing and sucking the sap from twigs. Some close relatives among the Hemiptera are able to puncture the skin and inflict exceedingly painful wounds, as the author can vouch for from personal experience. He has yet, however, to be bitten by either a lantern fly or a cicada, although he has handled hundreds of living and very active individuals.

Nevertheless, the Peruvian Indian has a very real fear of these insects. It is also a curious fact that all through the Amazonian jungles the native medicine man carries one or two lantern flies in his bag of tricks or fetishes, and sometimes he has an additional supply speared on a palm spike stuck up under the eaves of his hut.

STRANGE STREAMERS

There are several other species of large fulgorids in the American tropics, all peculiar in shape and habits. A number of them secrete a thick, waxy substance which hardens in the air and frequently trails out behind in whitish streamers two or three inches long. In flight these streamers look like tails, making the bug resemble a flying bird, although much slower in speed. The way in which these waxen strands serve the insect is unknown. Perhaps they protect it by filling the mouth of any pursuing hunter with something unpalatable.

LANTERN FLIES IN THE UNITED STATES

In the United States, there are no large members of the family. All are small, one-half inch or less in size, but rather peculiar in shape, exceeded in this respect by only one other family, the Membracidae, to which we will come very shortly.

Two common species are widely distributed. *Scolops sulcipes,* a dark-gray insect with a long, slender extension of the front of the head, can be swept in a net from wet grassy meadows. *Acanalonia bivittata* is a greenish insect, although some of them are pinkish, like the pink katydids. Less than half an inch in length, they have heads that are ordinary in shape and size; their eyes are large, and their wings very large, so that in flight they look like small moths. At rest, they hold their wings like tents over their tiny bodies. You will have to stand very still to observe them at rest, for they are wary little fellows, keen on playing hide-and-seek with you among the twigs and branches.

A few species can do some little damage to the particular agricultural crop on which they feed. As a rule they are not numerous enough to do any widespread damage, possibly because they are limited in their choice of food and occur only in rather widely separated spots throughout their geographical range.

TREE HOPPERS—COMICAL LITTLE HOBGOBLINS

The tree hoppers (family Membracidae) depend for their ludicrous effects, not on their head shapes, which are normal, but rather on curious distortions of the prothorax (that part of the insect's body that lies between its head and its wings). Some are adorned by a thornlike projection, half as long as the insect itself; some have two thorns. In others the prothorax is swelled up out of all reason to look like a shield, a crag, or a pup tent. To get real amusement out of them, you need only to look at a few species, head on or in profile, through a low-power microscope.

Unlike the lantern flies, none of the tree hoppers, not even the tropical species, go in for large size; most of them are about half an inch in length. Almost every color is represented in the family; most of the North American species come in the various shades of green and brown.

Many are very sociable, feeding together on a twig or branch like a flock of tiny sheep. The immature and the adults frequently flock together. When you approach them, all will dodge around to the opposite side of their branch or leaf. Go closer and you will see the adults hop off and then fly to some near-by tree or shrub.

The female lays her eggs by means of a sharp and powerful ovipositor which places them well into the tissue of the plant on which her species usually feeds. The insertion of the eggs sometimes does as much damage to the plant as does the actual feeding of the insects. One species, the Buffalo Tree Hopper, *Ceresa bubalus,* sometimes does considerable harm to young apple trees by depositing its eggs in such a manner as to kill or stunt the branches.

ENEMY OF THE APPLE TREE

The buffalo tree hopper is one of a large family of weird-looking insects, all small, all having various odd protuberances or swellings above the head and between the wings. In the summer you can find some kind of tree hopper on almost any plant or tree. Look for the buffalo tree hopper on apple trees. That is where it lays its eggs, often to the trees' serious hurt.

LEAF HOPPERS AND SHARPSHOOTERS

Comprising a large family (Cicadellidae) of small, torpedo-shaped bugs, these insects are abundant in all vegetated areas throughout the world. They feed more upon the foliage or very soft tissues of plants or low weeds and grasses than on the tough-fibered shrubs and trees. They do not adopt exaggerated shapes, but sometimes do wear bright colors, although most are green or greenish yellow. None of the North American species are very large, seldom measuring over half an inch.

Many species feed upon cultivated crops, and when numerous enough become serious pests. Some carry plant diseases from one plant to another, thus causing greater damage than they do by feeding on the sap.

They are lively little bugs, dodging around the plant stems, entirely confident that if you approach too close a hop will carry them beyond your reach. Sweep your net over any summer meadow, and you will collect more species of leaf hoppers than you would have supposed existed.

FROGHOPPERS, OR SPITTLE BUGS

The summer wanderer in grassy meadows, weedy fields, or young woodlands has undoubtedly met these insects, at least indirectly. He may never notice the bugs themselves, but he certainly will see the frothy homes of their young, little blobs of spittle fastened to grass or tender plant stems.

A SPITTLE BUG AND ITS HOUSE OF BUBBLES
The young spittle bug builds itself a house of bubbles on some plant or grass so that it can suck the juices in comparative safety. The adult is a small, neatly patterned brownish-green insect which flies around low-growing vegetation or hops upon it.

If you are very careful, you can scrape away the mass of bubbles and discover, sitting astride the stem, a little pale-green creature that looks somewhat like a tiny frog. This is the fellow responsible for the mass of spittle.

Hour after hour, with its beak buried in the plant, the froghopper sucks the sap for food. Lashing its little tail, it exudes a soapy liquid into which it pumps air by means of a curious bellows-like apparatus in its abdomen. As the bubbles are formed, the insect pulls and pushes them over itself in an orderly fashion until its soft body is completely covered.

For a vivid account of how one man got interested in the spittle bugs in his own back yard, and how he watched one build and rebuild its tiny house, you should read the chapter called "The Home of Bubbles" in Edwin Way Teale's *Near Horizons*.

The young (or nymph) of the froghopper spends its entire life of several weeks in this manner. After its final molt it leaves this protection and becomes another hopping bug, very much like the other hoppers we have just discussed. There are few species of this family (Cercopidae), and all of them are quite small.

APHIDS, OR PLANT LICE— OUR INTERESTING LITTLE ENEMIES

Everyone interested in plants, from the farmer with hundreds of acres of crops, the orchardist, and the greenhouse grower, down to the apartment dweller with a potted plant or a window box, has met and tried to destroy the little pests known as plant lice. They are extremely dangerous to all kinds of plant life.

Many of these insects are unattractive or even repulsive to look at, but some of them are rather lovely, especially in their winged form, and some are decidedly odd. They all have interesting, even puzzling, life histories. Some entomologists have divided the aphids into four families, but for this brief discussion we can safely lump them all into one common family, Aphididae.

There are many species, and in some cases many forms of a species. Most of our northern species pass the winter as eggs stuck in the crevices of bark, or other protected parts of plants. When spring comes, the eggs hatch. The little aphids start to feed. In three or four days each of these aphids, for every one of them is a female, produces a number of living young. A few more days and these latter are also producing living young. This method of reproduction is known as agamic, or asexual, and the females are called stem mothers.

If food becomes scarce, or sometimes for reasons no one seems to know, a generation of winged forms may be produced. These feed for a few days, then take wing and fly to new localities, sometimes to a different kind of plant. Here the whole life process is repeated. A number of these winged broods may appear during the course of a summer.

With the approach of fall and the general slowing up of all Nature, a new miracle takes place. Completely developed males and females appear. These are nearly always winged. They mate, fly off, and lay their eggs in the crevices of their favored plants.

HOW APHIDS SERVE AS "ANT COWS"

Wherever you find aphids on outdoor plants you are pretty certain to find ants. For, as nearly all gardeners know, ants like to drink the sweetish liquid which the aphids exude. Whenever the aphids are feeding they pass out droplets through two small tubes near the tip of the abdomen. This secretion is called honeydew because, if it is not gathered by the ants, it falls on the leaves like dew. If there is a scarcity of nectar in flowers, honeybees will frequently gather the honeydew instead. Honeydew does not make good honey, for it is thin and sours quickly.

So fond have ants become of this honeydew that many close associations have developed between certain species of ants and certain species of aphids. Not only do the ants benefit, but the aphids are relieved of a material that in time would bog them down. This mutually beneficial association is known as commensalism.

A remarkable case of this sort is that of the Corn-root Aphid, *Aphis maidi-radicis,* and an ant, *Lasius niger.* In the fall, the ants gather the aphid eggs as fast as they are deposited, carefully storing these eggs in the most suitable parts of their underground chambers. During the winter, they move the eggs from place to place as the weather changes. When the eggs start to hatch in the spring, the ants carry the little aphids to chambers along the roots of weeds and place them carefully on their temporary food plant. As soon as corn has been planted and is sprouting, the ants move the aphids to the corn roots, which are their preferred food. Here, their careful tending of the aphids pays off, and the ants can gather plenty of corn-sweet honeydew.

Aphids are frequently referred to as "ant cows," and well they might be, as the case just mentioned proves. In some species of aphids that feed in an exposed situation, the ants not only tend their cows by milking them, they also protect them by driving away various hunters, such as aphid lions and lady beetles.

THE APHID'S DEADLIEST FOE

From one enemy, the ants seem unable to protect their "cows." This enemy is the Chalcid Fly. Examine any colony of aphids and you will almost certainly see more than one individual that is only an empty shell of an aphid, with a small round hole in its back. A tiny grub has been feeding within the living aphid. Hatched from an egg laid by an adult chalcid fly on the body of an aphid, it has fed, pupated, and eventually emerged through the round hole to fly away and parasitize other aphids.

Although the aphids do not produce many young or lay many eggs at a time, their life cycle is so short, and the generations are so frequent, that, if it were not for their numerous enemies, they could in a very short time overrun the world and destroy all plant life. It has been estimated that, if they met with no accidents, the progeny of a single plant louse would amount in a single season to several million individuals. Before that staggering statistic one can only say, Be thankful for chalcid flies.

MEALY BUGS, SOFT-SCALE, AND SCALE INSECTS

This is a large and complex family of homopterous insects. It is such a diverse collection of odd and curious creatures that present-day entomologists, instead of considering it as a single family with three principal subfamilies, regard it as a superfamily, Coccoidea, breaking it up into at least nine families. Since we shall concern ourselves here with only a few of the most important members of this group, we can safely adhere to the old classification, family Coccidae.

The Coccidae are all plant feeders, sucking the juices of the plants upon which they feed. Practically all plants are attacked by one or more species of these insects. Since many of them do great damage to plants that are useful to man, the family is universally condemned. There are, however, a number of species of considerable value to man because they possess certain secretions which he has been able to utilize.

MEALY BUGS

Mealy bugs are in constant conflict with mankind because they like so many of the plants that man likes. They are soft-bodied creatures, less than a quarter of an inch long, oval in shape, and flat. A waxy coating, which covers the entire insect, makes them look as if they had been dusted with flour. Some of these insects have neatly notched edges. In most species the males have wings, but the females are wingless. Although able to move about somewhat, mealy bugs generally cling closely to the surface where they feed.

The Citrus Mealy Bug, *Pseudococcus citri,* is one of the most common of the several species that are found on greenhouse plants. As its name indicates, it is particularly partial to plants of the citrus family, but it can be found upon many of our household plants, especially those with tender, juicy stalks and leaves. A closely related species, *longispinosus,* is also common on house plants. Both of these species are widely distributed. The females deposit their eggs under the body in a mass of sticky or waxy threads. So large does this pile become, that the adult has to stand on its head to continue to feed.

Maple trees have a mealy bug, *Phenacoccus acericola,* which attacks the leaves, sometimes doing considerable damage. It is light yellow, and is covered with a mass of stringy white wax.

COCHINEAL INSECTS

The Cochineal Scale, *Coccus cacti,* was for many years the source of some of our most beautiful red and orange dyes. It lives in the drier regions of Mexico and the adjoining area as far south as Peru, wherever its food, the nopal and similar species of the opuntia cactus, is found.

The adult, male, cochineal insect is small, white-winged, incapable of eating, and is very rare. The female is larger, wingless, reddish, and numerous enough to cover the cactus plants on which it feeds.

The dye is made from the dried bodies of the females; seventy thousand of them are required to make one pound. Long before the arrival of the Spanish in the Americas, the Indians had learned how to produce the beautiful dyes. The Spanish quickly recognized the commercial value of the cochineal and demanded great quantities of it as tribute. For three hundred years or more, the gathering and exporting of cochineal was an important industry. But after the introduction of inexpensive aniline dyes, the commercial use of cochineal practically disappeared, except for the small amounts used for coloring cosmetics, foods, and drinks.

THE SHELLAC INSECTS

The Indian Lac Insect, *Carteria lacca,* is the most valuable of the scale insects. In the course of its scientific naming it has been placed in a number of genera. Readers may find it under *Coccus* or *Tachardia,* as well as others. *Laccifer* seems to be the one in use at the present time. The insects range over an extensive area, from India and Ceylon eastward through Indo-China, Formosa, the Philippine Islands, and down into the East Indies. They feed upon a great variety of plants, but seem to prefer the native banyan and other native fig trees.

The males are tiny insects, either winged or wingless. The females are larger, but are encased in such a mass of wax as to be scarcely noticeable. In fact, if there are a number of insects close together, the gummy excretions become so great as to completely engulf the insects and surround the entire twig to a thickness of three-eighths to half an inch.

To prepare the lac, these twigs are cut off and boiled in water. The lac separates and rises to the top. After being refined, it appears commercially as shell-lac or shellac. Average annual production is about four million pounds. Although a number of substitute products have been developed, none of them begin to approach the quality of the natural material.

THE MANNA INSECTS

The Tamarisk Manna Scale, *Trabutina mannipara* (also called *Coccus manniparus*), produces the famous "manna of the wilderness." This is the food mentioned in the Bible as appearing miraculously to the Israelites during their journey to the Promised Land. The insects feed on two species of the tamarisk shrub or tree, *Tamarix mannifera* and *gallica,* which grow in parts of Asia Minor and Iraq. The females secrete large amounts of honeydew, which, coating the leaves and ground, accumulates in this arid country into a thickened layer called manna. It is a sweet substance containing a high percentage of sugar. Manna is still collected by the Arabs of the Sinai Mountains and used as a substitute for sugar.

SOME INJURIOUS SOFT-SCALE INSECTS

The soft-scale group contains the giants of the Coccidae. They usually have curved or rounded exteriors, with a waxy covering, and no very distinct hard, scaly covering.

The Cottony Scale, *Pulvinaria innumerabilis,* is the most common scale found on maple, elm, Virginia creeper, grape, and a number of other plants. So plentiful is it at times that the honeydew dropping from the trees coats everything beneath with the sticky mess. This is quickly turned black by an interesting fungus which grows upon it. The cottony fungus material covers the eggs and protects the insect from its enemies.

The genus *Eulecanium* contains a number of species which do considerable damage. Among them are *tulipiferae,* which is found on the tulip tree and the magnolia and is the largest scale insect in North America; *nigrofasciatum,* the dreaded Terrapin Scale, that attacks many fruit trees but particularly the peach; and *pruinosum,* the common Frosted Scale, found on a variety of fruit and forest trees.

The Chinese Wax Scale, *Ericerus pe-la,* is famous for the white wax secreted by the male insect. This wax is used for making candles and many other purposes. Before World War II nearly three thousand tons were produced annually, most of it coming from the region of Shantung, China. Other areas also produce some wax, for this scale insect is found throughout a large part of China and Japan. In many places the natives rear the wax insects, carefully protecting them during the winter, and then carry them long distances to pasture them out on suitable plants in favorable places.

HARD-SCALE INSECTS

The true scale insects are those that are covered with a hard coating or shell, which is composed of the insect's molted skins cemented together with secretions from the body. For this reason, they are frequently called armored scales. The species are numerous, and we shall mention only a few of the most notable.

The San Jose Scale, *Aspidiotus perniciosus,* is one of the most serious scale pests that attack our fruit and forest trees. This insect is cir cular in shape and so small as to be easily overlooked until a tree is heavily infested. By that time the tree has a roughened or scaly appearance. When this rough surface is scraped with a knife, a yellowish secretion is pressed out, coming from the crushed insects. The San Jose scale has undoubtedly come to us from Asia. It was first noticed in California in 1880, but now has spread to nearly all parts of the country.

The Oyster-shell Scale, *Lepidosaphes ulmi,* is a common pest on trees and shrubs of the more temperate regions. A native of eastern Asia, it has been carried to the four corners of the world on ornamental plants and fruit trees. From these Eastern importations, the insects have spread to many of our native plants, which have suffered greatly because of their lack of resistance to this strange, invading enemy. This scale is well named, its hard, shell-like covering looking very much like a tiny oyster shell.

The Purple Scale, *Lepidosaphes beckii,* and Glover's Scale, *gloverii,* are also two Old World species which have spread by means of citrus stock to most of the citrus-growing regions. The Mediterranean Fig Scale, *ficus,* is a pest in the fig-growing areas around the Mediterranean Sea. It has recently managed to reach and become established in the fig-growing regions of California.

There are many other species, for this is undoubtedly the largest group of the Coccidae. Since the family is of such great economic importance, a great deal has been written concerning it.

The True Bugs

TO MANY PEOPLE, the word "bug" means any unattractive insect, and even anything that crawls. Historically, they are quite correct, for "bug" is a very old English word which originally meant any strange creature which was small and horrid. Nowadays, entomologists limit the term to one order of insects, the Hemiptera ("half wings"). This order contains many of our most beautiful species, several that are quite a nuisance to farmers and gardeners, and one that is indeed small and horrid, the bedbug.

The name "half wings" is given them, not because these insects have only half wings, but because the basal half of the fore wing is hard and horny, while the tip is thin and membranous. The thin parts of the two wings overlap, while the basal parts are usually widely separated by a broad, triangular, hard piece, called the scutellum, or shield. The lines between these parts form a cross on the back. The four triangular areas, together with the broad thorax and rather small head, are characteristic of the true bugs.

The antennae are five- or six-jointed; the mouth parts are beaklike, enabling the insect to suck plant or animal juices. This beak also serves the bugs as a pumping organ for forcing into their victims a saliva-like poison.

HOW TO COLLECT AND PRESERVE THE TRUE BUGS

If you enjoy curious shapes and delicate colors, you will enjoy collecting and studying the true bugs. Some look like the inventions of a comic artist. Many are exquisitely tinted. Many are extremely interesting to watch in action. When nicely mounted and arranged in a collection, they present a pleasing appearance.

Hemiptera should be killed quickly, and not left too long in the

1808

killing bottle, especially if the atmosphere is at all damp; otherwise they may lose their delicate tints and bright colors. Medium-to-large specimens should be pinned through the scutellum. Those too small to pin should be mounted on a paper point or triangle with a tiny speck of glue, shellac, or amberoid cement. Only the tip of the point should be permitted to touch the insect, and then only at a place between the second and third legs on the right side. When these points are pinned the insect should be to the left of the pin and facing forward.

You will find land-dwelling species on growing vegetation, under loose bark, or under leaves or debris on the ground. The subaquatic species (those which are somewhat aquatic) live in muddy spots, along the sides of ditches, or on the surface of ponds and streams. The species which are aquatic (all-around water animals) swim in ponds and lakes, sluggish streams, and, occasionally, in more rapid waters. Ponds with plenty of decaying vegetation and water plants will yield the largest number of specimens.

One of the larger orders, Hemiptera contains about thirty thousand described species, with perhaps three thousand of these in North America. New species are constantly being discovered and described, particularly from the tropical regions. Of the twenty-six families in the order, we shall discuss eighteen.

Separating the families into three groups according to the type of place in which they generally like to live, we have the land-dwelling group, comprising the Pentatomidae, Scutelleridae, Cydnidae, Coreidae, Corizidae, Lygaeidae, Pyrrhocoridae, Miridae, Aradidae, Tingidae, Reduviidae, and Cimicidae; the subaquatic, comprising the Gerridae and Gelastocoridae; and the aquatic, comprising the Naucoridae, Nepidae, Belostomatidae, Notonectidae, and Corixidae.

STINKBUGS

Anyone who has ever gone berrypicking knows about these little insect skunks (family Pentatomidae), for the stinkbug delights in berry bushes, particularly those of the raspberry, and only too often just before you have spotted a really luscious-looking berry, the stinkbug has sprayed it with a nauseating oil. The dreadful taste of a berry subjected to this treatment is not soon forgotten.

The stinkbug carries its two scent glands on the underside of its

thorax, with the openings near the base of its hind legs. When frightened, the bug opens the valves of the glands and floods its whole
neighborhood. This vile-smelling and vile-tasting spray undoubtedly
protects the stinkbug from insect-eating birds and animals. Since
many of the pentatomids are brilliantly colored, it is thought that
their bright colors have developed as a warning signal that this creature is not good to eat. Birds and animals after a few bad experiences may learn to associate bright colors with a nasty taste. An additional argument in support of this theory is the fact that many
brightly colored insects in widely scattered orders also have a disagreeable secretion that they exude when disturbed.

The pentatomids make up one of the largest of the families of the
Hemiptera. In North America, there are some two hundred species,
while the world boasts nearly five thousand. Some found in the tropics reach a length of one and a half inches.

The pentatomids are divided in their choice of foods. Some of
them are vegetarians, sucking the sap of plants with their piercing

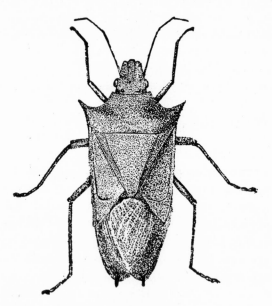

THE STINKBUG GIVES WARNING OF DANGER
Of the five thousand different kinds of stinkbugs, most are attractively colored, and some
are even beautiful. The colors serve as a warning signal to other insects; if the warning is
disregarded, the stinkbugs spray bad-smelling oils over their enemies. Most stinkbugs feed
on plants, but others, including the one pictured here, eat insects, particularly caterpillars.

beaks. A large number, however, feed upon a great variety of insects. They regard caterpillars as a delightful meal. It is a common sight to see a caterpillar impaled on the beak of a flesh-eating stinkbug. When disturbed, the bug will seldom abandon its meal, but, like a puppy with a gigantic bone in its mouth, will calmly stalk away with the caterpillar sticking out at right angles.

Many of the carnivorous species belong to the genus *Podisus*. Some of these have the pronotum (the cover just behind the head) extended in a sharp spine on either side. Members of sap-feeding species, the *Brochymena,* are broad and rough, usually brownish or dark gray. They are found on the trunks and branches of trees, where they look like loose flakes of bark. It takes sharp eyes to discover them. Several large species, slightly over half an inch long, are bright green in color. They usually belong to the genus *Acrosternum.* Another green species with yellow side margins and a yellow-tipped scutellum is *Chlorochroa uhleri.*

THIS STINKBUG DINES ON VEGETABLES

The Harlequin Cabbage Bug, *Murgantia histrionica,* a shining black or blue creature conspicuously marked with red, is in high disfavor with farmers because of the damage it does to crops. Its normal food was wild species of the mustard family of plants, and was never very plentiful. However, with the planting by the white man of enormous fields of cabbage, cauliflower, and related plants, and the smaller gardens of radishes and turnips, the insect has found an abundance of food available for it.

Gardeners have applied to it numerous names, some of which cannot bear repeating, but the commonest are harlequin cabbage bug, firebug, calicoback, and terrapin bug. The adult hibernates under rubbish, ready to sally forth as soon as young cabbage plants are set out in the spring. It feeds on these while laying its eggs in a double row. The eggs look like little barrels all standing on end and gaily decorated with two black bands and a white spot.

SHIELD BUGS

Closely related to the stinkbugs, the shield bugs (family Scutelleridae) wear a scutellum, or shield, so greatly enlarged that it covers practically the entire insect. The wings are tucked away under this covering, so that only their edges show. How does the insect ever manage to stow away its wings? Perhaps some day you may be fortunate enough to watch one.

The family is not large, but its few species range throughout the world. Many of them are brightly colored, particularly those found in the warmer countries. They are plant eaters, and many seem to prefer plants growing in wet, open places, where, with the full benefit of the sun upon their yellow, red, and blue backs, they glisten like little jewels.

NEGRO, OR BURROWING BUGS

This insect (family Cydnidae) is a smaller edition of the shield bug. Some of them are shiny black, and these are called Negro bugs. They look like small black hemispherical beetles and frequently fool the untrained observer. One has to look carefully to determine whether the shining back is all in one piece (called the scutellum), a feature which would place the insect in the Cydnidae group, or whether it is really split down the center to form the two elytra, or wing cases, of a beetle.

Their other common name, burrowing bugs, comes from the fact that these bugs are often found under stones. There are not many known species in the family. All feed on plants.

SQUASH BUGS

A large family of bugs, the squash bugs have more lengthened shapes than the pentatomids but are equally foul in flavor. Since they also love to promenade about on berries, one frequently knows of them by taste rather than by sight.

Most of this family (Coreidae) are plant eaters. Of these, a familiar example is the squash bug, *Anasa tristis,* from which the family gets its common name. It is dark brown, speckled with lighter brown. The very young are black, gaily decorated with red on their legs, head, and the front of the thorax. They lose their decorations as they grow older. The young tend to congregate, feeding like a herd of cows out to pasture.

August sees the first of the adults, which feed singly and usually at night, and hide during the day under rubbish. As the colder days of fall approach, and most of the squash plants have died, the bugs fly off to winter in a permanent accumulation of rubbish or old leaves. With the arrival of summer weather the following year, they seek out young squash plants on which to lay irregular clusters of oval, dark-yellow eggs. Here again, man's planting of extensive fields of squash and melon plants makes beautiful feeding grounds for squash bugs.

A smaller species than *Anasa*, light brown in color, with a flat, dilated area, a leaflike expansion, on each antenna, probably is *Chariesterus antennator*.

Species of the genus *Alydus* are largely animals that prey on others. They are slender, with a row of spines on the hind femora (upper parts of the legs). Larger species also having spines on the hind femora, with cylindrical hind tibiae (second parts of the legs), belong to the genera *Euthochtha* and *Archimerus*. In the genera *Leptoglossus* and *Acanthocephala*, the hind tibiae, instead of being cylindrical, are expanded into leaflike dilations, and members of this group are called leaf-footed bugs. Some of the tropical species are quite large, with huge dilated areas on their legs. Their brilliant color, as they stalk along, warns all comers, "I am a bad bug, leave me alone."

GRASS BUGS

Although the grass bugs are a small family (Corizidae), many of the species are cosmopolitan in distribution. They usually feed upon grasses or low weeds and often occur in unbelievable numbers. In general, they resemble the Coreidae, the family with which they were formerly grouped.

One very common North American species, the Black and Red Box Elder Bug *Leptocoris trivittatis*, feeds on the leaves and young seeds of box elders and maples.

CHINCH BUGS

These are long, soft-bodied bugs (family Lygaeidae), which suck the sap of plants. The most publicized one, which many of us have never seen (although we may have contributed to its control through taxes), is the common Chinch Bug, *Blissus leucopterus*. This insect exacts a tremendous toll in the damage it does to corn and other small grains, as well as grasses, particularly in the central United States.

Like so many of our pests, the chinch bug is small, measuring only about a quarter of an inch long. It has a black body with white markings on thorax and wings, red legs, and red at the base of the antennae.

The adults sleep away the winter under dry leaves or similar vegetation. When they emerge in the spring, the female lays up to five hundred tiny yellowish-white eggs on the roots or at the base of the stalk of young grain. The eggs quickly hatch, and the young, which may be either bright red or yellow marked with brown, start to work sucking on the juices of the tender plants. The stalks dwindle in growth, turn yellow, and frequently die. By early summer, this first brood has reached maturity. They start laying their eggs on corn if it is available. By late August or September, this second brood has developed, and as adults are seeking winter quarters in grass clumps or rubbish.

Adult chinch bugs are of two forms, the short-winged one that cannot fly, and the long-winged, or normal form, which can fly but seldom does, preferring to walk. The long-winged chinch bug is more numerous in the Mississippi Valley, while the short-winged form seems to take over in the southern states, on the eastern seaboard, and along the Great Lakes.

Several species of larger size are prettily colored in black with red lines. *Lygaeus kalmii*, for example, has a red basal area on the thorax and lines of red on the wings forming a cross on the back. *Oncopeltus fasciatus* is larger, bright red with a black spot on the center of the thorax, and a broad black band across the wings at about the middle. *Myodochus serripes* presents an odd sight with its long, thin neck, and its long, club-shaped antennae waving as it runs about on the ground. It prefers rather open meadows, where it is quite at home among the stones and trash.

FIREBUGS

As both the common name and the scientific name (Pyrrhocoridae) of this family indicate, these insects are largely fiery in color. The red markings may be warning signals to insect-eating enemies that they are not good eating.

Most of the members of this family are tropical. One of the northern species, *Euryopthalmus succinctus,* is believed by some people to feed upon the cottony-cushion scale, a scale insect which infests the orange and other plants. Other authorities disagree, saying that it feeds on plant juices. In any case, it is a beautiful insect dressed in brownish-black above, trimmed throughout with red. Underneath, it is covered with brilliant blue hairs.

Most of the species are very destructive of our cultivated crops. The "cotton stainers," belonging to the genus *Dysdercus,* are scattered throughout the world wherever cotton is grown. The one living in our southern states is *Dysdercus suturellus.* The damage in this case is caused by the insects' excrement, which stains the cotton a bright red. In addition to calling them cotton stainers, the exasperated cotton grower calls them "bordered plant bugs," "redbugs," and other similarly descriptive names.

LEAF BUGS OR PLANT BUGS

A very large family (Miridae) of rather small bugs, the plant-bug group has few members that are over a quarter of an inch long. There are innumerable species; some four hundred have been described in North America, while more than 1,200 have been listed throughout the world. New species are constantly being recorded, for, as yet, the tropics have just been touched. Even specialists who have spent their lives in studying this group are frequently confused by the vast numbers and the complexities of their relationship.

At one time, it was thought that the species were all plant feeders. We now know that some of them render valuable service to mankind by preying upon other insects or insect eggs. A few, however, do considerable damage to our agricultural crops.

The Tarnished Plant Bug, *Lygus pratensis,* a common insect in the United States, is one such creature. It is brown or yellowish brown, with variable darker markings. It is as varied in its diet as in its coloring. Garden crops, strawberries, fruit trees, and forest trees are all food for this bug. The bite the insect makes for the purpose of sucking the juices seems to have a poisonous effect upon the plant, killing the surrounding tissue. Even the eggs which are inserted in the plant affect its growth.

The Four-lined Leaf Bug, *Poecilocapsus lineatus,* is a very pretty species. The adult appears in June in bright-green, with the head, part of the pronotum (the cover just behind the head), and underside bright red. Four black longitudinal lines decorate the upper part. The young are dressed in brilliant red uniforms. Although they feed upon almost any plant, they seem to show a preference for the buds of roses, dahlias, and peonies, and are also quite fond of the currant family. Wherever the plant tissue is punctured it turns brown, the discoloration spreading rapidly until the entire bud or leaf shrivels and curls up, eventually dropping off. Whole twigs and shoots will wither and die in this manner.

FLAT BUGS

When hunting for insects under the loose bark of old logs or fallen trees, you can count on finding one or more of the flat bugs (family Aradidae). They are very much flattened, a condition well fitted for the place in which they live. Occasionally they will be seen walking slowly on the bark of dead trees or twigs, evidently exploring for suitable living quarters. It takes a keen pair of eyes to see them, for their irregular shape and dark-brown or black color blend in perfectly with the rough, moss-covered bark.

Little is known about the habits of the flat bugs, but it is thought that they feed upon fungus. The author has sometimes seen the mother hovering over a patch of her eggs and staying with the little ones when they hatch. Although she does not sit on her eggs, the odor from her scent glands undoubtedly repels any hungry beetle that may be foraging in the vicinity.

The young are reddish and look very much like bedbugs. Since these insects occur around freshly sawed lumber, the idea has arisen that bedbugs are brought into houses on new lumber when the house is built or repairs are made. True bedbugs are never found away from human settlements, and the little flat bugs that so closely resemble them never feed on human blood.

LACE BUGS

Although they are less than three-sixteenths of an inch in length, you will recognize these insects immediately by the odd projections over the back of the head and thorax, and by the front wings, all of which are transparent, with darker raised veins, making the insect look like a bit of Irish lace. Beating the foliage of trees or shrubs over an opened umbrella or a beating net is almost certain to yield some of these attractive tiny bugs, which are members of the family Tingidae.

They are weak fliers, and after getting into the air drift along on the breeze. Evening is their favorite time for sallying forth to look for fresh pastures. Each species usually feeds on only one species of plant or tree or on a group of closely related species. Only a small number of lace bugs occur in North America. The Eastern Hemisphere is much richer in species.

ASSASSIN BUGS AND KISSING BUGS

As their popular names indicate, these insects (family Reduviidae) assassinate and feed largely on other insects. Not only will they attack insects, but, in self-defense, they will bite human beings if carelessly handled or accidentally pinched. Their first act when they bite is to inject into the victim a saliva-like poison which immediately kills an insect and makes a very painful wound in large creatures.

The author can well state that our largest species, *Arilus cristatus*, which ranges throughout a large part of the southern three-fourths of the United States, has a most painful bite. A great many years ago he grasped in his bare hand, to prevent its escape from the net, the first of this species that he had ever collected. This was foolish, for the insect proceeded to give him a vicious jab in the ball of the thumb with its beak. Although the pain was terrific, he held onto the bug, until it could be transferred to a collecting bottle. No bee or wasp sting could ever hurt as much as that bite. The thumb swelled up and was stiff and helpless until the next day, when the pain gradually subsided and the swelling decreased.

Arilus cristatus sometimes reaches a length of one and a half inches. It is a grayish color, with a notched crest along the middle of the thorax, like the comb of a cock. It is sometimes called the wheel bug, probably from its habit of turning round and round as it lays its eggs, each egg standing on end, all side by side, forming a hexagonal or roundish patch.

KISSING BUGS

Another blackish bug that is capable of biting man and causing a painful wound is *Reduvius personatus,* commonly called the kissing bug. It seldom measures over one inch. These bugs frequently come into houses in search of other insects, particularly bedbugs, of which they are quite fond. The young are clothed with sticky spines on which they place the dry bodies of their victims; from this habit come two common names, the old-clothes bug and the masked bedbug hunter.

At about the beginning of the twentieth century, newspapers spread a great scare over the country as they reported person after person being bitten by these bugs during the night. One report had it that the bugs commonly bit ladies on the lips, and this gave rise to the name kissing bug. We hear nothing of these insects any more, for with improved sanitary conditions and improved control measures the bedbug is rapidly being wiped out, and with it its enemy, the kissing bug.

BUGS THAT CARRY DISEASE

Bugs much more to be feared are those of the genus *Triatoma.* The various species range from the southern United States through Mexico and Central America, into northern South America. Not only is their bite painful in itself, but they transmit several severe or dangerous diseases. Probably many so-called "spider bites" are actually given by this insect. Since many of them come into houses and have been found around beds, they have been named the "big bedbug." Their red, black, and gray colors also suggest a resemblance to the bedbug. Outdoors, all of the Reduviidae are on the whole useful bugs because they feed on other insects.

THE BEDBUG—AND HOW TO FIGHT IT

This little, flat, red, wingless bug (family Cimicidae), scarcely a quarter of an inch long, hardly needs describing, for at some time or other it has come to the attention of nearly everyone.

Cimex lectularius is the most widely distributed species, having traveled with man wherever he has gone. Another species, *Cimex rotundatus,* occurs in the tropics, particularly central Africa. There are about thirty other species in this family, all parasitic on birds and bats.

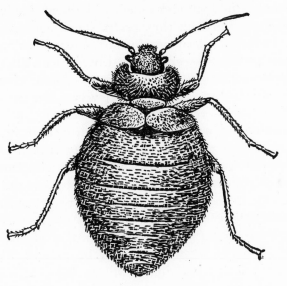

AN UNWELCOME GUEST
Improved habits of cleanliness have made the ugly, flattish, reddish bedbug less common than it used to be. The bedbug has no wings, and its mouth is a beak through which it sucks human blood. No newcomer, the creature has been bothering man since prehistoric times, and has hitchhiked with him wherever he has gone.

The continuous warm temperatures that man maintains in his homes allows the bedbug to be active throughout the year. In fact, it is quite dependent upon man-made housing, for it is not found outdoors. Reports that bedbugs have been found around firewood or lumber, under bark, and on bats probably result from the mistaken identification of other insects as bedbugs.

Liberal use of kerosene in the cracks or crannies, repeated at intervals about a home, will usually rid the place of these pests. The powerful insecticide DDT, either as dry powder or in a spray, has done wonders in reducing bedbug infestation.

WATER STRIDERS

One, and usually more, of these long-legged, feather-footed bugs are likely to be found on any body of water, large or small. They are, however, particularly fond of little pools along a woodland stream overhung with leafy branches.

Where the sun filters through, making spots of gold, here the pond-skaters, as they are also called, will collect in numbers. Their feet, densely covered with tiny, feathery hairs, never get wet. Like greased needles, they float on the surface film as they glide along, chasing each other or seeking any tiny insect that may fall into the water.

So light are the little creatures that they never break the surface film, only dimple it, even though they sometimes leap several inches into the air. These dimples are so slight as to be scarcely visible except for the shadow they cast upon the bottom of the pool. As seen from below, the insect appears to be resting with each foot of the second and third pair of legs in the center of a large disk. The front legs do not touch the water, but are held ready to seize any insect small enough for them to hold.

The water striders (family Gerridae) make fascinating aquarium inhabitants, but the aquarium should be covered with screening; otherwise, the winged individuals will fly away. An interesting fact is that in the adults of many species there are both wingless and winged specimens. While some are free to go wandering off in search of new waters, the other, wingless, ones have to remain where they grew up. If you wish to bring home water striders for your aquarium, do not carry them in a bucket of water, for the little creatures will be drowned in the splashing water. They will travel happily if placed in wet moss.

WATER STRIDERS THAT GO TO SEA

There are not many species of water striders in the United States, and most of them look pretty much alike and have the same general habits. One group is worthy of mention, however. This consists of the few species that are sea-going and live far from land. The most common of these belong to the genus *Halobates*. The author first saw them a number of years ago while on the Pacific Ocean, about seven hundred miles off the Mexican coast. The ship had just passed through a terrific storm in which the seas had been running mountain-high. It was calm, and the ship was at rest while repairs were being made. Over the side, hundreds of one of these species of

Halobates could be seen, gliding about on the surface. It seemed incredible that these curious little creatures, living on the open seas so far from land, could manage to ride atop the heavy waves and withstand the extreme weather conditions.

TOAD BUGS—THEY LOOK AND HOP LIKE TOADS

You will see these toadlike bugs on muddy, or wet, sandy beaches, or along the ruts of a wet country lane. Only a quarter of an inch or less in length, they are nearly as broad as long, with their backs roughened, very much like the warty backs of toads. They have two bulging, toadlike eyes. Not only do these little bugs look like small toads, but they hop like toads as they search for their prey, which consists of tiny flies or other small insects. They pounce on their prey and seize it in their tonglike front legs.

They are so agile as to be very difficult to capture. The easiest method is to place a hand, palm down, on top of them, and with the other hand reach under and pick them out of the mud.

Very little is known of their life habits. One species in the United States deposits its eggs in small burrows made by the mother in the wet sand; other species probably have similar habits. The adults, when not hunting, retreat to small burrows, which they can dig very quickly. Only a little over a hundred species are known, most of these in the Western Hemisphere, although this number should be greatly increased when the insects of the tropics have been thoroughly collected and catalogued. The family name Gelastocoridae comes from two Greek words, one meaning "laughable," the other "bug," and well do the animals of this family live up to their name.

CREEPING WATER BUGS

The creeping water bugs look very much like the toad bugs, but they lack the large, bulging eyes. Their habits are also quite different. Instead of living on the wet banks of ponds or streams, these bugs live in stagnant water, especially water filled with algae, or with other aquatic vegetation.

They are small bugs, never over half an inch long, and usually greenish yellow in color. The broad head is inserted so far into the thorax that the eyes just escape being covered. As in the toad bugs, the front legs are equipped to seize and hold their prey, while the middle and hind pairs are more slender and enable the insect to crawl or swim about the vegetation.

Since they live in the water, the creeping water bugs, members of the Naucoridae family, like most other water insects carry a supply of air in their "tanks," the space under their wing covers. When this is exhausted, they must then come to the surface for a fresh supply, which they obtain by pushing the tip of the abdomen up through the surface film.

The family is a small one, many of the species residing in the warmer regions. To date it has been neglected by students. When more extensive research has been made, we shall undoubtedly find many more species and know much more of their life histories.

WATER STRIDER, BACK SWIMMER, AND WATER SCORPION

Here are three of the true bugs that spend a large part of their lives in or on the water. The water strider (*top*) scoots on four legs across the surface of ponds and quiet streams; it uses its front legs to seize its prey. The back swimmer (*right*) is built like a boat, and travels upside down, using its hind legs as oars. Note the long, slender "tail" of the water scorpion (*left*) sticking up through the water. This is really a breathing tube, carrying air down to the submerged insect.

WATER SCORPIONS

A long respiratory tube extending from the end of the body at once distinguishes the water scorpions, members of the Nepidae family, from all other Hemiptera. This tube also gives them the name water scorpion, because it gives them a slight resemblance to the real scorpions. The breathing tube looks like an enormous stinger, but, actually, it is with their beaks that the water scorpions inflict death upon any insect or other small creatures that comes within reach of their tonglike front legs. They kill their victims by injecting a saliva-like poison; then they quietly settle down to drain out the victims' life blood.

The water scorpions are not active creatures. They may rest in one spot for hours, clinging to some submerged object, with only the tip of the breathing tube protruding above the water. When they do swim they make an awkward job of it. An up-and-down stroke of the front legs, and a wild kicking of the middle and hind legs propel them along an erratic course.

About two hundred known species are widely distributed throughout the temperate and tropical regions. Of the easily recognized genera, *Nepa* is fairly broad and flat, while *Ranatra* is more slender and cylindrical.

GIANT WATER BUGS

Of the many names given these insects, giant water bug is the most descriptive, for species living in the tropics sometimes reach a length of five to six inches. Here, in the United States, the largest is seldom over three and a half inches. The larger species belong to the genera *Lethocerus* and *Benacus*. The genus *Belostoma* has species which are usually shorter and broader than these.

On quiet nights the adults frequently leave the ponds in which they have been living and fly off in search of other waterways. Some of them, mistaking a shimmering greenhouse for a quiet pool, come plummeting down to kill themselves on the glass. Others are attracted to street lights, particularly those located near water, where they may collect in numbers. This has earned them the name of electric-light bugs. When one of them, attracted by a light, flies in an open window of some waterside cottage, it usually creates consternation among the rightful occupants by its mad threshing about against the walls and ceilings.

BITERS AND KILLERS

Toe biter is another appropriate name for these creatures, as many bathers can testify, for the giant water bugs love to lie half buried in the mud, ready to grab any creature that may wander near. On human beings, they can inflict a very painful, but not fatal, wound. However, when one of these water bugs seizes another insect or even a fish, it jabs the captive again and again with its beak, while holding on with its powerful front legs. The more the victim struggles, the tighter the front legs close, for their action is very much like that of a pair of ice tongs.

IT INFLICTS A PAINFUL WOUND
The giant water bug is one of the largest of the true bugs—it reaches a length of three and one-half inches in the United States and five inches in the tropics. Dark, mud-colored creatures, the water bugs have strong wings, and at night are likely to leave their pond in swarms and fly to the nearest bright lights. In the pond they live in the mud, where they grab at any human toes that come near them; their preference, however, is for frogs and fish. Note the bug's flattened, hairy legs—they make swimming easier.

Fishes up to five inches long can be killed by one of these three-inch bugs. A number of them in fish-hatchery pools can do considerable damage, making serious pests of themselves. Because of their fondness for fish, they have been called fish killers.

THE MALE CARRIES THE EGGS

The giant water bugs, members of the Belostomatidae family, are active creatures, propelling themselves through the water with strong strokes of their powerful second and third pairs of legs. These legs are flattened, and feathered along the edges with short, stiff hairs; they make very efficient oars. The bugs come to the surface at intervals of thirty to sixty minutes for a fresh supply of air, which is carried in the space over the abdomen and under the wings. In order to take on this stock of air, the tip of the abdomen is stuck up above the water surface. When resting quietly, the insect will remain submerged for longer periods.

In some species, particularly of the genus *Belostoma,* the female deposits her eggs on the back of the male. He carries these around with him until they are all hatched, when the little ones go off to shift for themselves. This care of the eggs is the extent of their parental duties.

In South America and in the East Indies, many of the natives eat the larger species of the Belostomatidae. The tough legs and wings are discarded, and the rest eaten either raw or toasted.

THE BACK SWIMMER—BUILT LIKE A BOAT

The back swimmer is the only water-dwelling Hemiptera that habitually swims upside down. Built like a boat, with the hind pair of legs much elongated, broadened, and feathered with short, stiff hairs, it dashes through the water at a great rate. The back swimmer (family Notonectidae) is a hunter, eager to capture any small creature that it can overcome with its poison beak while holding it with its thin front legs. It likes to cruise near the surface while it hunts for an insect that has fallen into the water. Pausing at intervals, it sticks its abdomen above the water and takes in more air, which it stores in two "tanks," each one consisting of a groove covered with hair and running along each side of the abdomen.

Most insects are darker colored on the back than underneath. Since the back swimmers live upside down, the general coloring is reversed. The back is light in color, frequently almost white, which makes the bug scarcely visible to any creature that might be below and looking toward the light sky. For the same reason, the underside is greenish or brownish, making the insect less visible to any creature looking down toward the darker background of the bottom of the pond.

BACK SWIMMERS DO WELL IN AQUARIUMS

The back swimmers make nice aquarium pets and will quickly learn to take a fly held in the fingers at the water surface. Tiny pieces of raw meat placed on the surface will be accepted as soon as the back swimmers learn that these are good to eat. Since the meat does not move as an insect does, it may be ignored. However, a piece held in fine forceps and gently wiggled will induce an immediate attack. Keep your aquarium screened, otherwise, the back swimmers will spring into the air ready to fly to some neighboring pond, and will be lost in the unnatural environment of a house. In handling your pets with your forefingers, be careful that you give them no opportunity to bite; for they can inflict a painful, though not fatal, jab.

THE WATER BOATMAN

The water boatman (family Corixidae) is much smaller than the back swimmer, and lacks the latter's long hind legs; in the water boatman, both the middle and hind pair of legs are fitted for swimming. It usually stays near the bottom. Since it is heavier than water, it has to swim up to the surface. Here, the surface tension holds it in place while it basks in the sunshine and absorbs air.

The corixids make nice additions to your insect aquarium. You may even be fortunate enough to hear the chirping, cricket-like noise made by some of them. They produce this sound by rubbing their beaks with their front legs, usually at night.

They lay their eggs on the surface of water plants or submerged objects. One species is common in the lake region near Mexico City, and around the "floating gardens" of the region. The many eggs the insects produce are collected by the natives and dried for food. They are then served in several ways. Toasting is perhaps the favorite method, but they are frequently added to soups or prepared as a dressing for meat.

Parasites on Birds and Domestic Animals — The Bird, or Biting, Lice

Considering the common attitude toward insects as mostly pests or "vermin," it is interesting to note how few of them really are parasitic. Among those few are the two orders we are now going to have a look at, the biting lice, or Mallophaga, and the sucking lice, or Anoplura.

Everyone has heard about lice, although in this age of sanitation very few have ever seen them. They are, however, well worth examining under a low-power microscope. Mallophaga (meaning "wool eaters") are often called "bird lice," but since several species feed upon mammals, it is better to call them "biting" lice to distinguish them from the following order, the "sucking" lice.

LICE HAVE LOST THEIR WINGS

The species of the biting order are all small, rarely reaching a quarter of an inch in length. Their bodies are flattened, heads broad and triangular, antennae short. They are quite hairy and range in color from whitish through yellow, brown, and reddish, to black. Although the Mallophaga are wingless, they have rather completely organized little bodies, whereas most other wingless insects, like the bristletails and springtails, have very primitive bodies. Entomologists believe that lice have lost their wings because of their parasitic habits. Eggs of many of the species look like anything except an egg; they resemble flowers, stars, and feathered arrows.

1827

TO EACH HIS OWN

Most of the biting lice live on birds, feeding on their feathers and skin. Others live on animals feeding on hair and wool. Practically every bird or warm-blooded animal is host to one or more species of louse. But each species of louse is usually restricted to one species, or closely associated species, of host. So we have the Chicken Louse, the Pigeon Louse, the White Swan Louse, the Turkey Louse, the Biting Dog Louse (*biting* here and in the next two cases referring to the louse and not the host), the Biting Cat Louse, the Biting Cattle Louse, and so on through some 2,500 known species. None of the biting lice attack man, except temporarily, when some migrant from a domestic animal alights on a human being and takes an experimental bite. Many louse species are of world-wide distribution, having traveled across continents on their hosts.

Damage done by biting lice is serious but not devastating. Every poultry farmer knows that his hens are weakened by the constant irritation caused by lice. Sheep Lice decrease the quality and length

BITING LICE AND BOOK LICE LIKE THEIR FOOD DRY

In contrast to the true louse that sucks blood, the biting louse (*left*) chews on the fur, feathers, or skin of its victim. (Each different kind of louse feeds on a different kind of bird or animal; there are chicken lice and turkey lice, biting sheep lice, dog lice, cat lice, etc.) This order of lice does not attack man except temporarily, when fallen from its true host. The book louse (*right*) does not belong to the bird louse order, although it is also wingless. It feeds on paste in books, on flour and prepared cereals.

of wool fibers. Modern sanitary farm and control measures have considerably lessened the incidence of the biting lice in domestic animals.

Man's Parasites—The Sucking or True Lice

THE SUCKING LICE are, on the average, rather smaller than the biting lice; the largest is only about seven millimeters long. The sucking louse (order Anoplura—"unarmed tail") is dirty white or yellowish white and slender or oval in shape, except for one family which is crab-shaped. Its head is small, with mouth parts built for piercing and sucking. Many species have no eyes; in others, the eyes are much reduced. The legs are short and stout, and end in claws especially constructed for grasping hairs. In contrast to the biting lice, the sucking kind lay simple, oval, or elongated, eggs. These are cemented to the base of the hair or wool of the host.

THEY ATTACK JUST FOUR KINDS OF MAMMALS

Only about five hundred species are known, but they enjoy a worldwide distribution. Their hosts are limited, for the most part, to just four orders of mammals: the primates, namely, man, monkeys, and apes; the hoofed mammals, domestic and wild, including horses, cattle, sheep, deer, etc.; the rodents, consisting of rabbits, mice, rats, and squirrels; a few of the carnivores, or flesh-eating animals, including dogs, wolves, coyotes, seals, and walruses. Curiously enough, the cat family (cats, tigers, and lions) is immune to these pests, as are some other large groups, such as the kangaroos and opossums, the sloths, anteaters and armadillos, the moles, and the bats.

Unfortunately, mankind enjoys no such immunity. Modern plumbing and our resulting sanitary habits have eliminated human lice from civilized homes, but they still persist in many parts of the world, and each generation of our soldiers has to fight the six-legged "cooties," as well as two-legged human foes.

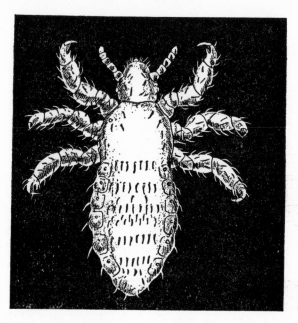

THE "COOTIE" IS A TRUE LOUSE
True lice have mouth parts built for sucking, and feed only on mammals. Some animals are immune to these pests—the cat family, the kangaroo and opossum family, bats, and some others—but not man. Fortunately, modern plumbing and ideals of cleanliness have pretty well destroyed the human louse in more advanced countries.

Two or three species of lice are recognized as parasitic upon man. The most common of these is the Head Louse, *Pediculus capitis.* Another, not so common, is the Body, or Clothes, Louse, *Pediculus vestimenti,* also called the grayback. Some recent entomologists have considered these as just one species, and have returned them to the old Linnaean term, *Pediculus humanus.* Whether they are one or two species, they have long been a terrible scourge to man, transmitting the germs of the deadly typhus fever, trench fever, and relapsing fever from one victim to another. The least common, the Crab Louse, *Phthirus inguinalis,* infests the pubic region and the armpits.

Most of the species that infest domestic mammals belong to one large family, the Haematopinidae. About 150 species are known; most of them are cosmopolitan in range. The use of DDT is liberating both man and beast from the louse.

The Thrips—Lovers of the Flowers

Look closely into almost any flower and you are sure to find one or several tiny, slender insects. These will probably prove to be thrips, members of a small order of insects which look much alike, but which show great variation in their habits. They love to gather in the deep recesses of bell-shaped flowers, but you should find plenty of them on daisy-shaped flowers, where it will be easier for you to observe them in action under a hand lens or even under a reading glass.

The first characteristic that you will notice in the thrips is their four wings, which look like so many tiny feathers. Under a higher-powered microscope you can see that the wings themselves are extremely narrow but are edged with a wide fringe of hairs. The name of the order, Thysanoptera, means "tassel wings."

Most of the adult thrips that you see on flowers have wings, but there are many species that are wingless, and, of course, none of the young have wings. All North American thrips are quite small, about one-twenty-fifth to one tenth of an inch in length. Tropical species are larger, and there is an Australian giant that reaches a size of more than half an inch. Thrips range in color from yellow through brown to black; the black ones are often miscalled "black flies." Many thrips carry a curious bladder-like structure at the end of their feet, or tarsi, which enables them to stick to smooth surfaces. The mouth parts of the thrip are built for piercing and sucking and are developed on the left side of the head only.

Some species are bisexual, and in some species the males are rare or absent, the eggs developing without fertilization. This method is called "parthenogénesis." Usually, the female lays eggs in the tissues of some plant or flower, or elsewhere near a food supply. However, several species give birth to living young.

The life span varies according to species, from two or three months to as long as a year. In the Pear Thrips, which is of the type that lives for a year, most of the insect's life is spent in the egg and immature stages. The adult comes forth at fruit-blossom time, lives and deposits its eggs in the flowers, and dies when the petals drop.

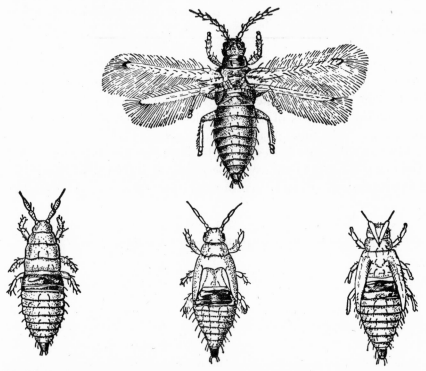

THRIPS—MANY ARE TROUBLEMAKERS

Look in the bottom of almost any flower and you will probably see one or more tiny live specks. One of these, examined under a microscope, will look somewhat like the insects in this illustration. Note that the wings are like little feathers, but not all thrips have wings. Some thrips feed on aphids, mites, and the eggs of other insects; some of them feed on farm crops, where they can do great damage. Lower figures are young forms.

THEY SETTLE LIKE LIVE SAND

Unfortunately, these tiny insects lead their interesting lives mostly on man's choicest cultivated plants. There are Greenhouse Thrips,

Onion Thrips, Gladiolus Thrips, Wheat Thrips, Carnation Thrips, and many others, which damage crops in several different ways. Feeding on leaves, they injure plants; feeding in blossoms, they prevent fruit from forming. They spread several different bacterial and fungus-plant diseases, particularly the tomato wilt. Both the grain and the onion, or tobacco, thrips tend to swarm on hot summer days, not only injuring the crops, but settling like live sand on everything and everybody. When they alight on human skin they are quite likely to bite it, apparently searching for moisture rather than blood; and while the bite of one thrip is insignificant the mass attack of several dozen can be quite disconcerting.

At least a few more of the many contradictions or variations in the thrips' way of life need listing. Not all thrips live on flowers and leaves. Some species feed on decaying vegetable matter, some on fungi; some live under bark. Some disdain vegetarianism and prey upon mites, aphids, other thrips, and on the eggs and young of larger insects.

They inhabit all regions of the earth except the very cold places. About 2,500 species have been described; doubtless there are just as many more that are still unknown to us.

Ancient Pests—Book Lice and Bark Lice

WHEN YOU RUMMAGE among old books or magazines, especially when they have been stored in a dampish place, you are almost certain to see one or more pale, fat-bodied little insects running for cover. These are the book lice, members of order Corrodentia. They have to run because they have no wings with which to fly. Two species, *Troctes divinatorius* and *Atropos pulsatoria*, belonging to the family Atropidae, are the ones commonly associated with man and his libraries, his museums, and sometimes his granaries and warehouses. They feed on glue, paste, fungi, and some other dried animal and vegetable materials.

Since the beginning of recorded history they have lived with us in the same form that we now know them. Were they also associated with primitive man? If so, what did they feed on? How long ago did they lose their wings? Interesting questions for which, as yet, we have no answers.

The other members of this order, belonging to the family Psocidae, all have wings. They live outdoors, usually on the bark of trees, and are believed to feed on mosses and minute fungi. They tend to stay in groups, each batch covered with a very fine silken net which they spin with their mouths. This net is of considerable value in protecting them from some of their enemies. Some forty species have been described from North America, while 650 species are known to exist in the world, and undoubtedly many new ones await discovery.

Scorpion Flies and Snow Flies — Insect Curiosities

Scorpion Flies. In shady spots along a sluggish stream, or deep in swampy woods, you will occasionally see what looks like an unusual crane fly resting on a broad leaf or fern. It will not be too difficult to capture, and when you can examine it in your hand you will see that it has four long, narrow, gauzy wings (instead of the crane fly's two), very long antennae, and a larger head than that of the crane fly. If your captive is a male, it will have at the end of its abdomen a pair of claws which it carries curved over its back, much as a scorpion carries its stinger. The scorpion fly's claws are not stingers, and this fly can hurt nothing except the smaller insects which it sometimes eats. It also sips nectar and the juices of decaying berries.

The larvae, which look like caterpillars, burrow in the ground, coming up to the surface to feed on small insects. They pupate in the ground, in the burrows they have dug. The pupae move up to the surface just before they are ready to emerge as adults.

Scorpion flies belong to the families Panorpidae and Bittacidae and some others. There are not many species. The most common in North American woods is *Panorpa nebulosa,* and in England, *communis.* All are members of the order Mecoptera.

Snow Flies. On a sunny winter day, you may see small black insects hopping about on the snow. They have the long antennae and long legs of the scorpion flies, but they do not have a clawed abdominal appendage, and in place of the scorpion fly's lacy wings, the males carry a pair of finely toothed spines, and the females a tiny pair of scalelike lobes. These are the snow flies, genus *Boreus,* and family Boreidae. They spend their harmless lives on the forest floor, living on dead vegetation, and possibly on springtails, which also hop around on sunny snow. Like the springtails, the snow flies are practically invisible except against the white background of the snow. Their larvae feed and pupate in much the same manner as those of the scorpion flies.

Not many species have been described. They range in North America from Alaska to as far south as Washington, D. C.

The Caddis Flies — Builders of Houses

IF YOU WISH to observe Nature at her best, an excellent method is to seat yourself in a peaceful place and quietly await what may happen. There is no better spot on a warm summer day than the bank of a woodland pool. Gazing into its depths, your eyes pick out a variety of objects. Last year's leaves in various stages of decay litter the bottom; fine twigs and pieces of weeds are scattered about.

As you watch abstractedly, your mind records a movement. You concentrate on this spot of activity until you make out what appears to be a tiny cylinder of leaf particles slowly moving along the bottom. What makes it move? As you wonder you discover a shining spot at one end of the cylinder. This shining spot is the head of a larva, with six tiny legs set close behind, all that is visible of a representative of one of the most interesting of the insect orders. The soft and succulent body of the caddis worm (the usual term for the caddis-fly larva) is safely protected in a snug home it has built of leaf fragments fastened together with its own spun silk.

CADDIS FLIES SPEND THEIR EARLY LIFE UNDER WATER
The immature caddis fly is soft and wormlike, and it builds around itself a house of pieces of leaves or tiny sticks or grains of sand (each different species constructs a different kind of covering). It changes to a pupa in the larval case. When it has come of age, the pupa swims to the surface and instantly the adult breaks out, ready to fly away. Now it looks like a hairy moth; the name "water moth" is often applied to it.

In the same pool, you will soon pick out other species of caddis-fly larvae, each identifiable by the type of house it builds. Some are lazy and simply cut off a hollow weed stem, into which the body snugly fits. When the creature outgrows its quarters, it moves to a slightly larger piece. All it adds to its prefabricated dwelling is a silken lining on the inside walls.

Another species selects minute pieces of weeds; that is, they are minute to us, but to the insect they must appear like giant logs. Members of this species carefully fasten the weed pieces together into a cylindrical home. When they need more room, they simply slit open one side and insert a new log.

Still another species likes to crisscross its logs, building up a turret-shaped home. One wonders how the larva is able to drag this cumbersome house about; the ends of the logs stick out in all directions, catching on every obstacle. These are but a few examples. In all quiet, somewhat muddy, debris-strewn pools, many kinds of caddis-worm houses are dragging along their muddy paths.

BUILDING HOUSES WITH SNAILS

Then there are stone masons among the caddis flies. To find these, we shall have to go to a sandy or gravelly pool. Here your eye, now trained to detect caddis-worm houses, will find a dozen styles to attract your attention. Some creatures have built simple, hollow cylinders of very fine grains of sand. Others use small gravel, which to them must represent huge boulders. As they build, the caddis worms may pick up minute snail shells, apparently mistaking them for gravel, and fit them into their stone houses.

Often enough the snail is still living in its shell, but off it goes, willy-nilly, as part of the caddis-worm castle. The snail reaches out for food or foothold but is usually too small to succeed. Given a big enough snail, however, and an opportunity for it to take hold of some substantial object, a true tug-of-war ensues. Sometimes the snail wins, and the caddis worm must find another nugget to fill the gap in its wall.

THE MASTER ARCHITECTS

The final achievement in architectural design is reached by one species which, using fine sand grains and silk, builds a house in the exact shape of a snail shell. So perfect is the imitation that it has even bewildered experienced shell collectors. Paleontologists, the scientists who deal with the life of earlier geological eras, have also been puzzled, for one of these cases without its owner might well be mistaken for a fossil shell.

The food of these larvae consists of minute insects, algae, and water vegetation. Each species seems to restrict its diet to certain types of food.

SOME REMARKABLE LARVAE

Before we leave the caddis-fly larvae we must try to discover a few of their more specialized forms. To do this, we shall have to find a rapidly flowing stream, with the water dashing over the rocks or a waterfall leaping over ledge after ledge of rocky outcrops. Here we shall find the fishermen of the group. In the swiftest water, they spin a silken net. Not a large web, for it would be torn away, but a small web that is seldom larger than a quarter. Some species make flattish webs, but most of them are cup-shaped; a few are elongated into a funnel. In the web, the larvae lie in wait for what the water may wash into their traps.

WHEN THE CADDIS FLY COMES OF AGE

But what of the adult, which soon must become an aerial creature?

When the larva is fully grown it closes itself in its case, or web, with a few silken threads. In a short while it turns into a pupa. At the right time, the pupa leaves its case and swims or crawls to the surface. Here, it molts, emerging as a fully winged caddis fly.

The caddis fly is a mothlike creature, covered with hairs, and mottled in patterns of brown or gray, with very long, slender, segmented antennae. The antennae are usually as long, and frequently two or three times as long, as the body. The legs are long, and the insects make ready use of them by darting rapidly here and there when not in flight.

Most of the species fly readily, although in a few the females are nearly wingless, and in others the rear pair of wings is greatly reduced in size. Although individuals do fly in the daytime, it is toward dusk or after darkness has set in, on still, warm spring or summer evenings, that they begin their wedding dance in numbers over the quiet waters. At this time, when bright lights divert them from their dance, we are more likely to see them as they come to the windows of our houses.

ANCESTORS OF THE MOTHS AND BUTTERFLIES

Over 3,600 species of the Trichoptera, the order to which these creatures belong, have been described throughout the world; undoubtedly many new ones, from little-known areas, are yet to be discovered. They have many common names such as caddises, caseflies, caddis flies, and water moths. This last name refers to their mothlike appearance. With the discovery of several fossil species, the order has proved to be an ancient one. It is generally thought that moths and butterflies are an offshoot of this ancient group.

AN AID IN FISHING

The caddis flies and their larvae have long been used for bait by fresh-water fishermen. Many of the artificial lures have been modeled after the adults. The country boy, however, gets the most use from the caddis worms. He collects the cases, which he can keep for several days, and then has a supply of excellent bait at hand. When he is ready for fishing, the larva is extracted from the case to adorn his hook, or even his bent pin.

Beetles—Most Numerous of the Insects

THERE ARE more beetles in the world than any other kind of insect. Over a quarter of a million beetle species (order Coleoptera) have been described, and new ones are still coming to notice. New species are probably not being found at the same rate as in some of the other orders, however, because beetles have been studied and collected more widely than most other insects. Two reasons are responsible for this interest in beetles. The collector finds them beautiful or odd, more durable than moths and butterflies, easy to collect and keep in good condition. The economic entomologist studies the habits and histories of the many beetles that are constantly taking over something that man has called his own.

HOW TO RECOGNIZE THE BEETLES

You can always recognize a beetle by the first pair of wings, which are hard, sheathlike coverings curving over its folded second pair of membranous wings and abdomen like a shield. In fact, the name of the order means "sheathed wings." Earwigs and some grasshoppers have wing covers, but do not in the least resemble the beetles, although their wing covers are a modification of the front wings, as in the beetles. Beetle wing covers are called elytra.

The hind wings are large and thin, as they must be to carry the large, heavy body of a beetle, and yet they fold compactly under the wing covers. Of course, in so large an order you can expect to find plenty of exceptions. A few species of beetles are wingless. In one of the largest families, the elytra are very short and cover only a part of the abdomen.

In every other characteristic, the beetles show great variation. In size, they range from a fungus beetle a hundredth of an inch long to the great six-inch Hercules Beetle of the genus *Dynastes*. You will find almost every kind of antennae in this order, some long and slender, others clubbed on the end, some consisting of thin layers, and others elbowed. Male beetles of some species have jaws, or mandibles, so enormously enlarged that they form pinchers. In some other species, they have large, hornlike formations on the head or thorax. Except for some blind cave-dwelling and parasitic species, beetles have large, round, or oblong, well-developed eyes.

WHERE BEETLES LIVE

Beetles live all over the world, except in the oceans and at the poles. They are mostly land dwellers, but some live in fresh water. They feed on every kind of animal and plant life, living or dead. Many species are in constant conflict with man, because there are few of the organic commodities that man has learned to use that do not also interest some beetle. All our vegetable food, natural or proc- essed; all our prepared meats, fats, leathers, furs, and feathers; our cotton, wool, and silk; our lumber and the trees we grow for any purpose; and our flowering plants and shrubs are just as desirable to some beetle or other as they are to us.

The larvae of beetles are often very large. Like fly larvae, they are commonly called "grubs." In some tropical countries, certain beetle larvae are a staple food. One that spends its life in the thick flesh of century-plant leaves, makes an excellent salad, tasting some- thing like shrimp salad.

THE VARIOUS KINDS OF BEETLES

Much work must still be done before the problems of classifying members of this order have been solved to the satisfaction of all. But the following rough grouping of all the beetle families into very large divisions shows the general relationship of each to the other. Only a few of the many families in each group can be discussed here, and only those few are named in this grouping. The arrangement is based on easily determined adult characteristics, and will assist you in making preliminary identifications.

Adephaga. The feet, or tarsi, have five distinct segments; the an- tennae are threadlike (except in the Gyrinidae). The group com- prises the families Cicindelidae, Carabidae, Dytiscidae, and Gyrin- idae.

Clavicornia. The segments of the tarsi are variable in number; the antennae are equipped with a more or less distinct club (the terminal segments being broader than the others). The group com- prises the families Hydrophilidae, Silphidae, Staphylinidae, Niti- dulidae, Histeridae, Coccinellidae, Endomychidae, Erotylidae, Langu- riidae, and Dermestidae.

Serricornia. The segments of the tarsi are variable in number; the third and following segments of the antennae are more or less saw- like. The group comprises the families Elateridae, Buprestidae, and Lampyridae.

Heteromera. The front and middle tarsi are composed of five seg- ments, the hind tarsi of four segments; other characteristics are variable. The group comprises the families Tenebrionidae and Mordellidae.

Lamellicornia. The tarsi have five segments; the antennae are leaf-like, with three or more terminal segments. The group comprises the families Lucanidae, Passalidae and Scarabaeidae.

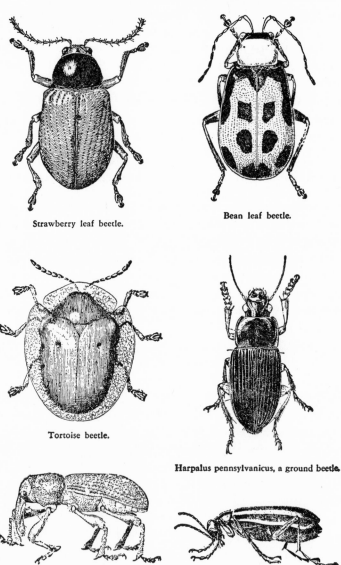

Strawberry leaf beetle.

Bean leaf beetle.

Tortoise beetle.

Harpalus pennsylvanicus, a ground beetle.

Pales weevil.

Striped blister beetle.

Phytophaga. The tarsi are apparently in four segments but actually in five (the fourth being quite small and barely visible); the third segment is grooved to receive the fourth and fifth; usually the three basal segments are densely hairy on the underside. The group comprises the families Cerambycidae and Chrysomelidae.

Rhynchophora. The head is usually more or less prolonged in front to form a snout or beak; the tarsi are apparently in four segments; the third segment is usually broad and hairy on the underside. The group comprises the families Brentidae, Anthribidae, Curculionidae, and Scolytidae.

The literature on beetles is enormous. Every textbook on insects must necessarily devote a large proportion of its pages to this important order.

TIGER BEETLES—BURROWERS AND EATERS OF FLESH

While walking along a sandy beach some sunny day, you may be surprised by suddenly flushing from the sand in front of you a long, slender-legged beetle. It will rise, fly twenty or thirty feet away, and settle, facing you. If you approach stealthily, you may succeed in getting near enough to see the large eyes, the long, slender antennae, and the sharp-toothed mandibles with which it seizes its prey, for the tiger beetle is a hunter.

The larva of the tiger beetle is also a flesh eater. Instead of running down its victims as the adult does, it resorts to stratagem. It rests at the mouth of a burrow it has dug in the ground, ready to seize any passing insect that ventures close enough.

If the intended victim looks too dangerous, the tiger-beetle larva can quickly withdraw into the burrow. Sometimes, however, it may misjudge and actually take hold of an insect that is almost too strong for it. This might be disastrous for the tiger-beetle larva, except that it is provided with a pair of hooks atop a hump on the back of the fifth abdominal segment. These hooks are recurved; in other words, they bend back and dig into the wall of the burrow, making a very effective anchor.

More than two thousand species of tiger beetles (family Cicindelidae) have been recorded. Nearly two hundred of these are found in North America, where they range well into Canada. Dr. Mont A. Cazier, an authority on the tiger beetles, has amassed in the collections of the American Museum of Natural History thousands of these insects, and the museum now has one of the finest collections of tiger beetles in the world.

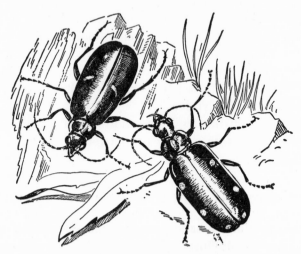

TIGER BEETLES—FIERCE HUNTERS OF OTHER INSECTS
Tiger beetles have slender bodies and long legs, and most of them spend their lives on the ground. Extremely speedy, they are probably the most difficult to catch of all the beetles. The green tiger beetle shown at the right, which is brilliant green in color with white spots, is very common on sunny woodland paths; next to it is the purple tiger beetle, which favors more open land. Tiger beetle larvae are fierce, frightful-looking creatures.

SOME WELL-KNOWN TIGER BEETLES

The genus *Cicindela* is the largest, with nearly one hundred species and numerous subspecies to its credit in North America. They vary in length from three-eighths of an inch to not more than three-quarters of an inch. Many are brightly colored; others are prettily marked with spots or curving lines.

Cicindela repanda is a common and widely distributed species found along the sandy margins of lakes or streams. Its gray-brown color is decorated with small, but distinct, whitish lines on the wing covers. This species is frequently found associated with *Cicindela generosa,* one of the larger species. The white markings in *generosa* are much more distinct, but quite similar in arrangement to those in *repanda.*

Cicindela dorsalis, a large, cream-colored tiger beetle, loves the white sands of the beaches along the Atlantic Ocean. The typical form ranges from Massachusetts to southern New Jersey. South of this area and along the Gulf states, other subspecies are found. The cream-colored wings blend well with the white sands. The wings are usually decorated with darker lines or markings which also help in the protective coloration pattern.

Cicindela lepida, a small, nearly white beetle, is at home only on the finest white sand of the shifting dunes. It is found, and rather rarely nowadays, in New York and New Jersey, and in Ohio and other states along the Great Lakes, and in Iowa and Kansas, wherever the right conditions prevail. This attractive beetle is becoming extinct as human beings invade or destroy the dunes where it lives.

The Six-spotted Green Tiger Beetle, *Cicindela sexguttata,* can be found in the spring along almost any forest pathway in the eastern United States, from Canada southward. Its shining green stands out conspicuously as it suns itself on the bare ground of the path. It is not asleep, however, and knows only too well that a short flight will land it among the surrounding vegetation where it will be safe from prying eyes.

Other Tiger Beetles. A black-brown beetle with a row of very faintly impressed green pits along the suture (the margin where the two wing covers meet) is another common species. Instead of frequenting sandy beaches, *Cicindela punctulata* prefers dry clay soils. It loves to hunt in our gardens along the rows of carrots and beets, and the corn and potatoes. Here also, if you look closely you may find the burrows of the larvae, each with a head and jaws blocking the entrance.

The genus *Tetracha* is represented in the United States by two rather common species, both somewhat southern. *Tetracha virginica* is the most widely distributed. It gets as far north as southern New Jersey and southern Ohio and Indiana. It is a large species nearly one inch long. A gold-green color, it has wing covers that are blackish near the middle, and metallic green along the sides. The underside of the insect is a brownish yellow.

Tetracha carolina is slightly larger and lighter green, with the tip of the wing covers, legs, and antennae yellow. It ranges along the Gulf states.

The *Tetrachas* are night prowlers, spending the day under boards or other shelter. They like sandy country with a few scattered trees. While collecting in Alabama, the author dug holes about a foot deep, using a fence-post digger, and keeping the walls as straight as possible, in order to see what might wander into the pits. Each morning, he would find all manner of creatures, snakes, toads, frogs, scorpions, spiders, and beetles. Of the beetles, both species of *Tetracha* would be present, although no *Cicindelas* ever came to these traps. Ground Beetles (carabids) and Darkling Beetles (tenebrionids) were also present in numbers.

GROUND BEETLES—A GREAT AND REMARKABLE FAMILY

A very large family of swift-running beetles, the ground beetles are usually seen on the ground, when boards or stones are overturned, or running across a pathway, apparently intent only on reaching the other side.

Not all of these beetles remain upon the ground; some of them rest in flowers, feeding upon the pollen and nectar. Others ascend the tallest trees in search of caterpillars. A few take wing at the slightest disturbance, flying almost as well as their relatives, the tiger beetles. Still others try to bury themselves in the ground. Indeed, a number of these have stayed so closely attached to the soil as to have lost their ability to fly, even, in some cases, losing their wings and having wing cases that are firmly joined together.

Most of the species are somber-colored blacks, browns, and grays. A number, however, wear bright yellows, reds, or greens, with the greens predominating. Some are even iridescent blue, brown, and gold, with brilliant reflections. In general, the ground beetles are medium sized, although a few are quite large, and several are very small.

Over 21,000 species have been described and more than two thousand of these make their homes in North America. The family (Carabidae) is widely distributed, ranging from the polar regions to the tropics. The more temperate regions of North America, Europe, and Asia have the greatest concentration of species. They prefer the moist regions, becoming quite scarce in the desert spots.

The Green Caterpillar Hunter, *Calosoma scrutator,* is one of the largest of the Carabidae. It is one and a half inches long. The head and thorax are purplish; the wings are bright green, finely margined with red, and dotted with several rows of golden pits. *Calosoma will-coxi* is quite similar, but much smaller, usually measuring slightly less than one inch. Both of these species climb trees in search of caterpillars, and do a great deal of good by destroying the Spring Canker Worm, the Fall Canker Worm, the Web Worm, and others.

TRYING TO DISCOURAGE A GIANT ATTACKER

A large number of the black or dark brown insects you see running on the ground are carabid beetles. But there are many different kinds, and some live on plants and bushes. Among them are brilliantly colored creatures like the bombardier ground beetle (*left*), which is bright blue, with a red head and thorax. When disturbed, it shoots off a smoke-screen of whitish, stinging gas in an attempt to discourage an intruder, in this instance a large *Carabus* beetle. This strategy is frequently successful.

The Fiery Caterpillar Hunter, *Calosoma calidum,* is about one inch long and black, with three rows of distinct gold or greenish pits on each wing cover. This is a ground-loving *Calosoma,* and you will frequently meet it while you are hoeing or weeding in your garden, where it undoubtedly does a great amount of good by killing cut-worms. This beetle is frequently attracted to lights in houses, star-tling the owners by its size and rapid movements. If you catch it in your fingers, it will eject a slightly caustic and strong-smelling secretion difficult to wash off.

Other Ground Beetles. *Calosoma sycophanta* is an introduced species from Europe. It was brought in because in its native home it feeds upon the Brown-tail Moth's larvae.

Carabus is a genus of large and usually attractively colored ground beetles. In North America, there are about a dozen species, plus numerous subspecies. In Europe and Asia, the genus is much better represented. These beetles may occasionally be seen wandering about in the daytime, although they are more active at night.

Cychrus is a genus of rather large beetles, usually bluish or purplish in color. A long and narrow head and thorax allow the beetle to insert its head into the opening of a snail shell, for the *Cychrus* beetles feed upon the soft bodies of snails.

Pterostichus contains many species of black ground beetles. They range in size from three-eighths of an inch to three-quarters of an inch. All of them seek cover during the daytime under old boards or logs, coming out at night to hunt. The numerous species are determined by the type of grooves and pits on the wing covers. To any but a specialist, they look pretty much alike.

Lebia contains some small, but highly colored, species. Some are bright blue or green. They are usually found in flowers growing in weedy pastures.

Brachinus species look very much like *Lebias* but are slightly larger. They are bright blue, with a reddish head and thorax. The wing covers are truncate (cut off square at the tip). When disturbed, the Bombardier Beetles (as *Brachinus* beetles are called), like a number of other carabids, give off an acrid secretion. The bombardier beetles go one better by releasing it with a distinct pop as a cloud of whitish gas. This so confuses the pursuer that the bombardier quickly makes its escape.

Most of the Carabidae prey on other insects. There are, however, some that are seed or plant eaters. These vegetarians mostly belong to the genera *Harpalus* and *Agonoderus,* and a few other closely related genera.

PREDACEOUS DIVING BEETLES

The larvae of these beetles (family Dytiscidae) are called Water Tigers, a name descriptive not only of the larvae, but equally appropriate for the adults. Both have exceedingly large appetites, preying upon any water life they are able to master. Even very small fish are captured and devoured.

They are oval in outline, flattened, brownish or greenish-black, and frequently marked with indefinite yellow lines. They may be distinguished from all other water beetles by the slender antennae, the long, flattened hind legs, fringed with long hairs, making an excellent pair of oars.

The adults sometimes leave their watery home, normally at night,

WATER BEETLES LIVE IN STREAMS AND PONDS

The diving beetle (*left*) spends most of its time in the water, but sometimes it leaves home at night and flies awkwardly around street lamps or automobile headlights; this insect will devour every creature it can capture. You can see groups of whirligig beetles (*top right*) gyrating at great speed on the surface of quiet pools; when disturbed, they drop to the bottom. The great water scavenger beetle (*bottom right*) hunts for insect larvae, slugs, or small fish, besides eating water plants.

flying off in search of another pond. Sometimes they are attracted from their course by bright street or house lights and come blundering down. On land, they are awkward and almost helpless, pushing themselves about with their big hind legs. In the water they are right at home, swimming easily or diving to the bottom to hide in the water plants. Before diving they take in under their wing covers a supply of air which enables them to remain below for some time.

If you approach a pond carefully, you may see some dytiscid beetles quietly resting with the tip of the abdomen protruding through the surface film. The wing covers are slightly raised, allowing the air to enter and reach the spiracles, or breathing openings.

The dytiscids represent the largest family of water beetles. Over 2,100 species are known, four hundred of them in North America. While the great majority are small to medium in size, some of the dytiscids reach two inches in length. Most of the larger species belong to the genus *Dytiscus*. In China, these larger dytiscids, which are found in the rivers in large numbers, are much used for food, and the collecting and drying of them is a minor industry. They are exported for sale in the Chinese quarters of London, New York, and San Francisco.

WHIRLIGIG BEETLES—SPEEDSTERS OF OUR PONDS AND STREAMS

Everyone who has wandered about our ponds or streams must at some time have seen whirligig beetles gyrating on the surface of the water. They are fond of each other's company, and hundreds of them will gather in a quiet backwater or sheltered spot. Slowly they circle about, in and out.

At the slightest disturbance or approach of danger, the placid group becomes a seething mass, the beetles dashing in interlacing circles. So rapidly do they swim that the water fairly boils with their mad twisting and turning. No eye is quick enough to follow any one beetle. If the danger becomes too acute, they can always dive below the surface for protection in the weeds and debris.

The whirligig beetles are a small family (Gyrinidae) of some five hundred species, with less than fifty of these living in North America. However, some of the species are widely distributed, being almost cosmopolitan. They are easily distinguished from all other beetles by their long front legs, which are slender and fitted for holding their prey while feeding. The second and third pairs of legs, although short, are broadly flattened and fitted for swimming. The beetles themselves are oval, flattened, a greenish or bluish black above, and have a distinct sheen. On the underside they are usually light brown. None of the species are large, three-quarters of an inch being the maximum, while the smallest is about one-quarter of an inch.

Among the most interesting gyrinid characteristics are the divided eyes. Each eye is separated into two parts by the side margin of the head. This is a very convenient arrangement, for one pair watches for enemies above the surface of the water, while the other watches for danger from below.

WATER SCAVENGER BEETLES

The hydrophilids (family Hydrophilidae) make up the third most important family of water beetles. Members of this group resemble the Dytiscidae in their elongated, oval, or elliptical, shape, and their black, or greenish-black, color. Their bodies are, however, slightly more arched in shape, with the second, as well as the third, pair of legs fringed with hairs, and fitted for swimming. Instead of slender antennae, as in the water tigers, they have clubbed antennae. However, the palpi, the segmented pieces attached to the mouth, are long and slender and might be mistaken for antennae, a fact which is somewhat confusing to the beginning insect observer.

The method of swimming used by the hydrophilids is different from that of the dytiscids, for the former use their legs alternately instead of together. This leg motion gives them an erratic course, rather than the straight powerful dive of the dytiscids. In addition to carrying air under the wing covers, they carry a supply clinging to the hairs of the underside. This gives them a silvery appearance from below, perhaps making them less visible to enemies lurking down near the bottom. It is also said that some carry a bubble of air under the head. Perhaps this makes them more buoyant at the head end, a condition which might account for their manner of swimming with the head up.

At one time it was thought that the adult beetles fed entirely upon decaying vegetation. It is now known that some, at least, catch and eat insects, snails, even small fishes, and other small creatures they may meet. The larvae are usually flesh eaters, and when young, frequently devour their companions.

A few of the smaller hydrophilids have left their watery homes for the land. They cannot desert their watery life entirely, so they live in moist earth, decaying vegetation, and the dung of animals.

The family is not a large one, numbering only about 1,800 species, with about two hundred of these living in the region north of Mexico. The largest species measures about two and a half inches, while the smallest may be about the size of a pinhead.

CARRION BEETLES, OR BURYING BEETLES

This interesting family (Silphidae) is not a group made up of very similar members. You will find in it as many different types as you can imagine. The beetles range in size from one-twentieth of an inch to nearly two inches. Some are flat; others are not. Some have five segments in the feet, others, only four. Still others have a combination of four segments in the hind feet, with five in the front and middle feet. Some have excellent eyes, others live in caves and have no eyes at all. Many have clubbed antennae, while others have slender, threadlike antennae. They all agree in leaving at least three segments of the abdomen uncovered by the wing covers. This characteristic is shared with about fifteen other families of beetles, however, and does not aid greatly in identification.

Most of the adults and larvae feed upon decaying flesh, but some feed upon fungi and decaying vegetable matter. A few, just to be different, feed upon beets, spinach, and other garden vegetables. A very few, when they are able, attack and devour snails, insects, and even their own brothers and sisters. Some have become very lazy, and have found living in ant nests a convenient life. They probably are tolerated by the ants because of the good they do in cleaning up waste material in the nest.

HOW CARRION BEETLES DO THEIR WORK

When an animal dies the silphids seem to know it very quickly, for they soon begin to arrive from several directions. They circle in ever-narrowing rings, with clubbed antennae stretched out to th limit to aid them in locating the body. Dropping to the ground, they carefully tuck their membranous wings under their wing covers and then, like calculating contractors, walk over the carcass to see how best to start the work.

If the ground is suitable, they begin to excavate beneath the remains. If the ground is hard or rocky, the dead animal must be moved to a new location, provided it is small enough to be dragged by several couples, for they almost always work in pairs. There are cases on record where two burying beetles have dragged a rat several feet to suitable soil. Silphids almost always prefer smaller animals, leaving the larger ones to other scavengers.

As the silphids excavate the soil, the body sinks lower and lower. Soon it is low enough for the excavated dirt to begin to roll over the

BURYING BEETLES AND ROVE BEETLES—INSECT GARBAGE COLLECTORS
Burying or carrion beetles dispose of a small dead animal by digging a grave under it. Several beetles work together, and will, if necessary, drag the body to soil that is suitable for digging. When the grave is deep enough they deposit eggs on the body and cover it with earth. A *Silpha* burying beetle is shown at upper left, a *Necrophorus* beetle at lower right. Upper right is one of the many kinds of rove beetles. They also are scavengers. Carrion beetles are frequently noteworthy for their bright colors.

body. When the carrion beetles have finished the job the only evidence remaining is a little spot of newly turned soil. An animal the size of a mouse can be buried in two or three hours, while a rat may receive a decent interment in five or six hours.

The silphids work fast, for, if they do not, flies and other scavengers will soon be on the scene to get their share. If flies arrive before the burying beetles have covered the body, they will deposit their eggs, and the resulting larvae will quickly devour the food before the silphid larvae have even hatched.

The true burying beetles belong to the genus *Necrophorus*, of which we have about a dozen species, with a number of subspecies, in North America. They are all large beetles from one to one and three-quarters inches long. Black in color, they are usually marked with one or two spots of red on each wing cover. In some, the spots merge into red bands. In a few, the thorax is decorated with fine golden hairs.

In the genus *Silpha*, the species are flat and well fitted for crawling under or into the bodies of the carrion. In these beetles, it is frequently the thorax that is decorated with red or yellow. They vary in size from one-half to three-quarters of an inch. The species of a number of other genera are usually much smaller, and are found in decaying material or on living plants.

The family is not a large one; only about 1,600 species are known, with 140 of these living in North America. The collector of these and other scavenger insects can secure specimens by placing pieces of meat or dead animals out as bait. If vultures or other scavengers are near, it is a good idea to cover the bait with an overturned box. A visit to the bait at least once a day will yield a multitude of silphids, staphylinids, histerids, and other beetles.

ROVE BEETLES—INCLUDING THE "DEVIL'S COACH HORSES"

These small-to-medium-sized beetles are easily recognized by their very short wing covers. In most of the species, the wing covers extend back over only about two of the basal abdominal segments; in a few, they extend farther, leaving only three segments exposed. The second pair of wings is of normal length, and it is remarkable the way these wings can be folded and tucked away completely out of sight under the small cases. The beetle uses its hind legs and the tip of its turned-up abdomen to place its wings under its wing cases.

The rove beetles (family Staphylinidae) are all rather slender, straight-sided beetles, largely black, some dull, others shiny. Some are conspicuously marked with red, yellow, and other bright colors. A few have golden hairs in patches in various places, giving them a wasplike appearance. To add to this effect, many of them have the habit of raising the end of the abdomen as if about to sting as they run along the ground. Because of this habit, the English call them "devil's coach horses." They are unable to sting, but many, when picked up, eject a brownish secretion which stains the fingers and has a strong odor. This is undoubtedly a protective device against birds and small animals.

The fact that the rove beetles are largely scavengers has earned them another common name, the short-winged scavenger beetles. A good way to collect these insects is to make up a pile of grass, lawn clippings, or old leaves amounting to the size of a bushel basket, on a bare spot of ground. After a few days, this can be turned over, and numbers of staphylinids will be seen scurrying in all directions, many of them with their abdomens elevated in a threatening attitude. Carrion or old meat placed under boards will yield other species.

HOW THEY HELP THE ANTS

A great many of these beetles have found it convenient to live in ant or termite nests, where they probably aid the ants in cleaning up waste material. In any case, the ants do not object to their presence. Over three hundred species have been taken from ant and termite nests, making this the largest group of myrmecophilous insects, in other words, insects fond of ants.

Over twenty thousand species of rove beetles are known, with new ones constantly being described and added to our lists. Out-of-the-way places, when more thoroughly explored, will yield additional thousands. North America has more than 2,700 species.

SAP-FEEDING BEETLES

An outdoor place containing old logs, or a spot where a tree has recently been cut down, is an excellent location for finding some of the sap-feeding beetles (family Nitidulidae). Others you will have to look for around old fruit, decaying fungi, and carrion. Some prefer flowers, where they dine upon the pollen and nectar.

An easy way to collect these beetles is by spreading a mixture of brown sugar and molasses, thinned with a little stale beer or vinegar, on the top of old logs in the woods. Over this, place some old chips or small pieces of wood. In a short while and for days after, nitidulid beetles will collect for the banquet.

You will notice that most of them are small, oval, flat beetles. In many, the thorax and wing covers have wide, thin, side margins, and the wing covers are more or less squared off at the tip, leaving a little of the abdomen exposed. The antennae have eleven joints, the last three joints of each antenna being enlarged into a distinct club.

The family is not a large one, for it numbers only about 2,500 species, with about 130 occurring in North America. Several species are almost world-wide in distribution, for they have hitchhiked everywhere, traveling in man's food products.

HISTER BEETLES

These beetles are mostly small-to-medium-sized creatures, the largest being three-quarters of an inch or less in length. They are round or oval beetles. Most are black, but a few are decorated with red or yellow spots or markings. Some are flat and can crawl under loose bark, where they live, feeding on the decaying part of the cambium layer. (The cambium layer of a tree is normally the green, growing part just under the bark.) It is also thought that they prey upon other small insects under the bark.

Most of the hister beetles, (family Histeridae) however, are hemispherical. They do not need to be flat, for these species live in all sorts of waste products, decaying animal and vegetable matter, and dung. As with staphylinids, a few invade ants' nests, where it is believed they may prey upon the eggs and young, snatching them out from under the very noses of the ants.

When disturbed, a histerid either lies very still or rolls over on its back, pulls its little legs close to its body, and plays possum. In this state it looks more like a little black seed than a beetle.

The family is not a large one, containing only about three thousand known species. More than 375 of these live in North America.

LADY BEETLES—THEIR COLORS GIVE WARNING

The lady beetles (family Coccinellidae) are the "ladybugs" of nursery rhymes. They are also called ladybirds, this name sometimes being lengthened to ladybird beetles. The Germans know them as *Marienkäferchen* (Mary beetles) and also *Sonnenkälbchen* (sun calves). The scientific name is a good descriptive term, for it comes from the Greek word meaning "scarlet," and refers to the color of many of the adults.

Although many lady beetles are bright red or yellow, decorated with spots or lines of black, almost as many are exactly the reverse in coloring. These are black, spotted with red or yellow. As we have mentioned before, brilliant colors in the insect world seem to indi-

LADY BEETLES OR LADYBUGS—SOME EAT PLANTS AND SOME EAT INSECTS

The beetle pictured coming down the branch is the squash beetle, which can be quite a pest to the gardener. The other two feed on aphids, or plant lice. You can sometimes see great numbers of the two-spotted ladybug (*bottom right*) gathered on a sunny brick wall in late fall. The convergens ladybug (*bottom left*) is a very common species.

cate that their wearers are bad tasting. So it is with the lady beetles. You can easily find this out for yourself by holding one in your hands for a few minutes, particularly if you should slightly pinch it. The beetle will expel a strong-smelling liquid from its leg joints and various other parts of its body, which will stain your skin yellow.

The coccinellids are generally rounded or oval, and more or less hemispherical in shape. They are frequently confused with the chrysomelids (Leaf Beetles) and with the endomychids (the Handsome Fungus Beetles). The three-jointed feet (actually there are four joints), and the broad, hatchet-shaped, or somewhat triangular, terminal joint of the palpi (segmented mouth attachments) will at once distinguish them from the chrysomelids.

The lady beetles are perhaps less easily separated from the endomychids, for you will have to look at the tarsal claws. The endomychids have simple claws, while the coccinellids have claws that are enlarged or toothed at the base. You will need a lens in order to see this detail. Once you are familiar with the two families, you will be able to recognize a new specimen after only a superficial examination.

Coccinellid larvae are narrow or oblong grubs, armed with tufts of branching and rebranching spines. Although usually rather dull in color, some of them are spotted or banded with red, yellow, or black. They are frequently seen walking around on the foliage and flowers of plants. The eggs of many of the species are a bright, orange-yellow color and are usually laid in a cluster almost anywhere, wherever the mother wanders, but usually near a food supply.

SOME LADY BEETLES PREY ON OTHER ANIMALS

Most coccinellids, both larvae and adults, prey on other animals. The red and yellow species, both adults and their larvae, feed largely on plant lice. The blackish species prefer scale insects. Consequently, all of these species are considered beneficial. Lady beetles occasionally whet their appetites for more aphids or scale insects by lunching on pollen and nectar.

SOME FEED ON PLANTS

Unfortunately, there are some coccinellids that are plant feeders. These belong to the genus *Epilachna,* a very large group, numbering over 450 species and scattered in all parts of the world, from the tropics to the colder temperate regions, or wherever the many plant species on which they feed are growing. It is in this group that we find some of our most serious economic pests.

Two notable pests in this genus, the Squash Beetle, *Epilachna borealis,* and recently the Mexican Bean Beetle, *Epilachna varivestris* (given in the older books as *Epilachna corrupta*), are doing considerable damage throughout the United States. This is particularly true of the latter, which, moving from the Southwest northward and eastward, from bean patch to bean patch, has now spread over the entire United States and southern Canada, from the Rocky Mountains to the Atlantic Ocean. It is creating tremendous havoc in the growing of beans, both commercially and in back-yard gardens. So great has this hazard become that many growers have entirely given up trying to raise beans.

Epilachna and a few closely related, but small, genera make up one of the subfamilies, Epilachnidae, of the Coccinellidae. Some entomologists would like to separate this group and establish it as a family, because of its great difference, both biologically and in its habits, from other coccinellids. They are too closely alike in body formation, however, for these black sheep to be disowned by the good little lady beetles.

The Two-spotted Lady Beetle, *Adalia bipunctata,* is a small, arched, red species with a black spot in the center of each wing cover. The species is common everywhere, both in Europe and North America. The adults hibernate in a protected spot where they can congregate, for the species' odor is augmented by the greater number of individuals present. This odor warns all enemies to beware of eating them, for these beetles are bad tasting.

The woman who is a better housekeeper than entomologist is frequently distressed when, upon opening a window on a winter day, she sees a great mass of these little beetles on the ledges. Immediately she thinks, and is probably so informed by less intelligent neighbors, that these bugs are bedbugs. Then brr-r-r-r, the author's telephone rings. And again he has to assure a panicky woman that her bugs are kindly little lady beetles only wanting to eat the aphids from her begonias.

The Nine-spotted Lady Beetle, *Coccinella novemnotata,* is one of our larger species. Hemispherical and nearly round, it has four black spots on its bright-red wing covers. This species, with its three sub-species, ranges throughout the United States and southward into Mexico. It is commonly seen resting on a grass blade or leaf, like a little red jewel.

Other Coccinellids. *Ceratomegilla fuscilabris,* a pretty, rather flat, red lady beetle with six black spots on each wing cover, is a common insect around gardens. It is particularly fond of aphids that feed on corn. Many amateur gardeners, seeing these lady beetles on the corn tassels, run for the spray gun, thinking the beetles are eating their corn plants. Actually, if you look closely, you will see hundreds of little yellow-green aphids dining on the corn, and the lady beetles dining on the aphids. This beetle is common throughout the United States and Canada.

The genus *Hippodamia* has a number of common species, widely distributed in North America. They are generally more oval and less hemispherical than some of the other species. *Hippodamia con-vergens* is named for the two converging lines on the thorax; *paren-thesis* for the comma-like marks on its wing covers; and *tredecim-punctata* for its thirteen spots. The species mentioned are all aphid eaters.

The Twice-stabbed Lady Beetle, *Chilocorus bivulnerus,* a scale eater, is one of our largest and most brilliant species. It is shiny black, with two rather small red spots, one in the center of each wing cover. It is found throughout the United States and Canada, although it is not one of the commonly seen species.

PLEASING FUNGUS BEETLES

On a sunny day in late spring, while resting on a fallen tree or log after walking in the woods, you may be surprised to see some brightly colored, rather small, hemispherical beetles exploring or just sun-ning themselves on the log beside you. These beetles will probably belong to the family Erotylidae and are commonly known as the pleasing fungus beetles. Their colors are usually black and red, in an alternating pattern which makes the beetles very conspicuous. Since these beetles have bad-tasting secretions, they need fear no birds and may sun their bright bodies in comparative safety.

The food of these beetles is largely fungi. Almost any type of fungus shaken over a white cloth will yield some of the smaller species. Staphylinids and nitidulids, as well as representatives of other beetle families, will also be found in this way. The larger species usually make their homes under loose bark, where they undoubtedly feed upon fungi that attack old logs.

A rather small family, containing about 2,800 species, the pleasing fungus beetles live mainly in hot climates; a large percentage of them live in the South American tropics. Many of these are slightly over an inch in length and, with their bright colors, when nicely mounted, make an attractive-looking collection. The North American species number sixty, with most of these measuring under half an inch.

Megalodacne fasciata is one of the largest and most conspicuous of the northern members of the family. It is shining black, with two reddish bars across the wing covers. The basal bar is irregular and broken, surrounding three small black spots. This beetle is found around old stumps or logs in the fungus stage of disintegration and varies in size from half an inch to five-eighths of an inch. It ranges throughout the eastern half of the United States, from Canada into Mexico.

Megalodacne heros is similar to *fasciata* but is larger and less shining. Found in the same location, it is more limited in distribution. Its length is three-quarters of an inch to seven-eighths of an inch.

THE HANDSOME FUNGUS BEETLES

A group of beetles that might well be confused with the erotylids, the handsome fungus beetles (family Endomychidae) are found in the same places and also feed upon fungi. On close examination, they can be easily identified, however, for they have only three joints in the tarsi, or feet, while the erotylids have four joints. They also differ in that they are usually rounder, their hemispherical bodies making them look like lady beetles. Endomychids are rarely as brightly colored as the lady beetles, and do not frequent gardens or flowers but live in deep woods around old logs or dead trees.

The endomychids are also frequently mistaken for Leaf Beetles, which belong to the family Chrysomelidae. Here again, the tarsal joints will at once answer the question, for the leaf beetles have the third segment distinctly divided into two lobes, while in the endomychids, the second segment is divided in two, and both first and second segments are enlarged.

Only about 950 species have been described, with a little over thirty-five of these from North America. Little is known about their life histories.

STEM BORERS

If you should find some brightly colored beetles that look like erotylids but are very long and slender, they undoubtedly would not be any of the pleasing fungus beetles, but members of the family Languriidae. For many years the langurids were considered a subfamily of the Erotylidae, and are still so considered by a few beetle experts. Structurally, they are very closely related, but biologically, they are quite different.

The narrow, cylindrical shape of their bodies suggests that langurids are well fitted to live in burrows or tunnels. And that is exactly where the few whose life histories we have studied do live. Actually, we know little about the habits of most of the species. These few that we have watched are stem borers, preferring plants that have a pithy stem, meaning a stem that has its center filled with spongy tissue. These insects are not seen around old logs, but are usually collected by sweeping grass and vegetation with a heavy insect net. Sweeping, incidentally, is also a good way to collect other insects. As you walk along, you swing your net back and forth in front of you, sweeping the tops of the grass, bushes, and other vegetation.

The larger species, some up to an inch in length, are found in the tropics, where the family, which numbers about four hundred species, is richest. The twenty species living in North America are all less than half an inch long.

The Clover-stem Borer, *Languria mozardi,* is not only a pest on the clovers, alfalfa, and other leguminous plants that are cultivated, but probably does some good by attacking weed plants that are not useful to man.

A small species, about a quarter of an inch long, it is slender and dark blue, with a distinctly reddish thorax. It is widely distributed, ranging over the entire eastern half of the United States, from Canada to the Gulf states.

SKIN BEETLES—THEY CAUSE ENORMOUS DAMAGE

We are all familiar with the family Dermestidae, perhaps not with the insects themselves but certainly with the damage they do. There is hardly a person who has not had occasion at some time to "cuss" these beetles and their larvae.

Perhaps the coat you put away in a closet, but neglected to look at for a time, is discovered to be full of holes. Or the new rug and the upholstered furniture may seem to have lost their nice appearance. Examining them closely, you are amazed to find they have been eaten here and there. Certain dermestid beetles, but particularly their larvae, cause millions of dollars in damage to goods manufactured from any animal product, such as wool, fur, feathers, and even leather. Dried food products made from meat, and occasionally grain and vegetable products, are also considered fine food by dermestids.

Since so many of the Dermestidae have been associated with man or his products for so long, it is only natural that we should find many of the species nearly cosmopolitan. Out of the 550 known species, at least one hundred have traveled all around the world.

SKIN BEETLES ARE FOND OF POLLEN

None of the dermestids are large; in fact, many are quite small, not much larger than a pinhead, while the largest is not over three-quarters of an inch. They are plump, oval, or round beetles, densely covered with very short, black, brown, or gray hairs, and frequently mottled with white or red modified hairs or scales. These are frequently aranged in patterns characteristic of the species.

You will find many of the smaller adult species when they feed upon pollen. They normally existed by feeding on pollen before taking up with man, and they still like to return to their ancestral homes from time to time. The larger species (all of these belong to the genus *Dermestes*) usually live around carrion, dead animals, or old meat.

The larvae are more destructive than the adults, for they are exceedingly greedy if food is plentiful. If food is scarce, they are able to survive for long intervals without eating. Ordinarily, for most species, the life cycle is one year, but it may be extended for two or three years, if the temperature is considerably lowered. The grubs are hairy with the hairs frequently arranged in tufts or bunches. Longer hairs, which are sometimes barbed and arranged in bunches or patches of very close hairs, decorate the larvae on the tail end or in various other places. When ready to pupate, they frequently remain partially within the larval skin. Tanners call the *Dermestes* larvae "skin worms."

The Larder Beetle, *Dermestes lardarius,* is three-eighths of an inch long and black, except that the basal half of the wing cover is yellow brown, crossed with a row of six blackish spots, three to each wing cover. These beetles are frequently found in pantries, where they feed upon dried meat, and particularly bacon, that may have been overlooked or forgotten.

Dermestes cadaverinus, vulpinus, and a number of other species are about the size of *lardarius,* but are dull black on the upper side and densely covered with white scales below. The arrangement and pattern of these scales identify the numerous species. An interesting scientific use is made of some of the *Dermestes* beetles, particularly *vulpinus.* Museums, in preparing bones for study, place the bones nearly cleared of all meat in tight cages containing *Dermestes* larvae. The larvae quickly eat off all remaining pieces of meat, leaving the bones well cleaned.

DESTRUCTIVE HOUSEHOLD PESTS

The genus *Anthrenus* contains a number of species much smaller than the *Dermestes.* The adults are little, round beetles, mottled with red, yellow, brown, and black scales. About an eighth of an inch long, or slightly less, and nearly as broad, they are attractive insects, especially when viewed with a lens, for then their real beauty is brought out. They play possum when disturbed; folding their legs close to the body, they look like little, round seeds. Look for them in flowers of all kinds, because they love to dine on pollen. Look for them also on your window sills. If you find any, start looking for the larvae, hairy grubs about a quarter of an inch long, in your rugs, woolen clothing, and your upholstered furniture, for these are destructive household pests.

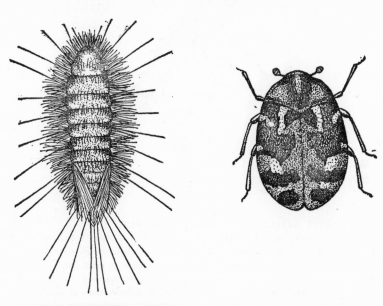

ONCE IT FED ON BUFFALO HIDES
The buffalo carpet beetle got its name because it used to damage buffalo hides. It is now found in homes and warehouses, where its grub feeds on wool, fur, and feathers. The grub (*left*) is whitish, but so covered with black bristly hairs as to look dark. The adult beetle (*right*) is clothed with scales variegated in red, black, brown, and white. In the picture this pest is drawn much enlarged.

The Buffalo Carpet Beetle, *Anthrenus scrophulariae,* sometimes called the buffalo moth, and a close relative, *verbasci,* are two of the most damaging. Liberal use of paradichlorobenzene around the house will discourage them.

The Black Carpet Beetle, *Attagenus piceus,* is just as serious a pest, if not more so. The adults are dull-black insects, half an inch in length. You should look for them around the house, on the window sills, or in bathrooms, where they can easily be detected. On the rugs, or on clothes in closets, they are harder to see. The larvae, which do the damage, are hairy, red-brown grubs, and have a long brush of hairs trailing from the tail. Although they prefer animal products, they do very well on dry vegetable products, especially if some animal fats or oils are near-by to stimulate their appetites.

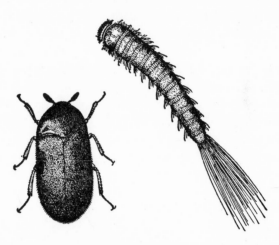

THE BLACK CARPET BEETLE—ANOTHER SERIOUS PEST

The larva or grub (*right*) is whitish, but covered with red-brown hairs, and also has a long red-brown tail, which it may lose. The adult (*left*) is larger than the buffalo carpet beetle and is dull black. This beetle's larva, which feeds on wool, fur, and feathers, is also fond of oily vegetable products, flour, noodles, macaroni, and the like. Buffalo and black carpet beetles are estimated to do millions of dollars' worth of damage annually.

CLICK BEETLES OR SKIPJACKS— POPULAR INSECT ACROBATS

Who has not marveled at the way these beetles (family Elateridae), when placed on their backs, are able to snap into the air? The author remembers his delight as a child in forcing a skipjack to do this, time after time, until the poor beetle was completely worn out. Undoubtedly, the beetle enjoyed it far less than did its audience.

When disturbed, the click beetle lets go its hold on leaf or twig and falls to the ground. With legs folded close to its body (and in many species they fit into special grooves), it lies still, usually on its back, looking like a chip of wood. When danger is past, the beetle slowly returns to activity, reaching out with its feet to grab any stick or stone within reach that will enable it to turn over. Should nothing be convenient, it then resorts to its snapping apparatus.

WHAT MAKES THE CLICK BEETLE CLICK

This apparatus consists of a spine on the underside of the prothorax (the front portion of the thorax), which slides in a groove on the underside of the mesothorax (the middle portion of the thorax). The beetle is loosely jointed between the prothorax and the rest of the body.

When lying on its back, the beetle straightens out, bending the thorax farther and farther back, as in cocking a gun, until the spine is at the very end of the groove. Suddenly, there is a snap, accompanied by an audible click. The release of the muscular tension forces the shoulders or base of the wing covers against the ground with such force as to throw the insect into the air to the height of four or five inches. If it lands on its feet when it comes down, it hurries off for the nearest cover. It may have to try two or three snappings, however, before alighting properly.

A CLOSE LOOK AT THE ELATERS

Elaters, as these creatures are sometimes called, are usually longish beetles; their bodies have parallel sides but are rounded or tapering behind. They have long, slender, but distinctly serrate (saw-toothed) antennae; and the hind angles of the thorax in most species are prolonged into a distinct spine. The marked separation between the thorax and the base of the wing covers, and the thoracic spine will at once identify them.

Many of them are somber brown or gray. However, almost as many are shining and brilliantly colored in greens, yellows, reds, and blues. These brilliant species are usually confined to the tropical rain-forest regions (those having an annual rainfall of one hundred inches or more) of South America, India, and the East Indies. Elaters range in size from little species less than a quarter of an inch to giants of two and a half inches or larger. Of the nine thousand known species, nearly seven hundred occur in North America.

THE STIFF LITTLE WIREWORMS

The larvae are long and slender, cylindrical and smooth, usually light brown or straw colored, and would look like very stiff and strange earthworms, if it were not for the three pairs of small feet. Because of their stiffness, the larvae are called Wireworms. A great many will be found in old stumps, rotting wood, or decaying vegetation. A number are underground animals, feeding upon seeds, bulbs, and the roots of plants and trees. Some of these are serious pests because of their fondness for agricultural crops. A few live in ant and termite nests.

The Eyed Elater, *Alaus oculatus,* is one of the most conspicuous snapping beetles in the United States, where it ranges over the entire eastern half of the country. Individuals vary from one and a half to two inches, although very small ones of one inch have been found. This beetle is black in color and flecked with fine white scales. On

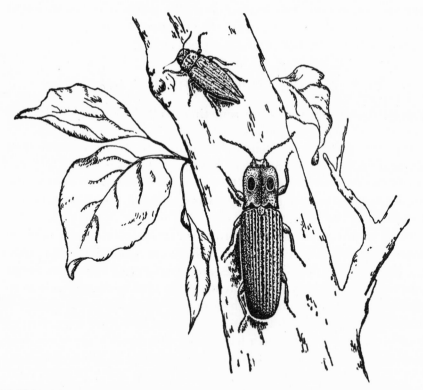

BEETLES THAT LIVE IN WOOD—AN EYED ELATER AND A WOOD-BORER

Those are not eyes you see on the back of the eyed elater or click beetle (*bottom*), but simply black spots—perhaps these make-believe eyes serve to scare birds. The wood-borer fleeing from the click beetle is clad in bright metallic colors. It deposits its eggs in the bark of trees, where the grubs develop and eat the living wood.

the upper surface of the thorax are two velvety-black spots ringed with a circle of white scales. These spots are nearly three-sixteenths of an inch across, and look like two glaring eyes, this being the reason for the insect's common name. The larvae are sometimes uncovered in old apple-tree stumps.

Other Interesting Click Beetles. *Alaus myops* is slightly smaller than *oculatus,* with much smaller eye spots. Instead of having white scales, it is flecked with brown or red-brown scales. *Myops* is more common throughout the southern states.

Alaus melanops replaces *oculatus* in the Pacific states. It is generally smaller and less brightly marked.

Alaus lusciosus, found in Mexico and the extreme southwestern states of Texas and Arizona, has the white scales collected in several small patches.

Alaus miszechi makes its home in the Congo region of Africa. It has no eye spots but is confusedly mottled with white, gray, and brown scales.

Melanactes piceus, a large, shiny, black elater, one to one and a quarter inches long, is frequently found under loose bark or on the ground under old logs or stones.

Semiotus is a genus of very brightly colored beetles ranging from the middle of Central American countries into southern Brazil and northern Chile and Argentina. Beetles in this group are mostly large species from one inch to one and three-quarters inches in size. A few measure less than one inch. Nearly a hundred species are known, dressed largely in yellow and black, or red and black, and polished. They are slender and taper sharply to the tip of the wing covers.

Chalcolepidius is another genus of large, bulky, brilliant elaters. They occupy the same region of South America as *Semiotus,* but extend up into the southwestern United States, and one species is found in Virginia and surrounding states.

FIRE BEETLES

Pyrophorus, a genus of luminous elaters, commonly called Fire Beetles, or by the name of *cucujas* (there are several spellings), is widely distributed from the southern United States to Argentina and the West Indies. It comprises mostly large beetles, easily recognized by the luminous organs, which are two yellow spots, more or less elevated, one near each hind angle of the thorax. At night, these spots glow with a soft, green light as the beetle rests on a tree trunk. A glimpse of a fire beetle in flight is a sight never to be forgotten, for in most species, when the wings are spread, the abdomen fairly flames with a brilliant, orange light. Nearly a hundred species have been described, but it is quite certain that when the genus is intensively studied, with working material available in the collections, many of these species will be found to be identical. A closely related genus, *Photophorus*, with similar luminous organs, is found only in the East Indies, and has only two species.

In the various regions in which they occur, these fire beetles are often used by the natives as a source of illumination and decoration. Three or four of them in a bottle will give considerable light. The author has been able to read print by the soft glow that they give off. At local dances, the native women sometimes fasten a number of these beetles to their clothing, and even in their hair, to give additional charm to their black hair and their plain dresses.

METALLIC WOOD-BORING BEETLES

These close relatives of the click beetles resemble them to a considerable extent. They differ by the lack of the prosternal spine (the spine on the underside of the prothorax, or front portion of the thorax). There is no loose-jointedness between the prothorax and the rest of the body. The rear angles of the thorax are not sharply prolonged, the antennae, although saw-toothed, are generally much shorter, the eyes more protuberant.

Members of the family Buprestidae, these insects are medium-to-large beetles, often brightly colored, with metallic, and frequently iridescent, greens, blues, reds, and yellows. Because of the bright colors and hard bodies, they are frequently used for decorative purposes, both by the natives of the less civilized regions, who fasten them in their hair and clothing, and by dealers, who use them in jewelry and art work, and to sell to collectors.

These beetles love the sun, the larger ones resting on dead or fallen timber, the smaller species on leaves and flowers of more herbaceous plants. They are extremely active, and the collector must approach with caution, for they are gone at the slightest disturbance.

On cool or cloudy days, they frequently drop to the ground, where, with legs retracted and close to the body, they are practically invisible. The buprestid collector must be speedy with his net, to get those that he sees. Many of the smaller species can be obtained by sweeping or beating the vegetation and particularly the branches and leaves of dying trees and shrubs.

The eggs are placed by the mother in a hollow she has chewed in the bark of the particular host her species feeds upon. Immediately after hatching, the little grub bores into the bark, feeding as it bores. Its very small head is set into the next segment, which is much enlarged and flattened. Behind this larger segment, the body narrows down. In this stage, the grubs are spoken of as Flat-headed Borers, or Hammer-heads. They have no eyes and no legs.

The grubs follow the cambium layer of a tree and sometimes penetrate the sapwood. Because of the flattened, but enlarged, segment, the resulting burrow conforms to this shape. As the larva matures, it works to the outer surface, leaving only a thin shell of wood separating it from the outside world. It pupates here, and then, as an adult, cuts its way out.

The family is rather large, with over eight thousand species, nearly six hundred of these being found in North America. Many of the species are of considerable economic importance because of the damage that they do to growing plants and trees. Actually, however, most of the species attack diseased or dead and dying trees.

The Flat-headed Apple-tree Borer, *Chrysobothris femorata,* attacks not only apple trees but numerous other fruit trees and forest trees. Wherever it occurs in numbers, considerable damage is certain to result. In the spring, the adults love to rest on tree trunks, sunning themselves. Their brown color and roughened wing covers blend in with the bark, making it difficult to see them. When they fly, and they do so with extreme speed, the green abdomen shows like a streak of light. This species is about half an inch long.

Other Notable Buprestids. *Euchroma gigantea* is probably the largest of the buprestids. It is two and a half to three inches long and one to one and a quarter inches broad. The coloring is quite variable in the individuals, but red and green are the dominant colors. The head and thorax are greenish, with the discal part of the thorax darker. In the subspecies *goliath,* this dark area is more or less broken into two smaller spots. The wing covers are reddish or coppery, with greenish highlights. This beetle is found from the more tropical part of Central America throughout the northern half of South America, and in the West Indies.

The genera *Chrysochroa* and *Sternocera* have many brilliant species living in the tropics of eastern Asia. These beetles are much sought after by collectors and consequently command a good price.

Dicerca divaricata is perhaps the most common species of buprestid in the eastern part of the United States. It is nearly one inch long, with the tips of the wing covers prolonged into two blunt projections. It is a shining coppery or brassy color above, with flecks of darker brown scattered over the surface. These beetles are frequently seen on dead or dying beech, maple, cherry, peach, apple, and other trees not of the evergreen group.

Chalcophora virginiensis is one of the largest species in the eastern United States, reaching a length of one and a quarter inches. It is not as brilliantly colored, being blackish bronze, the thorax and wing covers presenting a brassy impression. The head and thorax have a deep middle groove. The wing covers have four to six impressed spots. A species seen in the western United States is *Chalcophora angulicollis.*

FIREFLIES—NATURE'S EVENING SPARKLERS

Everyone, even the city dweller, is familiar with those small, flat, soft-bodied sparklers of our early summer evenings, the fireflies. In the largest cities, you have only to go on a muggy July evening to the nearest park, or any place where vegetation is at all plentiful, to see at least one lightning bug, as they are often called.

Wet meadows or swampy woods will sometimes fairly teem with them. Although the light is not as long lasting or as brilliant as that of the luminous elaters of the tropics, it is very pleasing to see and excites much interest. One of the most remarkable facts about the fireflies is that the light they produce is without any heat or loss of energy, a strange accomplishment that man, with all his forms of light, has not been able to achieve.

HOW THE FIREFLIES PRODUCE LIGHT

The luminous organs are located on the sixth and seventh abdominal segments, also sometimes to a lesser extent on others. They are distinguished by the lighter-yellow color of this area. It is in these segments that a special fatty tissue permeated with numerous tracheae (little tubes through which air is conveyed) lies. This fatty tissue contains a substance called luciferin, which is acted upon by the enzyme luciferase, producing this nearly cold light. The light is controlled at the will of the insect and is believed to be a signal between the sexes.

Each species is thought to have its own code of signals. Recent investigation seems to indicate that it is not so much the light—either color, brilliancy, or length—but rather the length of the interval that makes the code. Experimenters have tried flashlights, cigarette lighters, and even matches. As long as they kept the interval between flashes the same as that used by the surrounding fireflies, they could get a response from them. Other workers think that the undulations of the insect when in flight might represent a code used by the various species. The problem still awaits more study.

WHY GLOWWORMS ARE GROUNDED

There are some species of lightning bugs in which the females are wingless. These are called glowworms, and are doomed to a "grounded" life, rather than the aerial delights of their mates. Actually these females are very much like their larvae, but differ in that they possess compound eyes, rather than the simple ocelli of the immature. Some of the larvae show traces of luminosity.

Not all members of this family (Lampyridae) are luminous; in fact, the greatest percentage are not. These are usually placed in other subfamilies than the true fireflies, the groupings being based on their structural differences. The lampyrids, both larvae and adults, are flesh eaters, preying upon small insects and insect larvae, small arthropods, and snails that they find in old leaves, humus, or on the ground.

More than two thousand species have been described. About sixty of these are found in North America. The rain-forest regions of the tropics are rich in species, the largest of them reaching a length of an inch or slightly more.

The European Glowworm, *Lampyris noctiluca,* is the glowworm we read about in English and European literature. The male is winged, dark brown, and half an inch long. The female is larviform (wingless and grublike), light brown, and three-quarters of an inch long. It glows with a soft, bright light, quite delightful and amazing to see. No wonder it has been the inspiration of poets and other writers.

The genera *Photinus* and *Photurus* are North American and contain most of the luminous species. They range over the entire eastern United States, from the Atlantic Ocean to the Rocky Mountains and from the Great Lakes southward. Both sexes are winged and luminous. These are our familiar lightning bugs.

Phausis splendidula occurs in Europe and North America. The male is winged, but the female is larviform.

DARKLING BEETLES

These beetles are frequently confused with the Carabidae, or ground beetles, for they are usually found wandering about on the ground. In fact, the darkling beetles (family Tenebrionidae) are sometimes called the darkling ground beetles. Most of them, however, prefer conditions entirely different from those sought by the ground beetles. The darkling, or tenebrionid, beetles like dry and even semi-desert surroundings, while the carabids like moist, humid places. Both like darkness and usually do their active hunting at night.

SOME DARKLING BEETLES LIKE LIGHT

Not all of the darkling beetles are night prowlers. Some are lovers of daylight and may be seen walking sedately along in arid regions. A few of these, when touched, lower the head to the ground and elevate the abdomen, like a small boy trying to stand on his head. Smell your fingers, and you will probably detect a strong, offensive odor, undoubtedly useful as a protective device. These head-standers are called pincate beetles.

The Tenebrionidae belong to the heteromerous group (mentioned at the beginning of the discussion of beetles), which have five-jointed tarsi, or feet, on the front and middle pairs of legs, but only four-jointed tarsi on the rear pair. The antennae are usually beadlike (each segment rounded), instead of long and slender as in the Carabidae.

Many of the species have become so closely associated with the ground as to have lost their membranous wings through disuse; and in some the wing covers have even grown together, retaining only as an indentation the line where they met. Nearly all are black, gray, or brown. A few are decorated with red or yellow spots or marks, while in the tropics some look like brilliant gems. They vary in size from tiny creatures one eighth of an inch to giants of two and a half to three inches. Most of them are medium-sized.

DARKLING BEETLES ARE SCAVENGERS

Most tenebrionids are scavengers, feeding upon dry or decaying vegetable material, seeds, cereals, fungi, dung, and occasionally on living plants. Some live in pleasant association with ants in the latter's nests. Since so many feed upon waste material, the family as a whole can be considered beneficial.

The larvae are generally long, smooth, and slender, yellowish or straw colored, and resemble the wiry larvae of the Elateridae. For this reason, they are called False Wireworms. They feed upon the same material as the adults.

The Tenebrionidae are a large family, numbering more than fourteen thousand species. More than 1,100 of these are found in North America.

The Meal Beetle, *Tenebrio molitor,* is a well-known brownish-black beetle, three-quarters of an inch long, commonly seen around granaries, flour mills, stores, and barns. Sometimes you will find meal beetles in your home where flour and cereal products are kept for a long time or overlooked. The larva, known as the Meal Worm, is raised in large numbers for feeding birds and some animals. So great is the demand for meal worms that a supply industry of size has developed.

The Red Flour Beetle, *Tribolium ferrugineum,* the Confused Flour Beetle, *Tribolium confusum,* and the Broad-horned Flour Beetle, *Gnathocerus cornutus,* are all small, reddish-brown species, less than a quarter of an inch long. Any or all of these may invade your home, coming in as stowaways in packages of cereal, flour, or similar products. They have traveled in this manner to all parts of the world in man's products and by his commerce.

The Churchyard Beetle, *Blaps mortisaga,* is a dull-black, one-inch-long, European beetle, found frequently in damp places such as cellars and churchyards.

The genus *Eleodes* is North American and contains about 125 species, all occurring in the West and Southwest. They are rather large, smooth, black species, feeding upon growing plants, and sometimes, when numerous, doing considerable damage.

TUMBLING FLOWER BEETLES

If you examine almost any composite or flat, open flower, you are certain, sooner or later, to see a tumbling flower beetle, a curious little humpbacked creature, with a very sharp-pointed abdomen. When first seen it will have its head buried in the stamens of the flower.

Not for long will it stay in this position, however, for it is prompt to sense your presence. With a few quick kicks of its strong hind legs, it goes rolling head over heels in wild somersaults until eventually it tumbles out of the flower and is lost in the grass, or spreads its wings and flies elsewhere.

All of these beetles (family Mordellidae) are small, seldom measuring more than half an inch, and silky black from the very fine black hairs which cover them. Some of the species are mottled with whitish or yellowish spots or lines. Their tarsi (feet), which can be distinguished only with a lens, are of the heteromerous type, with five segments on the front and middle pairs, but only four on the rear pair.

Only about nine hundred species are known, nearly two hundred of these living in North America.

STAG BEETLES—A VANISHING RACE

The stag beetles are so named because of their greatly developed mandibles, or jaws. Nearly as large as the beetle itself, in some species, and branching as they do, these jaws very much resemble a stag's antlers. As in the deer family, it is only the males that have this odd development. These beetles (family Lucanidae) are also called pinching beetles by country boys, who find them very useful in livening a dull moment, as is so well related in Mark Twain's *The Adventures of Tom Sawyer.*

As to what the actual purpose of these large, and sometimes grotesque, mandibles may be, we have only the most vague ideas. We do know, however, that in some species a male will use them in fighting another male. This fighting is not a pinching process, but a butting maneuver. Two males will face each other and start pushing and butting, their strong-muscled legs braced for the final push that will either overturn or shove aside the weaker combatant.

The vanquished one then usually retires from the field, leaving the female, who has been standing quietly near-by, to the winner. The pair usually stays around the old stump or log which to them is home. Here, the female will probably lay her eggs in a little pocket she excavates in the wood with her short, but very powerful and efficient mandibles. Perhaps another male rival will appear, a situation which usually calls for another fight.

FINDING THE RIGHT NURSERY

Both sexes are able to fly in a sort of undirected flight. He is in search of a mate, and she is in search of an old tree or a stump in the right stage of decay to fit the needs of her children. It must be exactly right, for her children, in the form of fat, white grubs, must live in it for two years, and in some species, even longer. During this period, the wood must not become too wet, or, more important, must not dry out.

Finding such a nursery is becoming an increasingly difficult task, for with man's desire (through inadequate knowledge and understanding) to "clean up" every remaining wood lot, there are few old trees, in any condition whatsoever, left on the forest floor. "Burn and destroy" seems to be the modern watchword. When old logs and fallen trees are burned, much of the value of the wood is lost into the air, whereas the slow disintegration by insect and fungus attack returns these valuable elements to the soil.

BRIGHT LIGHTS ARE THEIR DOOM

Stag beetles were common in the author's childhood, but they are seldom seen today. Another cause for their disappearance, in addition to the decrease of suitable breeding locations, is the increased number of powerful lights along our highways.

Stag beetles, like many another insect large or small, are attracted by the bright lights. They fall to the ground and are either run over by passing autos, or, what is more likely, are stepped upon by some passing individual endowed only with the idea, through lack of knowledge, that all insects are harmful and should immediately be exterminated.

STAG BEETLES PREFER MOISTURE

The family has representatives all over the world, but the majority live in the humid rain forests. Here, also, the species reach their greatest size, some being nearly four inches long. Even in the temperate regions many of the species are quite large. Only about nine hundred species are known, with thirty of these living in North America.

Odontolabis alces, found in the East Indies, is probably the largest species. Large specimens are four inches long, one and a quarter inches broad, and rather flattened. They are a very dark brown, nearly black.

Lucanus capreolus (in some books *Lucanus dama*) is widely distributed over most of the United States east of the Rocky Mountains. It is a beautiful, rich, reddish brown, with the upper legs a lighter shade. Specimens vary in size from an inch to one and a half inches. The mandibles in the male also vary, from a quarter of an inch to half an inch.

Lucanus placidus, common in the central United States, is similar to *capreolus* but is a very dark reddish brown; the legs are not lighter in color. The surface of the wing covers is rather rough.

The Giant Stag Beetle, *Lucanus elaphus,* is the largest of the lucanids in the United States. It resembles *Lucanus capreolus* in its rich, brown color, but the mandibles are twice as long, curved and branching, and very antler-like in appearance. One wonders how the beetle can manage such awkward appendages and even fly with them, for they are frequently two-thirds the length of its body. A large specimen of *Lucanus elaphus* will measure two to two and a quarter inches. This beetle lives only in the southern half of the United States.

BEETLES THAT LIVE IN LOGS AND STUMPS—A STAG BEETLE AND A BESS BEETLE

Stag beetles are among the largest beetles in the United States. The males' "horns" are really greatly enlarged jaws, and no one knows for sure just why the beetles need them. However, the males push each other around with them. You can find these bright brown insects wherever there are extensive forests with plenty of decaying logs. The black bess beetle lives in the same environment. When picked up, it makes a peculiar hissing noise.

The Stag Beetle, *Lucanus cervus,* is very much like the giant stag beetle of the United States, but is European, ranging southward from England and Germany. The male has extremely long and branching mandibles.

The Giraffe Stag Beetle, *Cladognathus giraffe,* has slender mandibles as long as its body, sharply toothed on the inside. It is reddish brown to black and lives in Java and southern India.

BESS BEETLES—THEY SING A WARNING SONG

When you are exploring old logs for other insects, you will undoubtedly see some of the Passalidae. All of the species of the family look very much alike, and, once seen, will always be remembered.

All these beetles are black, except the newly emerged adults, which are a rich brown until they can develop their full pigmentation. Their wing covers are deeply striated, or grooved, and the body is squeezed together just behind the prothorax, making them appear almost as if cut in two. There is only one other group of beetles that are deeply constricted and resemble the passalids, and these are ground beetles belonging to the genus *Scarites.*

The passalids are generally larger, ranging from three-quarter-inch individuals to tropical giants three inches long. Although a small species of Passalidae may look like a *Scarites,* they can be instantly identified by the antennae. In the Passalidae, the last three segments are lamellate, or platelike, very much as in the lucanids, to which they are related, but coil up in an arc shape.

A SOCIAL GROUP OF INSECTS

When you find one passalid you are very likely to find more. You will probably also find larvae and pupae, and, if you look closely, you may even find the eggs. Passalids are beetles that show social tendencies. The adults care for the eggs, feed the larvae, by giving them chewed-up wood, and herd them deeper into the burrows, when disturbed, away from danger. If left to themselves, the larvae would probably be unable to survive.

THE SONG OF THE PASSALIDS

When disturbed or if taken in the fingers, a passalid beetle makes a creaking or hissing noise, produced by rubbing its abdomen up and down against the wing covers. The larvae are able to make a somewhat similar noise by rubbing the small third pair of legs against a ridged plate near the base of the second pair of legs.

It is from this sound that the passalids get their name bess beetles. Listen, and see if you do not think they are saying, "bess, bess, bess." Although this sound is probably useful in frightening off some enemies, it is believed to be a community signal, both for warning of danger and for social communication.

DWELLERS IN THE TROPICS

About four hundred species of passalids have been described, but only four in North America north of Mexico. Most of the others are in the rich, humid, rain-forest country of the tropics, where plenty of old trees remain.

Passalus cornutus is the only species of this interesting family in the eastern United States. If the author were to adhere exactly to the rules of nomenclature, he would drop this old and well-established name and use the newer name *Popilius disjunctus*. But since the insect is so well known under the former name, it is used here.

Measuring one and a quarter to one and a half inches, this beetle is among the largest in the North American fauna. Black, like all of its family, it has short, thick antennae, curved so that they are almost elbow-shaped. Their grubs, or larvae, are very large, bluish white, and have only two distinct pairs of legs. The third pair are merely small flappers and are used only to make noise.

SCARABS—THE COLLECTOR'S FAVORITES

This large family (Scarabaeidae) is one of the most popular with collectors. Their generally large size, bright colors, and unusual shapes make them very attractive beetles to study, when properly mounted. The males of many species have grotesquely shaped protuberances or horns on the head or thorax, and sometimes on both. These horns, in some species at least, are used for fighting, in much the same way the stag beetles use their enlarged mandibles. In these combats, as among the lucanids, the males butt and ram until one is vanquished. In some, the legs are fitted for digging.

The brightly colored species are usually plant feeders and may be found in flowers or browsing on the leaves of their favorite food plant. They all have one structural character in common, their lamellate, or platelike, antennae. The last three segments of the antennae are broadly flattened, but unlike the lucanids and the passalids, to which the scarabs are closely related, they are able to fold these segments or plates together into a compact ball. The surface of the plates is extremely sensitive and serves the insects as an effective sense organ, especially in detecting odors.

The family reaches its greatest development in the tropics, as is true of many insect groups. Here are found the species with the most brilliant colors, the most unusual development of horns, and the largest beetles known. In fact, these large beetles are probably the bulkiest of all insects.

More than thirty thousand species from all over the world are known, with 1,300 recorded from North America. Every country has its share of these interesting beetles. The family is divided into some twenty subfamilies, only a few of which we shall have space to discuss here.

THE DUNG BEETLES—USEFUL SCAVENGERS

These are the dung rollers, those useful scavengers that, in providing for their own life and activities, do so much in keeping the world clean and sanitary. The famed scarab of the ancient Egyptians, *Scarabaeus sacer,* belongs in this group, which is classified as subfamily Coprinae.

Usually, a female dung beetle, but sometimes a male and a female, working together, will form a ball of dung, and then roll it to a burrow the female has excavated near-by. Here it is kneaded, and an egg is placed in the center. Other balls and eggs will be added, and then the mother sometimes remains in the nursery to watch over the brood. Sometimes, however, a hungry adult will retire with a ball to a safe retreat, to dine at leisure.

OTHER INTERESTING SCARABS

Another very interesting group of scarabs is the subfamily Aphodiinae. Small, black, brown, or reddish beetles, these insects are seldom over half an inch long. They can be seen swarming in numbers over dung. On warm summer evenings, they take wing in countless numbers in search of new pasture, in our woods and fields.

We find quite a contrast in the habits of the subfamily Troginae. These beetles are scavengers, usually preferring carrion. They are roughly sculptured beetles, under three-quarters of an inch in length, decorated with numerous small knobs. Their heads are turned downward and covered with a shield, as if they were ashamed of their scavenging profession.

Very well known are adult scarabs of the subfamily Melolonthinae. You may also have heard of these beetles as May Beetles, May Bugs, or Rose Beetles. The adults are plant feeders, usually coming out at night. They are big-bodied, burly beetles, attracted to light. If one gets into your house, it buzzes and bumps around the room in an aimless way until caught and evicted. The larvae are seldom seen because most of them spend their lives underground, where they feed on the roots of grass and shrubs, or on decaying vegetation.

Somewhat similar to the Melolonthinae, the Rutelinae are generally dressed in bright colors. Metallic greens, blues, and reds, instead of the more somber browns, are more frequently seen. They are also plant feeders, and include the notorious Japanese beetle.

The Japanese Beetle, *Popillia japonica,* is an undesirable immigrant from Japan which became established in New Jersey a number of years ago and is rapidly becoming a major pest, as it continues to spread westward. It is now appearing in many localities throughout the Middle West. Were it less abundant and destructive, it would be considered an attractive insect.

The Japanese beetle is, however, not nearly as beautifully colored as some of its relatives, still citizens of eastern Asia, where in its native home the Japanese beetle was not a serious pest. Belonging to the genus *Popillia* are some forty other species, all found in various localities in Japan, China, Mongolia, Korea, and other countries of eastern Asia and the East Indies. Let's hope that if any of these should become established in the United States they will not be as serious a pest as the Japanese beetle.

The Cetoninae, another group of plant feeders, exceed even the Rutelinae in the brilliance of their coloring. Metallic, and sometimes iridescent, greens, blues, reds, and yellows are utilized to make one of the most beautiful groups of beetles known. Their very large, triangular shield piece is a conspicuous group characteristic. Many of the males go in for grotesque horns, in addition to their bright colors. The genus *Goliath* belongs in this subfamily. It has some of the largest species of beetles, certainly the largest to be found in Africa and eastern Asia.

In many ways quite different from preceding groups is the subfamily Dynastinae. This group also contains some gigantic beetles, as well as those with curious horns. Some of these protuberances are so large and cumbersome that one wonders how the beetles can manage to fly.

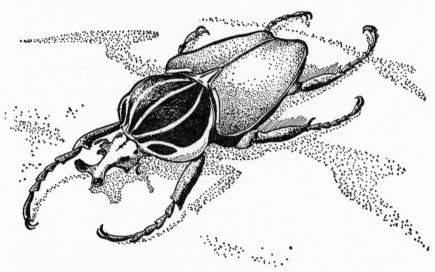

THE GOLIATH BEETLE OF WEST AFRICA—BIGGEST ON THE CONTINENT
The Goliath, largest beetle in Africa, is about four inches long; it is velvety reddish brown with white decorations on the back. The adult, it is said, loves to sit in the top of a palm tree, eating the heart of the growth bud, and thus killing the tree.

The Hercules Beetle, *Dynastes hercules,* of Central America and northern South America and the West Indies, is one such beetle. It has a very long thoracic horn, and curving up to meet it from the head is another horn. The male has an over-all length of four to six inches, a shining black body, and dull-green, or yellowish, wing covers. The female is unarmed and dull brown.

Dynastes tityus, one of the largest beetles in the southern United States, is attractively colored a greenish-gray, spotted with brown. It measures two to two and a half inches. The horn on the thorax, however, is only half an inch long.

The giants of the Dynastinae are the Elephant Beetles belonging to the genus *Megasoma.* Some of the largest of these are four inches long, big, bulky creatures as large as a man's fist. Large and heavy as they are, they are capable of flying, as are all of these massive, awkward-looking beetles. There are seven species of *Megasoma,* and they range from Central America throughout northern South America, each species in general occupying a well-defined area in this region.

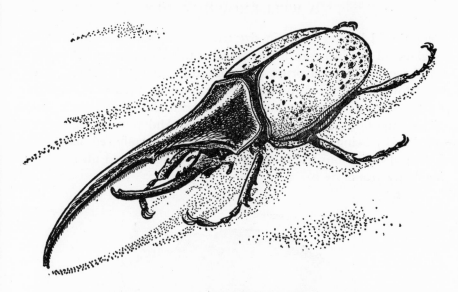

THE HERCULES BEETLE OF THE WEST INDIES MAY BE SIX INCHES LONG
The first explorers who collected the impressive-looking Hercules beetles, it is said, made a lot of money selling these big insects to enthusiastic museums and private collectors. The upper horn on a large male Hercules beetle is sometimes two and one-half inches long, and the whole insect may be six inches in length. The horns and prothorax are black, the upper wings are greenish; the prongs and underside of the upper horn are lined with amber-colored hairs. Beetles reach their greatest development in the tropics.

LONG-HORNED BEETLES

The beetles of this family (Cerambycidae) are well named, for they can at once be recognized by their very long antennae, which always reach at least to the base of the abdomen and often to the tip of the body. In a great many species the antennae have developed to extreme lengths, ranging up to two, three, and occasionally four, or more, times as long as the insect. Another name frequently used for these insects, especially in England, is Longicorns.

The tarsi, or feet, appear to have only four joints. Actually, they have five. The fourth is so small and so firmly united with the fifth, and so hidden between the deep divisions of the third joint, as to be scarcely visible. The first three segments are usually densely hairy.

A WELL-KNOWN FAMILY

Cerambycid beetles range in size from an eighth of an inch or less to giants of five inches or more. Many of them are attractively colored and have long been favorites with collectors. Student and professional collectors have scoured the remotest regions in search of new species. As a result, we probably know more about this family than about almost any other similar group of beetles. And yet, new species are continually being discovered, either from newly collected material or from old collections where the specimens have reposed unrecognized for many years.

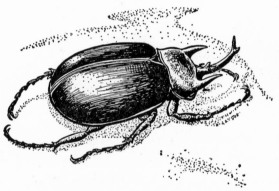

SOUTH AMERICA'S ELEPHANT BEETLE HAS A "TRUNK"
Broader than the Hercules beetle, but not so long, this heavy insect has a wingspread of eight to ten inches and is quite able to fly. The horn extending out from the front of the head suggests the trunk of an elephant, and the side prongs suggest the tusks. Nearly every natural history museum has specimens of this giant beetle, as well as of the Hercules and Goliath beetles. All three are members of the great scarab family.

We know very few complete life histories; but from the few species whose life cycles have been studied intensively, we have learned a little of the general family biology. The female lays her eggs on the bark of the particular host plant or tree that her species prefers, or inserts them into pockets she has cut with her mandibles. The larva bores in, penetrating deeper and deeper, growing as it feeds. As it nears maturity, it works toward the outer part of the bark and pupates just under the outer surface. The larval life may last for one year, but in some species it may last for three or four years. After emerging from its pupa, the adult beetle quickly cuts its way out of the bark.

A FAR-SIGHTED PARENT

Every part of a plant is attacked by the various species. The larger species attack the trunks or roots of trees, while the smaller ones are usually in the branches or twigs. In some, the parent, after laying her egg or eggs, goes just below and circles the branch, removing the bark to stop the growth, so that the young larvae will not be endangered by the growing and swelling wood.

A LONGHORN WITH TRULY LONG HORNS

American servicemen stationed in New Guinea and adjacent islands during World War II were so impressed by the long antennae of this curious insect that they brought home many specimens of it. Note the length of the "horns." Although the creature's front legs may be four inches long and its body three inches, its antennae may grow to a full seven inches. Like all longhorns, this one (called *Batocera*) lives in forests; it usually flies at night, and is attracted to lights.

In many countries, the larvae of some of the cerambycid beetles are eagerly sought for food. The Australian natives and lowland Indians of South America regard these grubs as a delicacy. The larvae are usually toasted until brown and crisp, and are somewhat like certain of our well-known commercial cocktail-snack preparations.

HOW TO FIND THEM

Adult cerambycid beetles are found resting on tree trunks or old logs; fallen timber is an ideal place for them. Smaller species may be found in flowers, for many of them are fond of nectar and pollen. Beating and sweeping the foliage of trees and shrubs will yield the species that live in them. Many species are attracted to light.

More than twenty-four thousand species have been described, 1,100 of them from North America. It is in the rain-forest tropics of the East Indies, Africa, and South America that the family reaches its greatest abundance, not only in the number of species, but in individuals. Here, also, the largest and most brilliant species are found.

The Harlequin Beetle, *Acrocinus longimanus,* from northern South America, is a remarkable long-horn. It is orange, with red and black markings on the thorax and wing covers. The body measures two and a half to three inches. The antennae are nearly twice the length of the body, while the forelegs are very long and slender, at least one and a half times the length of the insect. Those of the male are somewhat longer.

Other Long-horned Beetles. *Titanus giganteus* is usually considered the largest of the cerambycids. It is a huge, reddish-brown beetle, five inches long, one and a half inches broad. It makes its home in Brazil and the Guianas. This large species is scarce in collections, although the British Museum has three trays of them. The American Museum of Natural History has only one specimen.

Macrodontia cervicornis is another large species. Although the author has seen individuals in this species which measure more than *Titanus giganteus,* the average measures slightly less. It is tan or light brown in color, with darker-brown longitudinal lines on the wing covers. The mandibles are long and slender, varying from three-quarters to one and a half inches long, and armed along the inner edges with small teeth, making them quite ferocious looking. These beetles are not as bad as they look, however. Although one could give you a bad pinch if you placed your finger in its mandibles, they will not deliberately attack you.

ONE OF THE LARGEST LONG-HORNED BEETLES IN THE UNITED STATES
Large specimens of this big longhorn may be two inches long. The adult is black, with beautiful mahogany-colored antennae, but it spends its younger days as a fat white grub in the roots of various trees and shrubs. The shrimplike grubs of many of the longhorns are eaten by Indians, and are said by white cooks to be very good in a salad.

Prionus laticollis, about one and a half to two inches, is one of the largest long-horned beetles in the United States. It looks somewhat like a dwarf *Titanus giganteus,* although it is darker brown, almost black. The larvae live for three years in the roots of various trees, and even such small plants as the blackberry. The male has magnificent antennae, each segment being pectinate, or toothed, like a comb.

Orthosoma brunneum, about one and a half inches long, is a light reddish brown and somewhat shining. The larva, a white grub, is sometimes found feeding in oak stumps and logs, and perhaps on other dead trees.

Tetraopes tetraophthalmus is a pretty beetle found on milkweed. It is about half an inch long, dressed in bright-red, with six black spots, three on each wing cover. When the beetle sees you looking at it, it quickly folds its legs and slides off the smooth milkweed leaves to the ground, playing possum.

LEAF BEETLES

Look for these beetles on the leaves of plants. Almost every kind of plant will have one or more species of leaf beetles feeding on it.

You will have to look carefully, for many leaf beetles are quite small. A great many also have the habit of releasing their hold on the leaf at the slightest disturbance, folding their legs under them, and falling to the ground. A number have rear legs capable of leaping, and use these to propel themselves away from danger.

Others stay where they are when you approach, although they are very conspicuous, dressed in reds, yellows, and blues. Pick up one of these bright-colored beetles in your fingers, and a yellow juice, usually accompanied by a strong odor, will ooze out of the leg joints. This is believed to be ill-tasting to birds, their principal enemy, which quickly learn through experience to leave such good-looking morsels alone.

These beetles (family Chrysomelidae) are closely related to the cerambycid, or long-horn, beetles. They have the same type of tarsi, or feet; that is, feet that are apparently four-jointed, the third joint deeply divided, and the first three joints hairy beneath. They differ in never having the long antennae which are characteristic of the long-horns. In the chrysomelids, the antennae seldom reach the base of the thorax.

There is, however, one subfamily, the Donaciinae, whose members do have moderately long antennae. They also have a long, slender body, and in many ways resemble a cerambycid. One quickly learns to recognize at a glance the respective members of these two families.

The leaf beetles comprise one of the very large families of beetles, with over twenty-five thousand catalogued species in the world, about a thousand of these having been found in North America. The species fall readily into some twelve or more subfamilies, depending upon the personal views of the cataloguers studying the group. In fact, many specialists in the study of insects are inclined to break this family made up of groups having rather similar characteristics into several families based upon the subfamilies and the larval characteristics. Perhaps they have some good reason for doing this; but in this book we shall follow the old method, and list some of the subfamilies so that the reader may have a better understanding of this attractive family.

The subfamily Donaciinae, already mentioned, is quite a notable one. This group contains long, golden-brown or purplish (usually iridescent) beetles that are found upon plants living in, or near, water.

LEAF BEETLES ARE BEAUTIFUL PESTS

The roundish beetle (*bottom right*) so brightly striped and spotted is the infamous Colorado potato beetle, which has spread from its early home in the Southwest to wherever potatoes are grown in the United States; nowadays it is also found in parts of Europe. The two other insects are cucumber beetles, common in the eastern and central United States. Both adults and larvae feed on the vines of cucumber, squash and melon; the pollen in squash and pumpkin flowers is also popular with the adults.

The adults of many species go below the surface of the water to lay their eggs in the submerged stems of water lilies and the like, for their larvae live underwater, feeding sometimes near the roots. This sub-family is best represented in the temperate areas.

Special interest attaches to the beetles in the subfamily Sagrinae. Some of the largest of the leaf beetles are in this subfamily. The Kangaroo Beetle, *Sagria papuana* of the Melanesian islands, is an inch long. Nearly all the members of this group live in tropical climates. Only four species are listed in the United States, and they are all in the Southwest. Sagrinae beetles are brightly colored; a deep-blue shade is one of the most commonly seen. The upper part of their hind legs is long and greatly thickened. The larvae of many species live in plant stems, which become greatly swollen around their tenants.

Farmers have some acquaintance with the subfamily Chrysomelinae. Round, strongly hemispherical beetles, these insects are usually brightly colored in contrasting combinations. They delight in sunning themselves on the upper surface of a leaf, especially early in the morning while the dew is still heavy. Species in the temperate climates are seldom more than half an inch in length. In the South American tropics, some reach a length of one inch, are nearly as broad, and are half an inch high.

Some of the agricultural pests of the United States belong in this group, including the famous yellow and black Colorado Potato Beetle, and the tiny brown and yellow Turnip Beetle, which has migrated to the southern states from Argentina.

Another very important group of leaf beetles are the Galerucinae. This group contains softer-bodied leaf beetles. They are somewhat oval and only slightly arched, except in a number that have an abdomen so enlarged that the beetles appear to be resting on their heads. It is in this subfamily that many of our serious economic pests belong, including the Elm Leaf Beetle. Most of the species are rather dull in color, although a few are metallic yellow, red, or blue.

Perhaps not quite so impressive is the next subfamily, Halticinae. Beetles in this group are generally quite small. They are known as Flea Beetles because of their great leaping powers. A leap of two feet is not at all unusual. The uppermost segment of the hind legs is greatly enlarged and muscular.

No giants either are the leaf eaters in another group, Hispinae. Members of this subfamiiy are attractive little beetles, seldom over half an inch long. They are easily recognized by the short, stiff antennae which stick straight out in front. The tips of the antennae are usually slightly enlarged. The wing covers of many are broader at the end than at the base, making the beetle appear wedge-shaped. The wing covers are frequently pitted, with distinct ridges between the rows of pits.

Most of the Hispinae measure less than half an inch. One genus, *Alurnus*, occurring throughout northern South America, comprises the largest chrysomelids known. They range from one to one and a half inches. All are brightly dressed in contrasting colors of red, yellow and blue-black.

TORTOISE BEETLES

The beetles in this group (subfamily Cassidinae) are round or oval and flattened, with the edge of the wing covers and thorax dilated, or expanded. This expanded edge fits rather closely to the leaf on which they rest and usually covers the legs and head of the beetle, in very much the same way that the tortoise shell covers the tortoise, hence the common name. Most of the cassids are brightly colored, and many yellow species shine like burnished gold. This iridescence is the result of body fluids close to the surface, which break up the light rays. For this reason, when the insect dies, the lovely brilliance and shine of its coloring disappear.

WEEVILS—BEETLES WITH SNOUTS

There are some beetles whose heads are prolonged into a beak or snout. The extension may not be distinctly visible; then again it may be very pronounced. The beak may be short or long, broad or slender. It may curve downward, or stick straight out in front. No matter what the shape or size may be, the mouth parts are placed on its very end.

This beak takes a definite part in the activities of each of the various species, for they use it to make an opening in which to lay their eggs. Because of this distinctive feature, these insects have been called snout beetles. Weevil is a more familiar term, however, although this name is frequently applied to any damage-doing insect.

So universal is the belief that all weevils are injurious, that the entire group is condemned by mankind. Actually, only a few of the species are injurious; a great many serve in the very necessary business of controlling plants and in reducing plant material back into soil. All weevils are vegetarians.

There are six generally recognized families, although there has been a recent tendency among insect experts to raise some of the lower groups to family rank. We can mention only four of the families here.

PRIMITIVE WEEVILS

These curiously shaped beetles are called primitive because their activities are not quite as highly organized as those of other weevils. Actually, these weevils are fairly specialized, and are well designed for their own particular type of life.

They are all quite slender. Their antennae are not elbowed, as in many weevils, and sometimes are slightly clubbed. The members of a species are not at all uniform in size. Some individuals will be only half an inch long, while others may measure over two inches. The snout is equally variable in length, as well as the position of the antennae on the head.

How the Male Helps the Female. The sexes differ quite markedly in the shape of the head. In the male, the head is short and thick, and has a pair of large jaws; in the female, the head is prolonged straight out into a slender snout with a pair of small jaws on the tip.

This beak serves the female well, for, with it, she chews out a hole in a recently fallen or dying tree. When ready, she deposits an egg in the bottom, safe from hungry enemies and with an abundance of food available for her hatching offspring. The male seems to enjoy watching his mate at work; at any rate he lurks near-by. If another male comes by, he attacks the rival at once, pushing and prodding with his head, the rival returning push for push. The vanquished one crawls away, leaving the conqueror to stand guard.

Sometimes, when the boring is deep, the female is unable to extricate her jaws; then the valiant male comes to her rescue. The female braces her front legs and stiffens her body. The male presses down on her abdomen, literally prying her out of her dilemma, and showing a remarkable knowledge of the principle of leverage.

Most of the species are sociable, collecting in numbers under loose bark. The author has seen a hundred or more in a favorable location of this sort. It is here that all sizes and variations are to be found. Since they are always associated, we know them to be a single species, something it would be hard to believe if only the extreme variants from distant places were known.

WEEVILS PROVIDE A HOME FOR THEIR BABIES

The beak of the slender female nut weevil (*top*) is sometimes longer than her body; she uses this extraordinary snout to drill a deep hole into a nut so that she may deposit her eggs in the kernel. The adult is about half an inch long, dark brown, and covered with yellowish hairs. Lower down we see a female wood-boring weevil—*Eupsalis minuta,* a reddish-brown creature with yellowish spots. Watching at the left is the male, who guards her while she is boring into a dead tree to deposit her eggs.

The family (Brentidae) is a small one, containing only about nine hundred species. Most of these make their home in the tropics, only about six being found in North America.

Eupsalis minuta is the most interesting species of this family that we find in the United States. It ranges from New England, southern Canada, and Nebraska, southward to Florida and Texas. The weevils are dark reddish-brown creatures, with long, yellowish spots (sometimes joined together) attractively decorating the wing covers. The individuals vary in size from a quarter of an inch to three-quarters of an inch. The females all look alike, but the males have at least three named forms, differing in the style and arrangement of beak and antennae.

FUNGUS WEEVILS

At first glance, you would scarcely suppose many of the species in this family (Anthribidae) to be weevils. For, in most of them, the beak is very short and broad; the antennae are not elbowed, and, in some species, are very long (frequently longer than the insect itself) and slender. These are sometimes taken to be long-horned beetles (Cerambycidae), and have even been confused in large museum collections. A simple way to distinguish between the two families is by counting the segments of the beetle's leg (tarsus). The tarsi of longhorn beetles have five segments that appear to be only four; the fungus weevils have four segments that appear to be only three.

You can find some adults about woody fungi, where their larvae will be feeding. Others will be in smut fungi, while many species bore in dead wood on twigs or old fallen trees. Some also feed upon seeds or beans.

The Coffee Bean Weevil, *Areocerus fasciculatus,* has become quite a pest, particularly in coffee beans, and to a lesser extent in cacao, cotton, senna, and dried fruits. Shippers and shipping agents are constantly in trouble because of this small brown beetle. It has been carried by man's commerce from India to the far corners of the world, becoming established and breeding everywhere. But it cannot continue to survive where the winters are rather cold.

Most of the 2,000 species that compose the Anthribidae family live in the tropics. A great many from Queensland, Australia, have been described, and doubtless a great many are still to be discovered in New Guinea and elsewhere. We know of eighty-three species living in the United States.

SNOUT BEETLES

These are the true snout beetles, weevils, or curculios, as they are frequently called. It is thought that this family (Curculionidae) is the largest in number of species of any of the numerous families of beetles. Since many beetle families are rich in species, this family must go very high to top them, and it does; more than forty thousand snout beetles are known at this time.

New species are constantly being described, and when more remote areas have been thoroughly explored it is estimated that the number may be raised to 70,000 or even 100,000 species.

While these figures are tremendously impressive, not so with many of the beetles themselves. The majority are rather dull in color, although some are real jewels, decorated with iridescent colors reflected from the finely ridged scales.

The snout beetles vary considerably in size, ranging from very minute species about the size of a pinhead to gigantic and startling-looking creatures three inches long. The snout is also quite variable, but always distinguishable, and in the nut weevils it is frequently longer than the insect itself. One wonders just how they manage this snout. You expect them to go stumbling over it at any moment.

The curculios are plant feeders, attacking chiefly fruits, seeds, and nuts; but no part of any plant is exempt from one or another of their many species, both larvae and adults. It is only natural that in this great horde of plant-eating insects quite a number should prove to be serious agricultural pests. Among these may be mentioned the Rose Snout Beetle, *Rhynchites bicolor,* which breeds in wild and cultivated roses, throughout a large part of the United States. It is red and black and a quarter of an inch long.

The Cotton Boll Weevil, *Anthonomus grandis,* a native American insect, is very destructive to cotton in the South. A close relative, the Apple Blossom Weevil, *Anthonomus pomorum,* does much damage in orchards. The Plum Curculio, *Conotrachelus nenuphar,* feeds on apples and cherries, as well as on plums.

Stored grain products come in for their share of weevil pests. The Granary Weevil, *Sitophilus granarius,* and the Rice Weevil, *Sitophilus oryza,* together eat or damage annually some forty million dollars' worth of food man has prepared for himself.

The Palmetto Weevil, *Rhynchophorus cruentatus,* the largest curculionid in the United States, is found in the southern states, from South Carolina to Louisiana. This beautiful insect is usually about one and a quarter to one and a half inches long. Wherever the palmetto and date palm grow, these beetles are rather common, for the larvae bore into the trunks of those that are dead or dying. Most of the specimens are black; a few, however, are a rich shade of maroon on the sides, with black remaining as a central thoracic line, and with three spots on each wing cover.

BARK BEETLES AND AMBROSIA BEETLES

These are very small weevils (family Scolytidae) that would not be mentioned except for the great destruction they cause, and for the interesting lives that many of them lead.

Bark Beetles. The bark beetles are the creatures that put curious designs under the bark of a tree, incidentally loosening the bark and killing the tree, or the limbs, for the various species attack different parts of the trees from the roots to the twigs.

The mother beetle bores through the bark, then excavates a tunnel parallel with the grain, in the cambium layer, the green, growing part just under the bark. At regular intervals along this tunnel, she lays her tiny, white eggs. When the eggs hatch, each little grub starts to feed, eating out at right angles to the main tunnel, growing fatter, and consequently making a larger burrow as it travels. None of these burrows ever join, but gradually diverge from one another.

If many beetles attack the same tree, they very effectively circle the trunk or branches in which they have been feeding, (girdling the tree) as they go. The author has seen acres of timber killed by these tiny beetles in just this way. The United States Department of Agriculture estimates that in fifty years the value of the timber destroyed by these beetles would be over $1,000,000,000. Because of the rather pretty designs these beetles make under the bark, they are also called "engraver beetles."

Ambrosia Beetles. These are scolytid beetles in which the adults as well as the larvae do not confine their attentions to the bark and cambium layer, but penetrate deep into the wood. They usually prefer dead or dying trees. It is believed that these beetles, besides eating the wood, feed upon a fungus, yellow in color and known as ambrosia, which the beetles grow in the passages they have dug.

According to some studies made of a few species, the female beetle even carries the ambrosia spores with her when she flies from the burrow where she was born to start her own nursery burrow. Soon the new passages are lined with the fungi, which looks to the unassisted eye like a coating of sulfur, but when examined under a lens shows up as a mass of short stems, each topped with small round swellings. Eggs, larvae, pupae, and adult beetles live in the ambrosia-lined passages. Their tunnels spoil the value of the logs. It is not unusual to have the beetles continue to live in the wood long after the logs have been sawed into lumber, and the lumber incorporated into hurriedly and cheaply constructed houses.

Moths and Butterflies — Handsomest of Insects

Of ALL THE INSECTS, the popular favorite is undoubtedly the butterfly. Small boys and girls start their insect collections with butterflies, and many adult collectors specialize in these bright and exquisite beings. As a result, we have a wider knowledge of them than of any of the other insect groups.

Concerning moths, which are both more diverse in form and more numerous in species, we know almost as much; this is also partly because of their beauty, but largely because some of them are great pests and have required much patient study by our economic entomologists.

The butterflies and the moths form one of the largest orders in number of species and of individuals, Lepidoptera (meaning "scaly wings"). It has members that live in lands of nearly perpetual cold, as well as the steaming tropics. It is in the tropical regions, however, that the greatest number of species live, and it is here too that the species develop the brightest colors and largest sizes within the order.

The poetic phrase "clothed in color" is quite literally true for moths and butterflies. When the adult emerges from its cocoon or chrysalis it wears a bright, fresh costume in the color pattern of its kind. As it grows older and engages in a day-by-day tussle with the elements, it loses much of its brilliance, partly through fading, it is true, but largely through the dislodging of the colored scales that cover its wings and body. Only these tiny dustlike scales are colored. Without them the insect's wings are drab or transparent. It is from these scales that the order takes its scientific name.

To appreciate the beauty of a butterfly's wing, you have only to study it under a medium-power lens. The scales, each a tiny jewel hung by a slender stalk, lie side by side in evenly arranged rows, an upper row slightly overlapping the base of the row just below, in a manner suggestive of the shingles on our roofs. The broad wings are strengthened by veins, which radiate more or less from the base to the outer margins. It is on the arrangement of these veins that a system of classification has been founded. In other orders of insects, the arrangement of veins in the wings also is an important characteristic of family demarcation.

HOW TO TELL THE MOTHS FROM THE BUTTERFLIES

Butterflies fly during the daytime, but seldom at night, although they will flutter off to a new location if they are disturbed. Most moths fly at night. However, all those insects flying in the daytime that look like butterflies may not actually be butterflies, for there are a number of day-flying moths. These day-fliers are usually so brightly colored that they are easily confused with the butterflies. Nevertheless, there is one sure way to differentiate between butterflies and moths. All butterflies have a knob, or enlargement, at the tip of their antennae. The moths have either slender, tapering antennae ending in a sharp point, or feathery, or fernlike, antennae. In general, moths tend to have thicker and heavier bodies.

There is still another group of day-flying Lepidoptera that might be confusing to the casual observer. These are the Skippers. They have thick bodies, and their wings are usually brown or dull in color. They also have the knobbed antennae; their antennae, however, have at the end of the knob a tiny, slender hook that curves back. This group is a connecting link between the butterflies and the moths. Entomologists, in general, concede the skippers to be more closely allied to the butterflies.

The Lepidoptera, therefore, fall into two suborders, Rhopalocera, from the Greek words *rhopalon,* meaning "club," and *keras,* meaning "horn"; and Heterocera, from *hetero,* meaning "otherwise," and *keras,* meaning "horn." The butterflies and skippers thus belong to Rhopalocera, and the moths to Heterocera. Well over a hundred thousand species of Lepidoptera have been described, with numerous subspecies, varieties and forms. New species are constantly being set up by specialists working upon their particular small groups.

FROM EGG TO CATERPILLAR

The butterfly and the moth, like all other insects, start life as eggs. The mother is a very good botanist, for she lays her eggs on a host plant which will properly nourish her offspring. The identification of the food plant is probably accomplished through odor association. Each Lepidoptera species, or related group of species, is usually restricted in its feeding to one plant species or closely related species.

The eggs of a few butterflies and moths are roundish and smooth, but most of them are beautifully sculptured with pits or grooves, or decorated with lines or ridges, and even spines. The designs are so varied that one could spend an entire lifetime in studying the eggs in relation to the species and recording them by drawings or photographs. The eggs of only a few species have been studied.

The need for more study also applies to our knowledge of the caterpillars, the term generally used for the larvae (the forms which are produced from the eggs) of the butterflies and moths. Here, we find creatures of curious and bizarre shape, strangely, and sometimes gaudily, colored, although most of them are of the greenish tones that blend so well with the foliage upon which they feed. Not only do the caterpillars differ according to their species, but also according to their age. A caterpillar sheds its skin several times during its growth, and each time the new skin is differently shaped and colored. A full-grown caterpillar may not resemble in the least one that is newly hatched.

THE PUPA COMES INTO BEING

The third stage in the life of the butterflies and moths is the pupa. In color, most of the pupae are reddish or brownish, but many are gray in order to blend more neatly with the mosses on the tree trunks where they are usually found. Others are green or even bluish.

Some pupae hang by the tail. Others stand upright, with the tail secured in a little pad of silk, and with a silken strand around the waist, very much like the life belt of a lineman or a window cleaner. A great many of the moth caterpillars burrow into the ground to pupate. Others content themselves by hiding under loose bark, a crevice in a tree trunk, a hollow log, or debris on the ground. The pupae that excite our curiosity the most when we are children are the beautiful cocoons spun by the caterpillars of a few of the members of the family Saturniidae.

MILKWEED BUTTERFLIES

Although it is one of the smallest families of butterflies in species, the family Danaidae is one of the most widely distributed. Members will be found in most of the lands between the Arctic and the Antarctic. Cold limits their ascent of mountains to not much beyond nine thousand feet. Some member of the danaids will be found, wherever its caterpillars' food plant, the *Asclepias*, or milkweed, grows, or has traveled. Our common *Danaus plexippus*, the Monarch Butterfly, is one of the most experienced of travelers, for it has immigrated into many new lands within the last century. It voyages to foreign places as a pupa, probably in bales of American hay.

FASCINATING HABITS OF THE MONARCH BUTTERFLY

The migrating habits of the monarch butterfly are extremely fascinating. As warm weather develops in Florida and the states along the

Gulf of Mexico, this butterfly pushes farther north, laying its eggs on young milkweed plants. The butterflies developing from these eggs again push farther north, until, by late June and July, they have reached the northern limit of their dispersal, which is southern Canada. Another brood then develops, reaching maturity in August.

THE MONARCH BUTTERFLY GOES SOUTH FOR THE WINTER

The wings of this lovely American butterfly are orange-colored, with black borders and white spots. When the weather gets cool in the northern United States, the monarchs move south to deposit their eggs. Next spring a new brood flies north. The caterpillar, which develops from the egg, is yellowish green, with black bands and black legs, and it feeds on milkweed leaves. Later, it transforms itself into a pupa or chrysalis—now it looks like a beautiful jade ornament decorated with gold.

With the colder days of September, these butterflies turn their wings southward, and, governed by some instinct we can hardly guess at, begin their long journey to the Gulf. This is not a mass flight of the sort exhibited by migrating birds, but a series of individual actions as one by one they fly steadily southward. They differ also from the migrating birds in that they fly during the warmer hours of the day, instead of at night. When night comes, the monarch butterflies settle down to sleep, sometimes thousands upon thousands collecting on a single small tree or group of trees, much to the amazement of all their human observers.

This sleeping together is of distinct advantage to the monarch, for, like all of the danaids, it is protected from butterfly-eating birds by its disagreeable-tasting secretions. This characteristic is advertised in the daytime by its bright colors, and at night by odor. Numerous individuals collected together accentuate this warning odor.

Another odor that is characteristic of these butterflies, but confined to the males, comes from the scent pouches usually located on the rear wings, close to one of the veins. Elongated scales on the wings scatter the scent in the presence of the females.

The monarch has had many scientific names bestowed upon it by various authors. *Danaus* and *Anosia* are two of its commoner generic names, while specifically it appears in books under *archippus* and *menippe,* as well as others. A closely related species known as the Queen Butterfly, *Danaus berenice,* is found in the Gulf states and southwest into Mexico, each summer spreading only a short distance away from this restricted area.

Each of these species has a butterfly species from a different family, a family without disagreeable secretions, which resembles the danaid species rather closely. The edible butterflies, through close resemblance to bad-tasting species, are supposed to gain some protection. This is called protective resemblance, or mimicry.

Many of the Danaidae have a characteristic color pattern. This is a basic color of transparent white, yellow, or reddish, with the veins outlined in black, and frequently with a black border. Others are brown, marked with white, blue, or violet.

Since most of the species in this family are largish, and their scales are firmly attached, they need less care in collecting than is necessary for most Lepidoptera. The beginner will find it easier to have good specimens in his collection if he starts with the milkweed butterflies.

THE HELICONIANS

Closely related to the danaids, the long, slender-winged heliconians are gaily decorated with yellow, crimson, or blue luster bands across a black background. This family (Heliconidae) is confined to the tropics of the Western Hemisphere.

The Zebra Butterfly, *Heliconius charitonius,* ventures as far north as Florida and the Gulf states. It is a deep-black beauty, striped longitudinally across both wings and body with lemon-yellow bands. Its caterpillars, equally startling, with black spines on their white bodies, feed on the leaves of the passionflower. The chrysalis makes a creaking noise if it is disturbed, and male butterflies will hover around the chrysalis of a female, waiting for her to emerge.

Observers say that no bird or animal is willing to eat a heliconian, apparently because of the unpleasant odor emanating from these butterflies. Therefore, the butterflies tend to collect in swarms to accentuate this odor. Many of the species, including the zebras, gather in large groups at night to sleep on vines and Spanish moss. The place selected takes on the protecting odor, and night after night the individuals return to the same sleeping quarters.

Heliconians love to fly along the trails through tropical forests, visiting a jungle flower for a sip of nectar, where a spot of sunlight filters through the dense canopy. On such visits they are easily captured, but if the first sweep of the collector's net fails, they are off, seldom permitting a second opportunity for capture.

Although a nicely mounted collection of heliconians makes a striking display, nothing compares with the thrill of seeing them alive in their jungle home.

BRUSH-FOOTED BUTTERFLIES

The largest family of butterflies, the Nymphalidae, comprises about five thousand species. You can easily recognize members of this family by the greatly reduced front legs, a characteristic which makes them seem to have only two pairs. For this reason, they are frequently called "four-footed butterflies." The family is so large that special names, such as fritillaries, anglewings, tortoise shells, peacocks, sovereigns, emperors, leaf butterflies, and others have been applied to groups which the names very well describe.

THE FRITILLARIES

Medium-to-large tan or brownish butterflies with silver spots on the underside, the fritillaries sport with others among the blossoms in weedy meadows during late summer and early fall.

The Great Spangled Fritillary, *Argynnis cybele,* and the Aphrodite Fritillary, *aphrodite,* are the most common species. *Argynnis cybele* has a very wide, tan band completely filling the space between the two outer rows of silver spots, while *aphrodite* has a very narrow, pale area. Some lepidopterists think that the New World species do not belong to the genus *Argynnis* and have placed them in the genus *Speyeria.* However, some of the fritillaries are so well known under the genus *Argynnis,* appearing as such in nearly every popular book that they have been retained as such in this one.

The Regal Fritillary, *Argynnis idalia,* is the most beautiful, and one of the largest. It cannot fail to attract your attention as it flashes by. The red forewings, bordered with black, and the rear wings, suffused with black and trailing far behind the forewings, at once identify this rather rare butterfly. It displays a nervous temperament, pausing momentarily for a sip of nectar at a pasture flower, then darting off on flashing wings to other fields. Perhaps it is this habit of seldom remaining long in one spot that makes it rare in collections. Many of the *Argynnis* caterpillars feed on violets.

The genus *Brenthis* has two common species in the eastern United States. The Meadow Fritillary, *bellona,* has no silver spots underneath it, while the Silver-bordered Fritillary, *myrina,* looking much the same as *bellona* on the upper side, is spotted with silver on the underside, particularly on the rear wings. *Brenthis* has about one-half the wing spread of *Argynnis,* and *Phyciodes* is even smaller. This last-named genus also has two common and widely distributed species, *nycteis* and *tharos.* Almost any weedy field has dozens of these species visiting its flowers.

THE ANGLEWINGS

The anglewings look as if Mother Nature had dextrously used pinking shears in cutting out their wings. The upper side of the wings is mottled in browns and tans, with traces of reds and yellows thrown in to make the coloring more brilliant. The underside is minutely flecked with specks of gray, brown, and black, while in the middle of the rear wing is a small dash of silver. This pattern, together with the notched edges of the wings, disguises the butterfly as an old leaf or a moss-covered scrap of bark. It is a good example of protective coloration, enabling the butterfly to disappear as it alights, snuffing out like a candle the brighter colors shown while flying.

All of our anglewings pass the winter in the adult stage, hibernating in a hollow log or tree, an old shed, or a deserted cabin. Occasional warm spells in midwinter may coax them out from their hiding places for a few minutes of flight in the noonday sunshine.

These butterflies belong to the genus *Grapta* (*Polygonia* in recent lists). *Grapta interrogationis* is the largest. The silver spots on the underside of its rear wings are, with a little imagination, a pair of Spanish question marks. *Grapta comma,* somewhat smaller, has a comma-like mark, and *Grapta progne,* an angled mark.

There are two broods of *Graptas* a year, one reaching the adult stage in the summer, the other in the fall, and the latter, of course, is the hibernating form. These are known as the summer and winter forms. Strange to say, they differ in color, the summer *Graptas* usually being darker. When butterflies differ in this way, they are called seasonal dimorphic forms.

THE TORTOISE SHELLS

Tortoise-shell butterflies have delicately scalloped wings, splotched and dotted with red, yellow, and orange, in a manner faintly appropriate to their name. They belong mostly to the genus *Vanessa* (recently given as *Nymphalis*).

The Mourning Cloak, *Vanessa antiopa,* is our largest hibernating butterfly, and perhaps the most interesting of the tortoise-shell group. This somberly beautiful creature should be familiar to every wanderer in the out-of-doors, for it is our commonest butterfly in early spring. Leaving its winter quarters on the first warm day, it rests along a sunny pathway, slowly fanning its wings, and absorbing the delicious heat. You may also find it on a willow tree, just before the first tender leaves appear, for it is here that you will see its blackish egg clusters around the young twigs. Failing to find willows, however, the mourning cloak is willing to accept poplars and elms as food for its young.

It is only in the sunshine that we can appreciate the beautiful velvety-brown upper surface of the wings, margined with a yellow band. Look carefully, and you will see a row of purplish spots just inside the band. The underside is a finely mottled brown and gray, the coloring of dead leaves, an arrangement which completely disguises the resting butterfly. Mourning cloaks are quite confident of their invisibility; the author has often slipped up behind a resting mourn-

BUTTERFLIES THAT MIMIC DEAD LEAVES

The mourning cloak (*top*) is so called because the underside of its wings is dull dark brown, mimicking a dead leaf. The upper side looks dull, too, unless the sun shines on it, when it shimmers with purple and gold overtones. The mourning cloak lives through the winter in old buildings and in hollow trees, coming out with the first sunny days of spring. The anglewing (*bottom*) is brighter in color than the mourning cloak, but it, too, can look like an old leaf, and it also hibernates.

ing cloak and taken it in his fingers. They have another scheme in their bag of tricks, for, when captured in this way, they play dead, flopping over lifelessly if placed in the palm of your hand. You can even poke them around a bit; they will still remain limp. Just as you begin to think the butterfly is actually dead, frightened to death, perhaps, there is a flash of wings, and your captive is gone.

The mourning cloak ranges throughout North America and southward into Guatemala. It also occurs in the north temperate belt of the Old World. It is quite common in Europe, but very rare in England, where it is called the Camberwell beauty. English collectors are naturally anxious to obtain native specimens, but they laugh at their own eagerness and love to tell the following improbable joke. Once upon a time, they relate, a collector imported living specimens from Europe. Releasing them on his own grounds, he recaptured the butterflies, so that he could truthfully say he had collected Camberwell beauties on English soil.

The American Tortoise Shell, *Vanessa milberti,* is frequently seen in wet meadows, for here its caterpillar can be found feeding on nettles. It is dark brown above, with a broad band of orange across each wing, and two orange spots near the front margin of the front wings; the under surface is a mottled slate-gray color.

The Compton Tortoise Shell, *Vanessa j-album,* is larger than *milberti,* but not as large as the mourning cloak. It is a light tan above, this coloring being broken by three large patches and a dash of white on the front margin. The gray-brown under surface with a conspicuous silver "J" on the rear wings explains its species name. Its caterpillar does not confine itself to nettles, but feeds also on the false nettle, hop vines, and elm. It is restricted to northern North America. California has a tortoise shell all its own, and named for it. This is *Vanessa californica,* at times very abundant throughout western North America. Although its caterpillars prefer ceanothus (a prickly shrub), they will feed on other plants.

The Painted Lady, *Pyrameis cardui,* is perhaps the most widely distributed butterfly of the Nymphalidae. It is almost cosmopolitan, for it is found throughout the habitable world, with the exception of most of South America. It is also called the thistle butterfly, because it delights in sitting on a thistle blossom, probing into the depths of the flower for nectar with its long snoutlike appendage. Tan and orange, dappled with black, it has a row of circled spots on the hind wings. This species can be recognized by the four distinct, eyelike spots on the underside of the rear wing.

The painted lady has probably been able to spread to the far corners of the earth because it is not at all particular about its food. Its caterpillar feeds on a great variety of plants, including the thistle, sunflower, burdock, and hollyhock. It spins a little tent of silk and particles of the plant upon which it feeds, later drawing the leaves together into a larger canopy.

The Red Admiral, *Pyrameis atalanta,* is the largest species of this genus. It prefers the temperate weather of the middle Northern Hemisphere, and is quite common there, but it sometimes ventures into the hotter areas of the tropical belt by following the mountain ranges southward.

The background color of the red admiral is a rich, purplish black. The front wings are crossed with a band of orange-red, with white spots near the tip. The rear wing is margined with paler orange-red. The under surface is a maze of wavy lines, with a number of obscure eyespots on the rear wings. It has two broods in a season, passing the winter in either the adult or the pupal stage. Hop growers do not like this butterfly, for its caterpillar delights in a diet of hop leaves.

THE PEACOCK BUTTERFLIES

These are called peacock butterflies because of the extremely large eyespots on their wings.

The Buckeye, *Junonia coenia,* is a common butterfly throughout the southern United States. As you travel northward you find it becoming rarer and rarer, until along the Canadian border and southern New England, you scarcely ever see one. As a boy, the author was quite elated when he captured his first buckeye near his home in Ohio, the "Buckeye State."

The three conspicuous, eyelike spots on the forewing, and the two on the rear wing, at once identify this pretty butterfly. In addition, the forewing is crossed by a pale-white band, and has several smaller orange spots, and on the rear wing there is a narrow, but bright-orange, band a short distance from the margin. Wherever plantain or snapdragons are plentiful you can find the buckeye, for its caterpillars feed upon these plants. The peacock butterfly of Europe is somewhat similar to our buckeye; but it is usually placed in the genus *Vanessa.* Its specific name is *io.*

BASILARCHIA BUTTERFLIES

We now come to a group of butterflies that has long delighted and puzzled both the student and the collector, because of its many color variations and because of its remarkable habits. These butterflies belong to the genus *Basilarchia,* called *Limenitis* by some authors.

The Red-spotted Purple, *Basilarchia astyanax,* is the most representative of the genus. It ranges throughout the United States as far north as Canada. The rich dark-blue or dark-green, and a black band along the margins of the upper wings, quickly identify this beautiful butterfly. It also likes to show its under surface as it rests on a leaf or flower. The underside is brown with a submarginal row of red spots. There are two more red spots at the base of the forewings, and four at the base of the rear wings.

The Banded Purple, *Basilarchia arthemis,* has its principal home grounds in northern New England and southern Canada, but it often ventures southward into New York and Pennsylvania, keeping to the upper ridges of the mountains. Its common name refers to the wide and conspicuous white band crossing both the forewings and the rear wings. Without the band it would be quite similar to the red-spotted purple. Where the two species overlap we find a wide variety of intermediate forms. The difference is usually in a reduction of the white band, which begins to disappear from the rear wings first. A number of these forms have secured specific names. Perhaps it is better to consider them all as hybrids.

The red-spotted purple and the banded purple and their hybrids may be considered typical species of the genus. To add to the confusion, *Basilarchia* has another species, *archippus,* which is found in the United States. Instead of the typical purple shade, this species is a bright red, and, although slightly smaller, it is almost the exact duplicate, superficially, of *Danaus plexippus,* the monarch butterfly. It differs in that it has a shorter forewing, and that the markings on the tip are arranged differently. The rear wing has a narrow, black line crossing the middle, yet following the curve of the margin.

The Viceroy, *Basilarchia archippus,* is, therefore, said to mimic the monarch for the protection it might gain through its resemblance to a protected species. *Basilarchia hulsti* in the western states is believed to mimic *Danaus berenice,* which it resembles, for the same reason. Strange to say, the range of these last two butterflies almost exactly coincides.

THE DEAD-LEAF BUTTERFLIES

Before leaving the Nymphalidae, we should look at one other group, the dead-leaf butterflies of Asia. They belong to the genus *Kallima* and are sold as curiosities of Nature. The upper side is velvety brown; the forewings show bright-red bands. The rear wings are elongated to make a stubby tail. The underside, which is all you see when the butterfly is resting, is marked to resemble a dead, brown leaf. The central vein of the leaf is represented by a line running from the tail, which forms the stem of the leaf, to the apex of the wing. Lines angle off from the central line to form the branching veins of the leaf. As if to gain additional protection, the butterfly frequently, or wherever possible, settles on a twig that actually has dead, brown leaves.

SATYRS AND NYMPHS

The satyrids are small-to-medium-sized butterflies, dressed in soft browns or grays, resorting only to ringed circles or eyespots for decorative effect, much as women use buttons on their dresses. Other common names for this unobtrusive family (Satyridae), such as graylings and meadow browns, are more descriptive and more appropriate than the names satyrs and nymphs. In general, they are weak fliers, but excellent dodgers, slipping away almost without effort into tangled bushes or vines, as the experienced butterfly collector can well recall. Recent lists have changed many of the names of the satyrids, but for ease in comparison the names familiar to most of us are being retained here.

The Little Wood Satyr, *Neonympha eurytus,* is undoubtedly our most common species. It is dark brown above, tan below; the eyespots are ringed with yellow. It loves the shady forest pathways. You will find it there, flying close to the ground or along the forest edges, wherever there is grass to feed its light-green caterpillars.

The Common Wood Nymph, *Satyrus alope,* is our largest species. There are numerous color varieties, but all of them are probably one species. Some entomologists, however, regard them as several distinct species. The most distinctive feature of the common wood nymph is the conspicuous, large, yellow area on its forewings. In this area, are two dark eyespots. A larger, paler form lives in the Gulf states. Along the Atlantic coast a form called *maritima* has an orange, instead of a yellow, area; another form, *nephele,* ranging from the northern United States up into Canada, has no yellow area at all.

The Pearly Eye, *Debis portlandia,* is a soft tan with eight black eye-spots, three on the forewing and five on the rear wing. The spots are arranged in a row following the curve of the outer edge of the wing. On the underside, the spots are distinctly eyed.

The Grass Nymph, *Satyrodes canthus,* is soft brown. The spots on the under surface are larger than those above. It lives in wet meadows or grassy swamps.

The Glass-winged Butterflies, *Cithaerias* and *Haetera,* have transparent wings, to which they owe their common name. They are at home in the dark rain forest of tropical South America. Flying lazily, close to the ground, along a jungle trail, they seem easy to capture. But at the swing of your net, they are off into the dense side growth where you can never hope to get them. Their transparent wings make it almost impossible for the eye to follow them.

Along the Amazon and its upper tributaries, the Indians or natives of the region refer to these butterflies as the souls of their departed children, and, naturally, do not like to have them taken. While collecting insects in the interior of Peru, the author was able to secure a number of species of the genus *Haetera.* He was always careful, however, not to advertise this fact, and also to make certain no Indian was present when he did collect one; this was done out of respect for the feelings of the people among whom he was living, and to whom he was a foreigner.

BLUES, COPPERS, AND HAIRSTREAKS

Forming a large family of small butterflies, the members of this group (Lycaenidae) live all around the world, delighting collectors and confusing the insect experts of every country. They wear brilliant, metallic blues, greens, coppers, and various shades of these colors. The under surface is usually lighter than the upper side, and is decorated with dots, spots, and lines in patterns which identify the species. The exact determination of all the genera and species has proved very difficult, so that scientists are not at all agreed on the technical names of many of them.

As in most families of butterflies, there have been many changes in the generic and specific names to conform to recent research and to the international rules of nomenclature. This leads to considerable confusion of the amateur when consulting both the new and older books on insects.

Lycaenid larvae differ from those of most butterfly babies; they look more like hairy slugs than like ordinary caterpillars. Some are predatory creatures, feeding on scale insects, aphids, and perhaps other insects. Most, however, are vegetarians, particularly fond of the plant called dock and members of the pea family. The larvae of many species exude a secretion sought by the ants.

The Pygmy, *Brephidium exilis,* smallest of the North American lycaenids, is frequently sold mounted whole in a locket or brooch. Its wing expanse is only about five-eighths of an inch. Its brown wings have a white spot at the inner angle of the front pair, and are fringed with white.

The Spring Azure, or **Common Blue Butterfly,** visits flower after flower, in garden and field, all summer long. You are sure to see several on every field trip. As the summer progresses, or if you collect over a wide area, you will find numerous variations of this pretty butterfly. Entomologists have struggled to separate its innumerable sexual, seasonal, and climatic variations into named groups, but without unanimity as yet. Many authorities call it *Lycaena pseudargiolus,* but even its generic name is questioned.

The rear wings of the spring azure are rounded. If you find a small, blue butterfly with a tiny, threadlike tail, it is probably a close relative, the Eastern Tailed Blue, *Lycaena comyntas.* Examine its tail closely with a lens, for the little white tip is well worth looking at. Unfortunately, many of the specimens you collect will have lost their fragile tails. The females of this species are brown. The larvae are brownish green and feed on clover and similar legumes, whereas the larvae of the spring azure are light green and feed on the flowers of many plants.

The American Copper, *Chrysophanus hypophlaeus,* is a pretty butterfly, its red forewings spotted with black, and its black rear wings margined with red. Although its wing expanse is less than one inch, it is fearless and even pugnacious in defending its home territory. You will see it often during the summer in worn-out fields and meadows. Its stubby, bright-green larvae feed on sorrel, and retreat under stones to pupate.

SWALLOWTAILS

These are all large, strong-flying butterflies. Many of us are familiar with at least a few of them, for they sweep in to pause a moment at our favorite lilac, weigela, or butterfly bush. Only a moment and the swallowtail is off again, rising superbly to pass over our neighbor's house, as if its short sip of nectar had given it a tremendous burst of energy. It is impossible to follow the vagaries of its flight. It may be gone from our sight forever, or the next moment it may be back at the same flower for another taste of the delicious brew.

The caterpillars are large, fleshy, and smooth. Some of the species are decorated with two large, eyelike spots upon the thoracic region, giving them an appearance quite ferocious to human eyes, and one which is believed to frighten their enemies. A more effective means for warding off approaching attackers is the Y-shaped, orange-colored scent gland (called the osmeterium), which the caterpillar is able to push out through a slit in its thorax upon the slightest provocation. Not only is the sudden appearance of this weapon alarming; it also shoots out a disagreeable odor.

Many of the members of this large family (Papilionidae) have tails on their rear wings; at least, there is the place where the tails have been, for they are easily broken. Some species have two tails; one has three tails; some have no tails. Most of the tailless species inhabit the tropics, particularly the East Indies; but there is one, *Papilio polydamus,* found in the Gulf states.

The great bird-winged butterflies, the *Ornithoptera* of Malaysia, belong in this family. These are very large butterflies, sometimes having a wingspread of ten inches. The forewings are long and slender, the tip frequently curved back, making them very graceful creatures. In many species, the males and females are so differently colored that it is hard to believe that they can be mates. When the first collections of these bird-wings were received in the various museums of Europe, about two hundred years ago, this unusual difference caused considerable confusion in the naming of the species.

Naturally, the large size and remarkable colors of the *Ornithoptera* make them much sought after by collectors. Since the demand is heavy and specimens are scarce, dealers ask very high prices for them.

These butterflies are hard to capture because they fly so high. Some professional collectors have built high platforms over jungle trails used by the butterflies. From this position, and with long-handled nets, they are able to capture a few of those that fly past. All of this family in North America belong to the genus *Papilio*.

The Tiger Swallowtail, *Papilio glaucus* (called by some *Papilio turnus*), is one of our most familiar butterflies, not only because it is fairly common, but also because of its conspicuous yellow wings, barred with several black bands.

The female tiger swallowtail has two color forms. One form is yellow and black, like the male. In the other, the yellow is replaced by sooty-black, with dark-black bands. This variation has caused some confusion in the scientific naming of the butterfly. It happened that the black female form was discovered first and given the name *Papilio glaucus*. Later, the typical yellow form was described as a new species, *Papilio turnus*. Collectors, rearing the butterflies from eggs, soon learned that one batch of eggs could produce both color forms.

The Giant Swallowtail, *Papilio cresphontes,* is the largest species in the United States. It is black, with a yellow bar close to the margin, and another yellow bar crossing diagonally from the tip of the forewing to the base of the rear wing. The yellow bars are broken by the black veins, making a bar of spots. This is in contrast with *thoas* (with which it is frequently confused), in which the yellow bars are quite broad and well defined. *Papilio thoas* ranges from Florida and Texas southward, while *cresphontes* ranges northward to the Canadian border. It is rare in the North, but the author has collected it in the sand dunes along Lake Erie, and similar places in the vicinity of the Great Lakes. In the North, the caterpillar feeds on the hop tree and prickly ash, while in the extreme South, it feeds on orange leaves, frequently doing considerable damage. Citrus-fruit growers call the caterpillar the "orange dog."

THE SWALLOWTAIL IS HARD TO CATCH

Swallowtail butterflies have strong wings and can rise nearly straight up in the air—catching them requires more than a little craft and agility on the collector's part. Pictured is the tiger swallowtail; it has light yellow wings banded with black, but sometimes the female is all black. The caterpillar is large, smooth, and green, and has two large, eye-like spots behind its head. It feeds on such fruit trees as cherry, plum, and apple.

The Papaw Swallowtail, *Papilio marcellus,* also called the zebra swallowtail, ranges throughout the central United States, wherever the papaw, food of its caterpillars, grows. It is marked in much the same pattern as the yellow tiger swallowtail, except that the yellow is replaced by an exquisite, translucent white. This butterfly has seasonal variations, and the tails are twice as long in the summer form. Many of the older books call the butterfly *Papilio ajax.*

The Pipe-vine Swallowtail, *Papilio philenor,* is a beautiful, dark velvety-green, with a row of white, slightly crescent-shaped spots set in from the margin of the rear wing. The female is less brilliant and has a row of spots on the forewing as well as on the rear wing. The pipe-vine swallowtail is a common butterfly throughout temperate North America, wherever the pipe vine is abundant. It also feeds on asarum, or wild ginger.

The Parsnip, or **Carrot, Swallowtail,** *Papilio polyxenes,* is perhaps the most common *Papilio* in the eastern United States. It is black, with a double row of yellow spots, one close to the margin, the other set in from the margin. On the rear wings, blue fills much of the area between the two rows of yellow spots. This species is called *asterias,* and sometimes *ajax,* in various books. Subspecies and varieties of this beautiful butterfly live in some of the islands of the West Indies, as well as in Central America. They are found in northern South America, and follow the mountain ranges into Peru.

A somewhat similar specie, *zelicaon,* is found in western North America, and another, *bairdi,* in the Southwest.

The caterpillars of all of these species feed upon the various species of the carrot family. The European Swallowtail, *Papilio machaon,* is the corresponding species found in Europe.

The Spicebush Swallowtail, *Papilio troilus,* whose caterpillars also feed upon sassafras and laurel, is another common *Papilio* in eastern North America. It is sometimes called the green-clouded swallowtail, because of the greenish color of the upper surface of its rear wings. It resembles *polyxenes* but can be easily distinguished by the lack of the inner row of yellow spots on the upper surface of its wings.

The Western Swallowtail, *Papilio daunus,* lives in the western mountains of North America. It is one of our largest butterflies, frequently having a wing expanse of over five inches. It has two tails. The *Papilio pilumnus* of Arizona, a three-tailed species, is quite rare.

WHITES AND YELLOWS

These are the familiar, rather small, white and yellow butterflies that flutter about fields and pastures from early spring until late fall.

THE SPICEBUSH SWALLOWTAIL VISITS A ZINNIA

The spicebush swallowtail, a common butterfly throughout the eastern United States, is sometimes also called the green-clouded swallowtail because the male has greenish rear wings. This may be a good name for the male, but not for the female; her rear wings are clouded with blue.

They are particularly abundant when the clover is in bloom, and gather by the hundreds to picnic in its fragrant fields. Other names, such as sulphurs, orange tips, and brimstones are given to certain groups of them. All these pretty little butterflies belong to the family Pieridae.

All of the species have at least two broods, and some even produce three generations during the season. None of those living in our northern climates pass the winter as adult butterflies, but there are several species, which spend the long cold months as pupae or tiny chrysalises, waiting for the first warm days of spring before making their debut. The succeeding one or two generations then live their entire lives in the summer months.

The Imported Cabbage Butterfly, *Pieris rapae,* is undoubtedly the most abundant, and, therefore, the one we most commonly see, throughout a large portion of the United States. It is the only pierid that damages our crops to any extent. Accidentally introduced into Canada from England in 1860, and into the United States in 1868, it spread in a few years from coast to coast, and north to the limits of man's cabbage patches; it is now rapidly pushing its way into Central American countries. It has also immigrated with man into other continents.

The cabbage butterfly is white, with the tips of the forewings blackish, one black spot on the wing of the male, and two spots on the wing of the female. Both sexes have a single black spot near the front margin of the rear wing. In Europe, it is frequently called the turnip butterfly, and the name cabbage butterfly is then applied to *Pieris brassicae,* which is quite similar in appearance.

The Common White Butterfly, *Pieris protodice,* is a native species, ranging throughout the southern part of the United States, and very seldom seen in the northern states. As its name indicates, it was once quite common, but it is now becoming rare, driven out by the competition with the foreigner. It is also known as the southern cabbage butterfly and the checkered white. The latter name is very descriptive, for the white wings are blotched with black spots, more so in the female, where they are frequently connected by black extensions from the spots.

The checkered white does very little damage to the cabbage crop, for it feeds only on the extreme outer edges of the leaves and does not penetrate into the center of the head as *rapae* does. This habit accounts for its rapid reduction in numbers, for the cabbage grower, in spraying his cabbages, covers the outer leaves with his poison spray, killing off the larvae of the comparatively nondestructive *protodice,* but is unable to reach the inner leaves, where the real culprit is feeding.

Perhaps our native species persists only because individuals still feed on the wild species of the plant family to which the cabbage belongs, the wild cabbage having been its normal food before the numerous cultivated members of the cabbage family were introduced in the United States.

The Gray-veined White, *Pieris napi,* also has a number of other common names, such as mustard white, and old-fashioned cabbage butterfly. It was named the cabbage butterfly by the white settlers who first brought the cabbage plant to the New World, and for this reason is now sometimes called the old-fashioned cabbage butterfly. Believed to have been originally confined to Canada and the extreme northern United States, it rapidly spread southward, feeding on these new-found cabbage plants, until it covered the entire country.

Like the checkered white, this butterfly feeds only on the outer leaves, doing very little damage. The gray-veined white, now greatly reduced in numbers, has literally retreated to the woods, where it exists on wild species of Cruciferae, such as mustard and cress. *Pieris napi* is also a native of Europe, where it is known as the rape butterfly because there it feeds upon rape, a European herb.

The gray-veined white has many varieties, depending on season, climate, and location. It seems unable to decide whether it will be all white, or outline its veins with gray; keep the tips and front margins of the wings blackish; put one black spot on each front and hind wing, or a black blotch on each wing. Some of its varied forms have received special names.

The Gulf White, *Pieris monuste,* is a much larger species occurring throughout the Gulf states. The male is white, with a narrow brownish outer margin on the forewing, making a broad margin, and also a narrow brown margin on the rear wing.

The Falcate Orange Tip, *Euchloë genutia,* is a small butterfly with a wing expanse of slightly more than one inch. Only the male has the orange tip; on the under surface, both sexes are greenish, flecked with brown scales.

The Common Sulphur, *Colias philodice,* is slightly larger than the more plentiful cabbage butterfly, and is easily recognized by its yellow color, margined with solid black in the male, broken with lighter spots in the female. On the underside, in the center, is a silvery spot. Dozens of these butterflies fly over any clover field as you pass. The females also lay their eggs here, for the caterpillars feed upon clover. More, however, hover or drink at every puddle or wet spot in the few back-country roadways that still exist.

The Dog-face Sulphur, *Meganostoma caesonia,* is larger than the common sulphur. It has a much broader black band on the forewings, and this band is deeply indented, so that the yellow of the base extends into the black in two prolongations, looking, if you stretch your imagination, somewhat like the head of a high-browed poodle. In the female, the poodle silhouette is less sharply outlined.

Some other entomologists have thought the poodle looked more like a duck. When you see one of these butterflies, you can decide for yourself. It ranges throughout the eastern half of the United States from southern New Jersey and Wisconsin to the Gulf states.

The Little Sulphur, *Terias lisa,* is a dainty creature. With an expanse of about an inch and a quarter, its bright-yellow wings are broadly margined with black. It has three broods a year, and the last is believed to migrate southward, as the monarch does. No wintering stage has been discovered. Furthermore, great flocks have been recorded in Bermuda as arriving from the northwest. If they had traveled from this direction, the nearest land would be the northeastern part of the United States, six hundred miles away. Such a flight represents a long nonstop journey for these fragile butterflies to make.

There are a number of other *Terias* species in the United States and along the Gulf, which are described and illustrated in books devoted to the butterflies of North America.

Tropical South and Central America have some larger sulphurs measuring three inches or more across the wings. These butterflies have larger, conspicuous reddish or orange spots on their wings. Most of them belong to the genus *Callidryas.* They are remarkably strong fliers. One afternoon, while sitting on the deck of a ship anchored in the bay off Puerto Barrios, Guatemala, the author saw a steady stream of these butterflies passing overhead until twilight came, and the light failed. They were coming out of the south from unknown points, and disappearing toward unknown points in the north.

The Brimstone, or **Lemon, Bird,** *Gonepteryx rhamni,* is a very pretty European species. It looks somewhat like a small edition of one of the *Callidryas,* with its pale-yellow wings, marked with orange spots. It expands to only about one and a quarter inches.

THE MORPHO

Butterflies tax a writer's stock of superlatives, and none more so than the gorgeous *Morpho* (family Morphoidae). Its great wings, spreading six or seven inches from tip to tip, and almost as far from tip to tail, are an intensely iridescent blue. Sometimes the blue mass is broken with small opalescent spots, sometimes with a margin or patch of black or brown. The black or brown colors are pigments imbedded in the scales that thatch the wings; but the blue and red result from structural pattern. Each small scale is lined with minute ridges (called striae), which break up the light rays, refracting only blue and red to the eyes of the beholder.

Colors so produced can never fade. It is because of their enduring brilliance that thousands upon thousands of *Morpho* wings are used in making the countless lockets, plaques, trays, and other ornaments that we see offered for sale. So great has been the demand for these butterflies, that most of their native countries have tried to prohibit their collection, fearing that they will become extinct.

The *Morpho* lives only in the American tropics, ranging from central Mexico to southern Brazil. The greatest concentration of species is found in the Amazon and Orinoco valleys.

The *Morpho* is delightful to watch. It drifts along a forest pathway, its great wings undulating with languid grace. Looking at one you feel positive that if you lift your net this butterfly will sail right into it. Try your luck at netting one, and experience the surprise of your life. For, with the first movement of the net, the *Morpho* is gone. Gone where you least expect it. The lazy-looking insect has doubled back on its track, soared heavenward over the treetops, ducked under the net or over the net, and is continuing slowly up the trail. Only rarely will it leave the path to disappear in the dense side growth.

Occasionally, the *Morpho* takes to our paved roads. Once, while riding in a bus near Tamazunchale, Mexico, the author saw a small flock of them floating effortlessly ahead. They continued in this way for several rods, until with a furious burst of speed the shamed bus was able to overtake them.

SKIPPERS OR HESPERIDS— HALF BUTTERFLY AND HALF MOTH

Fuzzy, brown fliers dart rapidly back and forth, in and out among the tall grasses in a wet meadow, or along the banks of a locust-lined road. These are the skippers (family Hesperidae), half butterfly and half moth. They have the stout bodies and the blended shades of brown and yellow that we associate with moths. But they fly—and rapidly—in the daytime, and their antennae are clubbed like those of the butterflies. When you examine the antennae closely, however, you will see that at the very tip of the club there is a hooklike projection.

When at rest, some of the skippers hold their wings vertically; others, out flat. Still others hold their wings partly spread, with the upper wings at a sharper angle to the body than the lower pair, so that all four wings are plainly visible. Male skippers carry a little pocket of perfume along the outside edge of their forewings.

Studying all these and other, less obvious, characteristics, entomologists have placed the skippers as the last family of the butterflies, coming just before the moths.

About three thousand species are spread all over the world in the hot and temperate zones. Almost any locality in the United States can offer fifty or more species.

The female skipper lays dainty, green, dome-shaped eggs on leaves of grass or vetch, or locust trees, or other legumes. Within a few days the caterpillars hatch and start eating. They are queer-looking creatures, with long, thin, yellow bodies that taper in both directions from the middle and are fronted by large, dark-brown heads.

Some skipper caterpillars build themselves little tents of leaves fastened with silk, into which they retreat to rest or to molt. When full grown, the caterpillar spins a loosely woven cocoon among dead leaves on the ground. One generation of adults emerges in the late summer. Its offspring will spend the winter as pupae, and emerge early in the following summer.

HAWK MOTHS OR SPHINX MOTHS

Nearly everyone has at some time seen one of these heavy-bodied, long, tapering-winged moths dashing in circles about a street light, or hurling itself against the screens of our windows as it vainly tries to reach the light within. Or perhaps you may have seen one of the day-flying (diurnal) species when it visited your flower bed. Other species are crepuscular, flying just at dusk. Most of them, however, are active only at night and are seldom seen unless they are attracted to a light.

These moths are powerful fliers, with their long forewings and very small hind wings, driven by powerful muscles encased in a solid, torpedo-shaped body. The thick, fuzzy abdomen is usually brightly colored in shades of red and yellow; it is sometimes banded in a contrasting shade of the base color, sometimes lined on each side with a row of alternating black and white spots. The thorax is often decorated with tufts of brightly colored hair. The small rear wings are also vividly marked and colored. However, the large forewings are mottled or streaked in harmonious shades of tan, brown, or gray that blend with their surroundings. When the moth rests, these forewings fold rooflike over the body, effectively disguising it from prying eyes.

Hawk Moths with Sucking Tubes. The adults visit afternoon- or night-blooming flowers, and a number of species have very long sucking tubes, called proboscises, enabling them to reach the depths of flowers with deep corollas, such as the Nicotianas and the trumpet flowers. One species has a proboscis ten inches long. When the insect is not feeding, its proboscis lies under its head, coiled up like a watch spring.

Hawk, or sphinx, moths range in size from a California species, *Euproserpinus phaeton*, with a wing expanse of one and a half inches, to an Australian species that spreads nearly nine inches. The more than nine hundred known species in this family (Sphingidae) are widely distributed throughout the world, from the colder regions to the tropics, reaching the greatest number and the largest size in the latter regions.

Tomato Worms. The larvae are fleshy, heavy caterpillars, reaching lengths of four and five inches in the larger species. Many of them are greenish, frequently decorated with diagonal lines along the sides. Others are brownish, and some are rather brightly colored. The familiar tomato worm, as well as several others in this family, wears a horn on its terminal segment, making it look quite savage. The horn is quite harmless. Many of the caterpillars, when disturbed,

THE TOMATO WORM AND ITS NECTAR-LOVING MOTH
Wherever there are tomato or tobacco plants, or even potato, pepper, or eggplants, you are likely to see this large green caterpillar with a horn on its rear. When the creature has eaten its fill, it burrows into the ground to change into a pupa. It emerges as a large moth (*left*) with a heavy, fuzzy body brightly colored in shades of tan; its wings are also fuzzy, but more delicately colored.

rear the front half of the body upward, with the head arched downward, in what is thought to be a sphinxlike attitude. Tickle the next tomato worm you find, with a grass stem, and see if you agree.

When ready to pupate, the caterpillar burrows six or eight inches into the ground, or, in some species, contents itself with hiding under a pile of debris. The chrysalis is usually a dark reddish-brown, and in some cases it has a curved, handle-like protuberance, making it look like a little brown pitcher. The protuberance encases the proboscis. The tomato worm is among the insects making such a chrysalis.

HUMMINGBIRD MOTHS

Hemaris thysbe belongs to a group in the Sphingidae family popularly called hummingbird moths. (In some books they are placed in the genus *Haemorrhagia*.) They are pretty creatures, their fat bodies warmly dressed in green and red fuzz, their wings scaleless and transparent in the center, but thickly margined with red. Late in the afternoon, they start visiting our gardens, hovering like hummingbirds over the blossoms, as they sip the nectar through their uncoiled proboscises.

The Tomato Worm Sphinx, *Protoparce quinquemaculata,* and the Tobacco Worm Moth, *Protoparce sexta,* are typical examples of this family. You may find them under different names in other books. They feed upon a number of plants, including tomatoes, peppers, potatoes, and tobacco, and are frequently plentiful enough to do considerable damage. They are largely responsible for pollinizing long tubular flowers like the jimson weed and Nicotiana, and causing these plants to seed. In return, the plants produce foliage upon which the caterpillars feed. These two species range over a large part of North and South America, and the first has been able to reach Europe and Hawaii, where it is well established.

The Death's-head Moth, *Acherontia atropos,* is a European species. Its appearance was once regarded as a bad omen by the superstitious, for the brown-and-black pattern on the top of the thorax bears a remarkable resemblance to a human skull. In addition, by forcing the air across an opening in its proboscis, the moth produces a squeaking noise, supposedly prophesying a death rattle.

The White-lined Sphinx, *Deilephila lineata,* is a common moth, flying from June until cool weather. It flies not only at night but also during the day, particularly in dull or cloudy weather. It is widely distributed throughout North America and far into South America. It has also spread to many countries in the Eastern Hemisphere.

The veins of this moth's tan forewings are lined with white, and a pinkish band extends from the apex to the base. The rear wings are dark brown, crossed with a wide, reddish band. The moth has a spread of slightly more than four inches. The larvae feed on many kinds of plants, including grape, apple, Virginia creeper, and currant.

GIANT SILKWORM MOTHS

Forming a large family (Saturniidae) of very broad-winged moths, ranging from large to giant in size, the giant silkworm moths include some of the largest members of the insect world. Many of them are vividly colored in contrasting designs; others are clothed in somber dark-brown or gray. Many also have a transparent spot or window, called a fenestra, near the center of the wings. The males are usually smaller than the females, and are adorned with great feathery, fern-like (plumose) antennae. The antennae of the females are less plumose and sometimes only slightly pectinate (comblike).

Saturniid moths usually begin to fly just at dusk, continuing into the early part of the night. Unlike most of the moths, these big fellows never eat after they get their wings. They are attracted to lights and frequently come blundering against our window screens. Here, you can collect them rather easily, but you will find that your catch has beaten off some of the scales on its beautiful wings. A male will fly long distances in search of a female, frequently traveling a number of miles, especially up wind, for odor seems to be the guiding beam.

FEROCIOUS-LOOKING CATERPILLARS

The caterpillars are large and stout, some of the large species reaching a length of over six inches, and more than an inch in diameter. Many of them are green, decorated along the sides with silver or other bright markings. Although each species has its own method, all saturniid caterpillars contrive to look as hideous and ferocious as possible, with horns and spines and bristles and threatening postures.

When fully grown, the caterpillar spins around itself a large, warm, silken cocoon and enters that inactive, reorganizational stage in which the insect is called a pupa or chrysalis. Many of our northern species fasten their cocoons to the branches of the trees where they have been feeding, and we see them swinging on the leafless twigs all winter long. There the wings slowly take shape, and the following summer, if all goes well, what went into the cocoon as an ugly worm will emerge as a beautiful moth.

Frequently, however, all goes ill for the helpless chrysalis. While still in the caterpillar stage, about half of the individuals become the repository for eggs deposited by other insects, chiefly chalcid and ichneumon flies. What emerges from the cocoon of a parasitized caterpillar will be, not a moth, but a flock of tiny, wasplike flies.

COLLECTING SILKWORM COCOONS

Amateur collectors are likely to snatch every cocoon they see, and take it home with them, hoping to see the lovely moths emerge. Half the time, it is the parasitic flies that come out. Frequently, also, many of the healthy pupae will emerge as imperfect moths because the collector kept them in a room that was too hot or too dry. The few perfect specimens that emerge are speedily killed and added to collections. For these reasons, the larger moths once so common in the United States are now very rare.

In tropical climates, the pupation period is very much shorter, and the danger from parasites is greater. However, some tropical saturniids are cultivated, or at least protected, for their silk. Although none of these yield a product as fine as that of the true silkworm, which belongs to another moth family, about thirty Asiatic species and a few in South America are used in making textiles of various grades.

The Cecropia Moth, *Samia cecropia.* For many of the saturniid moths the specific name serves also as the popular or English name. This is true for the Cecropia, the largest moth in North America north of Mexico. It has a stout, fuzzy, rich-red body, with white stripes across the abdomen. Its wings are a duller red near the bases, and banded along the outer edges in varying shades of white and red. Near the center of each is a light, or white, crescent-shaped spot. Individuals have been seen with a wing expanse of seven inches.

The bluish-green caterpillar, with red knobs on its front segments and yellow knobs on its back segments, grows to about four inches. It feeds on a variety of plants, but prefers elderberry leaves. Its cocoon, frequently three inches long, is securely fastened along its whole length to a twig or branch.

Cecropia ranges over North America east of the Rocky Mountains. *Samia gloveri* replaces Cecropia throughout the Rockies, and *Samia euryalus,* along the Pacific coast.

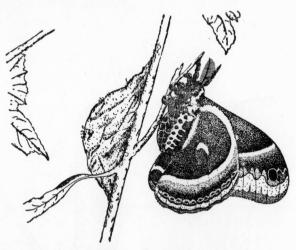

THE CECROPIA IS THE LARGEST MOTH IN THE UNITED STATES

The Cecropia has a heavy, furry, red-and-white body, large, feathery antennae, and wings banded and spotted in varying shades of tan and red. The largest specimens have a wingspread of seven inches. The caterpillar grows to four inches, and is blue-green, with red and yellow knobs on its back. Note how the cocoon is fastened to the branch.

The Promethea Moth, *Callosamia promethea.* Although it has nearly four inches of wingspread, the Promethea is one of our smaller saturniid moths. It is also among the commonest throughout its range, which comprises the entire eastern part of North America. The male is dark maroon, almost black. It has no windows (fenestrae) in its wings. The female is a light, reddish brown, and each wing has a triangular, or irregularly shaped window. The caterpillar is about two and a half inches long, bluish green, with four red knobs projecting from the front segments, six black ones on each of the middle segments, and a yellow one on the eleventh segment, making it a creature of startling appearance. It feeds on a variety of trees and shrubs, particularly sassafras, the tulip tree, the wild cherry, the lilac, and the spicebush.

When ready to pupate, the caterpillar carefully fastens a leaf to the twig by covering twig and leaf stalk with silk. It then wraps the leaf around itself, fastening the edges together. Within this leaf-tent it spins its cocoon, leaving a small opening at the top, through which the moth can emerge. All winter long, the cocoon rocks in the stormy winds.

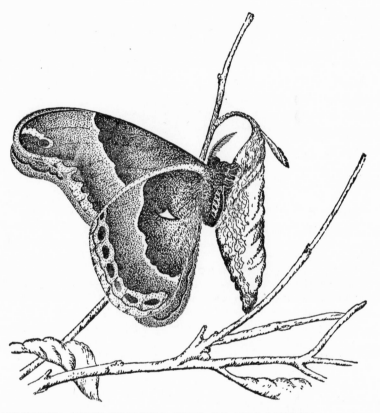

THE PROMETHEA MOTH EMERGING FROM ITS LEAF-COCOON
The male Promethea is very dark red, almost black, the female is reddish brown—creatures quite different from the caterpillar, which is blue-green and has four red, one yellow, and six black knobs on its back. When ready to become a pupa, the caterpillar uses strong silk to fasten a leaf to a twig, wraps the leaf around itself, closes the edges with silk, and spins its cocoon inside.

The Ailanthus, or **Cynthia Moth,** *Philosamia cynthia*. The patient artisans of China, Japan, and the East Indies made an excellent silk from the cocoons of the Cynthia moth. In the hope of establishing a silk industry in the Occident, commercial interests introduced the moth into Europe and the United States in the 1860's. High labor costs soon killed this plan.

However, the beautiful fawn-colored moth, whose caterpillar feeds on the imported ailanthus tree, has spread into many parts of the country, particularly around our large industrial cities, where the "tree of heaven," the tree that "grows in Brooklyn," thrives so well. On these trees or neighboring trees, you may find the cocoons dangling from the twigs in the winter time.

The author mentions neighboring trees, because caterpillars do not always spin in the tree on which they have been feeding. In fact, these large silkworms, as well as other insect larvae, seem to get the wanderlust at about the time they are ready to pupate, and scatter in all directions. This may be advantageous to them, for when they are widely scattered there is less likelihood that all of them will be destroyed. Cynthia is rapidly learning to feed upon a number of native American trees, such as lilac, sycamore, linden, and wild cherry.

The Polyphemus Moth, *Telea polyphemus.* A large moth, with a wing expanse of about five inches, and not uncommon, the Polyphemus is colored a beautiful buff or tan, with pinkish shades. Its caterpillar feeds on a great many trees, including birch and oak. The caterpillar has the habit, when disturbed, of rearing up and clicking its jaws. This terrifying attitude is not effective against the ichneumon flies, which make a sneak attack from behind.

The cocoon is solid, and its silk can be readily unreeled, but at too great a cost, in this country, for commercial use. Polyphemus almost always secures its cocoon to the twig with silk so that it will not fall to the ground in the fall when the leaves drop. This is a good general rule of identification to remember in distinguishing between the Polyphemus and Luna cocoons.

The Luna Moth, *Actias luna.* With its soft, green color, its two long, slender tails, and antennae that are like golden ferns, a freshly emerged Luna is one of our loveliest moths. However, the green quickly fades into a dull gray, especially if exposed to light, and the delicate tails are soon frayed. Nevertheless, the Luna is much desired by the young amateur collector, and the author is constantly asked the difficult question, "How can one be found?"

——WHERE TO FIND THE LUNA MOTH. Perhaps the best suggestion is to search for the caterpillars on hickory, walnut, sweet gum, persimmon, and other trees, and to rear the caterpillars. Do not mistake a Polyphemus caterpillar for a Luna, for they are somewhat similar in appearance. A Polyphemus caterpillar has seven slanting stripes on the sides; a Luna has a yellow band along the side. The cocoons almost always fall to the ground.

A BEAUTIFUL MOTH FROM AN INDUSTRIOUS CATERPILLAR
The wings of the Polyphemus are colored in harmonious shades of yellowish and pinkish tan. Each wing has a transparent spot; those on the hind wings are bordered with blue and black. The large green caterpillar has enormous silk glands, from which it spins half a mile of silk for its big cocoon.

The author has been successful in finding them by scratching about among the leaves under one of their favorite food trees at the edge of woods somewhat isolated from other trees. The Luna ranges throughout the eastern part of the United States.

The Io Moth, *Automeris io.* As vividly colored and marked as any butterfly, the male Io moth has clear, yellow forewings; the female, which is larger, has cloudy, lavender forewings. A large, bluish spot occupies most of the center of the rear wing in both sexes. It is among the smallest of the saturniids, large individuals spreading only three inches.

The Io caterpillar grows to a length of about two inches. One of our most attractive caterpillars, it is bright green, with a red-and-white band all along the side, and it wears a regular forest of green bristles on its back. It is so pretty that it will tempt you to try to collect it. But if you touch it with your bare hand, you will be sorry, for the closely packed bristles are poisonous and will leave an irritating rash on your skin. The caterpillar feeds on a great number of herbaceous plants, especially grasses and corn.

SOME EXOTIC MEMBERS OF THE SATURNIID FAMILY

Since the saturniid family is so intriguing and its tropical members appear in all museum collections, we will mention a few of the more exotic species.

The Atlas Moth, *Attacus atlas.* The female has a wingspread of ten and a half inches. It is regarded as one of the largest lepidopterous insects, especially if the wing area is considered. The huge Atlas caterpillars appear to be powdery or dusty, and feed on a great number of plants. The Atlas is found in southern Asia and the Malay regions. *Attacus edwardsi,* from Australia, is about equal in size.

The Hercules Moth, *Coscinoscera hercules,* which makes its home in Australia and Papua, is believed to hold the record for size. This dark and lovely creature measures fourteen inches from tip to tip of the forewings. In addition to having all this breadth, the male Hercules moth sports long tails from its rear wings.

The Luna Moth, *Actias selene,* of the Orient, ranges throughout Japan and China, and down into India and Ceylon. Europe is not blessed with many of the large, showy moths. *Saturnia pyri,* with an expanse of about three inches, is the largest in Europe, while the Emperor Moth, *Saturnia pavonia,* with wings about two inches across, is the only representative in Great Britain.

SOUTH AMERICAN SATURNIIDS

South America has a great many saturniids. *Rothschildia aurota* is the only species from which South Americans have attempted to produce silk, and then not very extensively. The genus *Rothschildia* has a number of beautiful species. Its members range from northern South America into the southern United States. *Rothschildia orizaba* and *jorulla* come northward into Arizona.

Copiopteryx semiramis, in the mountains of South America, from Colombia to Bolivia, and the genus *Argema*, in the Eastern Hemisphere, are remarkable for their exceedingly long tails, which are a little longer than the spread of their wings.

RELATIVES OF THE GIANT SILKWORM MOTHS

The members of this family (Citheroniidae—they have no common or English name) look very much like the saturniids, with which they were once classed. Their main difference is that their caterpillars do not spin cocoons but burrow into the ground to pupate.

The Royal Walnut Moth is the common name of the adult *Citheronia regalis;* its caterpillar is the Hickory Horned Devil. You will agree that it is well named when you first meet one. The fully grown horned devil is an alarming object, five inches long, greenish, with strong black-and-white spots, and decorated with six long, red-and-black horns that curve back. Decorated is the proper word to use here, for the horns are harmless. But how the caterpillar loves, when disturbed, to display its horns.

If you are trying to find one of these horned devils, search not only on walnut and hickory trees, as the names suggest, but also on butternut, sweet gum, ash, and sumac. The reddish-brown moth has a very large, stout body and large wings, with the veins of the forewings broadly lined with tan.

The Imperial Moth, *Basilona imperialis,* also, and more appropriately, called the yellow emperor, is a beautiful canary-yellow, mottled with spots and bands of purplish-brown. The male shows much more purple than the female. The hairy caterpillars are sometimes brown and sometimes green, and have four small horns on the thorax. They feed on nearly every kind of tree or shrub they can find; maple, elm, pine, hemlock, sumac, and chokecherry leaves are equally enjoyable to them.

THE SYNTOMIDS—OFTEN MISTAKEN FOR WASPS

The family Syntomidae, also sometimes called Amatidae, is a small one, reaching its greatest development in the hotter countries. A few species extend northward into the eastern United States. The syntomids are small, brightly colored, day-flying moths, found around field flowers. They are frequently mistaken for wasps or other hymenopterous insects, because their bright colors usually show a great deal of contrast, including such combinations as black, red, and yellow.

TIGER MOTHS AND WOOLLY BEARS

To the layman, the caterpillars of the tiger moth are perhaps more familiar than the adults, for these caterpillars are the familiar Woolly Bears. In the fall, many of them leave their eating places and start out in search of a new home, some looking for a place to hibernate, and some for a nice place to spin a rough cocoon. As they spin, the hairs on the body are mixed with the silk.

These creatures are also called "hedgehog caterpillars," for, when disturbed, they curl into a compact mass presenting to the disturber an armor of hairs. The adults are quite variable, but they are mostly thick bodied and hairy. They are white, brown, red, yellow, or combinations of these colors, frequently with black dots or lines added. In this family (Arctiidae), there are about 2,500 known species. They range from the colder regions to the hottest.

The Salt-marsh Caterpillar, *Estigmene acraea,* is common throughout North America. Its popular name was applied many years ago when numbers of them were seen in salt marshes. However, they feed on a great variety of plants and have become a serious pest on vegetable crops.

Nevertheless, one is tempted to forgive these caterpillars for the damage they do, because of the beautiful moths that they are going to become. The male is all white. The female's rear wings are yellow, spotted with small black dots, and she has a reddish abdomen.

The Virginia Tiger Moth, *Diacrisia virginica,* has white wings, flecked with a few faint, black specks, and a yellowish abdomen. This moth may be seen resting in your garden, for its caterpillar is the familiar yellow woolly bear that loves to feed on many garden plants. *Diacrisia vulpinaria* is the European representative and is rather similar in appearance.

The Isabella Tiger Moth, *Isia isabella,* has all-yellow wings, flecked with a few tiny, brown spots, and a reddish abdomen. This is the woolliest of all woolly bears, the one we see in the fall hurrying to cross the road in front of our automobile.

THE RAMBLING WOOLLY BEAR GROWS INTO AN EXQUISITE TIGER MOTH
Have you ever tried the woolly bear as a forecaster of the winter's weather? If the rust-colored band around this caterpillar's middle is broad, it is supposed to be a sign that the winter will not be cold. A walk along any path in the fall may show you woolly bears mostly with wide bands—but a walk the next day along another path a mile away may show you woolly bears mostly with narrow bands! The woolly bear spends the winter under leaves and debris. In the spring it spins a cocoon from which it will emerge as a lovely little orange-colored moth.

This woolly bear is hurrying, not to beat the car (thousands of these creatures, incidentally, are killed every fall on our highways), but to find a snug place in which to curl up and pass the winter. If everything has gone well with it, it comes forth on sunny days, eats a little more of its favorite food, plantain, and finally spins its cocoon under a loose stone, a log, or bark.

As almost everyone knows, the woolly bear is black at both ends and reddish brown in the middle. Some years this bright center will be unusually broad, and then we can remember a bit of old weather lore: that the more brown on the woolly bear, the milder we can expect the winter to be. Any resemblance between this insect and future temperatures is purely coincidental.

The Fall Webworm, *Hyphantria cunea,* is a grayish-white moth, flecked with brown spots. These spots may be plentiful or almost lacking. The caterpillars are equally variable, and live in a colony-nest of loosely spun silk entirely covering the branches of a tree. It is often confused with the Spring Webworm, *Malacosoma americana.*

FORESTER MOTHS

This family (Agaristidae) is mentioned here only because of one important species, the Eight-spotted Forester, *Alypia octomaculata.* Other *Alypias* are also called foresters and occupy other regions, but the eight-spot occurs in the northeastern United States. It is a small, velvety-black moth, one and a half inches in wingspread, with eight yellow and white spots, two to each wing, the largest at the base of the rear wings. We see them near grapevines because the caterpillars feed on these and on the Virginia creeper and are frequently very destructive.

NOCTUIDS, OR OWLET MOTHS— THEIR EYES HAVE AN ORANGE GLOW

The name noctuid comes from the Latin word *noctua,* meaning "night owl," and a more appropriate name for these moths could hardly have been found. They fly at night, and their eyes shine with a beautiful orange glow stimulated by any reflected light. They are largely phototropic (meaning that, like certain plants, they turn toward light) and you can usually find them around lights.

WHEN AND HOW TO COLLECT THEM

Another and more exciting way of collecting them is by "sugaring." A mixture of brown sugar or molasses, with enough water to make a thick syrup, added to a little stale beer or rum, to soothe the insects that gather for the feast, is spread with a large brush on tree trunks or fence posts at dusk. The trees selected should be along a convenient, open pathway or trail, or margin of woods, rather than in the deep forest, although a few trees in thick woods may be tried experimentally. A lone tree in a field often attracts many moths. A circuitous trail of half a mile or a mile makes a fine route.

Warm, muggy summer or fall nights usually yield best results. After dark with flashlight and net, start your rounds. Approach each bait tree quietly with flash unlit. Hold the net under the spot baited, and then turn on the flashlight. If conditions are right, you may be amazed at the things gathered for the banquet. There will be moths, mostly noctuids, beetles, grasshoppers, crickets, millepedes and centipedes, and ants. If ants collect, they tend to drive away other creatures with their scurrying around and will even attack them.

The reaction of the insects to the light is also interesting. At your first approach, on the flash of the light some will drop, perhaps into the net as intended. Others may fly upward. If you are quick enough you may catch some of these on the wing. Others will sit calmly, allowing you to place a widemouthed killing jar over them. Hold it there a moment until the insect flutters back into the jar. At first you will attempt to secure everything in sight; but after a few experiences your eye will quickly select what is rare from among the throng. At any rate, the author hopes you will have many enjoyable evenings, as he has had, taking them.

The Noctuidae family is one of the largest. More than twenty thousand species have been described, at least 2,500 of them living in North America. They are largely small moths with wingspreads of two inches or under, mottled brown or gray in color. However, a few are brightly colored, and some reach a considerable size.

FACTS ABOUT NOCTUID CATERPILLARS

The caterpillars are sometimes called Army Worms and Cutworms. Many of them do considerable damage, and gardeners "cuss" all caterpillars for this reason. You may be assured, however, that not all noctuid caterpillars are injurious; in fact, many are quite beneficial because they control vegetation that might become too possessive of the ground.

HOW TO DESTROY THEM

Cutworms may be destroyed by placing a poison bran mixture in various spots in the garden in the spring before plants are set out or seed is sown. The mixture is prepared by mixing one part, by weight, of Paris green, to twenty-five parts of bran and sufficient molasses thinned with water to make a thick mash. Chickens, as well as dogs, cats, and other pets, like this poisonous mixture, so precautions should be taken to prevent them from getting at it. You can do this by placing the mash under heavy, or weighted, boxes or pails that cannot be overturned. A few handfuls of mash should take care of the average garden.

In this book, we have space to mention only a few of the noctuids. If you wish to study the family more intensively, there are many specialized reports and papers on the group. If you should become deeply interested in the noctuids, you could spend a lifetime studying the North American species alone, without ever attempting to become acquainted with the exotic ones about which little is known.

TUSSOCK MOTHS

The Liparidae, also called Lymantriidae, is a small family, but important and well known for its destructive species. The moths are small and not particularly outstanding in appearance. The caterpillars frequently occur in such numbers as to completely strip the leaves from the trees where they cluster.

The White-marked Tussock Moth, *Hemerocampa leucostigma,* is perhaps the best known of this family, for it is widespread over the entire eastern part of North America. In the West, it is replaced by the California species, *vetusta.* It is the caterpillar, from which the moth gets its name, with which most people are familiar, and a most exquisite creature it is, with its four white tussocks of hairs, its red head, and pencils of long, black hair standing erect, two from the thorax, and one on the last segment, not to mention the yellow and black stripes on the body.

When grown, it spins a rough cocoon of silk interlaced with the hairs from its body, placing it usually in a crevice on the trunk of a tree, or in any other sheltered place. Under the eaves, or the edges of the clapboards, of a house is a favorite spot. Sometimes four or five cocoons are massed together.

It is estimated that only ten per cent of the caterpillars live to reach maturity. In addition to the predatory birds that destroy countless numbers, the caterpillars are beset by parasites. Over twenty hymenopterous and dipterous parasites on these caterpillars have been discovered, these parasites being attacked by hyperparasites, and these in turn by parasites. This pageant of animal existence is one of the most interesting cases of insect parasitism.

Very few people are familiar with the mature male moth, for it is a small, drab insect. The female is wingless, a fat little ash-gray creature who crawls out of her cocoon house and sits on the doorstep awaiting her lover. She then deposits her four hundred, or more, eggs on the top of the cocoon, covers them with a frothy secretion, which hardens into a waterproof covering, and dies. There may be as many as three generations a year. The winter is passed in the egg stage.

The Gypsy Moth, *Porthetria dispar,* was introduced into the United States in 1868 by an amateur entomologist experimenting with some material he had obtained from Europe. It was to prove a very costly and disastrous experiment.

Some of the moths escaped from captivity, and in no time a colony was established in Massachusetts. Rapidly spreading, the gypsy moth had caused immense destruction before control measures were started. These controls have been successful in confining it to the New England states, but there is no telling when it may accidentally become established in another area. If it is discovered in a new area, this fact should be immediately reported to the insect authorities.

The moths appear in July but may be seen for several months. The male is brown, with a wingspread of less than two inches. The female is larger and whitish. It seldom flies, a fact which has been an important factor in preventing the spread of the insect.

The eggs are laid in masses ranging in number from several hundred to nearly a thousand. The mass is covered with scales from the body of the adult and appears as a rounded, whitish object. You can find the egg masses usually on the underside of foliage, tree limbs, and stones, as well as on wagons and cars, and wherever the female can crawl after emerging from its pupa. The caterpillars feed at night and congregate during the day in masses on the limbs of trees or other protected spots. They are known to feed on over five hundred species of plants, including the cone-bearing trees.

The Brown-tail Moth, *Euproctis chrysorrhoea,* is also an emigrant from Europe. How it arrived in America no one knows, but it is now firmly established from Connecticut and Rhode Island northward to Nova Scotia.

The female brown-tail flies readily, and new colonies may easily become established from a wind-blown insect. Fortunately, the prevailing winds are from the west so that drifting insects would be blown out to sea rather than inland. The moths are whitish and can be distinguished by the brown hairs on the end of the abdomen. These are less conspicuous in the male. These moths appear in July and are attracted to lights more frequently than the gypsy moth.

The egg mass, usually on the underside of a leaf, is covered with the brown scales from the moth's abdomen. Hatching in a couple of weeks, the tiny caterpillars live in a colony on the tender terminal foliage, which they cover with a webbing of silk. It is in this same nest that the half-grown caterpillars pass the winter. In the spring, they resume their feeding, pupating in late spring.

The larvae are covered with brownish hairs, with a row of white tufts along each side. The hairs, particularly the brown ones, are barbed and poisonous. One need not come into direct contact with the insects to be attacked by them, for the hairs are carried by the wind, causing intense irritation to the skin, where they lodge. Some individuals are more allergic than others to these hairs.

TENT CATERPILLARS

A medium-large family (Lasiocampidae) found throughout the world, the tent caterpillars are poorly represented in North America by a few small species. What the family lacks in species it makes up in numbers. Some of the most destructive species are found in America.

Asia, Africa, and South America have some larger moths of this family. A few of the tropical species are valuable for the silk they produce, for the family is closely related to the true silkworms.

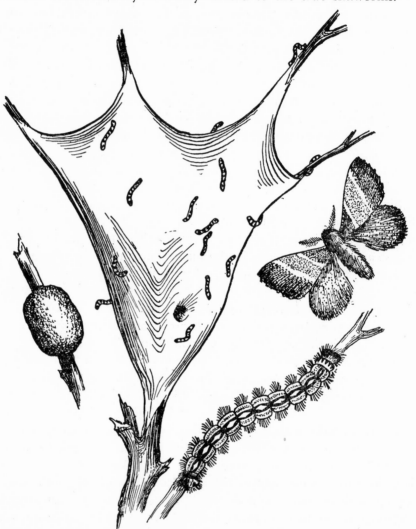

TENT CATERPILLARS LIKE TO CAMP ON WILD CHERRY TREES

Tent caterpillars lead an interesting communal life, generally on a wild cherry tree, but when they cannot find one they may disfigure our cultivated trees with their curious webs (*center*). The grown caterpillars leave their tents to find a place to weave a papery cocoon and, as there are a great many of them in each tent, they can create quite a bit of activity for yards around an infested tree. The moth is yellowish or reddish brown. Pictured at the left, encircling a twig, is the egg mass—it contains three hundred eggs or more.

The Tent Caterpillar, *Malacosoma americana,* is familiar to everyone in the East, because of its destructive larvae and the unsightly nests they spin in our trees, usually in the fork of a tree.

To the caterpillars, the nest is a wonderful structure. They sally out from it at night to feed, returning to the nest during the day or stormy weather for protection.

Each caterpillar, as it travels along a branch, spins a thread of silk; others follow, until trails of silk radiate from the nest to the feeding stations. These trails then provide convenient return routes.

When full grown, the caterpillar gets the wanderlust and, either crawling or dropping to the ground, starts hunting a place in which to pupate. When it has found a suitable crevice or protected spot, it builds a paper-like white cocoon and fastens it in a mesh of scattered threads.

The small, inconspicuous brown moths emerge in July. They can be recognized by the two fine, white lines which cross the front wings. They soon lay their eggs in masses which completely encircle a slender twig on one of their favorite food trees. They are partial to apple, pear, and wild cherry.

The Forest Tent Caterpillar, *Malacosoma disstria,* is sociable, but constructs no compact nest like that of the *americana.* It feeds on a variety of leaf-shedding forest trees and ranges over a large part of North America. The Great Basin Tent Caterpillar, *fragilis,* replaces the eastern species in the West. The Lackey Moth, *nuestrium,* is the European tent caterpillar and is also very destructive.

The Syrian Silkworm, *Pachypasa otus,* was a valuable silk-producing insect. The silk was used by the Greeks and Romans long before the introduction, about A.D. 550, of the Chinese silkworm. Its silk, which is a beautiful white, competed with that produced by Chinese silkworms until the late 1800's. *Borocera madagascariensis,* known as the Bibindandy, produces a beautiful silk. As its scientific name indicates, it is a native of Madagascar.

SILKWORMS—SPINNERS OF THE ORIENT

Less than a hundred species make up the silkworm family (Bombycidae), and they are all confined to eastern Asia.

The Chinese Silkworm, *Bombyx mori,* is the outstanding example in this group. It has so long been associated with man that it is almost domesticated and probably could not live by itself outdoors. Individuals have been liberated in what were thought to be favorable areas, but always failed to survive. Through the ages, many silkworm races have been developed to fit certain requirements, such as climate, productiveness, and the quality of the silk.

The adults are creamy white, heavy abdomened, and have a wing expanse of less than two inches. They never fly. About three hundred eggs are laid in a scattered space around the female. Commercial growers feed the larvae on mulberry leaves spread out in a thin layer on trays which slide into supporting frames. The larvae do not roam but feed contentedly on the leaves. A new supply of leaves is provided each day. In addition to the white and black mulberry normally used, they will also feed on osage orange and lettuce. In some cases, there may be as many as six broods a year.

The larvae feed for about forty-five days and spin their cocoons, from which the adults emerge in about two weeks. The cocoons to be used for commercial purposes are soaked in hot water, a procedure which kills the pupa but allows the silk to be unwound and reeled with ease.

GEOMETERS, OR MEASURING WORMS

A very large family (Geometridae) of smallish (though sometimes large in the tropics), more or less fragile moths, the geometers are usually seen resting on tree trunks or fences with their wings spread out flat. They depend upon the maze of zigzig lines or other baffling designs on their wings to prevent detection.

The caterpillars have no legs in the middle of the body, as do most other larvae. They therefore travel in a series of loops, by stretching out and taking firm hold with the three pairs of true legs on the thorax. The body is then looped, with the rear end brought forward to take hold with its two pairs of legs. It is this looping of the caterpillars that has given them such names as measuring worms, inch worms, spanworms, spanners, and loopers. The scientific name means "earth measurers," and it fits them well, for they seem to be forever on the move. As the old saying informs us, no summer picnic is complete without a few measuring worms taking your measurement for a new suit of clothes.

Although the family is very large (a thousand species have been described in North America alone), the coloring of many is so similar, that we will consider only two of the more common species.

The Fall Cankerworm, *Alsophila pometaria,* is a conspicuous moth in wooded areas in the fall, not through its beauty but because of the numbers that flutter about. The male is small and tan, with darker lines and markings. The female is a stay-at-home and a drab little creature. She is wingless, and for her view of the world she is content to crawl slowly along a tree trunk.

This little lady makes up for her lack of beauty by the batch of exquisite eggs she lays in November. The late Dr. Frank E. Lutz, the well-known entomologist, likened the appearance of the individual egg to a tiny "gray flower pot having a gray cover decorated with a dark central spot and a dark ring near the edge." The batch of eggs is placed carefully in close, regular rows and must be studied with the aid of a lens.

In the spring, from each of these "flower pots" instead of a lovely flower, a voracious caterpillar pushes up the lid and crawls out to spend the spring feasting on the leaves of a great number of trees.

When the hot days of July come, the caterpillar drops to the ground on a silken thread and burrows into the cool soil, spins a rough cocoon, pupates, and does not emerge until late fall. A few do not emerge until spring, when they may be seen flying with the Spring Cankerworms, to the confusion of the amateur collector.

The Spring Cankerworm Moth, *Paleacrita vernata,* is a small, pale-tan moth that flies in the early spring, shortly after the snow is off the ground. As in the case of the fall cankerworm, the female is wingless. In most localities, the spring cankerworm is much more common. Its caterpillar is responsible for great damage, for it strips the leaves from many trees. It was largely because of this species, together with some other geometrid larvae, that the English sparrow was introduced into the United States, to feed upon the insect. The American caterpillars did not appeal to the birds, which turned out to be destructive in other ways themselves.

BAGWORMS—MOTHS WITH UNUSUAL HABITS

This family (Psychidae) of medium-sized moths is interesting, not so much for color or shape, as for its unusual habits. As soon as its caterpillars are hatched, they proceed to build about themselves little homes of silk, into which are woven bits of twigs, leaves, bark, or other debris. From this habit come their common names, bagworms, bag moths, case moths, and basketworms. Each species makes its characteristic type of case. In most species, the case of the female moth differs from that of the male moth.

The females, as far as is known, are wingless, and spend their entire lives in the cases they started for themselves as very young caterpillars. The males have dark bodies, and for a short time after emerging from their pupae, they have dark wings. Their wing scales, however, are so loosely attached that they are soon lost, leaving the moth with transparent wings. It is in this condition that you usually see them.

The species are not numerous in the temperate region. Tropical and subtropical countries have several hundred, some of which construct bags several inches in length. Australians complain about bagworms each with a case as large as an ordinary cigar hanging side by side on trees from which they have eaten the leaves.

The Common Bagworm of eastern North America is not nearly as long as its technical name, *Thyridopteryx ephemeraeformis*. The adult male has long, feathery, antennae; a black, slender, tapering body; and smoky, transparent wings that were dull black when it first emerged. The adult female has no wings, no legs, no eyes, no antennae. She is just a soft, yellowish-white, maggot-like creature. She deposits her numerous white eggs in the case where she lives, and then dies, her body plugging the case up against intruders.

The caterpillars do not hatch out until the following spring. Then they weave their little cases and fasten them to the twigs of almost any kind of tree or shrub, although they prefer evergreens. Their bags can be seen everywhere and at any time, hanging even on the trees along our city streets and on other isolated trees and shrubs. Where there are enough of them they can strip the leaves from a tree, but this does not happen often.

SLUG CATERPILLARS—SOME HAVE DANGEROUS SPINES

Its curious sluglike caterpillars are the most remarkable thing about the family Limacodidae. With practically no feet, they slide around on the surface of the leaf. Beware of them if they belong to a species with spines, for the spines are easily broken off and can become imbedded in your flesh, causing extreme irritation. The author is inclined to believe they are not poisonous, although many books claim they are.

People vary widely in their reactions to the spines. Not only is the caterpillar to be avoided, but the thin cocoon it spins has the spines interwoven in the silk, making it a dangerous object to handle carelessly. Fortunately, not many of the species are so armed. The family has had a number of scientific names, including Cochlidiidae, Eucleidae, and Heterogeneidae.

SOME WEIRD CATERPILLARS AND THEIR TINY MOTHS

The odd caterpillar on the left is well named the "saddleback"; the saddle is brown, on a pale green "saddle pad"; the rest of the body is reddish brown. Note the hairs or spines on the saddleback—they sting like nettles. Above this larva is its small moth, which is light-and-dark reddish brown. The creature at the lower right is also a caterpillar—it is called the "hag moth," or "monkey slug caterpillar," and you have to see one to believe it. You can find both of these caterpillars on fruit trees.

The Saddleback Moth, *Sibine stimulea,* is a common species in the eastern United States, and its caterpillar is one greatly to be feared. Don't, however, let this prevent you from finding one of these creatures to look at from a safe distance. About one inch long, it is green, with each end brown, and with a brown saddle mark in the center of its back. Pointing outward from each end are two prominent, spine-covered, fleshy protuberances. Along each side are a number of tufts of yellow spines which can sting you far worse than nettles.

Every summer, some of these attractive caterpillars are brought or sent into the author's office, carefully housed in an old pickle bottle. The universal question is, "What can it be? I've never seen anything like it."

This caterpillar feeds on a variety of vegetation. Look for it this summer on cherry, apple, or pear tree, or on corn. When full grown, the caterpillar wanders some distance, seeking a place to spin its cocoon. The author knows of one case where a saddleback caterpillar wandered into a bureau drawer, and deciding the soft underclothing was a good place to pupate, carefully spun its cocoon. Not noticing the cocoon, the owner of the apartment, a woman, donned the garment from the drawer and soon suffered a severe case of skin irritation which hospitalized her for some time. The adult moth is small and of a rich brown color.

The Green Slug Moth, *Euclea chloris,* is a pretty little moth, with its brown forewings crossed by a broad, green band. The caterpillar is equally attractive, for it is red, with four black lines on the back, and the spines are yellowish.

CLEARWINGED MOTHS—THEY LOOK LIKE BEES OR FLIES

Small, but very attractive, these moths (family Aegeriidae) resemble bees, wasps, or flies. Their slender wings are very often transparent, the legs and abdomen brightly scaled in red, yellow, blue, or black. The moths fly in the daytime, with a rapid circling flight, and as they come near, you instinctively duck, so well do they remind you of angry wasps. This is another case of the protective mimicry described earlier.

The caterpillars, so far as is known, are borers in plants. Some species prefer the succulent tissues of herbaceous plants; others attack the harder wood of trees and shrubs. Their boring habit makes this a family of great economic importance, for many of the species attack plants in which man is interested.

The Squash-vine Borer, *Melittia satyriniformis,* is one of our most beautiful pests. With its metallic-green forewings, and transparent rear wings, its red abdomen and red legs fringed with black, this striking moth may be seen hovering around almost any member of the melon family. It seems to prefer squash and pumpkins. The red eggs are placed singly near the roots of the plants. When hatched, the little grub bores into the center of the vine stem, then follows along the stem, feeding on the tender inside tissue. The plant begins to show the effects of this disturbance by a wilting of the leaves. When fully fed, and about an inch long, the caterpillar leaves the plant and burrows into the ground, spinning a rough cocoon to which particles of earth adhere. The moths emerge the next summer, in late June or early July. In the North, this moth produces a single brood; in the South it is double brooded.

The Peach-tree Borer Moth, *Conopia exitiosa,* is another member of this family that is much too fond of the plants cultivated by man for his own use. The most conservative estimate of damage caused by the peach-tree borer is set at the unbelievable figure of $6,000,000 a year. With the planting of large peach orchards and the springing up of thousands of trees from tossed-away peach pits, the insect has increased tremendously in number. Originally, the larvae fed upon the wild cherry and plum trees.

The adults are attractive, but small, moths with a wingspread of a little more than an inch. In the male, the wings are transparent, with blue edges and blue veins. Its body is blue, each segment banded with fine white or yellow lines. In the female, only the rear wings are transparent; the forewings and abdomen are steel blue, except for the fourth segment of the abdomen, which is vivid orange-red. Strange to say, however, in specimens from the South it is the fifth segment that is so gaily decorated.

The female lays her tiny, pretty eggs, four or five hundred of them, scattered a few here and a few there, in crevices of the bark, usually near the base of the trees selected. The larvae bore in and then feed just under the bark, going up or down. Signs of attack can be detected by the oozing sap, which thickens into the peach gum which children are so fond of chewing.

"MICROS"—THE LITTLEST MOTHS

For everyday, nonscientific purposes, we are apt to divide the Lepidoptera into two groups. Into one we place all the beautiful, graceful, showy creatures, usually large and always charming, that hover over our flowers in the daytime or come to our window screens at night. Into another group go the Clothes Moths and all the other small, fuzzy, dizzy little demons, dull-colored, inconspicuous, and unattractive pests.

Even the scientist finds it easier to separate the little fellows for concentrated study. He has dignified his surrender to convenience by calling the small moths a long name, microlepidoptera, which he usually shortens to "micros." There are at least seventy families in this group. There are probably thousands of species, many of them as yet unidentified. They are the most difficult to study, the least known, and doubtless the most interesting of all their order.

Micros are all moths, all active during the evening and at night, flying in the daytime only when disturbed, as, for example, when shaken out of your coat. The smallest are only a fifth of an inch in length. The largest have a wing expanse of one inch.

Under a lens, many of these creatures show great beauty. The wings which look so dull to the unaided eye are actually brightly patterned with metallic spots and lines. Sometimes the wings are oddly shaped. Those of the Plume Moth are divided so that they look like outstretched feathers. Using the lens, you will see that the moth often wears a lovely headdress, has large, bright eyes, fancy mouth appendages, and long, delicate antennae.

The Yucca Moth, Gardener and Conservationist. On the plains and mesas of the southwestern United States and in many of their cultivated gardens, the Spanish bayonet or yucca lifts tall stalks of heavy, fragrant blossoms. Shake some of these flowers and watch a few very small, pale moths drop out and take off on the aimless, wiggle-waggle flight that characterizes the micros.

In one habit, however, the yucca micro is quite different from most of the group. The female gathers pollen in its mouth, which is specially modified for this purpose, and carefully places it on the stigma of the yucca flower, thus assuring seeds for her young. Then she deposits her eggs in the flower's ovary. The larvae feed on the seeds, always leaving some to provide for future crops.

MICROS OF ECONOMIC IMPORTANCE

With a few exceptions, like the yucca moth, only those micros have been studied whose interests conflict with man's. Among these are the three species of clothes moths that have bothered us for so long. They belong to the Tineidae family, many of whose members feed

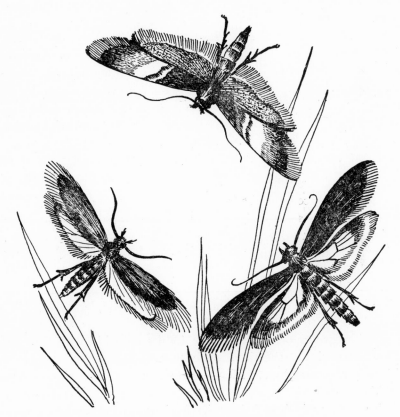

EVERY HOUSEKEEPER HATES THESE THREE CRIMINALS
There are only three kinds of common clothes moths. All have spread to the Western Hemisphere from their original Old World home. The adult moths look very much alike; the smallest has a wingspread of about half an inch, the largest, five-eighths of an inch. The caterpillars, however, build quite different kinds of cases or cocoons. *Top:* Case-bearing clothes moth, *Trichophaga tapetzella*. *Bottom left:* Webbing clothes moth, *Tineola bisselliella*. *Bottom right:* Old-fashioned clothes moth, *Tinea pellionella*.

on dead animal matter, particularly fur, feathers, and wool; but some feed on fungi and decaying vegetation.

Leaf Miners, belonging to several families, are beautiful, bright, or metallic-colored, moths, exquisitely shaped, whose caterpillars attack the leaves, twigs, and fruit of practically all our trees and shrubs, as well as many greenhouse plants.

Leaf Rollers, not so brilliantly colored, have small, pink, yellow, or green caterpillars which feed on leaves, fruits, and nuts almost to the despair of man. To this group belong the terrible Codling Moth, the Oriental Peach Moth, the Grape Moth, the Cranberry Blackhead Wireworm, and many another pest throughout the world. Here also belong the Mexican-jumping-bean Moth larvae, whose antics have delighted children for ages.

Larvae of a great many micro species feed on our dried and processed foods, on flour, meal, breakfast foods, macaroni, noodles, and the like, dried fruit, and shelled nuts. Their living adds greatly to the cost of ours.

Heroes of Australia. But in the same family, with the worst of the meal and dried-fruit moths, lives the famous Cactus Moth, *Cactoblastis cactorum,* true hero to the Australians. Years ago misguided persons introduced the American prickly-pear cactus into Australia. In an incredibly short time the cactus had covered sixty million acres of that continent's dry pasture land. In 1925 Argentina sent the suffering Australians 2,750 cactus-moth eggs. These were placed on the cactus leaves, hatched well, and the larvae burrowed in and set to work. Within the next few years, millions of moth eggs were distributed around Australia, and everywhere the larvae rapidly destroyed the cactus.

Another group of micros whose habits coincide with our desires are some species of the tiny, lovely Sun Moths. Their minute caterpillars have been observed feeding on mealy bugs, scales, and other coccids.

The great majority of the microlepidoptera are still unknown to us. As we learn more about them, we shall doubtless find many that we can call beneficial, because they feed on something that we want destroyed.

The True Flies—Biters, Scavengers, and Poisoners

Among English-speaking people, almost any insect that has noticeable wings, or one that makes much use of its wings, is called a fly, or some special kind of fly. So we have Butterflies, Dragonflies, Fireflies, Harvest Flies, and May Flies, as well as Houseflies, Bluebottle Flies, and Horseflies. Actually, only the last three named belong to the "true" flies (order Diptera). As we think about these for a moment, we may recall other only too familiar insects that are also true flies: Mosquitoes, Midges, Robber Flies, Fruit Flies, and many more.

HOW TRUE FLIES DIFFER FROM OTHER INSECTS

Look carefully at an assortment of these various flies, and you will see that they have one prominent characteristic in common: each has only one pair of wings. All other insects have either no wings at all or two pairs.

What has happened to the second pair of wings in the Diptera? Just back of the base of their wings you can see a pair of curious little knobs, mounted on slender stalks. These odd structures are called "halteres," or balancers. Since they occupy the approximate position where the second pair of wings would be, if present, and since they vibrate when the flies are flying, it is assumed by many insect experts that they are modified wings. Other entomologists believe that the halteres may be a more recent, and perhaps independent, development, appearing after the second pair of wings had ceased to function, had grown smaller and smaller, and had eventually disappeared.

It is this single pair of wings and the halteres that distinguish the Diptera from all other insects. They have one other noticeable characteristic, large eyes, sometimes occupying most of the head. In general, members of the Diptera do not differ as widely from one another as do the members of some other orders. Therefore we consider the Diptera as being "homogeneous," meaning that its members have very similar characteristics, as distinguished from the Hemiptera, which is a "heterogeneous" order (having widely varying members).

FLIES ARE ABUNDANT EVERYWHERE

Flies make their homes everywhere, from the lands of long winters and short summers to the steamiest jungles. Some are small, nearly invisible; others are large. Some are very dull in appearance; others dress brilliantly in yellows, greens, and reds. Some are beneficial to man as scavengers, or in their parasitic attacks upon other insects.

Others, however, are veritable demons, assailing you frontally as well as from both quarters and the rear. These little devils may be plain biters, leaving painful, but temporary, reminders of their presence. Or they may be insidious injectors of protozoans that will leave you suffering from dangerous diseases. Totaling up, however, the flies are probably more beneficial than dangerous to man's interests. The grubs of some species of flies are used as food by a number of primitive peoples.

Although the Diptera are not as numerous in species as the Lepidoptera or the Coleoptera, some seventy-three thousand have been described, and new ones are constantly being added to our lists.

CRANE FLIES—SUMMER DANCERS

At about sunset on a hot summer day, invite yourself to a dance of the crane flies. For an excellent view, take your seat near the top of a grassy bank above a marsh or pond. Even if such a location is not at hand, many such dances will be going on over wet meadows or at the opening of a small ravine.

Up and down, up and down, fragilely and clumsily, the crane flies dance until night falls, sometimes hundreds joining in the delicate rhythm. These are all males, and usually all of one species, although occasionally a straggler of some other kind will join in the gaieties. The dance is apparently a kind of courting entertainment, with the lady flies watching quietly from the side lines.

The crane flies (family Tipulidae) are easily recognized by their long, slender wings and bodies, but particularly by their very long legs. Sometimes they are called daddy long legs, but this name should be reserved for the long-legged spiders or harvestmen to which it is more generally applied.

The Tipulidae are weak fliers, their second and third pairs of legs dragging out behind, while the first pair is held doubled up in front. Once you have seen their curious flying appearance, you will always be able to recognize it.

COLLECTING CRANE FLIES

Since they get about so clumsily, you will find the crane flies easy to catch. However, few entomologists have bothered to collect them because they are so difficult to mount and keep. Some of the legs are sure to be lost. The safest method is to pin each specimen as soon as you catch it; if this is not possible, place each in a separate paper envelope. Pinned and dried specimens are still more fragile, and it is seldom that you see a perfect example in a collection.

CRANE FLIES AROUND THE WORLD

Contrary to the usual geographical variation seen in insects, the crane flies of the tropics are commonly smaller than those in the cooler climates. Note, however, a rule-proving exception, the Snow Fly, which is only about a sixth of an inch long and is found in such cold regions as northern Canada and also high altitudes.

The warmer temperate regions produce some truly enormous crane flies. China and Australia have the largest, but the author has seen several in the United States whose outspread legs would cover a small saucer. They look like giant mosquitoes. Every once in a while one of these large crane flies is brought into the author's office in New York City, usually in a milk bottle, its proud possessor certain that he has captured a dangerous New Jersey mosquito.

We are fortunate that crane flies cannot bite. If they could, they would undoubtedly be dangerous to have about. A few are pests, feeding on cultivated crops. Most of the species feed on vegetation growing in swampy areas.

Crane-fly larvae have cylindrical, grublike bodies, the largest over two inches long, protected by a body wall or integument so tough that they are often called "leatherjackets." Many live in the decaying vegetation in swamps, or in the humus of thick, damp woods, and quite a few are aquatic or semiaquatic. The larvae of some species feed on root vegetables and bulbs in Europe. The larvae of another are something of a pest to California grain crops.

Various Crane Flies. More than six thousand species have been described. One-third of these have been named by one man, Dr. C. P. Alexander, of Amherst, Mass. As a result of his energetic efforts, our

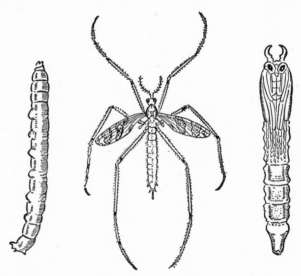

THE LONG-LEGGED CRANE FLY AND ITS FORERUNNERS

Sometimes you can see a host of crane flies dancing together over a warm wet meadow. They look like giant mosquitoes, but they cannot bite, and the legs of some species may be two inches long. The larva or grub (*left*) has such a tough covering that it is called a "leather jacket." It lives in wet ground or muddy streams or in decaying wood. The pupa (*right*) looks like a miniature totem pole.

knowledge of the crane flies has been far advanced, and new species are constantly being listed. Any collection of crane flies from a little-studied region will yield new members.

A few species are wingless, or have wings reduced to little wingless pads. One of these is the tiny snow fly, or snow gnat, *Chionea valga*, of the northern United States and Canada. In 1946 the author took two specimens of a wingless species that were clinging to the vegetation along a roadside ditch in the mountains overlooking Mexico City, at an altitude of twelve thousand feet.

A very pretty species, *Bittacomorpha clavipes,* black, with white bands all around the legs, has its legs thickly covered with very short, fine hairs. It is practically invisible when it flies, looking like an ethereal fluff of down. It has been called the phantom crane fly.

THE MOTH FLY

The attractive little moth fly is so called because its body, legs, wings, and antennae are densely clothed with fine hairs, making it look like a tiny moth. Since moth flies are so small, seldom over a sixth of an inch in length, they would scarcely be noticed except for their habit of flying to a window and there walking back and forth, spreading and folding their wings as they walk. Their wings are bent at a sharp angle at the base and lie rooflike over the body when the insects are at rest. This also adds to the mothlike appearance of these flies.

The moth fly's wormlike larvae live in decaying vegetation, fungi, sewage, and dung, and sometimes in flowing water. The adults can be found crawling or flying around.

This family (Psychodidae) is a small one, and, except for one genus, is rather beneficial to man, since its larvae assist in the disintegration of decayed animal and vegetable matter. The exception is the dreaded *Phlebotomus,* a bloodsucking genus, most species of which transmit disease. One of these carries an infectious skin ailment, the dangerous verruga disease, prevalent on the western slopes of the Peruvian Andes. Others transmit kala azar and the Oriental sore in Asiatic countries.

Phlebotomus flies have longer legs than the other moth flies and are less hairy. They fly only at night, hiding in dark caves or rocky crevices during the day. After their habit of night flying was discovered, the Peruvian government was able to reduce verruga mortality greatly by carefully screening village and railroad-camp sleeping quarters. The newer insect repellents should also serve to ward off the attacks of these flies.

THE MOSQUITO—CARRIER OF DREAD DISEASE

Of all the insects, the mosquito (family Culicidae) undoubtedly causes the most suffering, both to humans and to animals. Not only do mosquitoes disturb and annoy us with their persistent biting, but many species act as distributors for some of our most dangerous diseases.

Malaria, yellow fever, dengue, encephalomyelitis, filariasis, and other afflictions result from the microscopic protozoans which spend

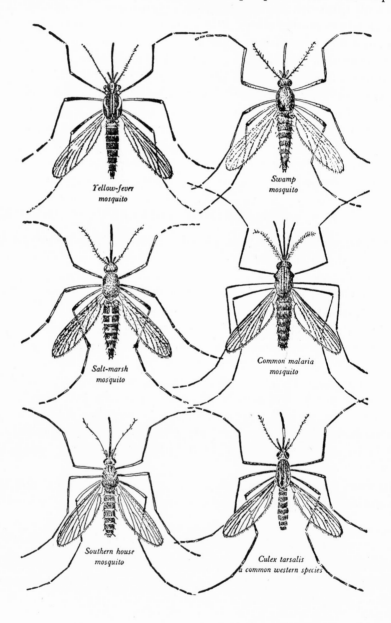

Yellow-fever
mosquito

Swamp
mosquito

Salt-marsh
mosquito

Common malaria
mosquito

Southern house
mosquito

Culex tarsalis
a common western species

part of their existence as harmful parasites in man or animals, another part, noninjuriously, in mosquitoes, and a third part, again harmfully, in a host similar to the first. The slightest bite of a mosquito carrying a supply of germs acquired from some individual already suffering from one of these diseases is sufficient to start a new case.

We all think we are familiar with mosquitoes, but only when we have closely examined one or more species under a good microscope do we realize how beautiful they are.

Even the beak of the female, for only the female bites, is an exquisite apparatus, more perfect than any man-made instrument for the same purpose could be. The feathery antennae of the males are lovely in the extreme. The wings are decorated with scales fastened to the veins in a very exact manner that differs with each species. The bodies are also covered with scales, each species having its characteristic design.

The larvae are water animals, each kind living under certain particular conditions, which are as varied as the number of species.

PHANTOM GNATS—ALMOST INVISIBLE

A little-known family of flies, closely related to the mosquitoes and formerly placed in their family, the phantom gnats (family Chaoboridae) differ, however, in having no scales on the wings or body. The missing scales are usually replaced by very minute hairs. These flies also are unable to bite.

The Chaoboridae are a group of insects helpful to mankind, because their larvae feed upon mosquito larvae. They also attack the young of other insects, and if these are scarce may become cannibalistic.

The larvae, although abundant at times, are not often noticed because they are so transparent as to be almost invisible, this being the reason for calling these insects "phantom gnats." They can occasionally be seen in quiet, shady pools, where your eye may be caught by the one or two airlike bubbles in their lucid bodies, and then by their dark eyes.

In some tropical regions, phantom gnats are so plentiful that they are strained from pools, pressed dry, and thus preserved for food.

MIDGES—SMALL BUT IMPORTANT

The midges are a large family of fragile, frequently minute, mosquito-like flies (Chironomidae). They usually occur in numbers along the borders of ponds and streams, for it is in the water that these insects, as larvae and pupae, have spent most of their lives. A few species, however, are not water-dwellers, but live in damp, decaying vegetation or wet, humus-filled soil.

The water-dwelling midges are one of the principal sources of food for small fishes, a fact for the fisherman to remember, as he curses and flails at the "pesky critters." Midge larvae are soft and wormlike and spend their hours burrowing in the oozy muck. Some are called bloodworms because they possess a hemoglobin which gives them a blood-red color. Those that live among water weeds are usually greenish.

It is usually on a warm summer evening that the pupa swims to the surface, its skin breaks open, and out crawls the adult midge. So many emerge during favorable seasons that vast hordes of them drift out over the land. Many are carried by the winds far from the water, never to be able to return to deposit their eggs. Most midges cannot bite, but by the numbers that lodge in hair, eyes, nose, and mouth, they can make one very uncomfortable.

Many a householder along the Great Lakes, delighting at day's end in his newly painted home, has awakened the next morning to find thousands of these little flies firmly embedded in the sticky paint. Street lights are sometimes capped with a crown of midges mixed with May flies, and office buildings may be draped with mantles of midges over their windward walls.

When examined closely, adult midges show up as attractive insects, with their long, slender legs, delicate wings, and especially the large, feathery antennae of the males.

Sand Flies, Punkies, and No-see-ums. Although it is true that most midges cannot bite, one small group belonging to the genus *Culicoides* more than makes up for what the others lack in this respect. These are the sand flies, punkies, and no-see-ums of the northern United States and Canada. You can scarcely see them, but you can certainly feel them, for it is their business to bite the moment they alight on your skin. Their bite feels like the jab of a red-hot needle.

The sand flies generally fly just at dusk or on muggy, overcast days. Since they are so small, they can pass through the average mosquito-proof screen.

Before the days of DDT, cottages located along waterways of swampy areas were regularly invaded by the no-see-ums every evening. Now, by spraying all screens with a 5 per cent DDT oil spray, you will kill the biggest percentage of these flies as they pass through the mesh.

GALL MIDGES

The gall midges are better known by their activities than by their appearance, because they are such tiny, fragile creatures. The smallest of all the flies, most of them are less than one-tenth of an inch long. Only a lens can reveal their delicate beauty. Hairy, long-legged, and equipped with long, beaded antennae, they fly about on transparent, gauzy wings. Their feeding habits are varied, and perhaps it is easiest to consider them from this angle. They belong to the family Cecidomyiidae.

The predatory species all fit in nicely with human needs, feeding upon plant lice, mites, coccids, and bark beetles.

A good number are saprophagous; that is, they feed upon decaying vegetation, dead trees, fungi, and dung. They are beneficial as scavengers, returning organic matter to a condition in which it can be reabsorbed by plants.

A great many gall midges are phytophagous; that is, they feed on living plant tissue. This makes them man's competitors, particularly when they attack plants which he has been cultivating.

The Hessian Fly, *Phytophaga destructor,* is a species belonging to the phytophagous group. As a destroyer of wheat, it has few equals; its annual damage is estimated at nearly $100,000,000. The Hessian fly does not confine its attentions to wheat; it is just as fond of rye and barley. The eggs are laid along the stem; the hatching larvae, protected under the leaf sheath, feed on the stem, injuring or killing the plant. Since there are two or three generations a year, tremendous destruction results.

The Hessian fly is believed to have originated in Asia, spreading to Europe in hay or cereals. It reached Long Island in the Revolutionary War, carried there in straw that the Hessian soldiers brought for bedding. By 1884, it had reached the Pacific coast, having traveled from wheat field to wheat field as the American settlers pushed farther and farther West.

Other Midges. Another wheat pest, the Wheat Midge, *Diplosis tritici,* was also imported from Europe, a short while after the Hessian fly.

The Pear Midge, *Contarinia pyrivora,* enters the pear fruit through the blossom. It causes a lumpy development in the fruit, particularly around the core. It also emigrated from Europe.

Many of America's destructive pests arrived from Europe years ago, before the establishment of the United States Bureau of Entomology and Plant Quarantine. Since this important government agency was set up and developed its thorough inspection of all plant material and other possible sources of infestation, fewer pests are able to reach America's shores. Nevertheless, in spite of this careful inspection, some foreign insects and plants still get established within them. Many never become pests; but there are always a few that, having left their natural controls behind, or finding conditions here favorable for their development, quickly spread until they become serious problems.

Many of the phytophagous cecidomyiids produce galls, those curious enlargements of the plant tissues. They attack the roots, stems, leaves, and flowers, showing particular interest in the plants belonging to the families Gramineae, the grains; Salicaceae, the willows; and Compositae, the chrysanthemums, daisies, sunflowers, and the like.

BLACK FLIES—SOME ARE BRILLIANTLY TINTED

Everyone who has vacationed in the North Woods has suffered from these stout, humpbacked, short-legged flies. Toward evening, or on overcast days, the female black fly, for it is only she who bites, starts her search for a possible victim. Noiselessly, she sneaks up on you and jabs you viciously on any exposed part, but preferably on the back of the hands or neck. A small blood blister is the visible result of the bite, but an intense itching is felt at the spot for hours.

These flies are bothersome not only in the North, but in the tropics as well. During a recent trip in eastern Peru, the author was troubled greatly just at dusk by swarms of black flies. One of the newly developed insect repellents was effective against mosquitoes but failed to ward off the simuliids unless the exposed skin was thoroughly doused.

Although most of the black flies do not cause any trouble other than their severe bites, a few are carriers of disease. *Eusimulium damnosum,* widely distributed in parts of Africa, transmits to man the Roundworm, *Onchocera volvulus,* which builds painful cysts under its victim's skin, especially in the eyes. There have been occasions when animals, both wild and domestic, and poultry, have died in numbers as a result of diseases carried by various species of these flies.

While many of the black flies are true to their color name, some are more brightly tinted with yellow, orange, and red. They have a number of other common names, such as buffalo gnat and turkey gnat. Only about three hundred species make up this family (Simuliidae), but, as is frequently the case when a group is limited in species, it more than compensates for this lack by the multitudes of its individuals.

Some Well-known Black Flies. The most widely distributed species, and the one you are most likely to meet, is named *Simulium vittatum*. A rather pretty species, called the White-stockinged Black Fly, *Simulium venustum,* because portions of the leg are marked with white, is also widely distributed east of the Rocky Mountains and as far north as Alaska. The Adirondack Black Fly, *Prosimulium hirtipes*, is found in the Adirondacks and northeastern states. The Yellow Gnat, *Prosimulium fulvum,* is a bad pest in the western states. A black fly which attacks turkeys as well as domestic animals and man throughout the southern part of the United States is *Simulium meridionale.*

INTERESTING WAYS OF BLACK-FLY LARVAE AND PUPAE

The larvae and pupae of the black fly lead interesting lives. The larvae inhabit swift flowing streams, clinging in groups to silken threads fastened to the rocks on the bottom. Sometimes they are so numerous as to make a black patch, looking almost like algae, covering square yards of the stream bed.

Here, they feed on the life that the rushing water brings them, sweeping it in with brushes on their heads. Each tiny larva clings by a sucker-like process on the end of its abdomen to the silken thread it is constantly spinning. If disturbed, it will let go its hold, but will not be washed away, because it has many other threads in the vicinity or can very rapidly spin a new thread, first having it very securely anchored.

When mature, the larva constructs a tiny, silken nest in which to pupate. At first, it is completely enclosed in this cocoon. When the larva has changed to a pupa, the downstream end is pushed out of the nest, making a convenient exit for what is about to be created. The pupa rests, with its fore part projecting into the stream, breathing the air from the well-aerated water, awaiting the day of its liberation.

Slowly, the pupal skin becomes inflated as air is filtered from the insect into the space just under the skin. The skin becomes rounded and buoyant. Rounded and more rounded, buoyant and more buoyant it grows, until this tiny pupal balloon pops from its nest and soars to the surface of the water, where it breaks open, releasing the fully developed, winged fly.

GADFLIES AND HORSEFLIES

Members of this family (Tabanidae) are mostly large, husky flies that announce their arrival by a loud "whir-r-r-r" as they circle their intended victim. One group, however, is more subtle, informing you of its presence only by a vicious jab on the back of the neck or some other vulnerable spot. These sneak attackers are smaller than most of their relatives. They belong to the genus *Chrysops,* and are popularly called gadflies, deer flies, clegs, breezes, or ear flies.

The *Chrysops* tend to have yellowish abdomens streaked with darker lines or blotches. A few have dark, or even black, abdomens. Their clear wings are usually marked with one or more dark bands or spots. Normally, they live in woodland places, where they attack all mammals, large and small, from rabbits to deer. They particularly relish human blood, as any hunter or fisherman can tell you. It is believed that some of the western *Chrysops* may transmit tularemia to persons. As with the mosquitoes and many other Diptera, it is the female that bites.

The genus *Tabanus* contains the larger, noisier species which are the true horseflies. Some are also called greenheads because of their very large, iridescent eyes, streaked with shooting lines of red, yellow, blue, and green. The eyes occupy most of the head, particularly in the males; you cannot help admiring the beauty of the greenheads, while despising the way they make their living.

TORMENTORS OF DOMESTIC ANIMALS

Tabanus species frequent pastures and more open country, where they prey upon horses, cattle, and other domestic animals. It is not at all uncommon to see open sores made by these flies about the neck, legs, and backs of domestic stock. The sores develop because the flies return again and again to feed in the same spot, always an area out of reach of the lashing tail and questing head. If the flies are numerous enough, as they often are, you can see the poor animals rushing frantically around pasture or pen to escape their tormentors.

DEER FLY, HOUSEFLY, AND HORSEFLY—PESTS TO MAN AND BEAST
Flies are attractive little insects in this picture, but their habits do not please us. The prettily marked deer fly (*top left*) attacks all mammals, and is thought to transmit tularemia to people. We are always fighting the housefly (*bottom left*) but it still survives, partly because it can produce many generations in one summer. The horsefly (*right*) is usually large, with enormous brilliant green eyes. Not only does this pest drive animals frantic— it also transmits anthrax.

The damage done by the horseflies is not limited to mere sores. They also frequently transmit anthrax, an infectious disease often attacking cattle and sheep, and sometimes man, and also the trypanosomes that cause the surra disease in horses.

SEA-GOING HORSEFLIES

Even though the horsefly is known as a pasture and meadow insect, a number of species of *Tabanus* leave the land to venture far out to sea. The author has seen them miles from shore on the Great Lakes, as well as incredibly far out on the Atlantic and Pacific oceans.

Seemingly, they come from nowhere to settle in sheltered places on a ship. After a short rest there, they sally forth to attack. One wonders where all these flies could come from.

The explanation that comes first to mind is that they stowed away on the ship before it left port. This is doubtless true in many cases; but vessels that have been thoroughly inspected and found free of flies at the start, very quickly begin to pick up a sizable quota. This seems to demonstrate that the flies are on the wing over the water. Since they are strong fliers, many may have flown away from land. Many more are carried to sea by strong winds. A passing ship can provide a welcome resting place for these tired insects. Undoubtedly, many flies, like butterflies flying over the oceans, settle on floating debris.

Other Black Flies. If you see a large, black horsefly with smoky wings, in the eastern United States, it is pretty certain to be *Tabanus atratus*. If you see a similar fly in the West, it is probably *punctifer*. These two are among the largest of the horseflies.

About 2,500 species of the Tabanidae family have been described, some three hundred of these being distributed throughout North America. They appear in every climate, although more commonly in the warmer countries, and at high altitudes as well as in the lowlands, but nearly always around water or damp places, because their larvae almost always live in the water or in mud. The eggs are long and slender and are laid in overlapping layers in masses attached to the foliage along the stream banks or in swampy places. As soon as they are hatched, the little larvae drop into the wet muck where they spend nearly a year feeding and growing.

BEE FLIES—THEY LOOK LIKE BUMBLEBEES

When you walk along a sunny woodland pathway during late summer, you are almost certain to see and hear one of the bee flies hovering close to the ground, its bright wings buzzing noisily. At first sight and sound, you may think it is a bumblebee.

It is a fuzzy fly, however, its largish abdomen decorated with short, thickset hairs which may be yellow, orange, white, black, or even a combination of several of these colors. The transparent wings are blotched with black in patterns peculiar to each species. Some species sport a long proboscis sticking straight out in front.

Their hovering will identify the bee flies more quickly than any description can; for, on wings vibrating so rapidly as to be nearly invisible, they remain absolutely fixed over a spot. Suddenly, with wings still vibrating, they dart off to hover over another spot a few feet away. Even in cities, above scorching sidewalks, you may see bee flies hovering.

FEEDING AND MATING

The adults eat pollen or sip nectar from flowers, but the larvae are parasitic on other insects. The newly hatched little maggot hunts energetically for a bee's nest, the egg mass of a grasshopper, a caterpillar, a beetle grub, or whatever that particular bee-fly species prefers. The parent bee fly, of course, drops her eggs as close as possible to the preferred host. If successful in its search, the larva settles down to feed and does not move again.

In this family (Bombyliidae), about two thousand species have been described so far. One of the largest of them, *Bombylius major,* is also one of the most common and one of the most widely distributed in the Northern Hemisphere. It is densely covered with black, white, and brown hairs, and the front halves of its wings are black. It is parasitic on the larvae of some of the bees. The history of another member of this family, the Anthrax Fly, also parasitic on bees, has been beautifully told by the great French writer, Henri Fabre. In compensation, to man, at least, for the family depredation on bees, several African species are parasitic on the pupae of the Tsetse Fly.

ROBBER FLIES—HEAVILY ARMED INSECT HIGHWAYMEN

All insects, except the very largest, fall easy prey to that swooping highwayman, the robber fly. Even the honeybees, wasps, and the smaller bumblebees, armed though they are with powerful stingers, are no match for a robber fly and its paralyzing proboscis.

Swift of flight, this fly overtakes its victim in the air and clutches it with all six powerful legs; at the same time the fly jabs its beak into the victim. Almost instantly, the struggles cease, and the robber fly carries the body to some convenient perch to suck it dry.

Only a violent disturbance can force the fly to drop its food before the last drop has been drained. A slight disturbance will only cause it to carry the carcass off to a quieter spot. The wanderer afield is certain sooner or later to see one of the robber flies in action.

Beekeepers are likely to fear robber flies, or assassin flies, as they are sometimes called, because of the destruction they are thought to cause in beehives. This is a questionable fear, because it would take a great many flies to make any considerable inroad into the population of even a single hive, and robber flies never appear to be very numerous. Perhaps in queen-bee rearing yards, the damage might become serious through the destruction of valuable queens.

HANDLE WITH CARE!

To the would-be collector of robber flies, a warning must be issued. Before the author learned to handle them, two species of this fly bit him every time he tried to take them out of his net. If the fly can get into the proper position, it loves to sink its beak into the ball of your thumb, creating a painful wound. Of course, one can bear this fly no ill-will, since it is acting purely in self-defense. If you are hesitant about experiencing a robber-fly bite, try to steer these flies into your killing bottle instead of seizing them in your fingers.

The larvae are also predatory, feeding upon insects and perhaps other small, soft-bodied creatures living in rotten wood, decaying leaf mold, or other vegetable debris.

The family (Asilidae) is a large one, with over four thousand species widely distributed throughout the world. A few of the species are quite small, but most of them are fairly large. One of the largest, an Australian species, *Phellus glaucus,* is over two inches long, with a wingspread of three and a half inches. It is steel blue in color. A smaller species, but perhaps the handsomest of all robber flies, also lives in Australia. It is *Blepharotes coriareus,* blackish in color, except for the abdomen, which is a brilliant orange, decorated with tufts of black and white hairs; it has smoky-gray wings.

ROBBER FLIES OF THE UNITED STATES

In the United States, there are three general styles of body design in the asilids. In the genus *Leptogaster*, represented by only a few species, the abdomen is elongated, with the last three segments much enlarged, giving the fly a wasplike appearance. In *Erax* and *Asilus*, to which most of the species belong, the reverse is true. Here, the abdomen is quite thick at the base, tapering toward the tip. In the male,

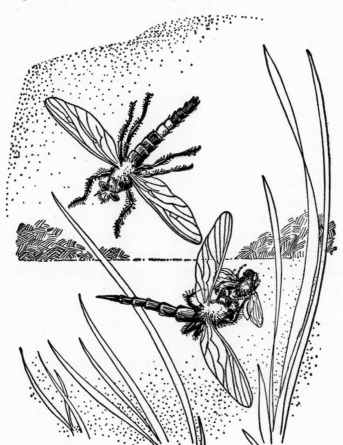

ROBBER FLIES—ASSASSINS IN THE AIR
　　Black, brown, or reddish insects, usually covered with bristles, these husky brigands can kill even wasps and bumblebees on the wing, for they are very fast, very strong, and big (some are two inches long). Their larvae live in rotten wood or vegetation, feeding on the larvae of other insects. You will find robber flies in open, sunny fields.

the extreme tip is rounded and slightly upturned. The female, however, has a tip that tapers to a very sharp end. She uses this tip to
insert her eggs into rotting vegetation or old logs.

The third style, illustrated by the genus *Dasyllis,* has a rounded
abdomen, which, together with the head and thorax, is covered with
a dense cloak of hairs. This plumage is usually gold and black, giving
the flies the appearance of bumblebees. Perhaps this resemblance to
bumblebees enables the robber flies to get close to their victims. Or it
may protect the flies from other predatory creatures, which mistake it
for a stinging insect.

It is also possible that this resemblance may just have happened.
There are many examples of mimicry throughout the insect world
which to our human eyes seem to serve a definite purpose, but we
have no reason to believe that insects see things as we do, or that they
would come to the same conclusions about them.

MYDAS FLIES—LARGE AND SPECTACULAR

The family Mydaidae is a small one as far as species are concerned,
and would be omitted from a general book of this sort, except for the
large and spectacular insects it contains.

Mydas clavatus is the only species found in the northern and eastern parts of the United States. It is velvety black with smoky wings.
For contrast, it wears a brilliant orange-red band on the second
basal segment of its abdomen. Its wing expanse of two inches gives it
plenty of power and speed and the capacity to create a startling noise
when it suddenly zooms across your path on a hot, sleepy afternoon.

A DISAPPEARING INSECT

The author first saw one of these flies during his boyhood. It was
basking in the sunshine on a dead beech snag standing in a dense
growth of blackberries, poison ivy, and young sassafras. Carefully, he
approached the lovely creature, breathlessly reaching out his net to
capture it. But the job was bungled, and the fly was gone.

Thinking there might be others around, the writer waited eagerly,
with his eyes glued to the beech trunk. Five minutes, ten, twenty,
passed. The spot of sunshine was shifting with the lowering sun. Only
a few minutes remained before all sunlight would be gone from the

trunk. Then a "whir-r-r," and the mydas fly was directly overhead. A quick sweep of the net, and this time there was no slip. This fly long remained the prize piece in the author's first collection, for he thought such an exciting fly must be something unknown.

It was only years later that he learned what this fly was, and that actually it was fairly common. Of late years, however, it seems to have become very rare. Nervous and erratic human beings, by continually redesigning the landscape to conform to short-sighted notions of land improvement, by cutting down trees, draining swamps, changing river courses, and building artificial dams (instead of letting the beavers do the dam building), are destroying the earth's great heritage, not only of mydas flies, but of wild flowers, birds, animals, and beautiful scenery.

In the southwestern United States and in northern Mexico, you can see another showy mydas fly, the orange-winged *Mydas luteipennis*, which is larger than the eastern species. Do not confuse it with the "tarantula hawk," a spider-killing wasp that inhabits the same regions and resembles the fly.

The largest mydas fly known is *Mydas heros*, a Brazilian species. With its two-inch body and three-inch wing expanse, it is truly a spectacular insect.

The family is best represented in the Americas, although Australia can claim nine species. The larvae, like those of the Asilidae, live in decaying wood and vegetation.

THE BEE LOUSE—EXTRA CARGO FOR THE BEE

In this queer family (Braulidae), there is only one common species. This is the brownish, hairy, minute bee louse, *Braula coeca*. It is wingless, undoubtedly having lost its wings because it had no further use for them; for it is parasitic on bees. Bee lice are so small that scores of them may hitchhike from beehive to beehive to flower to beehive on the body of a single honeybee. Mostly, however, they stay in the hive, crawling about from bee to bee, taking food from the mouths of their hosts.

HAVOC IN A BEEHIVE

The larvae burrow through the comb, feeding on the honey or pollen, or the bee bread, as the mixture of the two is called. When numerous, they can cause considerable damage to the comb.

The adults crawling about on the bees irritate them. So bothersome do these bugs become that a bee infested with them sets up a dance in the hive or on the alighting board. Round and round it turns, first in one direction and then in the other, trying vainly to rid itself of free riders.

The bee louse was first described in France in 1740, although it probably was known before this, and later was recognized as being widely distributed all over central Europe and along the Mediterranean. Man has transported it with his bees until it is now well established in most parts of the world where bee culture is practiced.

SYRPHID FLIES, HOVER FLIES, OR FLOWER FLIES

The syrphids are colorful flies, usually yellow and banded or lined with black, or black spotted with yellow. When not resting in flowers, feeding on the pollen, the flies may be found in the air, about eight to twelve feet above the ground, hovering on rapidly vibrating wings. They remain in a stationary position for minutes at a time, then dart off, too quickly to be seen, to a new location.

For this hovering, the syrphids select a sunlit woodland path, or a bright country lane, lined with trees, or occasionally an open weedy meadow. A dozen or more of one species will gather in a shaft of sunlight, to romp among themselves, chasing one another, hovering, then chasing again, seemingly on tireless wings.

LARVAE WITH CURIOUS HABITS

The larvae of the family Syrphidae are extremely variable in their habits. Some live in the nests of termites or ants, feeding on the dry pellets ejected by their hosts. Others live in the nests of bees and wasps.

One group lives in the liquids produced by decaying vegetable material or filth. These are the Rat-tailed Maggots, which have an extended, tail-like tube used for breathing while the larvae are immersed, head down, in the liquid. This apparatus may be from one to three times the length of the larvae. A European species, *Myiatropa florea,* has a respiratory tube ten inches long, or at least twelve times as long as the maggot.

Another group feeds upon aphids and mealy bugs or soft scab (the crusty spots on diseased plants and trees). Still others bore into wood and into the wounds in trees, into bulbs, and into the foliage of plants.

One of the largest and most beautiful species in the eastern United States is *Milesia virginiensis.* It is alternately banded with yellow, black, and brown. This syrphid fly used to be common a number of years ago, but of late very few have been seen. It enjoys resting in the sunshine on the trunks of dead trees.

The Drone Fly, *Eristalis tenax,* which has spread from its original home along the Mediterranean to the Western Hemisphere, is yellow and black and looks very much like the male honeybee, or drone bee. This resemblance, plus the fact that its larvae live and pupate in decaying flesh, fooled ancient Greek and Roman pastoral writers into believing that bees generated from the bodies of dead animals.

BOTFLIES AND WARBLE FLIES— COLORFUL BUT TROUBLESOME

Many present-day insect experts have split up the Oestridae family into a number of separate families. For convenience in this book, and because the botflies in general have quite similar habits, we are retaining the older classification and grouping them all in one family.

All botflies are medium-to-large, hairy, husky insects, somewhat resembling bees. Their eyes are smaller than those of most flies. All of their larvae are parasitic on mammals, including man. Since they lead extremely interesting lives, let us consider a few of them separately.

The Horse Botfly or **Nit Fly,** *Gasterophilus equi,* might be mistaken for a large bee, except for its white face. Although slow of flight, it usually succeeds in rushing in and laying its pale-yellow eggs and fastening them singly to the hairs of the legs, chests, and shoulders of horses, mules, and donkeys. This, in spite of the fact that the animals are trying constantly to drive the flies away.

When the eggs are hatching, the tickling young larvae are licked from the victim's hair. From the animal's tongue, they travel down its throat into its stomach. By means of hooks around their mouths, they attach themselves to the stomach walls. In badly infested stomachs the walls are completely covered with the wriggling larvae, which, when full grown, are three-quarters of an inch long.

The larvae spend the winter feeding. In the spring, they are full grown. Then, releasing their hold on the victim's stomach, they pass out with the droppings. Burrowing into the soil, they pupate, emerging as adults in the summer, ready to mate and lay eggs for the next generation.

The Nose Botfly, *Gasterophilus haemorrhoidalis,* a closely related species, lays its eggs on the lips of the horse. From here, it passes into the stomach of the animal, and the rest of its life is much like that of the horse botfly.

The Cattle Warble, or **Heel, Fly,** *Hypoderma lineata,* is a species which bothers cattle. These flies are large and heavy and are covered with black and white hairs, with extra tufts of white hair on each side of the thorax. The female fastens her small, white eggs to the hairs of her victim's forelegs and sides. Some of the newly hatched larvae are sure to be licked off the hairs and eventually to reach the animal's throat. From there, they work their way through the connective tissues until they reach the back.

Just under the hide the larvae stop and begin to feed. As they grow they form a lump, or "warble," which can be felt or seen quite easily. If you examine it closely you will discover a small hole in the top of the lump, through which the larva breathes and discharges its waste material. When full grown, the larva leaves through this opening, drops to the ground, and burrows in to form a pupa.

In the author's youth, one of the farm boy's chores was to pop the bot out of the cow's back by pressing the sides of the lump with his fingers. These holes heal, but they leave a weak place in the hide, greatly reducing its value. Tanners refer to skins with such weak spots as "grubby" hides.

Several other closely related species attack various other mammals, from field mice to deer.

The Sheep Botfly or **Sheep Gadfly,** *Oestrus ovis,* is usually the cause when you see sheep stampeding around the pasture on a hot summer's day. It is a husky, hairy, yellowish insect about half an inch long, and a very fast flier. The female sometimes carries her eggs until they hatch. She lays her eggs or deposits her larvae in the nostrils of sheep or goats. In spite of its desperate attempts the animal is seldom able to evade this persistent and speedy fly.

The larvae spend their entire lives, from summer through the winter and into the next spring, in the nostrils and sinuses of their hosts. Their presence causes great pain and frequently death, for they measure over an inch in length, and if a number are present can constrict the passages. This disease is known as "staggers," or "grub-in-the-head," or "false gid."

When mature, the larvae drop to the ground, where they burrow in to pupate. In a few weeks, the adult fly emerges, ready to start the next generation.

The sheep botfly originally made its home in the Old World, but it has traveled with its hosts until it is now cosmopolitan. Closely related species infest a number of animals, especially the deer group, but also kangaroos, elephants, rabbits, and man.

The Human Botfly, *Dermatobia hominis.* Most of the botflies live the simple, easy lives of ordinary parasites, but the one that lives on man leads a comparatively complicated and dangerous existence. Found only in the Western Hemisphere, it is a large, hairy fly with large wings, and, in contrast to many other botflies, large eyes.

The female of this fly lays its eggs on mosquitoes, other flies, or ticks; the eggs hatch on these animals. If one of these carriers comes in contact with man, the fly larvae transfer to man. Boring through the human skin, they establish themselves in the muscle tissues, and feed there until they are full grown, a matter of forty-five to fifty-five days. As you can imagine, this procedure is very painful to the victim.

If not successful in reaching their ultimate host, the botfly larvae soon die. This is the weak link in their life, and if it were not for this the fly would be more abundant and might become a serious pest.

——THE SPEED OF THE BOTFLY. One of the most frequent questions to come into the author's office concerns the reputed great speed of the botfly. Two hundred to seven hundred miles per hour are the usual figures appearing in fiction. Although botflies are rapid in flight, particularly the deer botfly, the actual speed of their flight probably does not exceed fifty miles, and probably reaches this figure only for short, darting flights. A more conservative estimate, and one probably nearer the truth, claims their flight to be about thirty to forty miles an hour.

TACHINA FLIES—OUR FRIENDLY SERVANTS

The author's introduction to the tachina flies (family Tachinidae) came years ago. He had collected a number of the spring caterpillars of the mourning cloak butterfly, which he kept in a screened box, carefully fed, and watched as they all selected spots and hung themselves up by the two legs at the tips of their abdomens. There they remained suspended, each from its little pad of silk, arching, head down in a J-shaped position.

The expected next stage in their transformation never occurred. There was no sign that the skin would split down the back, as described in books, to reveal the pupa. Instead, these caterpillars were gradually shriveling. And then it became apparent that a number of insects which at first appeared to be houseflies were in the cage. How did they get in?

Next, the author discovered they were not houseflies, and something he had read earlier came to mind; that these were tachina flies. The parent of these flies had laid her eggs on the caterpillars before the latter were collected. Hatching, the grubs had fed inside, four or five to each living caterpillar.

Tachina flies are a bane to all lepidopterists trying to rear butterflies and moths from field-collected larvae, but they are a blessing to the rest of humanity, for they destroy a great many of the insects that we consider pests. Not only do tachina flies attack many of the moths that feed on our food, but various species also feed on beetles, earwigs, grasshoppers, bugs, wasps, or other flies.

TACHINA FLIES IN ACTION

More than five thousand species of tachinas have been described, 1,500 of them having been seen in North America; many new ones are constantly being added. Among these thousands, their detailed habits are quite variable. A lifetime could be spent working out the life histories of just a few of them. As far as we know, however, all of the species prey upon other insects.

The tachina flies lay their eggs on, or in, the victim; or, sometimes, they deposit them on foliage, where they may be swallowed by their host, or where the hatched larvae may lie in wait to attach themselves to their prey. Fifty to as many as five thousand eggs may be deposited by the adult fly, depending upon the various species. Those that deposit the larger numbers of eggs are the species that drop them on grass and foliage, where, of course, the mortality to egg and larva is very high. Some species carry the eggs until they are hatched on the parent.

Once inside their host, the grubs live a life of ease until they are fully developed. Then they pupate, either in the remains of the victim or on the ground. The adults range in size from one-sixteenth of an inch to a full inch. Most of them are fierce-looking creatures, covered as they are with an armor of bristles.

Bombyliomyia abrupta is one of the attractive species in the eastern United States. It has a large, reddish-yellow abdomen, greenish-yellow thorax, and clear wings veined in yellow. Its body is covered with scattered, stiff, black bristles. You will find it along pathways on the edge of woods, basking in the sunshine, or scouting for a future host for its children.

It is impossible to list the numerous species in this family, but to the student wishing to specialize in a limited group, these flies are recommended as an intriguing and rewarding family to study. A collection neatly arranged offers a beautiful display to show to your friends.

BLOWFLIES, SCAVENGER FLIES, AND FLESH FLIES

Although all the members of this large family (Sarcophagidae) have disgusting habits, one group does the world an immense amount of good, for they are scavengers. They are quick to lay their eggs on dead animal matter. The larvae, equally quickly, reduce it from an obnoxious condition to one unnoticeable and readily blended with the soil. Some species apply the same clean-up methods to decaying vegetable material.

Dangerous to Man. Unfortunately, most of the blowflies are parasitic and dangerous to man and beast. Many of them place their larvae in the wounds of animals or man. Some of these cause infections of the eyes, ears, nose, and head. Even some of these parasitic species may be considered beneficial to man, however, because they destroy snails and grasshoppers. Others are parasitic on beetles, spiders, bees, and wasps.

In all there are about a thousand known species, ranging in size from very small to more than half an inch. Their gray-mottled abdomens bristling with scattered hairs, their striped thoraxes, and especially their reddish eyes will help you to recognize the members of this family.

ROOT MAGGOT FLIES—ENEMIES OF CROPS

An important family to the gardener is Anthomyiidae, for it contains a great many species that destroy his crops.

The Cabbage Maggot, *Phorbia brassicae,* produces larvae that are highly injurious to crops. They attack the stems and roots of young plants just set out, causing them to wilt and die. They also attack radishes, cauliflower, and others of the cabbage family. Old stalks or dead plants left in the garden harbor the insects over the winter and these should therefore be burned during the winter.

Phorbia fusciceps, introduced into the United States from Europe before 1856, is more general in its feeding habits. It not only attacks the cabbage family, but corn, onions, and other garden plants. *Phorbia cepetorum,* also introduced, and its native cousin, *ceparum,* do considerable damage to onions. Another, *rubivora,* girdles the tips of raspberry and blackberry shoots. Others, such as *Pegomyia vicina,* mine the leaves of beets and spinach, making blotchy leaves, unsuitable for market.

The Lesser Housefly, *Fannia canicularis,* together with some others of the same genus, is an immigrant from Europe. It breeds in dung and decaying material, making itself troublesome about houses in regions that do not possess proper sanitary facilities.

THE HOUSEFLY—AN AGE-OLD PEST

The Common Housefly, *Musca domestica,* is of course the most familiar representative of its family (Muscidae). It was probably associated with man long before he had acquired and domesticated animals. Undoubtedly, it has been one of the most serious pests with which he has had to contend.

This creature neither bites nor stings, but it contaminates our food by its unsanitary habit of walking over unclean material and then, perhaps the next moment, visiting the kitchen or dining room. It has been known to carry and transmit many diseases, the most common of which are typhoid fever, bacillary and amoebic dysentery, trachoma, cholera, and even tuberculosis.

MODERN METHODS KEEP THE HOUSEFLY IN CHECK. The author can remember the days when flies by the hundreds, yes, thousands, would congregate about every farmyard, house, or apartment. Screening had little effect, because usually it was so inadequately done. Now, however, with the automobile, and its resulting elimination of the old-style horse and cow stables, and the prevalence of sewerage systems, the fly has practically disappeared from many places. This is particularly true in the large urban areas.

Today, with adequate screens to prevent most flies and mosquitoes from entering, and with DDT sprayed in strategic spots in a house, to get the few stragglers that do make their way in, we need not worry about a fly invasion.

The female housefly lays five hundred to two thousand eggs, which may hatch in a few days. The larval period is less than five days, and the pupation stage about an equal time. Therefore, the entire life cycle, under favorable temperature and climatic conditions, can be as short as eleven or twelve days. Lower temperatures may extend the cycle to a month or more.

The family Muscidae at one time was one of the largest of the fly families. Recently, entomologists have been pruning it down by raising entire sections of it to family rank. For our purpose, we will consider these flies more or less as a whole group. In general, they all have pretty nearly the same habits, being primarily scavengers.

The Stable Fly, *Stomoxys calcitrans.* On those muggy days or evenings when the heavens seem all set to release the rain, everyone has noticed that the houseflies have gone crazy and turned biters. Vainly we drive them away, only to have them return with renewed vigor to the attack. Ankles, neck, and hands seem to be the selected spots.

Looking at the pests more carefully, we see at once that they are not houseflies. They are shorter, with a more rounded abdomen, and differ decidedly in having a long, piercing mouth part instead of the broad, rasping process of the familiar housefly. These are the stable flies.

Both sexes are bloodsuckers. Because they seem to be more vicious before, or during, summer rains, these flies have also acquired the name of storm fly. Domestic and wild animals suffer tremendously from these insects.

The Horn Fly, *Haematobia irritans,* is so called from its habit of sucking blood at the base of the horns of cattle. It is also called the Texas fly, because it was believed to have invaded the East from that state. Actually, the fly came from Europe and was first noticed about 1887. Of late years, it has become rather rare in the United States.

The Cluster Fly, *Pollenia rudis,* a fly that looks very much like a housefly, is frequently seen walking slowly about in the house. It received its popular name from its habit of collecting in numbers. It will gather, particularly in the fall, in groups of eight or ten, behind a picture, books, or among boxes. When disturbed, it does not attempt to fly but walks slowly away. The wings are carried overlapped, giving the fly an appearance of length.

The life history of the cluster fly is especially interesting because it is believed that its larvae feed upon earthworms, which in turn are living in manure or decaying vegetation.

The Screwworm, *Chrysomyia macellaria,* produces larvae which can be dangerous creatures. Normally, they feed on carrion, but occasionally they attack living animals. The eggs are laid in open wounds, or in the nose of an animal. If laid in the nose, the larvae may reach the head cavities, a condition sometimes resulting in death to the animal or man.

This fly is bluish in color and is frequently confused with the so-called "bluebottle flies" described below.

Blowflies or **Bluebottle Flies.** The genus *Calliphora* contains several flies known as blowflies, also as bluebottle flies. These flies hatch within twenty-four hours. Sometimes they have already hatched in the mother's body, in which case she deposits the living larvae. The larval and pupal stages each require from ten to twelve days, the pupal usually the longer. *Calliphora vomitoria* is the most common in the United States.

Lucilia has three common species of bluebottle flies: *sylvarum* is bright blue; *caesar* is greenish; and *sericata* has a bronze tint. Carrion is the principal food of all three, although they do breed in all types of offensive material.

THE DEADLY TSETSE FLY

Although the tsetse flies are found only in Africa, no book on insects could omit this family (Glossinidae), which is so deadly to man, his animals, and the wild animals of large areas in central Africa.

The tsetse flies are not outstanding in appearance, considering the reputation they have acquired. In fact, they might be mistaken for oversized houseflies, differing, to the layman's eyes, in being more brownish. It is with a feeling of disappointment that a museum visitor gazes for the first time at the innocuous-looking specimen labeled "tsetse fly."

The eggs develop singly. A larva is carried in the body of the mother and is fed by special glands. When mature, it is placed on the ground in a shady spot close to a stream or wet place. Burrowing in, the larva pupates; the adult emerges in about thirty days. Both sexes are bloodsuckers. Many of them carry the trypanosomes that are the cause of African sleeping sickness, a disease that is usually fatal to man and animals alike.

A Small But Dangerous Family. The family is a very small one, with only twenty-one species (all belonging to the genus *Glossina*). The species fall into three groups, each taking the name of the principal species of that group.

The *fusca* group, named after *Glossina fusca*, contains ten species. All of these play little part in the transmission of African sleeping sickness.

The *palpalis* group, named after *Glossina palpalis*, contains five species. The members of this group are instrumental in transmitting *Trypanosoma gambiense* to man, resulting in the Gambian sleeping sickness; *uniforme* to sheep and goats; and *vivax* to cattle and horses, causing the disease called souma.

The *morsitans* group, from *Glossina morsitans*, contains six species.

These flies transmit to man *Trypanosoma rhodesiense,* the cause of Rhodesian sleeping sickness; to cattle and horses, *brucei,* the cause of nagana, a fatal disease; to cattle and wild grazers, *caprae,* causing souma in cattle; to swine, *suis,* causing a similar disease.

PEACOCK FLIES

This small family (Trypetidae) is interesting only because of the adult flies, which strut about waving their wings back and forth in a very rhythmical manner. Although rather small, usually less than a quarter of an inch, many peacock flies are quite attractively marked. Their wings are marked with a variety of dark spots or bands, a feature which adds to their beauty as they gently fan the wings to and fro.

FLAT FLIES—HARDLY FLIES AT ALL

This family (Hippoboscidae) and two other small families are grouped here at the end of the flies, because those who specialize in the study of Diptera regard them as a distinct suborder. As the result of their long parasitic life on the coverings of animals, they have become so changed in structure and habits as to make them seem not to be Diptera.

Numbering about four hundred species, the Hippoboscidae are parasitic upon birds and mammals, sometimes killing their hosts. They live in the feathers or fur, sucking the hosts' blood. Most of them are flattened and are thus able to slip through the animals' covering.

The genus *Olfersia* contains winged species which are usually found on hawks and owls. If one host dies or is killed, the flies leave the body, flying off in search of another host. At this time, they may settle on almost any bird or animal that is near.

A PERSISTENT PEST

The author has had some of these flies settle on him. One in particular was determined to seek shelter on the author, and he was equally determined to capture it for a specimen. It would get under the collar or lapels of his coat, under his hat, or in his hair or clothing. Each time it would settle, he would try to grab it, only to have it slip through his fingers and fly away. It would then seem to leave the scene, but no, back it would come, and duck into some crevice.

Time after time the fly would escape the author's searching fingers. The chase lasted for fifteen minutes or more until success was finally achieved.

A FLAT FLY WITHOUT WINGS

If you wish to see a wingless member of this family, any flock of sheep will yield examples. This is *Melophagus ovinus*, commonly called the "sheep tick." Superficially, it does look like a tick, but can at once be recognized by the presence of only three pairs of legs. The adults are dark brown, with a long proboscis. They measure about a fifth of an inch long. Wherever sheep have been taken, this pest has traveled along. It irritates the sheep with its blood sucking, and if enough of these insects are gathered they kill the animal. They also stain and soil the wool, thus reducing its value.

BAT TICKS

With few exceptions, the members of the two families making up this group (Nycteribiidae and Streblidae) have no wings, although the halteres (the little knoblike organs) are present and well developed. Almost all of them live on bats, and that is how they come by their name.

The Fleas, Including the Jiggers

EVERYONE HAS HEARD about fleas. Many a person has met them, either on himself or on his pets. Yet we can hardly say that we know what they look like; all we see is a bouncing speck.

Under a microscope, however, a flea shows up as a most interestingly constructed insect. It is compact, wingless, usually reddish brown, with short forelegs and middle legs and very long hind legs, and the whole body is sparsely covered with short, stiff hairs all pointing backward.

Its flat sides enable the flea to slide easily through the hairs of its host. Its backward-pointing spines or hairs also assist its forward progress and hamper the host's efforts to scratch it out. The remarkable thing about fleas is their ability to jump. Like the leaf hoppers, grasshoppers, and other hoppers of the insect world, fleas can jump many times their own length. If man were endowed with proportionate skill, he could easily leap one hundred yards.

As we know only too well, adult fleas are bloodsuckers. The different species tend to feed upon different birds or mammals. Although they prefer a particular species of host, many are not averse to trying another if their favored brand of food is not conveniently near. On the other hand, they can live without food for a long time.

Contrary to the common notion, the larvae are not bloodsuckers, but feed upon the scales of skin and debris of plant or animal matter that collects in homes, stores, or factories. Even the dust in the floor cracks contains enough nourishment to feed many hundreds of flea grubs. These are small, white, wormlike creatures, under an eighth of an inch in length. When grown, the larva pupates in a round, flat, thin, silken cocoon. The eggs are white and barely visible on a black cloth. They are dropped at random by the female, wherever she may happen to be at the time. (Fleas make up the order Siphonaptera.)

COMMON PESTS

The Dog Flea, *Ctenocephalus canis,* is the most common of our household fleas. It is not partial to dogs alone, but is equally at home upon cats, rabbits, and rats, and is not at all reluctant to try man as a dwelling place. Just about as abundant, the Cat Flea, *Ctenocephalus felis,* also feeds on cats, dogs, rats, and man.

The Human Flea, *Pulex irritans,* is quite scarce in North America, but rather common in Europe and the rest of the Eastern Hemisphere. It has never seemed able to adjust itself to American conditions of living. Also chiefly confined to the Eastern Hemisphere are some eleven species of fleas that transmit bubonic plague from rats to man.

Jiggers—Different Feeding Habits. One family of fleas has feeding habits rather different from those of the fleas we have been considering. The chigoe, or jigger, *Dermatophilus penetrans,* originally from South America, is a typical species. The male feeds externally, but the female burrows into the flesh around the feet of domestic animals, birds, and man. There it lives, and deposits its eggs. It digs in under the toenails of the barefoot natives of the tropical countries, causing bad sores. This jigger is not to be confused with the mite of the southern United States, which is also called a jigger.

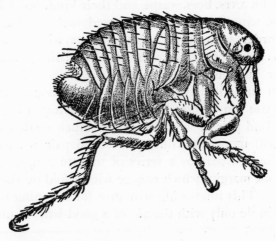

THE FLEA—FUSSY ABOUT ITS FOOD
Each kind of flea prefers the blood of one kind of animal or bird; there are dog fleas, cat fleas, rat fleas, and so on. If they are very hungry, animal fleas can and will attack persons. The flea shown above (greatly enlarged) has a special taste for human beings; it is an Eastern Hemisphere flea and has never been very successful in North America.

The Tropical Hen Flea, *Echidnophaga gallinacea,* is another flea that is parasitical on birds. It is also called the "sticktight flea" because it clings so closely to its host. It is a serious pest on poultry as well as on wild birds in many parts of the world. Hundreds of these fleas are sometimes seen adhering to the bare spots around the bill, eyes, comb, and wattles of domestic fowl.

Ants, Bees, Wasps, and Their Relatives

T HE ANTS, bees, wasps, and their kind, order Hymenoptera ("membrane wings"), are often confused with the Diptera, or true flies. Each order wears thin, membraneous wings with supporting veins. The Hymenoptera, however, have two pairs of wings, while the Diptera have but one pair.

Very often you will have to observe a hymenopterous insect carefully before you can be sure that it does have four wings. That is because the second pair of wings is usually much smaller than the first pair. And, still more confusing, the second pair is normally closely hooked to the first pair by a series of minute hooks, called hamuli, along the front margin, which engage with a fold on the rear edge of the forewings. This interesting structure for fastening the two wings together is visible only with the aid of a good lens, or under a microscope.

The commonest groups of the Hymenoptera, that is, the bees, the wasps (or hornets), and the ants, are very well known to most people for other distinctive characteristics, not the least of which are the very efficient stingers with which most of them are equipped. Some bees and many ants have no stingers, but ants frequently have a good pair of jaws, which they know only too well how to use.

Some Hymenoptera carry a most dangerous-looking weapon, apparently an enormous stinger, sometimes three or four inches long. This instrument is not a stinger but a combination drill and ovipositor, which its owner, a female ichneumon fly, will use to deposit her eggs under the bark of trees.

A GREAT GROUP—125,000 SPECIES

The Hymenoptera, with its 125,000 described species, is now the second-largest order of insects. It is exceeded only by the Coleoptera (beetles), which has 300,000 known species. It has been esti mated, moreover, that another 125,000 Hymenoptera, mostly very small insects, have yet to be described. Like most other groups of insects, they reach their highest development and numbers in tropical countries. About seven thousand species inhabit North America.

Since the Hymenoptera are divided into several groups called superfamilies, each superfamily composed of groups with fairly similar characteristics, it is the superfamilies that we shall discuss, instead of families, except when the latter are unusually distinctive or important.

SAWFLIES—THE FEMALE CARRIES A SAW

The sawflies differ from all other Hymenoptera in that they have no marked constriction at the base of the abdomen where it joins with the thorax. In other words, the sawflies are not "wasp-waisted." The females may also be recognized by their "saws," two flattened, pointed, usually yellowish plates sliding between two other external plates, the "saw guides," on the underside, at the tip of the abdomen.

This whole structure makes up the ovipositor, or egg-depositing apparatus. Some sawfly species have much larger ovipositors than others. With her ovipositor, the sawfly cuts an opening in the particular plant tissue she prefers for her young, and then inserts an egg. The place selected, depending upon the species, may be leaves, stems, tree trunks, or their branches. Some sawflies develop galls (enlarged plant growths) on leaves or stems, in which their larvae live and feed.

The larvae of all sawflies are plant feeders, and many of them look like the caterpillars of butterflies and moths. They can usually be distinguished from caterpillars by the absence of abdominal legs; if these are present, they do not have the circles of hooks that we see on the abdominal legs of caterpillars. A sure difference, however, is the presence of only one simple eye (ocellus) on each side of the head of the sawfly larva, whereas a caterpillar has several. Sawflies are classed as a superfamily, Tenthredinoidea.

The Elm Sawfly, *Cimbex americana,* is one of the common and larger species in the United States. The author would be inclined to call it the willow sawfly, for in his experience the larva is more commonly found feeding upon willow leaves than upon elm. But since elms are considered more valuable than willows, insect experts have taken this factor into consideration in applying a common name. The elm saw-fly also feeds upon poplar and linden, and perhaps occasionally on other trees.

The fleshy, greenish-white larva of this insect always clings with the end of its body encircling a stem or twig. When ready to pupate, it spins a rough cocoon among old leaves. The large, shining adult is steel blue-black, dotted with several white spots on the side of its abdomen, and has smoke-colored wings two inches across.

The Pigeon Tremex, *Tremex columba,* is one of a group of sawflies commonly called "horntails," because of the short, thick spine, or horn, at the end of the male bodies.

The pigeon tremex is a large, blundering insect nearly two inches long. It has a large head on a very slender neck. Its glistening, purplish-red abdomen is banded with yellow. Its many-veined, smoky wings may spread as much as two and a half inches. The female has a conspicuous ovipositor through which she inserts her eggs into the trunks of maple, elm, or other forest trees.

You will never see the horntail's larvae unless you have the time and energy to dig them out of the trees, for they bore into the wood, sometimes as much as several inches.

CHALCID FLIES—INCLUDING THE SMALLEST OF INSECTS

To mankind, the chalcid flies (superfamily Chalcidoidea) are just about the most important of all the insects. Not even the bees are more useful to us. For the chalcid flies are parasites that kill a great many of the insects that compete with us for our food supplies. They deposit their eggs in a great many plant-eating insects and insect larvae, from tomato worms and cabbage worms down to aphids and scale insects. They also parasitize ticks and spiders.

Not all chalcid flies are parasitic; a few are seed eaters. One of these, the famous *Blastophaga psense,* pollinates the Smyrna fig.

Looking at some of the chalcids, you will find it hard to believe that they wield so much power in the world of insects. The largest of them is scarcely an eighth of an inch long, and most are much smaller. There are chalcid flies that spend all their lives in the body of an aphid or a scale. What is supposed to be the smallest of all insects is the chalcid *Alaptus magnanimus,* eight one-thousandths of an inch long. It is a parasite on book lice.

CYNIPID FLIES—THEY PREY ON WEEDS

A big group of very small insects, the cynipid flies (superfamily Cyni-
poidea) are largely gall makers, especially on oak trees, although some
breed in the galls formed by others, taking no part in the formation.
Others are parasitic on a variety of insects.

In general, these flies are beneficial to man, even some of those of
them that are gall makers; for they attack plants that in the human
classification are called weeds, such as goldenrod and sunflowers.

THE "MAY BEETLE PARASITE" AND ITS KIN

Almost all of the insects in the next group, superfamily Serphoidea,
are parasitic. Most of them are very small, for many of them pass
their entire life cycle in an egg of another insect. For this reason,
few are ever seen except by a specialist studying these small insects.
There are still hundreds as yet unrecognized.

An Insect That Lives on May Beetle Grubs. One rather large species
fascinating to observe is *Pelecinus polyturator*. Although it has never
been given a common name, it might well be called the "May Beetle
Parasite," for this curious insect lives on May beetle grubs. The female, who always seems to know where to find her prey, inserts her
two-inch-long, very slender abdomen into the ground and lays an egg
upon the grub. She is shining black, with a wingspread of only one
inch. You wonder how those small, transparent wings can transport
this largish insect.

The male is entirely different, and for a long time was not known.
It has the same black color and the same transparent wings. Instead
of the long, slender body, however, it has a roundish abdomen, the
first two segments of which are short and slender, giving the insect a
wasplike look. Only a few specimens of the male exist in the large
insect collections of the United States. It is, therefore, believed to be
quite rare. Perhaps, we do not know just where to look for it.

ICHNEUMON FLIES—HELPFUL OR HARMFUL?

Man owes a great deal to this large group of ichneumon "wasps." They
work indirectly for us day after day by destroying other insects. Not

that they are intentionally beneficial to mankind. They simply like to eat the insects that like to eat our food plants. Actually, the ichneumon flies destroy just as many useful insects as harmful ones; but they serve an extremely important function in preserving what we call the "balance of nature."

The group (superfamily Ichneumonoidea) is so large and complex, with the species in many cases so closely resembling one another, that it is possible to give only a general idea of a few of the species. Perhaps the largest and most conspicuous species should be mentioned first.

SOME OF THE LARGE ICHNEUMONS

A number of these belong to the genus *Megarhyssa,* sometimes called *Thalessa.* You can recognize the female at once by the very long ovipositor, which varies, according to the species, from two to four, or

LONG-TAILED ICHNEUMON FLIES PROTECT OUR FORESTS
The female of these curious creatures has a tube two to five inches long which she can bore into a tree trunk until it reaches the tunnel of some wood-eating insect. Through the tube she deposits her eggs, which, when hatched, will eat the other insects.

five, inches in length. They are parasitic upon wood-boring larvae of the sawflies, and particularly the genus *Tremex.* With the long, slender ovipositor, the female is able to penetrate solid wood to a depth of several inches and deposit an egg in the burrow of the *Tremex* larva.

Extraordinary Ways of the Female. Another remarkable thing about the female is her ability to locate the exact spot where she should bore. Perhaps she can hear the sound the feeding *Tremex* larva makes.

When you are in a forest in the summer, you can easily observe the female exploring a tree trunk. Carefully, she examines a certain area, tapping gently with her antennae. Back and forth she moves, as she examines. Apparently satisfied, she firmly fastens the claws of her feet in the bark, then, rearing her abdomen upward on her widely stretched legs, she places the tip of her ovipositor directly below the tip of her abdomen, with the drill guides, one on each side, forming a tube through which the ovipositor can work.

The insect is unable, however, to elevate her abdomen to hold the entire ovipositor vertical. She, therefore, has developed an ingenious adaptation of her abdomen and is able to retract the base of her ovipositor within the last two abdominal segments, which are quite membranous. More and more they stretch, as the ovipositor is curved within them, until they resemble a thin, transparent, flattened balloon.

At about the time you expect the balloon to burst, the insect has the ovipositor in position and ready to drill. Slowly but steadily, it starts to pierce the wood, for at the tip are tiny teeth that saw the fiber apart.

——A Dangerous Operation. Woe betide the ichneumon if anything disturbs her at her drilling, for she may not be able to withdraw the ovipositor, in which case it is torn away as the insect seeks to escape. Even in the ordinary course of events, she is sometimes unable to extract her ovipositor because of swelling of the wood, and she either dies or breaks loose, leaving her ovipositor in the tree.

Megarhyssa atrata is the largest species in this genus. It is black, with smoky wings. A few fine, yellow lines mark the thorax and the tip of the abdomen.

Megarhyssa lunatar is nearly as large as *atrata*. Its ovipositor is twice the length of its body. The body is very prettily marked with lateral stripes of yellow, brown, and a grayish shade.

A Careful Feeder. *Ophion macrurum* is a large icheumon fly, reddish in color, and possessing a very short ovipositor scarcely a quarter of an inch long. The lepidopterist rearing saturniid moths is certain sooner or later to have some of these parasitic wasps emerge from his cherished cocoons. The *Ophion* larva feeds within the caterpillar, careful not to kill it until the cocoon is finished. The *Ophion* then pushes the dead caterpillar aside and spins its own cocoon, a rough affair, inside the original.

A FAMILIAR ICHNEUMON

Familiar signs of an ichneumon parasite that many of us have seen are the tiny, white, silken cocoons of one of the Braconidae carried around on the backs of sphingid caterpillars, especially on the tomato worm. Sometimes a gardener imagines that these cocoons are the eggs of the tomato worm, and carefully destroys them, thus killing insects that could do much more damage to tomato worms than he.

THE BUSY, BUSY ANTS

The word "ant" at once brings to mind the familiar wingless insect that gets into our picnic lunches or into our houses. Ants of this type are the workers of the various species, foraging for what they may find to eat or to carry home to feed the rest of the colony. Few persons realize that in each ant nest there are three classes of society, or castes. The castes may have several forms.

QUEENS, WORKERS, AND SOLDIERS

Outstanding in any typical colony is the queen; she is not a ruler in any sense of the word, but is the mother, and frequently the founder, of the colony. She lays the eggs from which all the other ants develop.

Most of these eggs produce individuals known as workers. These workers are imperfectly developed females, and their duties are innumerable. They forage and bring home the supplies to feed the queen and the other members of the family. They care for the eggs and the young. They enlarge the nest, clean it, and, if necessary, defend it.

This last duty is, however, frequently shared with the soldier caste, in those colonies that possess soldiers. The warrior caste usually differs from the workers in having larger heads with formidable jaws. There may even be several forms of these soldiers, differing in the size of the head and jaws.

THE MARRIAGE FLIGHT AND AFTERWARDS

In nearly every nest at some time in the year there are winged individuals. These are generally of two sizes. The smaller are the males, the larger the perfect females. For some unexplainable reason, on a certain day, generally toward evening, all of the colonies of a certain species for miles around will drive out the winged individuals. These will then try out their wings, for the first time, in a tremendous swarm, or marriage flight.

After mating, all drop to the ground. The males, which far outnumber the females, quickly die or are eaten by birds or mammals. The females, after mating, tear off their wings and crawl under cover, and eventually seek a place to attempt to establish a new colony.

Constructing a small chamber, a female will lay a few eggs, which she herself will tend, and will feed the young until a small nucleus of workers has developed. These workers then take over the active duties of the nest. From this time on, the queen is simply an egg-laying machine.

HOW TO KEEP AN ANT NEST

You can keep a small colony of ants where you can watch them. They make intriguing pets. The simplest form of nest may be a tumbler, containing soil, and set in a pan of water. Into the tumbler, a small colony of ants (it must have a queen to be successful) is dumped. They will quickly build a nest to suit themselves. While this is the easiest arrangement, it is not the best, as only a small portion of the actual nest can be seen.

Two Kinds of Ant Nests. Two types of ant nests have been constructed by man in order to raise and study ant life. The Janet Ant Nest is of cast plaster with two or more shallow chambers with narrow connecting passageways molded in the plaster. These chambers are covered with glass and also an opaque cover to provide darkness. One or more chambers serve for the nest, and one is for food. The food chamber is not darkened.

The Fielde Ant Nest is constructed on the same principle, but has a sheet of glass for the bottom. On this are cemented strips of glass for walls, forming chambers which are connected by passageways. Cemented on top of the glass strips are strips of coarse toweling; smaller sheets of glass, one to each chamber, rest on the toweling, which makes an effective barrier. Each chamber has an extra opaque cover or a sheet of amber-colored glass to exclude light.

MANY KINDS OF ANTS

Although there are many species of ants, they are all quite similar in body formation. The ants are classed as a superfamily (Formicoidea), one family, the Formicidae, making up the entire superfamily.

Insects Mistaken for Ants. A number of insects are confused with ants. The Isoptera, or termites, sometimes called "white ants," are among these. Termites have habits and a social organization similar to those of ants, but are not at all like ants physically. It is remarkable that two such separate groups as ants and termites should have evolved along such parallel lines as are exhibited by their colonizing or social habits. Some flies, bees, and particularly the "Velvet Ants" (actually wasps) are also frequently mistaken for ants.

A true ant can be quickly recognized by the one or two roundish enlargements it has in the contracted part of the abdomen. The first enlargement or segment is called a petiole. If there is a second segment, this is called the postpetiole.

The Black Carpenter Ant, *Camponotus herculeanus pennsylvanicus,* is seldom noticed unless it has invaded our homes, where it makes a nuisance of itself by getting into food or calmly wandering about on the floors and crawling on the kitchen sink. These insects are black, as their name indicates. The workers are three-eighths of an inch long, while the queens measure nearly one inch in length. The males are somewhat shorter.

If the only nuisance they committed were to wander through our houses and get into our food, we might put up with them, but carpenter ants like to establish their colonies in the timbers of our houses. They chew out the wood fiber, forming chambers in which they live and raise their young. An extensive colony may so weaken part of the structure as to cause it to collapse. Carpenter ants frequently take over where termites have died out.

Black carpenter ants also frequently establish a colony in the heart of one of our favorite trees. To eradicate them without killing the tree is extremely difficult, but can be accomplished by feeding them a poison mash. This is made by adding Paris green or arsenate of lead to a mixture of bran and molasses, with only enough water to make a thick paste. This poison mixture is so placed that the ants will find it and so that other creatures cannot get at it. The ants finding it will carry enough of it home to feed the queen and poison the entire colony.

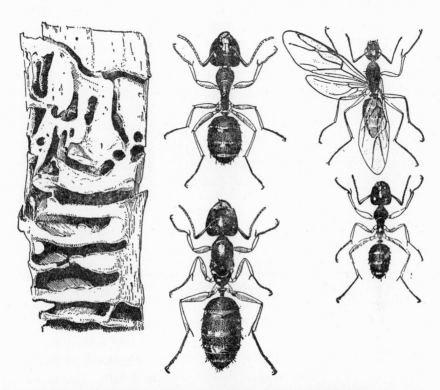

CARPENTER ANTS ARE ALMOST AS DESTRUCTIVE AS TERMITES

Usually the big black carpenter ants tunnel their homes in old logs and stumps; but as our forests have been disappearing, the ants have moved into our houses, weakening the timbers and raiding the kitchens for food. The illustration shows a cross section of carpenter ant tunnels, also four of the different castes. (*Top left*) Soldier or large worker. (*Top right*) Winged male. (*Bottom left*) Queen after she has torn off her wings. (*Bottom right*) Small worker.

The Herculean Ant of Europe, *Camponotus herculeanus,* is the largest species of this type in Europe. Other subspecies and varieties are found in other parts of the world.

1996 ANTS, BEES, WASPS, AND THEIR RELATIVES

The Black Honey Ant, *Camponotus inflatus,* is a closely related species. Ants of this type store honey for use during less bountiful times, and have a unique way of doing this. Volunteer workers, called repletes, engorge themselves until their abdomens are greatly distended. They remain like this until relieved of their loads by the other ants when food is not so plentiful.

In the southwestern United States and extending down into Central and South America, species of the genus *Myrmecocystus* also use repletes to store honey. These repletes cling to the ceilings of their underground chambers like miniature storage vats. Indians, as well as others in these regions, eagerly search out these nests to secure the swollen ants. Biting off the abdomen yields a sweet mouthful, as though one were eating delicious sweet grapes.

SOME FAMILIAR ANTS

The genus *Formica* contains many familiar species of ants. Although much smaller than the species of *Camponotus,* many of them are more formidable.

The Sanguinary Ant, *Formica sanguinea,* also called the red ant, or red slave maker, constructs no mound but loves an old stump or log. It is only three-eighths of an inch long or less, but does not hesitate to raid a colony of ants of much larger individuals and much greater numbers. Although it will attack the nests of a number of species, its favorite victim is *Formica fusca,* whose pupae it loves to steal. These are carried home by the raiders, and carefully raised so that eventually they can take over a large share of the work in the nest.

The Negro Ant, *Formica fusca,* has a great many subspecies and varieties, and is widely distributed throughout Europe and North America. It is a timid ant and constructs small nests.

The Common Red Ant, *Formica rufa,* also called hill ant, or horse ant, is also widely distributed in Europe and North America. It is easily recognized by the rather large mounds which it constructs. Open woods under tall trees are favorite locations. The pupae are gathered in large quantities, particularly in Europe, and when dried are sold in pet shops as the familiar "ant eggs" for bird and pet food.

The Allegheny Mound-building Ant, *Formica exsectoides,* is another species that builds large nests. These may be four or five feet in diameter and two feet high. A single colony may occupy several mounds in the vicinity. The mated queens cannot initiate a colony but get their start in a queenless or declining colony of *Formica fusca subsericea. Exsectoides* ranges from Southern New England and New Jersey westward into Ohio. It is most abundant in the Allegheny Mountains of Pennsylvania.

THE DARK BROWN ANTS AND THE CORNFIELD ANT

Lasius niger and *Lasius flavus* are common species in Europe, where they are called dark-brown ants. *Lasius niger* is represented in North America by the subspecies *Lasius niger americanus,* the Cornfield Ant. The cornfield ant is well known for its care of colonies of root aphids. In the fall, the aphids are carefully placed along the roots of various grasses reached by means of tunnels. Here they remain throughout the winter and early spring. As soon as corn is planted and sufficiently started, the ants transfer the aphids to the corn plants.

All summer the aphids are tended for their secretions, or honeydew, which the ants collect at frequent intervals.

THE DRIVER ANTS—MARCHERS OF THE TROPICS

The genera *Eciton,* of the American tropics, and *Dorylus,* of the African tropics, comprise the driver ants, which appear in adventure stories as the ferocious ants ready to pursue and attack us if we don't watch out! These tales are far from true, although it is a fact that the driver ants are voracious and prey upon insects. They will attack birds, mammals, or humans only if for some reason these creatures are injured and unable to get away.

The driver ants build no nests, and, when not on the march, cluster in what is called a bivouac. When on the march, they extend out through the jungle in long lines, while individuals forage on all sides. Their foraging habits are probably more beneficial than harmful to man, because they clean up the area through which they march.

The Indians and other natives living in their palm-thatch huts look forward to the appearance of driver ants. These people simply go outside and let the insects swarm through their homes, knowing that, when the ants have passed, every other insect, cockroach, fly, and spider will also be gone. Their only worry is that the colony might suddenly decide to bivouac for the night or longer in one of the houses, a situation not very pleasant for the occupants.

CUTTERS OF LEAVES

The Leaf-cutting, Parasol, or **Fungus-growing Ants** are interesting tropical species. They build underground nests, which in a prosperous colony may be of considerable size. The author has seen nests on the tributaries of the upper Amazon that honeycombed the ground for a diameter of thirty feet and to a depth of eight or nine feet.

The workers of this group travel out from the nest, along trails measuring three or four hundred feet, to species of trees which have leaves suitable for their use. Pieces of leaf of a size convenient for them to carry are cut out and carried back to the nest. This they do by holding the piece of leaf in their jaws, the edge resting in a groove on the top of the head. As they travel the trail homeward, each carries a piece of leaf which looks like a little parasol, which is why we call them parasol ants. To one seeing this for the first time, it is a strange and fascinating sight.

So numerous are the individuals engaged at this leaf-cutting work that large trees can be stripped of their foliage in a single night. Often, when such numbers of ants follow the same trail, a path six or seven inches wide and several inches deep is worn in the jungle floor.

The leaves are carried home, not for the ants to feed upon, but to make beds in which the spores of a certain kind of fungus will be planted and grown by the ants. It is this fungus upon which the ants feed.

ANTS THAT CAN SEW

Some species of the tropical genus *Oecophylla* can sew! They stitch leaves together to make their large nests in forest trees. For needles and thread, they use silk-spinning larvae. Holding the larvae in their jaws, the ants work the larvae back and forth to pull the edges of the leaves together and to fasten them with the silk.

SOLITARY WASPS

The solitary wasps (superfamily Sphecoidea), as their name indicates, live by themselves rather than in a colony. They dig a burrow in the ground, or construct cells of clay, or tunnel out a pithy stem. In these burrows, they store living spiders or almost any kind of caterpillar which they have paralyzed by stinging. On their victims, they lay their eggs, thus insuring that their larvae will be well supplied with fresh food.

The Giant Cicada-Killer, *Sphecius speciosus* is the largest wasp in this group. It has to be large in order to capture a cicada and carry it to the burrow it has dug in advance.

THE GIANT CICADA-KILLER SUBDUING A VICTIM
A large and beautiful wasp, the giant cicada-killer has a black body with yellow marks on it and its wings are shining amber. After digging a burrow, the female catches a cicada, paralyzes it with her poison sting, and deposits it in the burrow. Her egg is laid on the still living victim, so that the young wasp larva may have fresh food when it hatches.

A beautiful insect dressed in shining black, this wasp is patterned with yellow marks, and borne on flashing amber wings. It is not so beautiful to the impatient householder, however, when one, or more, of these wasps selects his recently established lawn as a suitable medium in which to make its three-quarter-inch-round burrows. The large size and the coloring of these wasps attract attention, and they are frequently brought into the author's office by people who have never seen them before.

There are a number of very pretty wasps in the genus *Sphex*. Many of them are marked with red, and their waists are long and very slender. They use caterpillars for the most part to stock their burrows.

Chlorion ichneumonea is a large wasp, beautifully colored, with a reddish abdomen, golden hair on its thorax, and amber wings. It is

**SOME WASPS BUILD APARTMENT DWELLINGS,
OTHERS LIKE TO LIVE ALONE**

In the upper part of the picture, Polistes wasps are building a paper-walled multiple dwelling, suspended from a rafter by a stem. (They chew wood pulp to make their strong paper.) As the apartment becomes larger, they will add more stems. Down below, a slender mud dauber builds its house of clay. Away over to the right are the rows of cells built by another kind of mud dauber.

frequently seen in the fall about the flowers of boneset and joe-pye weed.

Chalybion caeruleum, an iridescent, steel-blue wasp, is one of our familiar mud daubers that are continually building their clay nests under the eaves of our houses, and in attics whenever the windows are left open. In the nests of *caeruleum,* the cells are piled one on top of the other.

Sceliphron cementarius is another of our familiar mud daubers. It is a blackish wasp; the basal parts of the legs are yellowish. This wasp carefully arranges its cells in rows of about five to eight cells. The rows are laid side by side, making a flat mud nest. This and the preceding species collect spiders to stock their nests.

TYPICAL WASPS, HORNETS, AND THEIR RELATIVES

The superfamily Vespoidea is a division of the Hymenoptera with which most people have some acquaintance. Its members, wasps, hornets, and their kind, are usually called the social Hymenoptera, because most of them live in colonies or large families. A few of them are solitary, and none of them are genuinely socially inclined, especially if they feel that their personal activities are about to be interfered with. They defend their rights in a vigorous way with their powerful stingers. Left to their own devices, they will tend strictly to their own business.

VELVET ANTS—THEY ARE REALLY WASPS

The so-called "velvet ants" are not ants at all, but brightly colored wasps. If you don't believe this, just try picking one up. You will drop it in a hurry.

The females are wingless and densely covered with hair. Frequently a bright-red color, banded with black or white, and with a velvety sheen, they are attractive insects as you see them hurrying over a sandy spot or other dry or desert location. Some in the Southwest have white or yellow hair which may be long and shaggy. The males are winged, and although brightly colored are quite differently marked from their mates. They sport about, visiting the flowers on sunny days. You can pick up a male without fear, for he cannot sting.

The velvet ants belong to the family Mutillidae, numbering over three thousand species. They vary in size from a tiny one, *Mutilla lilliputiana,* which is about an eighth of an inch long, to the giant of the family, *Dasymutilla occidentalis,* an inch or more in length. This large species, occurring in the southeastern United States, is called the Cow-killer Ant. Although it is certainly a wicked stinger, its ability to kill a cow is doubtful.

Velvet ants are invaders of the nests of bees, where they feed upon the larvae of the rightful owners. On the whole, the family is a delightful one to study as well as to collect.

POTTER WASPS—THEY BUILD WITH CLAY

The sculptors of the wasp world, these wasps belong to the family Eumenidae. It is a large family, but few people are at all familiar with any of the species. Although all use clay in some way for the construction of their nests, only a few can be said to be true artisans.

The best of the potters is the eastern North American species, *Eumenes fraterna,* which builds a perfect clay jug. About half an inch in diameter, spherical in shape, with a contracting neck and a flaring top, the little jug perches on the upper side of a twig or leaf.

The wasp does not leave the jug open, for any possible intruders, but fits a perfectly modeled clay lid on it. Several paralyzed, but still living, cankerworms are stored within the jug. Suspended by a silken thread over the supply of food is the wasp egg, soon to hatch and feed upon the worms, but held safely out of harm's way in case a worm should suddenly lash its body about.

The Heath Potter, *Eumenes coarctatus,* builds its nest of three or four cells joined side by side on a twig. A great many of the family make use of hollow twigs or tubes, simply placing clay walls across the hollow, making a continuous row of cells. The family is widely distributed throughout the world; the heath potter is a native of Europe.

TARANTULA HAWKS AND THEIR RELATIVES

Long-legged, slender, solitary wasps, black or dark blue in color, and frequently ringed with a bright-orange or red band, might belong to the family Psammocharidae, in some books called the Pompilidae.

Psammochares atrox is a common species in the eastern United States. India claims the honor of having the smallest and the largest members of this genus yet known. They are *Psammochares mirandus,* less than a quarter of an inch long, and *ilus,* about one inch in length.

POTTER WASPS ARE SKILLED ARTISANS
The potter wasp builds a perfect little jug of clay about one-half inch in diameter on the branch of some convenient tree, fills the jug with paralyzed cankerworms, and suspends an egg within easy reach of the living food. Then it fits a lid over the mouth of the jug, to protect the egg. Potter wasps are valuable to us—they help keep down the pests that attack fruit trees, slaying great numbers of injurious insects each year.

All of the other species of the family are dwarfed by some of the genus *Pepsis.* These are the Tarantula Hawks. Some of them reach a length of two inches, with a wingspread of nearly four inches. *Pepsis obliguerugosa,* an all-blue insect, is the largest. A close runner-up is

Pepsis formosa, blue with red wings. Both occur in the Southwest of the United States, where the tarantula, their normal prey, is plentiful. The spiders are paralyzed by stinging, then stored in an underground burrow, where the wasp larvae feed upon them. The only species in the East, *elegans,* is much smaller. It is generally blue, with orange wings.

PAPER-MAKING WASPS

The family Vespidae is well known, for it includes most of the social wasps. It contains three genera which may be easily distinguished by the types of nests they build. They are, *Dolichovespula:* nest above ground, suspended from trees or shrubs; *Vespa:* nest above ground, but in hollow trees, stumps, old buildings, or caves; and *Vespula:* nest underground, occasionally in the base of stumps.

The White-faced Hornet, *Dolichovespula maculata,* is the most familiar member of the first group. It is the big, burly, black wasp, with white body markings and a conspicuous whitish face, that builds its paper nest in our favorite fruit tree or lilac bush. The well-known paper-making wasp, it uses the wood fiber from old weathered fences, buildings, or dead trees to construct its nest. The nest is started in the spring by a single queen and reaches its full size, usually larger than a football, by fall. The entire colony, except for a number of young mated queens which will hibernate in old logs or other shelter, dies at the first severe frost.

Somewhat similar species in Europe are *silvestris* and *media; arenaria* is not common in North America; while *norwegica* occurs in both Europe and North America.

The Giant Hornet, *Vespa crabro,* is as large as, if not larger than, the white-faced hornet. It is European, but was introduced into the United States sometime before 1854, for it was in that year that it was first discovered. The wasp has made itself right at home and is now reported from New England to Maryland; it has even crossed the Appalachians into Ohio. The queens are frequently seen in the spring, investigating old stumps and logs for possible cavities in which to start a colony.

There are half a dozen species of the genus *Vespula* in the United

States. They are the familiar yellow jackets, and all of the species look pretty much alike.

Although smaller than the other social wasps, these creatures make up what they lack in size by the viciousness of their sting and their seeming desire to use it. On the slightest disturbance of the everyday

THE BALD-FACED HORNET MAY JOIN YOUR PICNIC

Big black fellows with white faces, the bald-faced or white-faced hornets like to build their large paper nests in fruit trees or taller shrubs. The young queen starts her colony in the spring, and her offspring work at their nest (*shown in background*) until autumn frosts come. Now all die except next year's queens, which retire to sleep in some old stump until the following spring. Like all wasps, the white-faced hornet loves to sip fruit juices or other sweet liquids, and may join you at a picnic.

activities of the nest, the workers surge forth to do battle or die in the attempt. These black-and-yellow, uninvited guests at our picnic gatherings make themselves obnoxious as they dispute with us the right to our jelly sandwiches and sweet pickles, fairly crawling into our mouths to steal a bite.

Their nest is enclosed in paper and always placed underground, in a mouse's burrow, perhaps, or even in a slight hollow under a tuft of grass. The author has, on a few occasions, found a nest in a hollow stump and even between the walls of an old building (particularly where considerable debris had filtered down between the walls), and in the sawdust-filled walls of an icehouse. The common North American species are *Vespula pennsylvanica, maculifrons,* and *squamosa.* The European species is *vulgaris.*

POLISTES WASPS

One other important family of social wasps is Polistidae, with several common species living in the United States. They are largish wasps, about one inch long, reddish black or brown, with smoky wings. The combs or nests, without any enclosing envelope of paper, are hung by a short central stem, or, if very large, by several stems, in a corner of a building, under the eaves, around windows, or may even be placed in the corner of a door frame.

As is the case with most of the social wasps, the overwintering young queen starts the colony by building a few cells of the comb. In each cell, an egg is laid. The little grubs hatching from the eggs are fed by the queen until they pupate. When the young wasps develop, they are the workers or imperfect females and take over the work of the colony.

The two common species of this family in the eastern United States are *Polistes annularis* and *pallipes; texanus* and *aurifer* are two of the common western species.

THE BEES

THE BUMBLEBEES

Familiar insects to all of us are the bumblebees, also called humblebees or carder bees. Most people, however, think of them as the big, burly, yellow-and-black bees that visit our flower gardens, dragging the blossoms groundward with the weight of their bodies.

Although many bumblebees are as large as an inch or more, there are some species less than three-eighths of an inch long. In a single colony, there is also a great variation in the size of the individuals, for besides the queen, which is the largest, there are the workers, which are small to medium in size, and the males, which fall between the workers and the queen in size.

As with the wasps, the colony is started by the young queen, who has spent the winter season in a log, under debris, under brush, or in a sheltered corner. She starts her nest in a hollow in the ground or under a tuft of grass. Here she makes up a number of balls of pollen and nectar in which the eggs are laid. The bees from these eggs are workers that now take over the nest duties. Brood cells are built, and nectar and pollen are gathered to feed the hungry little larvae. From this modest beginning in spring, a nest occupying a hole ten to twelve inches wide may develop by fall.

The nests are nicely constructed. The hole in the ground is lined with bits of dry plants or straw. In the center of this, the nest proper is located. Unlike most of the social wasps, the bumblebees do not construct an envelope around their brood cells.

Bumblebees, having tongues much longer than those of honeybees, are very useful for pollinizing blossoms with long corollas. The clovers and alfalfa are among these, and without bumblebees it would be impossible for these plants to seed. Flower growers partial to long-tubed flowers like the columbine hate the bumblebees. These flowers are too long-tubed for even the bumblebees to reach, so the rascals go around behind and cut a slit in the flower's nectary, stealing the nectar without pollinizing the flower, instead of letting a long-tongued moth do the good deed.

THE HONEYBEES

The honeybee is undoubtedly one of man's most important insects. Having been associated with him for over four thousand years, it is frequently regarded almost as one of his domesticated animals. Only recently, however, has man been able, through breeding, to change to any great extent the character of the bee.

It is true that man has long put the bee to good use, and the bee has responded by adapting very readily to all the artificial devices invented, such as modern hives, section boxes, and innumerable other things to make beekeeping simpler and easier. But, left to themselves, bees will as readily desert all of these for a hollow tree and unconcernedly continue the same life they have followed for centuries.

The honeybees belong to the family Apidae, and the familiar species is *Apis mellifera*. (This name seems to have three years' priority over the name *Apis mellifica*, which was generally used a few years ago.) There are a number of other species of *Apis*, but none of them have been much used for beekeeping. There are, however, many races of the honeybee. Four of these are of outstanding importance.

BEES—TOP-RANK ASSISTANTS TO FARMERS
While earthworms pulverize the soil, making it possible for plants to grow, bees pollinize the flowers, enabling plants to fruit. All of the thousands of species of bees perform this service. The honeybee (*top*) also provides mankind with honey. Seventeenth-century colonists brought domestic bees to America from Europe, and the many wild honeybees now found in the United States are descendants of early imports. The gorgeous bumblebee (*bottom*) has a long tongue and pollinizes many of our tubular flowers, especially clover.

Four Important Honeybees. The German honeybee, which had its origin in central Europe, is blackish, very unfriendly, and little used now in the United States. The Italian honeybee, which originated in Italy, ranges from dark to golden in color, is gentle in temperament, and is now the most widely used in the United States. The Caucasian honeybee, which originated in the Caucasus, is grayish, the gentlest in temperament, but little used in the United States. The Carniolan honeybee, which originated in Austria, is gray with white bands, gentle, and very little used in the United States.

Castes Among the Honeybees. Like the bumblebees, the honeybees have three castes in each colony. The queen is a female and is the mother of the colony. She is developed from a fertilized egg through being fed a special food known as "royal jelly." The workers, of which there are a great number, frequently amounting to fifty thousand in an active colony, are abortive, or neuter, females, developed from fertilized eggs, but fed "bee bread," a mixture of pollen and honey. The drones are sexual males, developed from unfertilized eggs; they have no stings.

Unlike the bumblebee colony, the honeybee colony lives over the winter and may go on year after year, unless some interruption or trouble occurs. During the winter, a cluster of bees is maintained, the temperature in the center being kept sufficiently high so that brood rearing is carried on in a very limited way almost throughout the winter. The outer bees of this cluster act as insulators, and are constantly changing places with those nearer the center, thus seldom becoming chilled.

How the Honeybees Swarm. During the height of the summer season queen cells are built. Just before any of the queens are ready to emerge from their cells, the old queen leaves with a large collection of workers of various ages and functions, also some drones, to found a colony in a new location. This is called swarming. The first young queen to come out of her cell, if the colony is still quite populous, may leave with another swarm. This is called afterswarming. Some of these afterswarms may be so weak, having only a few handfuls of workers, as to be unable to establish a colony.

When the colony is reduced to a low point where no more swarming can be indulged in, the young queen then in the colony will be allowed to tear down the remaining queen cells and sting the occupants to death. Her sting is used only on a rival queen. You yourself can handle her, and she will never once make any attempt to sting. The workers will kill a queen by "balling" (surrounding her in a living mass of bees; but will never use their very efficient stingers on her. They will use their stingers in every possible way to protect their colony.

The Oriental Hive Bee, *Apis indica,* is the largest of the honeybees. It reaches a length of nearly three-quarters of an inch, and builds a single comb three to six feet long. This is fastened to the limb of a tree, a ledge of rock, or an old building. This bee occurs throughout India, Ceylon, and Malaysia. Distributed through the same area is the smallest bee, *Apis florae,* measuring three-eighths of an inch or less.

STINGLESS BEES

To most people, stings and bees are always associated, but there are some bees that are stingless. Although they cannot sting, to many people they are just as bothersome as the stingers. Ordinarily, they will not bother anyone, but disturb their nest, and they are out in numbers. They get into your eyes, ears, and nose; they crawl under your clothing, they crawl into your hair, digging with their legs, and biting with their mandibles. They love to nibble at tender places on your skin.

There are about three hundred species of stingless bees ranging throughout the tropical and warmer parts of the world. In the Americas, they extend from central Mexico to southern Brazil and northern Argentina. Like their close relatives, the honeybees, they are social insects, gather nectar and pollen, and build combs; their combs, however, are in horizontal layers, instead of vertical.

These creatures usually construct their nests in hollow trees, on rock ledges, old walls, or even among rocks on the ground, and in matted vines. The entrance is almost always a tube, frequently a number of inches in length.

The stingless bees (family Meliponidae) are much smaller than the honeybees. The largest is less than three-eighths of an inch, and the smallest is a tiny creature, a trifle more than one-twelfth of an inch. In some countries, the honey stored by these bees is gathered for use. Before the introduction of the European or German honeybee into the Americas, the Indians used this honey, and even went so far as to establish colonies of the bees in artificial hives. Attempts are being made to revive and commercialize stingless bees as honey producers.

Explorers or others should be careful in using such honey, for that made by some species is highly poisonous. Stingless bees are not at all averse to gathering secretions from other sources than the nectar of flowers. The author has frequently seen these insects collected by the dozens around the bodies of dead animals as well as other refuse.

OTHER BEES

There are many other species of bees, belonging to a number of families. (All make up a superfamily, Apoidea.) Many of these have extremely interesting habits. The Xylocopidae, the burly Carpenter Bees, look like big, black bumblebees. The Megachilidae, the dainty Leaf-cutter Bees, usually green in color, make cells of pieces of leaves in the stems of pithy plants or other small openings.

The rest of the bees, belonging to many families, are mostly solitary in habit. Each has its own life history, sometimes a rather complex one. You will find it fascinating to study any one of them that you happen to notice.

Index

NOTE:

Pages 1-680 are in Volume I
Pages 681-1390 are in Volume II
Pages 1391-2011 are in Volume III

Python, Mexican, 1328
  Queensland, 1329
  reticulated or regal,
    1328-1329, 1331
  rock, 1329, 1331
  See also Boa
Python amethystinus,
    1329
  molurus, 1329
  reticulatus, 1328
  sebae, 1329
Pythoninae, 1327

Q

Quagga, 665
Quail, 983-985
  button, 1007-1008
  common European, 984
  migratory, 984
  See also Partridge
Quetzal, 1077-1078
Quillback, 1457
Quiqui, 514
Quiscalus quiscula, 1151

R

Rabbit, 230-247
  Angora, 231-232
  briar, 244-245
  brush, 245
  chinchilla, 231
  common European, 231
  cottontail, 232, 236,
    244-245
  desert, 245
  eastern, 245
  Flemish giant, 231
  forest, 245
  Idaho pygmy, 245-246
  jack, 236, 238-241
  Mexican pygmy, 246
  mountain, 245
  New England, 245
  New Zealand white,
    231
  pygmy, 245-246
  pygmy Idaho, 236
  rock, 232-235
  snowshoe, 232, 236,
    241-242
  Sumatra, 247
  swamp, 245
  true, 235-236, 246-247
  See also Hare
Rabbit rat, 342
Raccoon, 479-482
  crab-eating, 482
Raccoon dog, 452
Racer, 1343-1344
Rackettail, white-footed,
    1075

Rail, 998-999, 1008-1011
  Bensch's, 999
  black, 1008
  clapper, 1009
  grass, 1010
  Iceland, 1010
  Schomburgk, 1011
  sora, 1009
  Wake Island, 1010
  wood, 1010
Rain bird, 1015-1017
Rainbow fish, 1519
Raja, 1415
Rallidae, 1009
Rallina eurizonoides, 1010
Rallus aquaticus, 1010
  longirostris, 1009
  torquatus, 1010
  wakensis, 1010
Ramphastidae, 1098
Ramphastos toco, 1098
Rana, 1219, 1228,
    1229, 1237
  capito, 1238
  catesbeiana, 1229
  goliath, 1229
  grylio, 1231
  palustrus, 1228
  sylvatica, 1228
Ranatra, 1823
Rangifer, 743
  arcticus, 747
  caribou, 749
  tarandus, 749
Ranidae, 1228
Raphicerus campestris,
    817
Raphidae, 1040
Rasboro, red, 1461
Rasboro heteromorpha,
    1461
Rasse, 541
Rat, 304-351
  African giant, 340
  African mole, 375
  Alexandrian, 335
  American kangaroo, 341
  Andean eight-toothed,
    372
  antelope, 305, 330
  Australian water, 342-
    343
  bamboo, 350-351, 373
  bandicoot, 338-339
  banner-tailed kangaroo,
    294
  brown, 334-335
  bushy-tailed, 315
  cane, 373-374
  cave, 313-315
  coffee, 340
  cotton, 305, 312-313
  crest-tailed marsupial, 43

Rat, crested spiny, 371
  dwarf kangaroo, 294
  fish-eating, 315-316
  Florida water, 324
  giant, 340, 1364
  grass, 340
  gray, 334-335
  great sand, 330
  greater cane, 373
  house, 334-335
  kangaroo, 292-294,
    341
  lesser cane, 373
  Mediterranean mole,
    350-351
  mole, 350-351, 373, 375
  mosaic-tailed, 340
  nest-building rabbit,
    342
  New Guinea water,
    342
  Norway, 334-335
  pack, 313-315
  pygmy rice, 306
  rabbit, 342
  rice, 305-306
  roof, 335
  sand, 330
  spiny, 371-372
  swamp, 341
  trade, 313-315
  true, 333-334
  tree, 370
  vesper, 305, 306-307
  wander, 334-335
  water, 305, 315-316,
    321-322, 324,
    342-343
  wharf, 334-335
  wood, 305, 313-315
Rat kangaroo, 59-64
Rat snake, 1346, 1347
  green, 1346
Ratel, 523-524
Ratitae, 886
Ratites, 886-894
  See Cassowary, Emu,
    Kiwi, Moa, Rhea, Os-
    trich
Rattail, 1500-1501
Rattlesnakes, 1291, 1323,
    1324, 1345, 1361-
    1362, 1379-1387
  Aruba, 1382
  canebrake, 1383
  diamondback, 1381,
    1383, 1384
  ground, 1384
  horned, 1291, 1361-
    1362
  long-tailed, 1384
  Mexican West Coast,
    1383